WATCH THE NEW
MIS VIDEOS ONLINE

Want to see how the information systems concepts you're learning apply to the real world? Use the password card in this textbook to check out relevant MIS video clips online at **www.course.com/mis/mis5**. Click on the video clip that corresponds to the chapter you're studying and discover more today.

If your book does not contain a password card, please ask your professor to contact their Thomson Course Technology representative.

Clip	Chapter
The Future of Design and Technology	Chapter 1: Business Information Systems: An Overview
Vehicle Tracking Devices	Chapter 2: Strategic Uses of Information Systems
Go Inside Krispy Kreme	Chapter 3: Business Functions and Supply Chains
Getting Started	Chapter 4: Hardware in Business
Software Vending Machines	Chapter 5: Software in Business
How to Start a Free Wiki	Chapter 6: Networks in Business
No clip	Chapter 7: Database Management Systems
Online Music Stores and Services	Chapter 8: E-Commerce
No clip	Chapter 9: Challenges in Global Information Systems
Google Maps Meet Craigslist	Chapter 10: Decision Support and Expert Systems
E-Voting	Chapter 11: Business Intelligence and Knowledge Management
Project Management with Web-based Tools	Chapter 12: Systems Planning and Development
Confessions of a Software Pirate	Chapter 13: Choices in Systems Acquisition
Emergency System Restore	Chapter 14: Risk, Controls, and Dis

D1088183

LOOK FOR THESE OTHER POPULAR THOMSON COURSE TECHNOLOGY
MIS TITLES

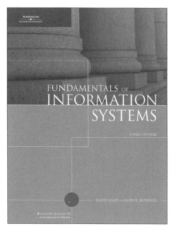

Fundamentals of Information Systems, Third Edition

by Ralph Stair and George Reynolds

ISBN: 0-619-21560-7

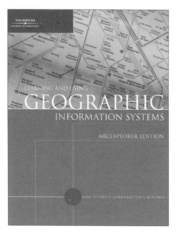

Learning and Using Geographic Information Systems: ArcExplorer Edition

by Wilpen Gorr and Kristen Kurland

ISBN: 0-619-21747-2

Systems Analysis and Design in a Changing World, Fourth Edition

by John Satzinger, Robert Jackson, and Stephen Burd

ISBN: 1-4188-3612-5

Database Systems: Design, Implementation, and Management, Seventh Edition

by Peter Rob and Carlos Coronel

ISBN: 1-4188-3593-5

Electronic Commerce, Seventh Edition

by Gary Schneider

ISBN: 1-4188-3703-2

Problem Solving Cases with Microsoft Access and Excel, Fourth Edition

by Joseph Brady and Ellen Monk

ISBN: 1-4188-3706-7

INSTRUCTOR EDITION

WELCOME   At Course Technology, our mission is to help people teach and learn about technology. This special Instructor Edition is all about helping YOU teach. We know you have a great deal to manage, and for this reason we provide you with great tools and resources with every text. This Instructor Edition will help you sort through all of this material, and will enable you to choose the right combination of tools to help you teach the way you want to teach.

CONTENTS AT A GLANCE

Page 2: **Instructor Resources for *Management Information Systems, Fifth Edition***

We provide you with an in-depth description of everything this textbook has to offer to help you teach, so you can choose what makes the most sense for your classroom.

Page 4: **Student Companion Web Site**

Do your students need additional concept reinforcement? The robust Student Companion Web site that accompanies this text includes a plethora of resources including Videos, Part Case Web Resources and Business Projects, Annotated Web Links, Hands-On Projects, and Practice Quizzes.

Page 5: **MIS Companion CD**

This exciting new tool, powered by SAM technology, allows students to experience FREE training in Microsoft Office Access 2003 and Microsoft Office Excel 2003, as well as additional MIS concept coverage using MIS Interactive Labs.

Page 8: **Annotated TOC for *Management Information Systems, Fifth Edition***

Is this your first time with this textbook? Or have you used this book in earlier editions and want to get a sense of what has been changed for the new Fifth Edition? The author has created an Annotated Table of Contents that includes a chapter-by-chapter guide to what each chapter of this book has to offer you and your students, as well as additional information to help you teach this course.

INSTRUCTOR RESOURCES

To effectively teach your class you need more than great textbooks. That is why we strive to provide you with outstanding instructor resources—developed by educators, for educators. Our goal is to make the teaching and learning experience in your classroom the best it can be. With these resources, you can spend less time preparing and more time teaching.

When preparing for your next class, the Instructor Resources CD-ROM is the best place to start. The CD-ROM contains everything you need to get your course up and running. Most of the materials on the Instructor Resources CD-ROM are also available for download at www.course.com at the instructor download section. And be sure to check this site before each semester for updates to the Instructor Resources for this title! The Instructor Resources CD-ROM for *Management Information Systems, Fifth Edition* contains the following:

INSTRUCTOR'S MANUAL

Need to compile a lecture for your class that's starting in an hour? Looking for ways to challenge your students with group projects? Searching for useful URLs to add substance to your lecture or assignments? Need to keep your students on track with assignments, class policies, and due dates? The electronic Instructor's Manual is a great place to look for all of these resources and more. The Microsoft Word document for each chapter can be easily customized to include your own notes, but it already comes chock-full of great ideas. For example, take advantage of direction from the author of the book about how to "hook" your students' interest at the start of the class. Or incorporate helpful teaching tips for each chapter into your lesson notes. The IM provides ideas for term projects, answers to review and discussion questions, and answers to end-of-chapter case questions. Separate Excel files provide solutions to quantitative questions.

POWERPOINT PRESENTATIONS

Need to deliver engaging and visually impressive lectures? It is easy with the professionally-designed PowerPoint presentations available for each chapter in this book. You can edit the files to fit your needs, post them to your network for students to review key concepts, or save them to the Web for your Distance Learning students.

FIGURE FILES

Looking for figures in the book that are not included in the PowerPoint presentations? Every figure in the textbook is available in electronic form. Use this ancillary to present a slide show in lecture or to print transparencies for use in lecture with an overhead projector. If you have a personal computer and LCD device, this ancillary can be an effective tool for presenting lectures.

SOLUTIONS TO EXERCISES

Need to quickly check answers to the hands-on work at the end of each chapter? Make homework corrections a snap with solutions to end-of-chapter work right at your fingertips.

TEST BANK AND TEST ENGINE

Looking for time-efficient ways to effectively test your students? ExamView features a user-friendly testing environment that allows you to not only publish traditional paper and LAN-based tests, but also Web-deliverable exams. Utilize the ultra-efficient Quick Test Wizard to create an exam in less than five minutes, take advantage of the Course Technology question banks, or even customize your own exams from scratch.

BLACKBOARD AND WEBCT CONTENT

www.blackboard.com

Blackboard and WebCT are the leading distance learning solutions available today. In the past few years, they've also become popular class-management platforms. Course Technology has partnered with Blackboard and WebCT to bring you premium online content. Content for use with *Management Information Systems, Fifth Edition* is available in Blackboard Course Cartridge and WebCT e-Pack format, and includes the following:

- Topic Reviews
- Case Projects
- PowerPoint Presentations
- Review Questions
- Practice Tests
- Custom Syllabus, and more!

STUDENT COMPANION WEB SITE

We have created an exciting online companion for students to utilize as they work through the fifth edition of *Management Information Systems*. This Web resource, located at *www.course.com/mis/mis5*, includes the following features:

- **PowerPoint Slides:** Direct access to the book's PowerPoint presentations is offered, which cover the key points from each chapter. These presentations are a useful study tool.
- **Videos:** Twelve topical video clips, linked to chapters throughout the book, can be found on this Web site. Questions to accompany the respective video clips are featured at the end of each corresponding chapter in the book. These exercises reinforce the concepts taught and provide the students with more critical thinking opportunities. Look for the video icon throughout the text.

    For extra video footage, you will also find clips that correspond to the part cases in the third edition of the text. These cases have been supplied on the site as well.
- **Glossary of Key Terms:** Students can view a PDF file of the glossary from the book.
- **Fifth Edition Part Case Projects:** Unique hands-on projects associated with the five Part Cases have been created to allow for first-hand participation in the businesses introduced in each Part. For each Part Case, there is a selection of hands-on projects that asks the user to become a "character" in the cases and perform small tasks to help meet business needs. The solution files for these activities are available to instructors at *www.course.com*, via the password-protected Instructor Downloads page for this textbook.
- **Additional Resources for the Cases:** Included here is a selection of interesting Web sites that pertain to subjects addressed in each Part Case, allowing for further research and exploration.
- **"Bike Guys" Business Cases:** For more examples of MIS concepts in action, we have supplied the popular "Bike Guys" cases from the third edition of the text.
- **Further Case Offerings:** Thomson Course Technology now offers cases from Harvard Business School Publishing and other leading case-writing institutions. Create the ideal casebook for your course by selecting cases, adding your own materials, and combining it with our best-selling Course Technology titles.

    Additional business articles and cases are offered through InfoTrac, the popular Journal Database, made up of more than 15 million full-text articles from over 5,000 scholarly and popular periodicals.
- **Additional Content:** Here you will find the following additional material:
    - Organizing Information Technology Resources
    - Measurement Units
- **Test Yourself on MIS:** Brand-new quizzes, created specifically for this site, allow users to test themselves on the content of each chapter and immediately see what answers were answered right and wrong. For each question answered incorrectly, users are provided with the correct answer and the page in the text where that information is covered. Special testing software randomly compiles a selection of questions from a large database, so students can take quizzes multiple times on a given chapter, with some new questions each time.
- **Hands-On Exercises:** Also created just for this Student Companion Web site, a selection of exercises asks users to apply what they have learned in each chapter and further explore various software tools. The solution files for these activities are also available to instructors at *www.course.com*.
- **Useful Web Links:** Access a repository of links to the home pages of the primary Web sites relative to each chapter for further research.

MIS COMPANION CD

Course Technology is committed to helping instructors effectively teach MIS concepts and related computer skills. With the Fifth Edition, we are proud to offer an exciting tool, powered by SAM technology, to enhance students' learning experience: the **MIS Companion CD** for student training. Students now have the opportunity to experience FREE training in Excel 2003 and Access 2003, along with access to additional coverage of MIS concepts using MIS Interactive Labs.

The MIS Companion CD is a unique, free tool on the back of every copy of this book. Tips for using this training tool can be found throughout the text.

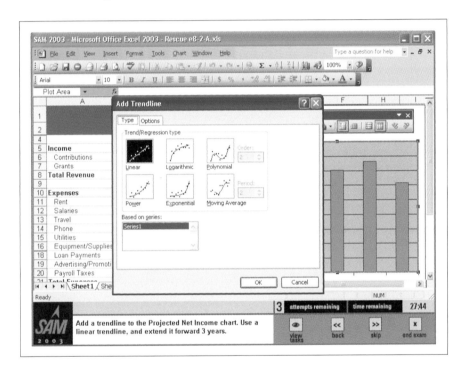

EXCEL 2003 AND ACCESS 2003 TRAINING

How many assignments in your course require basic knowledge of Excel and Access tasks? How much time do you spend reviewing these basic tasks? Spend your time teaching the fundamental concepts of MIS, and let the the MIS Companion CD reinforce training for you! Give your students the chance to get hands-on training and practice with Access 2003 and Excel 2003 tasks, ranging from the beginning through advanced levels. In addition, the MIS Companion CD will give your students the opportunity to learn and practice Access and Excel tasks *independently*.

MIS INTERACTIVE LABS

This CD also includes 12 robust interactive labs that reinforce key MIS-related concepts, enabling students to learn real-world computer-based activities in a simulated environment. The labs are designed to provide students with various options in absorbing concepts: through reading, observation, step-by-step practice, and hands-on application. Some of the exciting topics addressed in these labs include presentation software, networking basics, online privacy, project management, and Web design. These labs are also accessible via the new *Management Information Systems, Fifth Edition* Student Companion Web site.

TABLE OF CONTENTS FOR LAB INTEGRATION

The following table of contents illustrates which labs are best for reinforcing some of the content coverage in each chapter of this book. Use this list as a guide to match each MIS lab with its corresponding chapter:

Lab: Spreadsheets — Ch. 1: Business Information Systems: An Overview
Lab: Visual Programming — Ch. 5: Business Software
Lab: Networking Basics — Ch. 6: Business Networks and Telecommunications
Lab: Wireless Networking — Ch. 6: Business Networks and Telecommunications
Lab: Databases — Ch. 7: Databases and Data Warehouses
Lab: Electronic Commerce — Ch. 8: The Web-Enabled Enterprise
Lab: Creating a Web Page — Ch. 8: The Web-Enabled Enterprise
Lab: Advanced Spreadsheets — Ch. 10: Decision Support and Expert Systems
Lab: Advanced Databases — Ch. 11: Business Intelligence and Knowledge Management
Lab: Web Design Principles — Ch. 12: Systems Planning and Development
Lab: Project Management — Ch. 12: Systems Planning and Development
Lab: Keeping Your Computer Virus Free — Ch. 14: Risks, Security, and Disaster Recovery

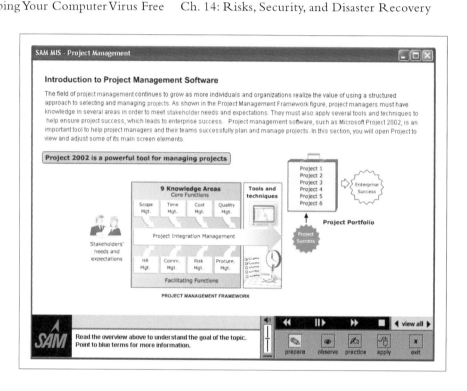

ASSESSMENT OPTIONS FOR INSTRUCTORS

Beyond this exciting MIS Companion CD for student training, Course Technology offers assessment options to further enhance student learning. SAM (Skills Assessment Manager) is the worldwide leader in online assessment and is proven to be the most effective tool to assess and train students in Microsoft Office tasks, Computer Concepts, Windows, the Internet, and more. SAM is a hands-on, simulated computer assessment and training tool that gives students the feeling of working live in the computer application.

WANT MORE? SAM 2003

Inject a wider breadth of applications, as well as additional Excel, Access, and Computer Concepts coverage into your MIS course with SAM 2003! Visit *http://samcentral.course.com* to learn more.

Please contact your Course Technology Sales Representative for more information regarding these assessment options.

WWW.COURSE.COM

Course Technology is the world's leading IT publisher. Because we focus solely on Information Technology, we have the unique ability to address the needs of customers like you.

Find out about the latest technology trends, products, and courseware solutions on the Course Technology Web site, *www.course.com*.

Visit often to:

- Connect with your peers through our Online forums
- Learn about the latest software releases and how they will impact you in the classroom
- Browse our online catalog
- Locate and contact your local sales representative
- Register for the next Conference for Information Technology Educators and our other educational events
- Download the files that are contained on this CD

Stop here before preparing for your class!

PASSWORDS AND SECURITY

INSTRUCTOR RESOURCES ON COURSE.COM

Depending on the type of Educational Institution you are a part of, please call one of the support services teams to obtain your password to our online Instructor Resources.

For colleges and universities in the United States:
Call Course Technology at **1.800.648.7450** and select option 3 for Support Services.

For High Schools:
Call Thomson Learning—School at:
1.800.824.5179

For Private Career Colleges:
Call Thomson Learning—Career at:
1.800.477.3692

For Corporations, IT Training Centers, and Federal Government Agencies:
Call Course Technology at **1.800.442.3692**

Password protection is of utmost importance at Course Technology. We monitor each and every caller requesting an instructor resources password by verifying their names with the school the caller indicates as their affiliation. This ensures that students never have access to the answers, test banks, or other resources that we provide for you on course.com.

OTHER RESOURCES AND PASSWORDS

Course Technology knows that protecting these passwords from students is critical, but keeping track of all the passwords for all the tools you may adopt in a given course (one for your online instructor resources, another for SAM, another for your schools' servers...) can be quite a hassle. For your convenience, we're providing space below for you to keep track of all your login information (either literally or with your own code that students won't understand!) for this course.

RESOURCE	USERNAME	PASSWORD

ANNOTATED TOC

Now you have a better understanding of all the tools that come with *Management Information Systems, Fifth Edition*. What about the text itself? What does each chapter have to offer you and your students? This annotated TOC highlights each chapter's main discussions and gives you some ideas on how to make the classroom experience for your students even more engaging.

In addition, it gives you an update on the Part Cases, which are updated for the Fifth Edition. In case you have not used this book before and are not familiar with these Part Cases, here is the background of this amazing teaching and learning tool!

PART CASES OVERVIEW

The cornerstone of this book and its new edition is a series of Part Cases that are carefully crafted to integrate all the IS principles that arise in business, to give students an opportunity to view IS issues in action, and to solve business problems related to IT just as they arise in the real world. The Part Cases are integrated into the text in every chapter, as they kick off each of the five parts in the book and are revisited at the start and end of every chapter, to put details and key lessons learned into real-world context.

The cases are built around companies that range in size from the entrepreneurial start-up to the multimillion-dollar corporate giant, reflecting a

wide variety of industries. These cases were created to show students how the full range of business functions operate within virtually every business setting.

NOTES:

_____

_____

_____

_____

CHAPTER 1: BUSINESS INFORMATION SYSTEMS: AN OVERVIEW

CHAPTER AT A GLANCE: This first chapter in a part of three chapters provides an overview of information technology (IT) and information systems (ISs) and a framework for discussions in subsequent chapters. It briefly reviews all the types of ISs that the students will meet in the rest of the book, as well as IT careers.

PART CASE UPDATE: The Part Case follows the story of a group of college students who start a fast health food business that becomes increasingly popular. As the business grows, they must strategize and move from manual operations to management supported by information technology. Students will most likely relate well to their portrayed peers. The story will help them appreciate the support that IT lends to such a growing business.

STUDENT COMPANION WEB SITE: Remember to send students to *www.course.com/mis/oz* for added resources to reinforce their learning, including access to self quizzes so they can test their own knowledge of the basics put forth in Chapter 1.

NOTES:

_____

_____

_____

_____

_____

CHAPTER 2: STRATEGIC USES OF INFORMATION SYSTEMS

CHAPTER AT A GLANCE: This entire chapter is devoted to one of the most important themes of this book: the strategic uses of information systems. The chapter provides more examples, all recent, of success and failure in harnessing IT to support or spearhead strategic initiatives. Strategy and strategic uses of IT are addressed many more times in subsequent chapters, often referring to the principles explained in this chapter. *Management Information Systems* was the first book to introduce this topic in an early chapter, and the successful pedagogy has been emulated by other introductory books.

STUDENT COMPANION WEB SITE: Remember to send students to *www.course.com/mis/oz* for added resources to reinforce their learning, including access to PowerPoint presentations to refresh the lessons put forth on information systems strategy in Chapter 2.

NOTES:

_____

_____

_____

_____

CHAPTER 3: BUSINESS FUNCTIONS AND SUPPLY CHAINS

CHAPTER AT A GLANCE: Chapter 3 provides a detailed discussion of how ISs are used in a variety of business functions and industries. It explains the concepts of enterprise applications such as enterprise resource planning systems and supply chain management systems, which are addressed throughout the book. The overarching pedagogy is to get the students to realize how interrelated business functions are in a modern commercial organization and the fact that current IT can facilitate integration of modules into a coherent corporate IS.

STUDENT COMPANION WEB SITE: Remember to send students to *www.course.com/mis/oz* for added resources to reinforce their learning, including access to an electronic copy of the Fifth Edition's glossary, which students can use to quickly access key terms from Chapter 3.

NOTES:

_____

_____

_____

_____

INSTRUCTOR EDITION

CHAPTER AT A GLANCE: This is the first chapter in a part of four chapters that discuss information technologies and their relevance to business. Chapter 4 covers the latest developments in hardware, from processing power to memory capacity to the various classes of computers and their importance in different business settings. The emphasis is on those aspects that are important in decision-making, such as which storage media meet what business needs.

PART CASE UPDATE: QuickBiz Messengers, the case for this part, is the story of a young entrepreneur and his team. It follows the development of the business from a small team of bicycle messengers to a fleet of trucks, and the steps management takes to keep the business competitive with information technologies that gives managers the information they need when they need it and in the form they need it. This is a classic case that demonstrates a growing need for state-of-the-art hardware, software, databases, and networks and the great dependency on these technologies to ensure survival and success.

STUDENT COMPANION WEB SITE: Remember to send students to *www.course.com/mis/oz* for added resources to reinforce their learning, including plenty of additional links to Web pages that offer tons of interesting information pertaining to the different subjects addressed in the Part II Case, "QuickBiz Messengers."

NOTES:

_____

_____

_____

_____

CHAPTER AT A GLANCE: The chapter begins with a review of programming languages from the very early machine languages to the latest object-oriented and Web languages. It discusses state-of-the-art applications and their importance for businesses, such as packaged applications, various operating systems, and virtual reality applications. It also explains trends such as organizations' move toward open source software. It ends with a discussion of considerations in purchasing software.

STUDENT COMPANION WEB SITE: Remember to send students to *www.course.com/mis/oz* for added resources to reinforce their learning, including a selection of robust labs that offer fascinating simulations on subjects addressed in Chapter 5, such as the basics of visual programming and spreadsheet software.

NOTES:

_____

_____

_____

_____

INSTRUCTOR EDITION

CHAPTER 6: BUSINESS NETWORKS AND TELECOMMUNICATIONS

CHAPTER AT A GLANCE: The chapter discusses the most important infrastructure of modern ISs. It also provides the technical foundation for later discussions that involve network-based applications. The chapter focuses on business uses of networking technologies, most of which the students are experiencing in daily life. The chapter also has extended coverage of the latest wireless technologies such as Wi-Fi and RFID.

STUDENT COMPANION WEB SITE: Remember to send students to *www.course.com/mis/oz* for added resources to reinforce their learning, including access to self quizzes so they can test their own knowledge of the technology that underlies telecommunications.

NOTES:

_____

_____

_____

_____

_____

CHAPTER 7: DATABASES AND DATA WAREHOUSES

CHAPTER AT A GLANCE: The heart of many ISs is a database or a data warehouse. These technologies and their uses are discussed in this chapter. The chapter discusses the different general models of databases with an emphasis on relational and object-oriented databases, and explains their advantages and disadvantages in terms of construction and maintenance. Discussion of data mining and online analytical processing have been moved to Chapter 11 in this edition, to expand the coverage of these important concepts.

STUDENT COMPANION WEB SITE: Remember to send students to *www.course.com/mis/oz* for added resources to reinforce their learning, including access to PowerPoint presentations that they can use to refresh on the lessons put forth about appropriately storing and managing data from Chapter 7.

NOTES:

_____

_____

_____

_____

_____

CHAPTER AT A GLANCE: Chapter 8 is the first of two chapters in Part III of the book. Much of the IT that students see and use is part of or related to the Web. This chapter explains the fundamentals of Web-enabled commerce, starting with popular Web technologies and continuing with online commercial enterprises. The chapter concludes with a survey of the options that companies have when establishing Web sites, especially when considering Web hosting services.

PART CASE UPDATE: It Fits Outfits, the case study for this part, follows the development of a young fashion designer's small business into a network of retail stores. The business increasingly depends on collaboration with suppliers around the globe, and its growth requires increasingly sophisticated information resources. Shari Steiner, the CEO, wisely adopts new information technologies to shorten cycle times and decision making of this successful business.

STUDENT COMPANION WEB SITE: Remember to send students to *www.course.com/mis/oz* for added resources to reinforce their learning, including multiple hands-on projects associated with the Part III Case. These projects give your students a chance to become a "character" in this case and make decisions to assist this business.

NOTES:

_____

_____

_____

_____

CHAPTER AT A GLANCE: This chapter is new in this edition, although some of the material was discussed in the Fourth Edition (in Chapter 11). It illuminates the challenges and efficiencies of managing business information systems on a global scale, and presents many new cases of the efficiencies accomplished with these systems. New technologies that support global supply chains, such as RFID, are highlighted, as well as the growing phenomenon of collaborative logistics. The chapter continues to emphasize the critical considerations in implementation of global ISs, especially Web-based systems. These issues include cultural, linguistic, and legal differences, as well as differences in standards and time and address notations.

STUDENT COMPANION WEB SITE: Remember to send students to *www.course.com/mis/oz* for added resources to reinforce their learning, including access to additional, brand new hands-on work, pertinent to Chapter 9, that they can use for practice or that you can use as additional homework assignments.

NOTES:

_____

_____

_____

_____

CHAPTER AT A GLANCE: This chapter is one of two that comprise Part IV of the book. The major focus of this chapter is decision support and expert systems, a topic covered in the Fourth Edition in two separate chapters. Many new examples of decision aides are given, especially of online expert systems. The students are introduced to the notion of unstructured problems and how these systems help solve such problems. The notions of model and sensitivity analysis are explained, and new examples are given to demonstrate them.

PART CASE UPDATE: The Part Case introduces the DeBoers, a family of farmers who learn to harness the power of IT to make decisions that may result in greater yields of their crops. The case accomplishes two goals: it introduces the students to some of the challenges of an important but little known segment of our economy, agriculture, and demonstrates how important IT has been in making the United States the world's most efficient food producer.

STUDENT COMPANION WEB SITE: Remember to send students to *www.course.com/mis/oz* for added resources to reinforce their learning, including plenty of additional links to Web pages that offer tons of interesting information pertaining to the different subjects addressed in the Part IV Case, "DeBoer Farms."

NOTES:

_____

_____

_____

_____

CHAPTER AT A GLANCE: This chapter introduces the students to the growing importance of business intelligence (BI), information about the business, its clients, and its competition, which is so important for executive decision making. The first discussion focuses mainly on the concept and use of online analytical processing and data mining. Many examples are given to demonstrate how these technologies have helped businesses stay competitive.

The second part of the chapter focuses on technologies that help organizations turn data into knowledge and help employees find sources of relevant knowledge, such as employee knowledge networks.

STUDENT COMPANION WEB SITE: Remember to send students to *www.course.com/mis/oz* for added resources to reinforce their learning, including access to additional, brand-new hands-on work, pertinent to Chapter 11, that they can use for practice or that you can use as additional homework assignments.

NOTES:

_____

_____

_____

_____

INSTRUCTOR EDITION

CHAPTER AT A GLANCE: This chapter is the first of three chapters that make up Part V of the book. IT planning and development have become increasingly important because of the fast advancing technologies and growing competition in the business world. The chapter outlines general approaches to IT planning and discusses the importance of integrating IT planning into the organizational strategic planning. While traditional "waterfall" approaches to developing information systems, such as the Systems Development Life Cycle, are discussed, the chapter devotes a thorough discussion to agile methods, which have become popular among software developers.

PART CASE UPDATE: The Part V case is the story of a hospitality enterprise that tries to stay abreast of technologies that will help it remain successful in a global market. Planning, systems development, consideration of alternative approaches to acquisition of applications, and coping with risks and security issues are demonstrated as Worldwide Host moves to open its systems for easy reservations of lodging and travel while being challenged with typical problems of moving from a legacy system to a new application and risks to a Web-based system.

STUDENT COMPANION WEB SITE: Remember to send students to *www.course.com/mis/oz* for added resources to reinforce their learning, including multiple hands-on projects associated with the Part V Case, "Worldwide Host." These projects give your students a chance to become a "character" in this case and make decisions to assist the development of this fictional new business.

NOTES:

_____

_____

_____

_____

CHAPTER AT A GLANCE: Assigning development to their own IT professionals is only one option organizations have in acquiring new information systems. This chapter discusses all the current alternatives: outsourcing, purchasing and licensing ready-made applications, software as a service (SaaS), and user-developed applications. The chapter presents the pros and cons of each option and explains the important points in managing each of them.

STUDENT COMPANION WEB SITE: Remember to send students to *www.course.com/mis/oz* for added resources to reinforce their learning, including access to self quizzes so they can test their own knowledge about other ways organizations can obtain new ISs.

NOTES:

_____

_____

_____

_____

CHAPTER AT A GLANCE: New disturbing risks to information resources increase the importance of this chapter, which has been extensively revised to reflect new threats and solutions. Viruses and worms, denial of service attacks, hijacking, phishing, identity theft, and other risks are thoroughly explained, and so are the methods to protect against them. Natural as well as man-made disasters in recent years have sent a clear message to organizations: they must plan for disaster recovery. The chapter discusses the topic in detail with many real examples. One section clarifies the economic consideration of security measures and explains how to calculate down time of interdependent and redundant systems.

STUDENT COMPANION WEB SITE: Remember to send students to *www.course.com/mis/oz* for added resources to reinforce their learning, including a selection of robust labs that offer fascinating simulations so students can expand their knowledge on subjects, including some addressed in Chapter 14, such how to keep your computer virus free.

NOTES:

_____

_____

_____

_____

_____

INSTRUCTOR EDITION

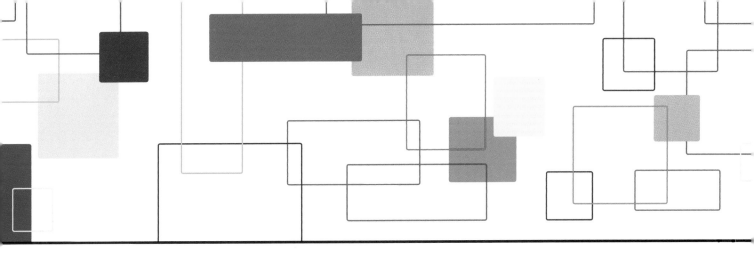

MANAGEMENT INFORMATION SYSTEMS

SYSTEMS

Fifth Edition

EFFY OZ

The Pennsylvania State University, Great Valley

THOMSON

COURSE TECHNOLOGY™

Australia • Canada • Mexico • Singapore • Spain • United Kingdom • United States

**Management Information Systems,
Fifth Edition**

by Effy Oz

Executive Editor:
Bob Woodbury

Acquisitions Editor:
Maureen Martin

Senior Product Manager:
Eunice Yeates

Developmental Editor:
Deb Kaufmann

Associate Product Manager:
Jennifer Smith

Editorial Assistant:
Allison Murphy

Production Editor:
GEX Publishing Services

Senior Marketing Manager:
Karen Seitz

Compositor:
GEX Publishing Services

Manufacturing Coordinator:
Justin Palmeiro

To Narda, my best friend and beloved wife:
It has been a great journey together, and it is only the beginning.

BRIEF CONTENTS

PART ONE   **THE INFORMATION AGE**   **1**

Chapter 1   Business Information Systems: An Overview   5
Chapter 2   Strategic Uses of Information Systems   36
Chapter 3   Business Functions and Supply Chains   68

PART TWO   **INFORMATION TECHNOLOGY**   **105**

Chapter 4   Business Hardware   109
Chapter 5   Business Software   145
Chapter 6   Business Networks and Telecommunications   178
Chapter 7   Databases and Data Warehouses   216

PART THREE   **WEB-ENABLED COMMERCE**   **245**

Chapter 8   The Web-Enabled Enterprise   248
Chapter 9   Challenges of Global Information Systems   288

PART FOUR   **DECISION SUPPORT AND BUSINESS INTELLIGENCE**   **313**

Chapter 10   Decision Support and Expert Systems   316
Chapter 11   Business Intelligence and Knowledge Management   351

PART FIVE   **PLANNING, ACQUISITION, AND CONTROLS**   **379**

Chapter 12   Systems Planning and Development   383
Chapter 13   Choices in Systems Acquisition   412
Chapter 14   Risks, Security, and Disaster Recovery   440

PART ONE	**THE INFORMATION AGE**	**1**
	Case I: *Eats2Go*	*1*
Chapter 1	**Business Information Systems: An Overview**	**5**
	Eats2Go: Business Systems and Information	*6*

The Purpose of Information Systems — 7

Data, Information, and Information Systems — 7
- *Data vs. Information 7*
- *Data Manipulation 8*
- *Generating Information 8*
- *Information in Context 9*
- *What Is a System? 9*
- *Information and Managers 11*

Why You Should…Be Well Versed in Information Systems — **12**
- *The Benefits of Human-Computer Synergy 13*
- *Information Systems in Organizations 13*
- *The Four Stages of Processing 15*

Ethical & Societal Issues: The Not-So-Bright Side — **16**
- *Computer Equipment for Information Systems 17*

From Recording Transactions to Providing Expertise:
Types of Information Systems — 18
- *Transaction Processing Systems 18*
- *Supply Chain Management Systems 18*
- *Customer Relationship Management Systems 19*
- *Business Intelligence Systems 20*
- *Decision Support and Expert Systems 20*
- *Geographic Information Systems 20*

Information Systems in Business Functions — 21
- *Accounting 21*
- *Finance 22*
- *Marketing 22*
- *Human Resources 22*

Web-Empowered Enterprises — 22

Careers in Information Systems — 22
- *Systems Analyst 23*
- *Database Administrator 24*
- *Network Administrator 24*
- *Webmaster 25*
- *Chief Security Officer 25*
- *Chief Information Officer and Chief Technology Officer 25*

Summary — 27

Eats2Go Revisited — **28**

Key Terms — 28

Review Questions	29
Discussion Questions	29
Applying Concepts	30
Hands-On Activities	30
Team Activities	30
Companion CD Questions	31
Video Questions	31
From Ideas to Application: Real Cases	**32**

Chapter 2	**Strategic Uses of Information Systems**	**36**
	Eats2Go: Using Information Strategically	*37*
	Strategy and Strategic Moves	38
	Achieving a Competitive Advantage	39
	Initiative #1: Reduce Costs 40	
	Initiative #2: Raise Barriers to Market Entrants 41	
	Initiative #3: Establish High Switching Costs 41	
	Initiative #4: Create New Products or Services 42	
	Initiative #5: Differentiate Products or Services 43	
	Initiative #6: Enhance Products or Services 44	
	Why You Should…Understand the Notion of Strategic Information Systems	**45**
	Initiative #7: Establish Alliances 45	
	Initiative #8: Lock in Suppliers or Buyers 47	
	Creating and Maintaining Strategic Information Systems	48
	Creating an SIS 49	
	Reengineering and Organizational Change 49	
	Competitive Advantage as a Moving Target 50	
	JetBlue: A Success Story	51
	Massive Automation 51	
	Away from Tradition 52	
	Enhanced Service 52	
	Impressive Performance 53	
	Late Mover Advantage 53	
	Ford on the Web: A Failure Story	54
	The Ideas 54	
	Hitting the Wall 54	
	The Retreat 54	
	Ethical & Societal Issues: Size Matters	**55**
	The Bleeding Edge	56
	Summary	58
	Eats2Go Revisited	**59**
	Key Terms	59

Review Questions	60
Discussion Questions	60
Applying Concepts	61
Hands-On Activities	62
Team Activities	62
Companion CD Questions	63
Video Questions	63
From Ideas to Application: Real Cases	**64**

Chapter 3	**Business Functions and Supply Chains**	**68**
	Eats2Go: Continued Growth and Specialization	**69**
	Effectiveness and Efficiency	70
	Accounting	72
	Why You Should...Know About Business Functions and Supply Chains	**73**
	Finance	74
	Cash Management 74	
	Investment Analysis and Service 75	
	Engineering	75
	Supply Chain Management	77
	Material Requirements Planning and Purchasing 78	
	Manufacturing Resource Planning 79	
	Monitoring and Control 79	
	Shipping 80	
	RFID in SCM 81	
	Customer Relationship Management	82
	Market Research 83	
	Targeted Marketing 84	
	Customer Service 85	
	Salesforce Automation 86	
	Ethical & Societal Issues: Consumer Privacy	**87**
	Human Resource Management	88
	Employee Record Management 88	
	Promotion and Recruitment 88	
	Training 90	
	Evaluation 91	
	Compensation and Benefits Management 91	
	Interorganizational Supply Chain Management Systems	91
	The Importance of Trust 93	
	The Musical Chairs of Inventory 94	
	Collaborative Logistics 94	
	Enterprise Resource Planning	95
	Summary	96

TABLE OF CONTENTS

Eats2Go Revisited	**97**
Key Terms	97
Review Questions	98
Discussion Questions	98
Applying Concepts	99
Hands-On Activities	99
Team Activities	99
Companion CD Questions	100
Video Questions	100
From Ideas to Application: Real Cases	**101**

PART TWO	**INFORMATION TECHNOLOGY**	**105**
	Case II: *Quickbiz Messengers*	*105*
Chapter 4	**Business Hardware**	**109**
	Quickbiz Messengers: Hardware Streamlines Processes	*110*
	Hardware Components	111
	Classification of Computers	112
	Supercomputers 113	
	Mainframe Computers 113	
	Midrange Computers 114	
	Microcomputers 114	
	Computers on the Go: Notebook, Handheld, and Tablet Computers 114	
	Converging Technologies 115	
	A Peek Inside the Computer	115
	The Central Processing Unit 116	
	Why You Should...Understand Some Technical Details	**118**
	Computer Power 118	
	Input Devices	119
	Keyboard 119	
	Mouse, Trackball, and Trackpad 119	
	Touch Screen 120	
	Source Data Input Devices 120	
	Imaging 122	
	Speech Recognition 122	
	Ethical & Societal Issues: Computers May Be Hazardous to Your Health	**123**
	Output Devices	123
	Monitors 123	
	Printers 124	

Storage Media 125
    Modes of Access   125
    Magnetic Tapes   126
    Magnetic Disks   127
    Optical Discs   127
    Optical Tape   128
    Flash Memory   128
    DAS, NAS, and SAN   129
    Business Considerations in Evaluating Storage Media   130

Considerations in Purchasing Hardware 132
    Scalability and Updating Hardware   133

Summary 136

QuickBiz Messengers Revisited **137**

Key Terms 137

Review Questions 138

Discussion Questions 138

Applying Concepts 139

Hands-On Activities 140

Team Activities 141

Companion CD Questions 141

Video Questions 141

From Ideas to Application: Real Cases **142**

Chapter 5 **Business Software** **145**
Quickbiz Messengers: Software Steers a Path to Stability **146**

Software: Instructions to the Computer 147

Programming Languages and Software Development Tools 147
    Visual Programming   149
    Object-Oriented Programming   150

Why You Should...Be Software Savvy **152**

Language Translation: Compilers and Interpreters 153

Application Software 154
    Office Productivity Applications   154
    Hypermedia and Multimedia   156
    Groupware   157
    Virtual Reality   157
    3-D Geographic Software   158

System Software 158
    Operating Systems   159
    Other System Software   163

Open Source Software 163

TABLE OF CONTENTS

Software Licensing 165

Ethical & Societal Issues: Software Piracy **166**

Considerations for Packaged Software 167

Summary 169

QuickBiz Messengers Revisited **170**

Key Terms 171

Review Questions 171

Discussion Questions 172

Applying Concepts 172

Hands-On Activities 173

Team Activities 173

Companion CD Questions 174

Video Questions 174

From Ideas to Application: Real Cases **175**

Chapter 6 **Business Networks and Telecommunications** **178**

Quickbiz Messengers: Communication Is Key *179*

Telecommunications in Business 180

Telecommunications in Daily Use 181
   Cellular Phones 181
   Videoconferencing 182
   Fax 182
   Wireless Payments and Warehousing 182

Why You Should...Understand Telecommunications **183**
   Peer-to-Peer File Sharing 183
   Web-Empowered Commerce 184

Bandwidth and Media 184
   Bandwidth 184
   Media 184

Networks 187
   Types of Networks 187
   PANs 189
   Networking Hardware 189
   Virtual Private Networks 190
   Switching Techniques 190

Protocols 191
   TCP/IP 192
   Ethernet 192
   Wireless Protocols 193
   Generations in Mobile Communications 196

Internet Networking Services   197
  Cable 197
  Digital Subscriber Line (DSL) 197
  T1 and T3 Lines 199
  Satellite 199
  Fixed Wireless 199
Ethical & Societal Issues: Telecommuting: Pros and Cons   200
  Optical Carrier 201
  Broadband over Power Lines (BPL) 202

The Future of Networking Technologies   202
  Broadband Telephoning 202
  Radio Frequency Identification 203
  Converging Technologies 204

Summary   207
QuickBiz Messengers Revisited   **208**
Key Terms   208
Review Questions   209
Discussion Questions   210
Applying Concepts   210
Hands-On Activities   211
Team Activities   211
Companion CD Questions   212
Video Questions   212
From Ideas to Application: Real Cases   **213**

Chapter 7   **Databases and Data Warehouses**   **216**
                Quickbiz Messengers: The Value and Uses of Databases   **217**

Managing Digital Data   218
  The Traditional File Approach 218
  The Database Approach 219

Database Models   222
  The Relational Model 222
Why You Should...Know About Data Management   **224**
  The Object-Oriented Model 225

Relational Operations   226
  Structured Query Language 227
  The Schema and Metadata 228

Data Modeling   229
Databases on the Web   230

TABLE OF CONTENTS

Data Warehousing   231

Ethical & Societal Issues: Every Move You Make   **233**

From Database to Data Warehouse 234

Phases in Building a Data Warehouse 235

Summary   237

QuickBiz Messengers Revisited   **238**

Key Terms   238

Review Questions   239

Discussion Questions   239

Applying Concepts   240

Hands-On Activities   240

Team Activities   241

Companion CD Questions   241

From Ideas to Application: Real Cases   **242**

PART THREE   **WEB-ENABLED COMMERCE**   **245**

Case III: *It Fits Outfits*   **245**

Chapter 8   **The Web-Enabled Enterprise**   **248**

It Fits Outfits: Setting up Operations on the Internet   **249**

Web Business: Growing and Changing   251

Web Technologies: A Review   251

HTTP 251

HTML and XML 252

File Transfer 252

RSS 253

Blogs 253

Why You Should...Know More About Web-Enabled Business   **254**

Podcasting 254

Instant Messaging 254

Cookies 255

Proprietary Technologies 256

Options in Establishing a Web Site   257

Owning and Maintaining a Server 257

Using a Hosting Service 257

Considerations in Selecting a Web Host 259

More than Meets the Eye 261

Web-Enabled Business   262

B2B Trading 262

B2C Trading 266

Supply Chains on the Web   273

Rules for Successful Web-Based Business   275

Target the Right Customers 275

Ethical & Societal Issues: Online Annoyances and Worse   **276**

Capture the Customer's Total Experience 277
Personalize the Service 277
Shorten the Business Cycle 278
Let Customers Help Themselves 278
Be Proactive and De-Commoditize 278
E-Commerce Is Every Commerce 278

Summary   279

It Fits Outfits Revisited   **280**

Key Terms   280

Review Questions   281

Discussion Questions   281

Applying Concepts   282

Hands-On Activities   283

Team Activities   284

Companion CD Questions   284

Video Questions   284

From Ideas to Application: Real Cases   **285**

Chapter 9   **Challenges of Global Information Systems**   **288**
It Fits Outfits: Expanding Globally   *289*

Multinational Organizations   290

The Web and International Commerce   291

Think Globally, Act Locally 292

Why You Should...Learn About Challenges of Global ISs   **293**

Challenges of Global Information Systems   293

Technological Challenges 293
Regulations and Tariffs 294
Differences in Payment Mechanisms 295
Language Differences 295
Cultural Differences 296
Conflicting Economic, Scientific, and Security Interests 296
Political Challenges 297
Different Standards 298

Ethical & Societal Issues: Legal Jurisdictions in Cyberspace   **299**

Legal Barriers 301
Different Time Zones 304

Summary   305

It Fits Outfits Revisited   **305**

Key Terms   306

Review Questions   306

Discussion Questions   306

TABLE OF CONTENTS

Applying Concepts   307

Hands-On Activities   308

Team Activities   308

Companion CD Questions   309

From Ideas to Application: Real Cases   **310**

PART FOUR   **DECISION SUPPORT AND BUSINESS INTELLIGENCE**   **313**

Case IV: *DeBoer Farms*   *313*

Chapter 10   **Decision Support and Expert Systems**   **316**
DeBoer Farms: Farming Technology for Information   *317*

Decision Support   318

The Decision-Making Process   318

Structured and Unstructured Problems   319

Why You Should...Be Familiar with Decision Aids   **321**

Decision Support Systems   321
    The Data Management Module 322
    The Model Management Module 323
    The Dialog Module 325
    Sensitivity Analysis 326
    Decision Support Systems in Action 327

Ethical & Societal Issues: Decisions by Machines   **329**

Expert Systems   332
    Expert Systems in Action 335

Geographic Information Systems   338

Summary   342

DeBoer Farms Revisited   **343**

Key Terms   343

Review Questions   343

Discussion Questions   344

Applying Concepts   345

Hands-On Activities   345

Team Activities   346

Companion CD Questions   347

Video Questions   347

From Ideas to Application: Real Cases   **348**

Chapter 11   **Business Intelligence and Knowledge Management**   **351**
DeBoer Farms: Harvesting Technology's Benefits   *352*

Data Mining and Online Analysis   353
   Data Mining   354
   Online Analytical Processing   357
   More Customer Intelligence   361
   Executive Dashboards   362
Why You Should...Learn About BI and KM Tools   **362**

Knowledge Management   363
   Capturing and Sorting Organizational Knowledge   364
   Employee Knowledge Networks   364
Ethical & Societal Issues: Knowledge and Globalization   **366**
   Knowledge from the Web   367
   Autocategorization   368

Summary   370
DeBoer Farms Revisited   **370**
Key Terms   371
Review Questions   371
Discussion Questions   372
Applying Concepts   372
Hands-On Activities   373
Team Activities   373
Companion CD Questions   374
Video Questions   374
From Ideas to Application: Real Cases   **375**

PART FIVE   **PLANNING, ACQUISITION, AND CONTROLS**   **379**

Case V: *Worldwide Host*   **379**

Chapter 12   **Systems Planning and Development**   **383**
Worldwide Host: A Vision for the Future   *384*

Planning Information Systems   385
   Steps in Planning Information Systems   386
   The Benefits of Standardization in Planning   387
   From Planning to Development   388
Why You Should...Understand the Principles of Systems Development   **388**

The Systems Development Life Cycle   388
   Analysis   389
   Design   392
   Implementation   396
   Support   397

TABLE OF CONTENTS

Agile Methods   398
   When to Use Agile Methods   400
   When Not to Use Agile Methods   400

Systems Integration   401
Ethical & Societal Issues: Should IS Professionals be Certified?   **402**

Summary   404

Worldwide Host Revisited   **404**

Key Terms   405

Review Questions   405

Discussion Questions   406

Applying Concepts   406

Hands-On Activities   407

Team Activities   408

Companion CD Questions   408

Video Questions   408

From Ideas to Application: Real Cases   **409**

Chapter 13   **Choices in Systems Acquisition**   **412**
Worldwide Host: Tapping Others' Expertise   *413*

Options and Priorities   414

Outsourcing   415
   Outsourcing Custom-Designed Applications   415
   Outsourcing IT Services   417
**Why You Should...Understand Alternative Avenues for the
Acquisition of Information Systems**   **418**
   Advantages of Outsourcing IT Services   418
   Risks of Outsourcing IT Services   420

Licensing Applications   422
   Software Licensing Benefits   422
   Software Licensing Risks   423
   Steps in Licensing Ready-Made Software   423

Software as a Service   425
   Caveat Emptor   427

User Application Development   428
   Managing User-Developed Applications   428
Ethical & Societal Issues: Computer Use Policies for Employees   **429**
   Advantages and Risks   430

Summary   432

Worldwide Host Revisited   **433**

Key Terms   433

Review Questions   433

Discussion Questions   434

Applying Concepts   435

Hands-On Activities   435

Team Activities   436

Companion CD Questions   436

Video Questions   436

From Ideas to Application: Real Cases   **437**

Chapter 14   **Risks, Security, and Disaster Recovery**   **440**
                 Worldwide Host: Battling Back from Attacks **441**

Goals of Information Security   442

Risks to Information Systems   442
   Risks to Hardware   443
   Risks to Data and Applications   444
Why You Should...Understand Risks, Security, and
Disaster Recovery Planning   **446**

Risks to Online Operations   450
   Denial of Service   450
   Computer Hijacking   450

Controls   451
   Program Robustness and Data Entry Controls   452
   Backup   452
   Access Controls   453
   Atomic Transactions   454
   Audit Trail   455

Security Measures   456
   Firewalls and Proxy Servers   456
   Authentication and Encryption   457
   The Downside of Security Measures   463

Recovery Measures   464
   The Business Recovery Plan   464
   Recovery Planning and Hot Site Providers   466

The Economics of Information Security   466
Ethical & Societal Issues: Terrorism and PATRIOTism   **467**
   How Much Security Is Enough Security?   468
   Calculating Downtime   468

Summary   470

Worldwide Host Revisited   **471**

Key Terms   471

Review Questions   472

Discussion Questions   473

TABLE OF CONTENTS

Applying Concepts   474
Hands-On Activities   474
Team Activities   475
Companion CD Questions   475
Video Questions   475
From Ideas to Application: Real Cases   **476**

Glossary   **479**
Subject Index   **495**
Name & Company Index   **523**

The goal of *Management Information Systems, Fifth Edition* is to provide a real-world understanding of information systems (ISs) for business and computer science students. Like its predecessor, this Fifth Edition provides students with a firm foundation in business-related information technology (IT) on which they can build successful careers regardless of the particular fields they choose. They may find themselves formulating strategic plans in executive suites, optimizing operations in businesses or on factory floors, fine-tuning plans for their own entrepreneurial ventures, designing ISs to optimize their organization's operations, working as consultants, augmenting business activities on the Web, or creating valuable new information products in any number of industries.

This Fifth Edition is more concise than its predecessor, yet not less complete. It is organized in fourteen chapters that contain the most important topics for business students.

The fundamental principle guiding this book is that ISs are everywhere in business. Information systems are pervasive because information is the single most powerful resource in every business function in every industry. Knowledge of IT is not always explicitly stated as a job requirement, but it is an essential element of success in virtually any position. Not everyone in business needs to have all the technical skills of an IT professional, but everyone needs a deep-enough understanding of the subject to know how to use IT in his or her profession.

Management Information Systems provides students with the proper balance of technical information and real-world applications. No matter what field they undertake, students will enter the business world knowing how to get information to work for them. They will know enough about IT to work productively with IT specialists, and they will know enough about business applications to get information systems to support their work in the best way possible.

APPROACH

Part Cases Show IS Principles in Action

In this edition Part Cases were carefully updated to integrate all the IT principles that arise in business, to give students an opportunity to view IS issues in action, and to solve business problems related to IT just as they arise in the real world. The cases are built around companies that range in size from the entrepreneurial start-up to the multimillion-dollar corporate giant, reflecting a wide variety of industries. These cases were created to show students how the full range of business functions operate within virtually every business setting. The Part Cases are integrated into the text in four ways:

- *The Case:* Each part of the text (made up of between two and four chapters) opens with the Part Case: the story of a business, including the business's IS challenges, the characters involved, and the issues. Everyone in business knows that almost every business problem has a human element; this aspect of managing IT-related challenges is realistically represented in each case.

- *The Business Challenge:* The presentation of each case is immediately followed by a succinct statement of the business challenge of the case and the ways the information in each chapter in the case will help the reader meet that challenge.

- *Case Installments:* Each chapter opens with an installment of the Part Case that focuses and expands on an aspect of the original story that relates most closely to the chapter content.

- *Case Revisited Sections:* Each chapter ends with a Case Revisited section, which includes a concise summary of the challenge in the case installment; a section called **What Would You Do**?, a series of questions that asks the readers to play a role in the case and decide how they would handle a variety of challenges inherent in the case; and **New Perspectives**, a series of questions that introduces a wide variety of "what ifs" reaching beyond the original scope of the case and again asking the students to play different roles to meet business challenges.

Emphasis on the Real World

Management Information Systems is not afraid to warn about the limitations of ISs. The text also explains the great potential of many information technologies, which many organizations have not yet unleashed. Of course, this book includes chapters and features that provide a thorough, concise—and refreshingly clear—grounding in the technology of information systems, because all professionals in successful organizations are involved in making decisions about hardware, software, and telecommunications. But, through current, detail-rich, real-world case studies throughout the book, and a dedication to qualifying each presentation with the real-world factors that may affect business, this book stays close to the workplace in its presentation.

Attention to New Business Practices and Trends

Large parts of the text are devoted to discussing innovative uses of information technology and its benefits and risks. Contemporary concepts such as supply chain management systems, data warehousing, business intelligence systems, knowledge management, Web-based electronic data interchange, and software as a service are explained in plain, easy-to-understand language. About 90 percent of the examples, case studies, statistics, and anecdotes are from the year 2004 and later.

Illustration of the Importance of Each Subject to One's Career

Business students often do not understand why they have to learn about information technology. The reason many students are frustrated with introductory MIS courses is that they do not fully understand how information technology works or why it is important for them to understand it. One of the primary goals of this book is for its entire presentation to make the answers to these questions apparent. First, all subjects are explained so clearly that even the least technically oriented student can understand them. Technology is never explained for technology's sake, but to immediately demonstrate how it supports businesses. For instance, networking, database management, and the Web technologies (Chapters 6 through 8), often confusing topics, are presented with clear, concise, and vivid descriptions to paint a picture of technology at work. In addition, each chapter includes a feature titled **Why You Should . . .** , which explains to students how being well-versed in that chapter's aspect of IT is important to their careers.

Emphasis on Ethical Thinking

The book puts a great emphasis on some of the questionable and controversial uses of information technology, with special treatment provided in the **Ethical and Societal Issues** boxes. The students are required to weigh the positive and negative impacts of technology and to convincingly argue their own positions on important issues such as privacy, free speech, and professional conduct.

Emphasis on Critical Thinking

Critical thinking is used throughout the text as well as in the book's many features. For instance, the students are put in the midst of a business dilemma relating to the running case of each chapter and required to answer **What Would You Do?** questions. The questions motivate students to evaluate many aspects of each situation and to repeatedly consider how quickly IT evolves.

ADDITIONAL EMPHASES IN THE FIFTH EDITION

Building on the success of the Fourth Edition, *Management Information Systems, Fifth Edition* includes a uniquely effective combination of features.

Updated and New Part and Chapter Case Studies

This Fifth Edition highlights again the well-received, powerful pedagogical tool: five **Part Cases** that clearly incorporate a wide array of real-world events and challenges that dramatize how information technology is integrated into everyday business.

Strong Foundation in Strategic ISs in Business Functions

In addition to a complete chapter on strategic uses of ISs (Chapter 2), strategic thinking is an underlying theme throughout the book. Current examples are used to illustrate how information systems can give businesses a strategic advantage.

Up-to-date Coverage of Web Technologies and Web-Enabled Commerce

Reflecting the use of Web technologies in so many business activities, the book integrates the topic seamlessly throughout the text, just as it has become integrated into business in general. But the text goes beyond the well-worn discussions of the topic (and the handful of sites everyone knows about) to tell the students what works about e-commerce and what doesn't work.

Thorough Discussion of Supply Chain Management Systems

As SCM systems are becoming pervasive in the business world, supply chains and their management are discussed both in a dedicated chapter (Chapter 3) and throughout the text. Related technologies, such as RFID, are clearly explained. In text and diagrams, the importance of these systems is underscored.

Current Real-world Examples Reflect a Wide Variety of Businesses

The text incorporates more applications, cases, and projects in the full range of business functions and industries throughout the book. The cases at the end of the chapter, in the **From Ideas to Application: Real Cases** sections, have been carefully selected to include critical thinking questions to guide students to apply what they have learned. Most of these cases are new to this edition and others have been updated and reflect technology and trends in 2005. In addition, for strong pedagogical reinforcement, examples are embedded throughout the book.

Coverage of Global Issues

Globalization has become an important issue both economically and technologically. An entire chapter, Chapter 9, is devoted to discussing challenges to global information systems, from legal discrepancies through cultural issues to time zone issues. The chapter also discusses how the challenges can be met successfully.

New Aspects of Ethical and Societal Issues

The coverage of **Ethical & Societal Issues** in *Management Information Systems* builds on the strong foundation started in the first four editions. However, new issues have emerged, such as phishing and offshoring, which are discussed in this edition.

New Hands-on Reinforcement of Material

This Fifth Edition continues to provide a large selection of assignments at the ends of chapters, mainly assignments that require the use of relevant software and the Web. Many of these assignments, including **Applying Concepts**, **Hands-on Activities**, and **Team Activities**, have been updated for the Fifth Edition. All-new hands-on features in this edition include **Companion CD Questions** and **Video Questions**. In addition to the hands-on exercises in each chapter, students and instructors will find a host of additional new hands-on work available at the Student Companion Web site, which is discussed later in this Preface.

More Points of Interest

Responding to instructors' enthusiastic reception of **Points of Interest**, we added a large number of sidebar statistics, anecdotes, and short stories that add an interesting and entertaining aspect to the main chapter text.

MIS COMPANION CD

 Course Technology is committed to helping instructors effectively teach MIS concepts and related computer skills. With the Fifth Edition, we are proud to offer an exciting tool, powered by SAM technology, to enhance students' learning experience; the MIS Companion CD for student training. Students now have the opportunity to experience FREE training in Microsoft Office Excel 2003 and Microsoft Office Access 2003 along with additional coverage of MIS concepts using MIS Interactive Labs.

The MIS Companion CD is a unique, free tool on CD in the back of every copy of this book. Integration of the CD can be found throughout the text; please look for the CD icon. There are also questions based on the CD material at the end of every chapter.

Excel 2003 and Access 2003 Training

The MIS Companion CD gives students the chance to get hands-on training and practice with Access 2003 and Excel 2003 tasks, ranging from the beginning through advanced levels. Instructors can now cover these software skills in their introductory MIS course by utilzing this Companion CD to help their students absorb and practice these skills. In addition, the tool also gives students the opportunity to learn and practice Access and Excel tasks independently.

MIS Interactive Labs

This CD also includes 15 robust interactive labs that reinforce key MIS-related concepts, enabling students to learn real-world computer-based activities in a simulated environment. These labs are designed to provide students with various options in absorbing concepts through reading, observation, step-by-step practice, and hands-on application. Some of the exciting topics addressed in these labs include presentation software, networking basics, online privacy, project management, and Web design.

Table of Contents for Lab Integration

The following table of contents illustrates which labs are best for reinforcing some of the content coverage in each chapter of this book. Use this list as a guide to match each MIS lab with its corresponding chapter.

Lab: Spreadsheets	Ch. 1: Business Information Systems: An Overview
Lab: Visual Programming	Ch. 5: Business Software
Lab: Networking Basics	Ch. 6: Networks and Telecommunications
Lab: Wireless Networking	Ch. 6: Networks and Telecommunications
Lab: Databases	Ch. 7: Databases and Data Warehouses
Lab: Electronic Commerce	Ch. 8: Web-Enabled Enterprise
Lab: Creating a Web Page	Ch. 8: Web-Enabled Enterprise
Lab: Advanced Spreadsheets	Ch. 10: Decision Support and Expert Systems
Lab: Advanced Databases	Ch. 11: Business Intelligence and Knowledge Management
Lab: Web Design Principles	Ch. 12: Systems Planning and Development
Lab: Project Management	Ch. 12: Systems Planning and Development
Lab: Keeping Your Computer Virus Free	Ch. 14: Risks, Security, and Disaster Recovery

ASSESSMENT OPTIONS FOR INSTRUCTORS

Beyond this exciting MIS Companion CD for student training, Course Technology offers assessment options to further enhance student learning. SAM (Skills Assessment Manager) is the worldwide leader in online assessment and is proven to be the most effective tool to assess and train students in Microsoft Office tasks, Computer Concepts, Windows, the Internet, and more. SAM is a hands-on, simulated computer assessment and training tool that gives students the feeling of working live in the computer application.

Want More? SAM 2003

Inject a wider breadth of applications, as well as additional Excel, Access, and Computer Concepts coverage into your MIS course with SAM 2003! Visit *http://samcentral.course.com* to learn more.

Please contact your Course Technology Sales Representative for more information regarding these assessment options.

STUDENT COMPANION WEB SITE

We have created an exciting online companion for students to utilize as they work through the Fifth Edition of *Management Information Systems*. In the front of this text you will find a key code that provides full access to a robust Web site, located at *www.course.com/mis/mis5*. This Web resource includes the following features:

PowerPoint Slides

Direct access is offered to the book's PowerPoint presentations, which cover the key points from each chapter. These presentations are a useful study tool.

 ### Videos

Twelve topical video clips, linked to chapters throughout the book, can be found on this Web site. Questions to accompany the respective video clips are featured at the end of each corresponding chapter in the book. These exercises reinforce the concepts taught and provide the students with more critical thinking opportunities. Look for the video icon throughout the text.

For extra video footage, you will also find clips that correspond to the part cases in the Third Edition of the text. These cases have been supplied on the site also.

Glossary of Key Terms

Students can view a PDF file of the glossary from the book.

Part Case Resources from the Fifth Edition

Gain access to a multitude of online resources tied to the five Part Opening Cases which have been updated from the previous edition.

Fifth Edition Part Case Projects

Unique hands-on projects associated with the five Part Cases have been created to allow for first-hand participation in the businesses introduced in each Part. For each Part Case, there is a selection of hands-on projects that asks the user to become a "character" in the cases and perform small tasks to help meet business needs. The solution files for these activities are available to instructors at *www.course.com*, via the password-protected Instructor Downloads page for this textbook.

"Bike Guys" Business Cases

For more examples of MIS concepts in action, we have supplied the popular "Bike Guys" cases from the Third Edition of the text.

Further Case Offerings

Thomson Course Technology now offers cases from Harvard Business School Publishing and other leading case-writing institutions. Create the ideal casebook for your course by selecting cases, adding your own materials, and combining it with our best-selling Course Technology titles. For further information please contact your instructor.

Additional business articles and cases are offered through InfoTrac, the popular Journal Database, made up of more than 15 million full-text articles from over 5000 scholarly and popular periodicals. Please speak with your instructor about accessing this database.

Additional Content

Here you will find the following additional material:

- Organizing Information Technology Resources
- Measurement Units

Test Yourself on MIS

Brand new quizzes, created specifically for this site, allow users to test themselves on the content of each chapter and immediately see what answers were answered right and wrong. For each question answered incorrectly, users are provided with the correct answer and the page in the text where that information is covered. Special testing software randomly compiles a selection of questions from a large database, so students can take quizzes multiple times on a given chapter, with some new questions each time.

Hands-On Exercises

Also created just for this Student Companion Web site, a selection of exercises asks users to apply what they have learned in each chapter and further explore various software tools. The solution files for these activities are also available to instructors at *www.course.com*.

Useful Web Links

Access a repository of links to the home pages of the primary Web sites relative to each chapter for further research.

INSTRUCTOR'S PACKAGE

Management Information Systems, Fifth Edition, includes teaching tools to support instructors in the classroom. The ancillaries that accompany the textbook include an Instructor's Manual, Solutions, Test Banks and Test Engine, Distance Learning content, PowerPoint presentations, and Figure Files. This textbook is one of the few accompanied by an Instructor's Manual written by the text author, ensuring compatibility with the textbook in content, pedagogy, and philosophy. All teaching tools available with this book are provided to the instructor on a single CD-ROM and also available on the Web at *www.course.com*.

The Instructor's Manual

The text author has created this manual to provide materials to help instructors make their classes informative and interesting. The manual offers several approaches to teaching the material, with a sample syllabus and comments on different components. It also suggests alternative course outlines and ideas for term projects. For each chapter, the manual includes teaching tips, useful website addresses, and answers to the Review Questions, Discussion Questions, and Thinking about the Case questions.

Solutions

We provide instructors with solutions to Review Questions and Discussion Questions as well as for quantitative hands-on work in each chapter. If appropriate, we will also provide solution files for various activities. Solutions may also be found on the Course Technology Web site at *www.course.com*. The solutions are password protected.

ExamView®

This objective-based test generator lets the instructor create paper, LAN, or Web-based tests from testbanks designed specifically for this Course Technology text. Instructors can use the QuickTest Wizard to create tests in fewer than five minutes by taking advantage of Course Technology's question banks—or create customized exams.

PowerPoint Presentations

Microsoft PowerPoint slides are included for each chapter. Instructors might use the slides in a variety of ways, including as teaching aids during classroom presentations or as printed handouts for classroom distribution. Instructors can add their own slides for additional topics introduced to the class.

Figure Files

Figure files allow instructors to create their own presentations using figures taken directly from the text.

Distance Learning Content

Course Technology, the premiere innovator in management information systems publishing, is proud to present online courses in WebCT and Blackboard.

- *Blackboard and WebCT Level 1 Online Content.* If you use Blackboard or WebCT, the test bank for this textbook is available at no cost in a simple, ready-to-use format. Go to *www.course.com* and search for this textbook to download the test bank.

- *Blackboard and WebCT Level 2 Online Content.* Blackboard Level 2 and WebCT Level 2 are also available for *Management Information Systems.* Level 2 offers course management and access to a Web site that is fully populated with content for this book.

For more information on how to bring distance learning to your course, instructors should contact their Course Technology sales representative.

ORGANIZATION

Management Information Systems, Fifth Edition is organized into five parts, followed by a glossary and an index. It includes major elements as described on the following page.

Part One: The Information Age

Part One of the book includes three chapters. Chapter 1, "Business Information Systems: An Overview," provides an overview of information technology (IT) and information systems (ISs) and a framework for discussions in subsequent chapters. Chapter 2, "Strategic Uses of Information Systems," discusses organizational strategy and ways in which ISs can be used to meet strategic goals. Chapter 3, "Business Functions and Supply Chains," provides a detailed discussion of business functions, supply chains, and the systems that support management of supply chains in various industries. Together, these three chapters address the essence of all overarching ideas that are discussed at greater depth in subsequent chapters.

Part Two: Information Technology

To understand how ISs enhance managerial practices, one must be well versed in the technical principles of information technology, which are covered in Part Two. Chapters 4, "Business Hardware," 5, "Business Software," and 6, "Networks and Telecommunications," provide a concise treatment of state-of-the-art hardware, software, and networking technologies in business. Chapter 7, "Databases and Data Warehouses," covers database management systems and data warehousing, which provide the technical foundation for a discussion of business intelligence and knowledge management in Chapter 11.

Part Three: Web-Enabled Commerce

Part Three is devoted to networked business and their use of the Internet. Chapter 8, "The Web-enabled Enterprise," is fully devoted to a thorough discussion of relevant Web technologies for business operations. Chapter 9, "Challenges of Global Information Systems," highlights cultural and other challenges in planning and use of the Web and international information system.

Part Four: Decision Support and Business Intelligence

Part Four provides a view of state-of-the-art decision support and expert systems in Chapter 10 and business intelligence in Chapter 11. Electronic decision aids have been integrated into other systems in recent years, but understanding of their fundamentals is important. Business intelligence applications, such as data mining and online analytical processing are fast becoming essential tools in a growing number of businesses. Plenty of examples are provided to demonstrate their power.

Part Five: Planning, Acquisition, and Controls

Part Five is devoted to planning, acquisition, and controls of information systems to ensure their successful and timely development and implementation, as well as their security. Chapter 12, "Systems Planning and Development," discusses how professionals plan information systems. It details traditional and agile methods of software development. Chapter 13, "Choices in Systems Acquisition," presents alternative acquisition methods to inhouse development: outsourcing, purchased applications, end-user systems development, and software as a service. Chapter 14, "Risks, Security, and Disaster Recovery," discusses the risks that information systems face and ways to minimize them, as well as approaches to recover from disasters.

PREFACE

NEW FEATURES OF THIS EDITION

We listened carefully to our adopters, potential adopters, and reviewers in planning and writing this Fifth Edition of *Management Information Systems*. The major changes and improvements in this edition are:

- More concise text, with 14 chapters instead of 17

- More brief, real-life examples within the text of chapters

- Updated and extended coverage of the latest technologies and trends in MIS, including information security

- New Point of Interest boxes throughout

- All-new end-of-chapter case studies

- New or revised end-of-chapter exercises

- A wealth of online, video, and lab resources to accompany the text

The first thing adopters will notice is that the text is shorter and the number of chapters is smaller. The 17 chapters of the Fourth Edition were condensed into 14 chapters in response to instructors' requests: they prefer succinct discussions followed immediately with brief current examples, and they now have somewhat different preferences of topics to be covered. However, the shortened text does not exclude any topic that is important for business students and students in other fields who must know how IT is used in business. Some chapter titles were changed to reflect the new materials covered.

The organization of the Fifth Edition into 14 chapters allows a discussion of one chapter per class meeting at schools with semester schedules, and leaves enough room for midterm and final exams. Instructors in quarter-system schools will find it easy to combine some chapters to accommodate shorter terms.

Some instructors would like students to consider careers in IT. Therefore, the discussion of IT careers was moved to Chapter 1, "Business Information Systems: An Overview." This allows the students to learn what IT professionals do early on.

Supply chain management (SCM) systems and customer relationship management (CRM) systems have become important staples in businesses. Therefore, they are now introduced early in Chapter 1, thoroughly explained in Chapter 3, "Business Functions and Supply Chains," and discussed widely throughout the text in various contexts. While we still discuss information systems by business function in Chapter 3, a large part of the chapter is devoted to enterprise applications such as SCM, CRM, and ERP systems.

Chapter 4, "Business Hardware," now includes shorter discussions of the innards of computers and extensive discussions on external memory devices and networked storage technologies such as SAN and NAS.

In Chapter 5, "Business Software," the discussion of programming language generations was significantly cut to make room for more important discussions of software that all students will encounter in most organizations. The growing trend of using open source software is extensively discussed and no longer focuses only on Linux. The students are exposed to a plethora of open source applications.

Chapter 6, "Business Networks and Telecommunications," no longer includes discussions of modulation and demodulation, and the technical aspect has been toned down. Most of the chapter now focuses on the use of various networking technologies in business. A new section covers the latest wireless technologies, as this is the future of networking in communities, businesses, and homes. A detailed discussion of RFID technologies is included to provide the technical foundation for further discussion of current and future application of this technology in business.

In the last edition, a separate chapter was devoted to e-commerce, but it has become so pervasive that in this edition e-commerce is a theme discussed throughout the book. The major Web technologies are discussed and demonstrated in Chapter 8, "The Web-Enabled Enterprise." The entire chapter was rewritten to reflect new technologies. The section on alternatives in establishing commercial Web sites reflects the latest array of hosting options. Chapter 9, "Challenges of Global Information Systems," is devoted to illuminating the challenges and efficiencies of managing business information systems on a global scale (a discussion that used to be only a part in Chapter 11 in the Fourth Edition).

The Fourth Edition's chapters on decision support systems and artificial intelligence were merged in this edition into a single chapter, Chapter 10, "Decision Support and Expert Systems." Plenty of current examples are provided.

Chapter 11, "Business Intelligence and Knowledge Management," combines discussions that were included in different chapters in the previous edition. Both business intelligence (BI) and knowledge management (KM) have assumed somewhat different meanings over the past two years. The new concept of employee knowledge networks is explained and demonstrated in examples.

Systems planning and systems development were merged into a single chapter that places more emphasis on systems development, as planning is usually taught as a full subject in other courses. While traditional "waterfall" approaches such as the systems development life cycle are discussed, Chapter 12, "Systems Planning and Development," devotes a thorough discussion to agile methods, which have become so popular among software developers.

User-led software development was cut from Chapter 13, "Choices in Systems Acquisition," because the approach is rarely practiced now. Other alternatives, such as Software as a Service, are discussed in detail.

Security and disaster recovery are still discussed with the same level of detail as in the Fourth Edition, but the discussion is more concise. The discussion of encryption methods in Chapter 14, "Risks, Security, and Disaster Recovery," is shorter and clearer. New risks, such as phishing, are discussed in this chapter as well as in others throughout the text.

Except for very few entries, all the Point of Interest box features are new. All Ethical and Societal Issues discussions have been updated, and some are new, such as a discussion of the offshoring of IT jobs. Discussion of threats to privacy were updated to address new technologies such as RFID tags.

Nearly all of the end-of-chapter Real Cases are new, predominantly from 2005. As in previous editions, all are real-world examples reported in a wide range of major business journals. About 90 percent of all the examples given in chapter discussions are new and recent. The only examples that are older than 2 years are those that are classic stories of strategic use of IT. Thus, the pedagogy of this edition is significantly enhanced.

In addition, almost all of the exercises at the ends of chapters are new or revised. The number of quantitative assignments is greater than in the Fourth Edition. Solutions to the quantitative problems are provided to instructors.

ACKNOWLEDGMENTS

This book is the fruit of a great concerted effort. A project such as this could not be successful without the contribution of many people. I would first like to thank my colleagues in the IS area whose ideas and opinions over all these years have helped me understand the educational needs of our students. I also recognize the indirect contribution of the many students I have taught. Their comments helped me understand the points that need extra emphasis or a different presentation to make subjects that are potentially overwhelming more interesting.

Many thanks go to Eunice Yeates for being so enthusiastic about this project. She was always there for me with advice and encouragement. Eunice exerted much energy when heading this project. Her active guidance and constant involvement made an immense contribution to this edition. Jenny Smith handled the smooth coordination of the instructor's package and Beth Paquin ably handled Web materials and more. Kelly Murphy at GEX Publishing Services shepherded the book through production, managing the process in a very orderly and timely manner. The design and art managers at GEX Publishing Services made sure the text and photos were visually appealing, and the team of artists there skillfully rendered our ideas. Abby Reip ensured that the text concepts were supported with photos. She was knowledgeable and agile. I applaud all of them.

Deb Kaufmann, the developmental editor has demonstrated again her excellent skills and high integrity. It was wonderful to work with an editor who excels not only in improving style and organization but who is also so knowledgeable in the subject matter.

Naomi Friedman helped updating the opening cases for this edition and provided her own original work in some of the chapters. Her contribution was refreshing.

Reviewers are the most important aides to any writer, let alone one who prepares a text for college students. I would like to thank the following reviewers for their candid and constructive feedback on the previous editions:

Gary Armstrong, *Shippensburg University*

Karin Bast, *University of Wisconsin/La Crosse*

Siddhartha Bhattacharya, *Southern Illinois University/Carbondale*

Douglas Bock, *Southern Illinois University/Edwardsville*

George Bohlen, *University of Dayton*

Sonny Butler, *Eastern Kentucky University*

Jane Carey, *Arizona State University*

Judith Carlisle, *Georgia Institute of Technology*

Jason Chen, *Gonzaga University*

Paul Cheney, *University of South Florida*

Jim Danowski, *University of Illinois/Chicago*

Sergio Davalos, *University of Portland*

Robert Davis, *Southwest Texas State University*

Glenn Dietrich, *University of Texas/San Antonio*

James Divoky, *University of Akron*

Charles Downing, *Boston College*

Richard Evans, *Rhode Island College*

Karen Forcht, *James Madison University*

Jeff Guan, *University of Louisville*

Constanza Hagmann, *Kansas State University*

Bassam Hassan, *Univeristy of Toledo*

Sunil Hazari, *University of West Georgia*

Jeff Hedrington, *University of Phoenix*

Charlotte Hiatt, *California State University/Fresno*

Ellen Hoadley, *Loyola College*

Joan Hoopes, *Marist College*

Andrew Hurd, *Hudson Valley Community College*

Anthony Keys, *Wichita State University*

Al Lederer, *University of Kentucky*

Jo Mae Maris, *Arizona State University*

Kenneth Marr, *Hofstra University*

Patricia McQuaid, *California Polytechnic State University*

John Melrose, *University of Wisconsin/Eau Claire*

Lisa Miller, *University of Central Oklahoma*

Denise Padavano, *Peirce College*

Leah Pietron, *University of Nebraska/Omaha*

Floyd Ploeger, *Texas State Univeristy – San Marcos*

Jack Powell, *University of South Dakota*

Leonard Presby, *William Paterson University*

Raghav Rao, *State University of New York/Buffalo*

Lora Robinson, *St. Cloud State University*

Subhashish Samaddar, *Western Illinois University*

William Schiano, *Bentley College*

Shannon Taylor, *Montana State University*

Wallace Wood, *Bryant College*

Zachary Wong, *Sonoma State University*

Amy Woszczynski, *Kennesaw State University*

In addition, I would especially like to thank the reviewers who carefully read every chapter of this edition and/or reviewed the revision proposal for this edition:

Efrem Mallach, *University of Massachusetts, Dartmouth*

Jennifer Nightingale, *Duquesne University*

Pat Ormond, *Utah Valley State College*

Colleen Ramos, *Bellhaven College*

Elizabeth Sigman, *Georgetown University*

Howard Sundwall, *West Chester University*

Barbara Warner, *University of South Florida*

Howard Sundwall, in particular, went the extra mile in reviewing chapters from previous editions and this new edition and provided very helpful advice that greatly enhanced both the material and its presentation.

Lastly, I would like to thank the members of my family. Narda, my wife of 31 years, as well as our children—Sahar, Adi, Noam, and Ron. Adi was instrumental in finding rich business cases and materials for our Points of Interest.

As always, I welcome suggestions and comments from our adopters.

Effy Oz
effyoz@psu.edu

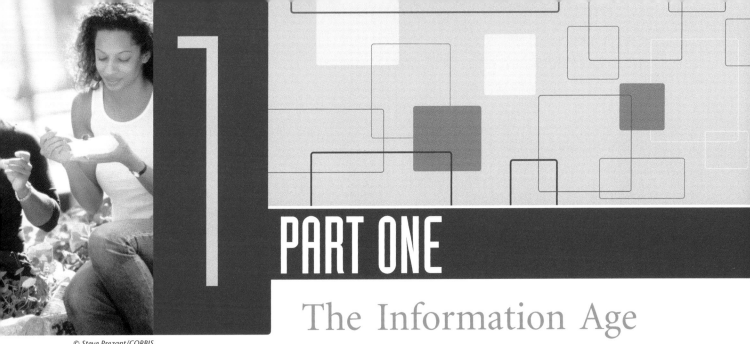

PART ONE

The Information Age

CASE 1: EATS2GO

"Maybe we should start our own business." As soon as Juan said it, his two friends put down their coffee and stared at him. Juan Moreno, Kendra Banks, and Dave Slater were hotel and restaurant management majors in their junior year at college, and they were looking over the business and travel news and lamenting the sluggish job outlook in their chosen field. They had always joked about starting a business together, but this time Juan was serious. With few prospects in the daily want ads, the three friends were worried that travel and entertainment wouldn't pick up by the time they graduated. They'd begun their job searches in the fall but weren't interested in the available positions. So, like many other young people, they considered heading out on their own and becoming entrepreneurs.

"Well, you know that I've always wanted to open a restaurant eventually, Juan," said Kendra. "I love being a chef. But aren't we getting ahead of ourselves? How could we get enough cash together to rent a place and staff it? Rental space is really expensive in Campus Town, and we don't have the funds to pay anyone right now. We still have student loans to pay off when we graduate."

"What about a pushcart in Robbins Park?" suggested Dave. "We could start small and take turns manning it ourselves. That'd keep our manpower costs and store rental low. Besides, you're always complaining about the greasy food at the burger place in Campus Town, Kendra. We could offer better alternatives to burgers and fries. Robbins Park across from campus has been improved recently with new benches and tables, too. It'd be a perfect spot to open a small lunch business."

"We'd still need a business plan to get a loan for start-up," Juan advised. He was excited about organizing a new firm, but knew they needed a detailed plan. "We have to think everything through carefully, and show people that we know what we're doing, or we'll never get off the ground."

Kendra laughed. "You're good with facts and figures," she said to Juan. "Must be the business and finance courses you took. With my restaurant management background, I'd love to develop the new menu. That's the fun, creative part of this for me. Dave, you have so many contacts through your student government experience. That could come in handy down the road, don't you think?"

"Looks like we each have some strengths that could help us get started," observed Dave. "So, what do you think? Shall we try it?"

The three friends stood up and raised their coffee cups in a formal toast to the new business—Eats2Go.

Assessing Business Needs

When Juan, Kendra, and Dave agreed to start their business, they had no clear idea of the amount of work involved. They each had certain skills to contribute—innate skills and skills they had polished in their courses—and they were excited about becoming entrepreneurs. But as they continued to meet to sketch out their plans, they quickly realized they'd need to collect quite a lot of information and allocate responsibilities:

- They needed facts and figures on the local lunch business to draft a business plan.
- They needed to negotiate a vendor's license with the city to set up their cart and rent the cart itself.
- They needed to plan a menu and price items, and then track which offerings generated the most revenue.
- They needed to advertise their business and print menus.
- They needed a system to record food inventory, plastic serving utensils, paper wraps, and napkins—both costs and quantities.

Keeping track of so much information could be a headache, but computer systems would provide part of the solution. The three friends had grown up using computers in their classes, surfing the Web for fun, and sending e-mails and instant messages to their families to keep in touch. But this was different. For the first time they were seeing computers as a critical tool for their success. Computer systems could track and store information they collected, help them calculate financial information, create forms and documents, and even assist in future planning and forecasting. The entrepreneurs knew they needed to become proficient in information systems so that they could concentrate on their real business—running the lunch cart and attracting customers. They were determined not to take shortcuts, and if information systems could help them, they would use them.

Formulating a Plan

Juan Moreno had gained some restaurant experience through his family. His uncle owned a small Spanish restaurant in the city that was open for lunch and dinner. Juan thought his uncle might be persuaded to allow the three entrepreneurs to use the kitchen early in the morning to prepare their cold sandwiches—for a small fee. So the three met with Juan's uncle, Julio, and convinced him that they were serious about their business and would not interfere with his; he was adamant that they had to leave the kitchen spotless and be out of the way by 10:00 each morning. They also agreed on a rental fee to compensate Julio for use of his facilities.

Kendra and Dave had participated in the university's Future Chefs lunch program, in which cooking and nutrition students prepared and served hot lunches to paying faculty members—to simulate a restaurant experience. Kendra loved selecting main dishes and their accompaniments and hoped some day to become a chef. Dave liked the organizational aspects of planning and wanted to concentrate on management.

Kendra began thinking about Eats2Go's menu. She thought that limiting their food to cold sandwiches, drinks, and side dishes simplified food preparation and storage—they would only need to keep items cold, not cook them on the spot. She discussed the menu with Juan and Dave and decided that pita wraps and small side dishes would work well for the cart—they weren't too bulky and would be healthful, lighter alternatives to burgers or pizza, which were sold nearby. Kendra also had heard about a computer application that could track and print calorie and nutritional information; that program would be useful for their menu later.

Dave, with his student government experience, had attended city council meetings as the university's student representative. He had made acquaintances with some members of the business community during those meetings. He remembered especially Kathy Slocum, First Capital Bank's loan officer, who sat on the council's finance committee. Maybe she could talk with them about a loan or refer them to someone who could. At least he wouldn't be a complete stranger to the banker.

Writing a Business Plan

Once Juan, Kendra, and Dave had their initial plans set, they turned to the task of writing a business plan. They knew a business plan would be the key to obtaining the seed capital from the bank to start their business. Loan officers would scrutinize every detail to be sure that the three students were worth the risk and were reliable. A good plan also needs to catch the interest of the lender—to generate excitement so that it will stand out from the other loan applicants. So, they began work, fleshing out the sections of the plan to provide an overview of their business:

- The Executive Summary provided a general synopsis of who the three entrepreneurs were, what business they planned to start, when they planned to start their operations, why they were qualified to own the business, why there was a need for it, and where they planned to place their lunch cart. It also explained their enduring interest in the restaurant industry and their eagerness to bring their ideas to life in the new business.
- The Introduction stated the general concept of the business, its purpose and general objectives, and an overview of the lunch business in the area. They also included general information on their own backgrounds—education, experience, and training.
- The Marketing section outlined the target market, the business's main competitors, and plans for advertising, pricing, food and supply procurement and preparation, and location of the pushcart. They also included information and statistics on the growing trend toward more healthful alternatives to fast food and the lack of healthful, organic lunch options near campus. Finally, they mentioned their spring start-up date, when outdoor pedestrian traffic volumes would grow.
- The Financial section detailed equipment and kitchen rental fees, the pushcart leasing fee, cost of the city vendor's license, and initial food and supply purchase costs. The partners explained their plan to staff the cart themselves and so avoid additional labor costs. They included a budget forecast, the estimated total lunch business market in the area and the percentage they thought they could capture with their new business, the needs for start-up capital, and a plan for spending the funds.
- The Résumé section completed the plan, listing all three partners' background, experience, and references.

Kathy Slocum of First Capital Bank reviewed their plan and was impressed with the work the three had done. She met with Juan, Kendra, and Dave and discussed their completed business plan. She told them she thought they had provided critical information overall, but she requested more details on foot traffic counts at Robbins Park and nearby lunch business competitors to be sure the cart could generate enough customers to be profitable. Also, she asked for more specifics on pricing details versus the competition and the point at which the three projected to break even on their business and begin earning a profit. Those details would help Kathy determine whether the business was a good risk and when the loan would be paid off.

Juan, Kendra, and Dave did additional research and recorded the details in the revised plan. Then they provided Kathy with this additional information. Their hard work paid off. First Capital approved their loan—they were in business! The three partners were excited but realized they needed to get started immediately to open their business in the spring—only four short months away.

BUSINESS CHALLENGES

In the next three chapters, you learn what Juan, Kendra, and Dave need to know to get started: how to harness information technology to help build and grow their lunch business.

- In Chapter 1, "Business Information Systems: An Overview," you learn what your role in information technology might be, which types of information systems you would need whether you are running a large or small business, and what information you need, in what form you need it, where you might find it, and how to process it. You also learn what computer-based information tools you need to build a business, and some of the major ethical and societal concerns about acquiring, using, storing, and reporting potentially sensitive information.

- In Chapter 2, "Strategic Uses of Information Systems," you learn how to use information strategically, how to initiate strategic moves, and how to deal with competitive challenges.

- In Chapter 3, "Business Functions and Supply Chains," you learn how you might best use information technology to help manage a business, whether you need to order inventory and track sales, generate financial statements, or automate payroll systems. You also learn how all the various business information systems work together.

© Steve Prezant/CORBIS

1

ONE

Business Information Systems:

AN OVERVIEW

LEARNING OBJECTIVES

Information systems pervade almost every aspect of our lives. Whether you are withdrawing money from a bank's automatic teller machine or surfing the World Wide Web, hardly a day goes by without our feeding data into, or using information generated by, an information system. In business especially, computer-based information systems generate most of the information we use. These systems have become essential to successful business operations.

When you finish this chapter, you will be able to:

- Explain why information systems are essential to business.

- Describe how computers process data into useful information for problem solving and decision making.

- Identify the functions of different types of information systems in business.

- Describe careers in information technology.

- Identify major ethical and societal concerns created by widespread use of information technology.

EATS2GO:
Business Systems and Information

Juan Moreno, Kendra Banks, and Dave Slater couldn't believe what they had accomplished in the five months since they obtained their small-business loan for their lunch pushcart business, Eats2Go. They'd made so many decisions and solved so many problems, it was hard to keep track of them all.

Solving Problems and Making Decisions

Juan rented a pushcart to place in the middle of Robbins Park near the campus and obtained a vendor's license from city hall. Dave investigated a new PC, software, and printer, and the partners selected a desktop system that would fill their current computing needs and still allow for growth. Juan and Kendra worked on the food service side of the business. Juan's uncle, Julio, had referred them to a food wholesaler who gave them a small discount because he could deliver Eats2Go's supplies directly to Juan's uncle's restaurant.

Kendra developed her own recipes for pita wraps that would offer more healthful alternatives to the cheeseburgers and pizza offered in Campus Town: chicken pesto with pine nuts, lean roast beef with spicy peppers, and smoked turkey with Dijon mustard and dill. She, Dave, and Juan arose at dawn three weeks before opening to do practice runs in the kitchen and work out a smooth production process. By the fourth practice run, they thought they had a good system—the sandwiches were prepared and packaged for storage in the cart, and the chips were cooked, seasoned, and bagged. Best of all, they were out of Julio Moreno's kitchen by the 10:00 deadline.

Generating Business Information

Dave and Juan worked up a simple printed menu for the cart and used the calorie-counting application to generate nutrition information for their customers. Key advantages of their food were the freshness of their ingredients and their health-conscious menu, so they made sure the menu highlighted those features. They set prices a bit higher than the burger and pizza places down the street because their ingredients were completely fresh—without preservatives or additives.

Dave designed and arranged for ads to run in the campus newspaper, both the paper and Web versions, two weeks before they opened for business. He also prepared simple flyers to hand out on campus and in Robbins Park.

Juan set up Eats2Go's computer programs: a word-processing program to create basic business stationery and forms; a spreadsheet to record and track sales, taxes, and profits; and a database to manage food inventory and supplies.

Managing Data

After the business had been operating for a month, sales started to pick up. Whoever was staffing the pushcart wrote out a receipt for all items in an order and placed the receipt in a small plastic folder to be entered into the business's computer later. But as the lunch customers multiplied, Eats2Go's owners realized that they were falling behind on their paperwork for the business. It was becoming inefficient to handwrite the many sales receipts and later record them into the spreadsheets.

As the backlog in sales receipts grew, Juan had to spend more and more time on weekends to input sales data so that they could order supplies from the wholesaler on Mondays. He also was bogged down at the end of the month, when he prepared Eats2Go's loan and rental payments, sales tax information, and expenses.

Gathering Useful Information from Customers

Kendra noticed that some of the items on the lunch menu sold better than others—the chicken pesto salad was a big hit, but the roast beef sold less well—and was surprised by the many requests for additional chip varieties and side dishes. And with summer on the way, they needed to consider adding some seasonal menu items to keep the customers coming back. Juan, Kendra, and Dave needed to consider the costs and profits of adding or dropping menu items, or repricing items. Also, several times the partners had had to place emergency calls to restock depleted ingredients and supplies. They had to find a better way to track all the data and forecast their needs so that they wouldn't run short of items or throw away unused ingredients. Dissatisfied customers meant lost sales and fewer profits. So, they thought that they could generate some reports on customer-ordering preferences.

THE PURPOSE OF INFORMATION SYSTEMS

People require information for many reasons and in varied ways. For instance, you probably seek information for entertainment and enlightenment by viewing television, watching movies, browsing the Internet, listening to the radio, and reading newspapers, magazines, and books. In business, however, people and organizations seek and use information specifically to make sound decisions and to solve problems—two closely related practices that form the foundation of every successful company.

CONTRAST w/ THE NOTION OF AN OPPORTUNITY?

What is a problem? A *problem* is any undesirable situation. When you are stuck in the middle of nowhere with a flat tire, you have a problem. If you know that some customers do not pay their debts on time, but you don't know who or how much they owe, you have a problem. You can solve both problems with the aid of information. In the first case, you can call a towing company, which might use a computerized tracking system to send the tow truck closest to your location; in the second case, simple accounting software can help.

DECISION METHOD DATA

An organization or individual that finds more than one way to solve a problem or a dilemma must make a *decision*. The problem "2 + 2 = ?" does not require decision making because it has only one solution. However, as a manager, you might face a dilemma such as "Which is the best way to promote the company's new car?" There are many potential ways to promote the new car—television advertising, radio advertising, newspaper advertising, Web advertising, auto shows, direct mail, or any combination of these methods. This dilemma calls for decision making.

Both problem solving and decision making require information. Gathering the right information efficiently, storing it so that it can be used and manipulated as necessary, and using it to help an organization achieve its business goals—all topics covered in this book—are the keys to success in business today. The purpose of information systems is to support these activities. As a future professional, you need to understand and apply these information fundamentals to succeed.

DATA, INFORMATION, AND INFORMATION SYSTEMS

We use the words "data," "information," and "system" almost daily. Understanding what these terms mean, both generally and in the business context, is necessary if you are to use information effectively in your career.

Data vs. Information *vs. KNOWLEDGE*

The terms "data" and "information" do not mean the same thing. The word **data** is derived from the Latin *datum*, literally a given or fact, which might take the form of a number, a statement, or a picture. Data is the raw material in the production of information. **Information**, on the other hand, is facts or conclusions that have meaning within a context. Raw data is rarely meaningful or useful as information. To become information, data is manipulated through tabulation, addition, subtraction, division, or any other operation that leads to greater understanding of a situation.

POINT OF INTEREST

A Paperless Society?

Although Americans make up less than 5 percent of the world's population, they produce nearly 25 percent of the world's office paper, and although Americans use more computers and Internet links than any other nation, they still produce and consume many tons of paper documents. The Information Age was supposed to reduce the amount of paper that offices use. The emergence of the Web was supposed to reduce paper use even further. Not so. In 2002, the United States produced 9,190 million tons of office paper. About 95 percent of the world's information is still printed or written on paper. The U.S. Environmental Protection Agency (EPA) is interested in such figures because a growing percentage of this paper becomes waste, from 1.7 percent of total solid waste tonnage in 1960 to the forecasted 6.5 percent in 2010 in the United States.

Source: American Forest & Paper Association, 2005; Canadian Pulp and Paper Association, 1998; U.S. Environmental Protection Agency, "Characterization of Municipal Solid State Waste in the United States," 1990.

Data Manipulation

Here's a simple example that demonstrates the difference between data and information. Assume that you work for a car manufacturer. Last year, the company introduced a new vehicle to the market. Because management realizes that keeping a loyal customer base requires continuously improving products and services, it periodically surveys large samples of buyers. It sends out questionnaires that include 30 questions in several categories, including demographic data (such as gender, age, and annual income); complaints about different performance areas (such as ease of handling, braking, and the quality of the sound system); features that satisfy buyers most; and courtesy of the dealer's personnel.

Reading through all this data would be extremely time-consuming and not very helpful. However, if the data is manipulated, it might provide highly useful information. For example, by categorizing complaints by topic and totaling the number of complaints for each type of complaint and each car model, the company might be able to pinpoint a car's weaknesses. The company then can pass the resulting information along to the appropriate engineering or manufacturing unit.

Also, the company might already have sufficient data on dealers who sold cars to the customers surveyed, the car models they sold, and the financing method for each purchase. But with the survey results, the company can generate new information to improve its marketing. For instance, by calculating the average age and income of current buyers and categorizing them by the car they purchased, marketing executives can better target advertising to groups most likely to purchase each car. If the majority of buyers of a particular type of car do not ask for financing, the company might wish to drop this service option for that car and divert more loan money to finance purchases of other cars. In this way, the company generates useful information from data.

Generating Information

In the examples just cited, calculating totals and averages of different complaints or purchasers' ages reveals trends associated with customers. These calculations are processes. A **process** is any manipulation of data, usually with the goal of producing information. Hence, while data is raw materials, information is output. Just as raw materials are processed in manufacturing to create useful end-products, so raw data is processed in information systems to create useful information (see Figure 1.1). Some processes, however, produce yet another set of data.

FIGURE 1.1
Input-process-output

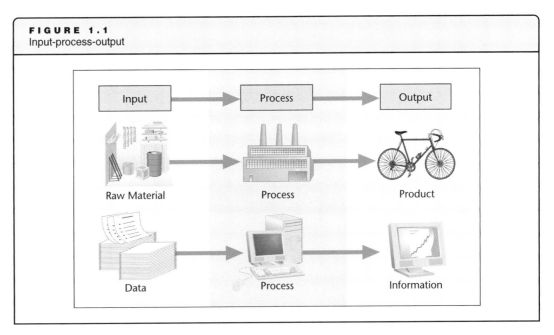

Sometimes, data in one context is considered information in another context. For example, if an organization needs to know the age of every person attending a basketball game, then a list of that data is actually information. But if that same organization wants to know the average price of tickets each age group purchases, the list of ages is only data, which the organization must process to generate information.

Information in Context

Information is an extremely important resource for both individuals and organizations, but not all information is useful. Consider the following story. Two people touring in a hot-air balloon encountered unexpected wind that soon blew them off course. When they managed to lower their balloon, they shouted to a farmer on the ground, "Where are we?" The farmer answered, "You are right above a cornfield!" The balloonists looked at each other, and one groaned, "Some information! Highly accurate and totally useless!" To be useful, information must be relevant, complete, accurate, and current. And in business, information must also be obtained economically, that is, cost effectively. Figure 1.2 lists characteristics of useful information.

What Is a System?

JAMES DOOGAN, "DATA, INFORMATION, AND KNOWLEDGE — RELEVANCE AND UNDERSTANDING"

Simply put, a **system** is an array of components that work together to achieve a common goal, or multiple goals, by accepting input, processing it, and producing output in an organized manner. Consider the following examples:

- A sound system consists of many electronic and mechanical parts, such as a laser head, an amplifier, an equalizer, and so on. This system uses input in the form of electrical power and sound recorded on a medium such as a CD or DVD, and processes the input to reproduce music and other sounds. The components work together to achieve this goal.

- Consider the times you have heard the phrase "to beat the system." Here, the term "system" refers to an organization of human beings—a government agency, a commercial company, or any other bureaucracy. Organizations, too, are systems; they consist of components—people organized into departments and divisions—that work together to achieve common goals.

Systems and Subsystems

Not every system has a single goal. Often, a system consists of several **subsystems**—components of a larger system—with subgoals, all contributing to meeting the main goal. Subsystems can receive input from, and transfer output to, other systems or subsystems.

Relevant — Information must pertain to the problem at hand. For example, the total number of years of education might not be relevant to a person's qualifications for a new job. Relevant information might be that the person has so many years of education in mechanical engineering and so many years of experience. The information must also be presented in a way that helps a person understand it in a specific context.

Complete — Partial information is often worse than no information. For example, marketing data about household incomes might lead to bad decisions if not accompanied by vital information on the consumption habits of the targeted population.

Accurate — Erroneous information might lead to disastrous decisions. For example, an inaccurate record of a patient's reaction to penicillin might lead a doctor to harm the patient while believing that she is helping him.

Current — Decisions are often based on the latest information available, but what was a fact yesterday might no longer be one today. For example, a short-term investment decision to purchase a stock today based on yesterday's stock prices might be a costly mistake if the stock's price has risen in the interim.

Economical — In a business setting, the cost of obtaining information must be considered as one cost element involved in any decision. For example, demand for a new product must be researched to reduce risk of marketing failure, but if market research is too expensive, the cost of obtaining the information might diminish profit from sales.

Consider the different departments of a manufacturing business. The marketing department promotes sales of the organization's products; the engineering department designs new products and improves existing ones; the finance department plans a clear budget and arranges for every unused penny to earn interest by the end of the day. Each department is a subsystem with its own goal, which is a subgoal of a larger system (the company), whose goal is to maximize profit.

Now consider the goals of a manufacturing organization's information system, which stores and processes operational data and produces information about all aspects of company operations. The purpose of its inventory control subsystem is to let managers know what quantities of which items are available; the purpose of its production control subsystem is to track the status of manufactured parts; and the assembly control subsystem presents the bill of material (a list of all parts that make up a product) and the status of assembled products. The entire system's goal is to help deliver finished goods at the lowest possible cost within the shortest possible time.

Figure 1.3 shows an example of a system found in every business: an accounting system. An accounting system consists of several subsystems: accounts payable records information about money that the organization owes to other organizations and individuals; accounts receivable records sums owed to the organization and by whom; a general ledger records current transactions; and a reporting mechanism generates reports reflecting the company's financial status. Each subsystem has a well-defined goal. Together, the subsystems make up the organization's accounting system.

Closed vs. Open Systems

Systems are closed or open, depending on the nature of the information flow in the system. A **closed system** stands alone, with no connection to another system: nothing flows in from another system, nothing flows out to another system. For example, a small check-producing system that prints and cuts checks when an employee enters data through a keyboard is a closed system. The system might be isolated for security purposes. An **open system** interfaces and interacts with other systems. For example, an accounting system that records accounts receivable, accounts payable, and cash flow is open if it receives its payroll figures from the payroll system. Subsystems, by definition, are always open, because as components of a bigger system,

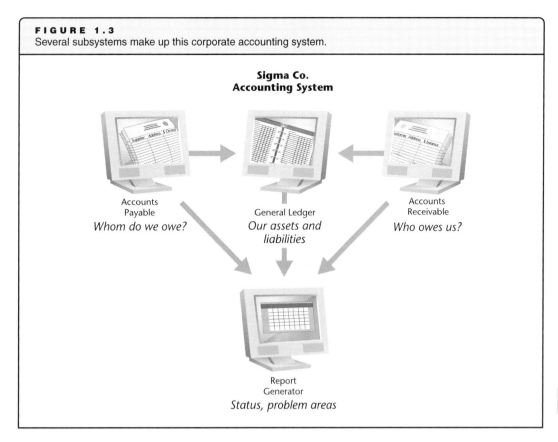

FIGURE 1.3
Several subsystems make up this corporate accounting system.

**Sigma Co.
Accounting System**

Accounts
Payable
Whom do we owe?

General Ledger
*Our assets and
liabilities*

Accounts
Receivable
Who owes us?

Report
Generator
Status, problem areas

they must receive information from, and give information to, other subsystems. Increasingly, companies are implementing open information systems that can be linked to other systems owned by business partners such as suppliers and clients.

Information Systems

With an understanding of the words "information" and "system," the definition of an information system is almost intuitive: an **information system (IS)** consists of all the components that work together to process data and produce information. Almost all business information systems consist of many subsystems with subgoals, all contributing to the organization's main goal.

Information and Managers

Thinking of an organization in terms of its suborganizations or subsystems—called systems thinking—is a powerful management approach because it creates a framework for both excellent problem solving and excellent decision making. To solve problems, managers need to isolate them, which they do by recognizing the subsystems in which the problems occur and solving the problems within those subsystems' constraints and strengths.

Systems thinking can also help keep managers focused on the overall goals and operations of a business. It encourages them to consider the entire system, not only their specific subsystem, when solving problems and making decisions. A satisfactory solution for one subsystem might be inadequate for the business as a whole. For example, when the sales department creates a Web site to take online customer orders, it automates a formerly labor-intensive activity of the sales subsystem. This saves cost. With systems thinking, improving the sales process could also improve other company processes. Without systems thinking, managers from other departments aren't involved in the decision, so they don't benefit. In the case of the sales department, if other managers are involved in planning for automated online ordering, they could suggest that sales data recorded on the **database**—a large collection of electronic records—connected to the Web also be accessible to other departments, such as shipping and manufacturing. The shipping department could use the records to expedite packaging and shipping, thanks to the information that appears on a computer monitor rather than a piece of paper. The manufacturing units could use the order records for planning resources such as laborers and inventory. Figuratively, by applying systems thinking, effective managers view their areas of responsibility as puzzle pieces. Each piece is important and should fit well with adjacent pieces, but the entire picture should always be kept in view.

One of an information system's most important contributions to the sound workings of an organization is the automation of information exchange among subsystems (such as departments and divisions). Consider the earlier example: customer orders taken via a Web site by the sales department could be automatically routed to the manufacturing and shipping units and processed by their own information systems for their specific purposes. In fact, such information exchanges make up a major portion of all interactions among business subsystems.

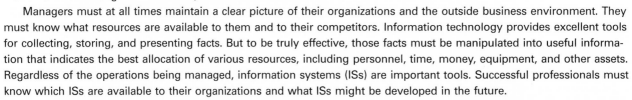

Why You Should...
Be Well Versed in Information Systems

You might be surprised at how much information technology (IT) knowledge your prospective employer will expect of you when you interview for your next job, even if the position you seek is not in the IT area. Today's corporations look for IT-savvy professionals, and with good reason. Information is the lifeblood of any organization, commercial or nonprofit; it is essential to sound problem solving and decision making, upon which business success is built. In fact, the main factor limiting the services and information that computers can provide within an organization is the budget.

Because of rapid changes in technology, information systems, unlike many other business components, are quickly changing in form and content. A computer considered fast and powerful today will be an outdated machine in 18–24 months. In 12–24 months, a better program will surpass one that is considered innovative right now. The dynamic nature of information technology is like a moving target. A professional who does not stay informed is of diminishing value to an organization. All knowledge workers, professionals, scientists, managers, and others who create new information and knowledge in their work, must be familiar with IT.

Managers must at all times maintain a clear picture of their organizations and the outside business environment. They must know what resources are available to them and to their competitors. Information technology provides excellent tools for collecting, storing, and presenting facts. But to be truly effective, those facts must be manipulated into useful information that indicates the best allocation of various resources, including personnel, time, money, equipment, and other assets. Regardless of the operations being managed, information systems (ISs) are important tools. Successful professionals must know which ISs are available to their organizations and what ISs might be developed in the future.

POINT OF INTEREST

Looking for More Skilled Graduates

A survey of 580 chief information officers by *CIO Magazine* reveals that college graduates are not prepared to work with business IT. Sixty-one percent said college graduates were unprepared for the real world of business IT. Seventy-four percent of respondents said young hires lacked knowledge of project management, 71 percent said the graduates lacked knowledge of business operations, and 71 percent said they lacked interpersonal skills. The general opinion was that new hires did not understand well the relationship of business and IT.

Source: D'Agostino, D., "Whose Job Is It to Teach Business Skills?" *CIO Insight*, November 1, 2004.

The **information map** of a modern business—that is, the description of data and information flow within an organization—shows a network of information subsystems that exchange information with each other and with the world outside the system. In an ideal organization, no human would need to retrieve information from one IS and transfer it to another. The organization would capture only new raw data, usually from its operations or from outside the organization. Then, data captured at any point in the system would automatically become available to any other subsystem that needs it. Thus, systems thinking is served well by **information technology (IT)**, a term that refers to all technologies that collectively facilitate construction and maintenance of information systems. Systems thinking is the basic reasoning behind equipping organizations with enterprise software applications. Enterprise software applications are systems that serve many parts of the organization by minimizing the need for human data entry and ensuring timely, useful information for the organization's entire supply chain, including taking customer orders, receiving raw materials, manufacturing and shipping, and billing and collection. In the service sector, companies often use document management systems, enabling workers from many departments to add information and signatures to a document from request to approval, or from draft to a final document. You will learn about these systems throughout this book.

The Benefits of Human-Computer Synergy

It is important to remember that computers can only carry out instructions that humans give them. Computers can process data accurately at far greater speeds than people can, yet they are limited in many respects—most importantly, they lack common sense. However, combining the strengths of these machines with human strengths creates synergy.

Some people call synergy the "2 + 2 = 5" rule. **Synergy** (from the Greek "work together") occurs when combined resources produce output that exceeds the sum of the outputs of the same resources employed separately. A computer works quickly and accurately; humans work relatively slowly and make mistakes. A computer cannot make independent decisions, however, or formulate steps for solving problems, unless programmed to do so by humans. Even with sophisticated artificial intelligence, which enables the computer to learn and implement what it learns, the initial programming must be done by humans. Thus, a human-computer combination allows the results of human thought to be translated into efficient processing of large amounts of data. For example, when you use a Web search engine to find articles about a topic, you, the human, enter a keyword or a series of keywords. By clicking the Search button you shift control to a computer program that quickly finds the articles for you. A human programmed a computer to perform an extremely fast search in a huge database of Web links; another human entered keywords and triggered the program; and the computer performed the matching of keywords with the links at a speed that is way beyond the capability of any human. The result is an efficient search that takes only seconds, which no human would be able to complete in a lifetime. Figure 1.4 presents qualities of humans and computers that result in synergy. It is important to notice not only the potential benefits of synergy but also what computers should not be expected to do independently.

Information Systems in Organizations

In an organization, an information system consists of data, hardware, software, telecommunications, people, and procedures as summarized in Figure 1.5. An information system has become synonymous with a computer-based information system, a system with a computer at its center to which peripheral equipment is connected. That is how this term is used in this book. In a computer-based information system, computers collect, store, and process data into information, according to instructions people provide via computer programs.

Several trends have made the use of information systems (ISs) very important in business:

- The power of computers has grown tremendously while their prices have dropped.
- The variety and ingenuity of computer programs have increased.
- Quick and reliable communication lines and access to the Internet and the Web have become widely available and affordable.
- The fast growth of the Internet has opened opportunities and encouraged competition in global markets.
- An increasing ratio of the global workforce is computer literate.

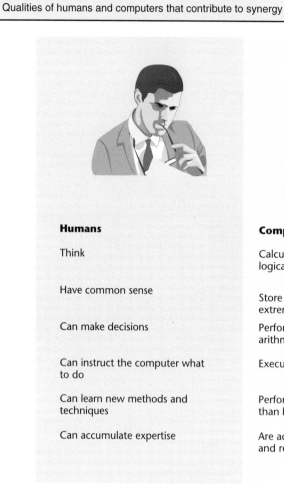

Humans

Think

Have common sense

Can make decisions

Can instruct the computer what to do

Can learn new methods and techniques

Can accumulate expertise

Computers

Calculate and perform programmed logical operations extremely rapidly

Store and retrieve data and information extremely rapidly

Perform complex logical and arithmetical functions accurately

Execute long, tedious operations

Perform routine tasks less expensively than humans

Are adaptable (can be programmed and reprogrammed)

FIGURE 1.5
Components of an information system

Data	Input that the system takes to produce information
Hardware	A computer and its peripheral equipment: input, output, and storage devices; hardware also includes data communication equipment
Software	Sets of instructions that tell the computer how to take data in, how to process it, how to display information, and how to store data and information
Telecommunications	Hardware and software that facilitate fast transmission and reception of text, pictures, sound, and animation in the form of electronic data
People	Information systems professionals and users who analyze organizational information needs, design and construct information systems, write computer programs, operate the hardware, and maintain software
Procedures	Rules for achieving optimal and secure operations in data processing; procedures include priorities in dispensing software applications and security measures

In this environment, organizations quickly lag behind if they do not use information systems and skills to meet their goals. Moreover, they must continuously upgrade hardware, software, and the skills of their employees to stay competitive.

The Four Stages of Processing

All information systems operate in the same basic fashion whether they include a computer or not. However, the computer provides a convenient means to execute the four main operations of an information system:

- Entering data into the IS **(input)**.
- Changing and manipulating the data in the IS **(data processing)**.
- Getting information out of the IS **(output)**.
- Storing data and information **(storage)**.

A computer-based IS also uses a logical process to decide which data to capture and how to process it. This process will be discussed later.

Input

The first step in producing information is collecting and introducing data, known as input, into the IS. Most data an organization uses as input to its IS are generated and collected within the organization. These data result from transactions undertaken in the course of business. A **transaction** is a business event: a sale, a purchase, the hiring of a new employee, and the like. These transactions can be recorded on paper and later entered into a computer system, directly recorded through terminals of a **transaction processing system (TPS)**, such as a cash register, or captured online when someone transacts through the Web. A TPS is any system that records transactions. Often, the same system also processes the transactions, summarizing and routing information to other systems; therefore, these systems are transaction *processing* systems, not just transaction *recording* systems.

Input devices (devices used to enter data into an IS) include the keyboard (currently the most widely used), infrared devices that sense bar codes, voice recognition systems, and touch screens. Chapter 4, "Business Hardware," describes these and other means to input data. The trend has been to shorten the time and ease the effort of input by using devices that allow visual or auditory data entry.

POINT OF INTEREST

Do it Yourself and Save Labor

Apparently, more and more of us prefer using a self-checkout system to waiting in line. Retailers love these systems because they save labor. In 2004, Albertson's, one of the world's largest grocery chains, installed 4,500 self-checkout terminals in its 2,300 stores. Business analysts say the machines could help Albertson's save $137 million annually by cutting two clerks per store.

Source: Duvall, M., and Nash, K. S., "Albertson's: A Shot at the Crown," *Baseline* (www.baselinemag.com), February 5, 2004.

Processing

The computer's greatest contribution to ISs is efficient data processing, which is essential to a robust IS. The computer's speed and accuracy let organizations process millions of pieces of data in several seconds. For example, managers of a national retail chain can receive up-to-date information on inventory levels of every item the chain carries and order accordingly; in the past, obtaining such information would take days. These astronomic gains in the speed and affordability of computing have made information the essential ingredient for an organization's success.

Output

Output is the information an IS produces and displays in the format most useful to an organization. The most widely used output device is the video display, or video monitor, which displays output visually. Another common output device is the printer, used to print hard copies of information on paper. However, computers can communicate output through speakers in the form of music or speech and also can transmit it to another computer or electronic device in computer-coded form, for later interpretation.

The Not-So-Bright Side

New technology almost always improves lives. But new technology often also has undesirable effects. This was true of the labor-saving machines that prompted the industrial revolution (introducing 16-hour workdays and child labor under harsh conditions), and it is also true about information technology. Think of the bliss of IT: it makes our work more productive because a few keystrokes on a computer keyboard prompt the computer to calculate and print what would otherwise take many human hours. It educates us via technologies such as multimedia classes delivered online. It opens new economic opportunities such as trading with overseas consumers via the Internet. It makes the world smaller by letting people work and socialize together over great distances via networks such as the Web. It democratizes the business community by making important business tools affordable to both rich and start-up companies. And it puts at our fingertips information on practically every imaginable subject. So, what's the dark side? There are quite a few dark sides, which we will discuss in the following chapters. Here is a sample of the main issues and the questions they raise.

- **Consumer Privacy.** The ability to inexpensively and quickly collect, maintain, manipulate, and transfer data enables every individual and organization to collect millions of personal records. When visiting a commercial Web site, chances are the site installs a little file, a "cookie," on your computer's hard disk. This file helps track every click you make on that site, so companies specializing in consumer profiling can learn your shopping and buying habits. When you purchase drugs, the druggist collects details about you. Before you send a warranty card for a newly purchased product, you are asked to answer some questions that have nothing to do with the warranty but much to do with your lifestyle. All these data are channeled into large databases for commercial exploitation. Your control of such data is minimal. While consumers, patients, and employees might consent to the collection of information on one aspect of their lives by one party and on another aspect by another party, the combination of such information might reveal more than they would like. For example, a firm can easily and inexpensively purchase *your* data from a druggist and several consumer goods companies, combine the data into larger records, and practically prepare a dossier about you: your name, age, and gender; your shopping habits; the drugs you take (and through this information, the diseases you might have); the political party to which you contributed; and so on.

Civil rights advocates argue that IT has created a Big Brother society where anyone can be observed. U.S. business leaders oppose European-style legislation to curb collection and dissemination of private data because this limits target marketing and other economic activities. Business leaders ask, "How can we target our products to consumers who are most likely to want them if we have no information about those consumers?" Are you willing to give up some of your privacy to help companies better market to you products and services you might be interested in? Do you accept the manipulation and selling of your personal data?

- **Employee Privacy.** IT helps employers monitor their employees, not only via the ubiquitous video camera, but also through the personal computers they use. Employers feel it is their right to monitor keystrokes, e-mail traffic, the Web sites employees visit, and the whereabouts of people whose wages they pay while on the job. So, while IT increases productivity, it might violate privacy and create stress. Which is more important: your employer's right to electronically monitor you, or your privacy and mental well-being?

- **Freedom of Speech.** The Web opens opportunities for many activities that people consider undesirable, such as the broadcast of violent and pornographic images and the dissemination of illegally copied digitized work. Almost anyone can become a publisher. If someone posts slurs about your ethnic group at a Web site, do you want the government to step in and ban such postings? And if one government legislates, can it impose its law on a network that crosses many national borders?

- **Online Annoyances.** E-mail is so popular because it allows easy and inexpensive transfer of ideas and creative work within seconds. However, more and more of us find our e-mail boxes clogged with unsolicited messages, popularly called spam. Spam now makes up about 80 percent of all e-mail. Do you accept this? And if you own a new small business and want to advertise via e-mail (because it is the least expensive advertising method), wouldn't you want the freedom to do so? While surfing the Web you encounter pop-up windows and pop-under windows. Your computer contracts spyware. Sometimes special software hijacks your browser and automatically takes you to a commercial site that you do not care for. Are these annoyances legitimate, or should they be stopped by legislation?

- **IT Professionalism.** IT specialists play an increasing role in the lives of individuals and the operations of organizations. The information systems they develop and maintain affect our physical and financial well-being tremendously. Are IT specialists professionals? If they are, why don't they comply with a mandatory code of ethics as other professionals (such as physicians and lawyers) do?

We will discuss these and other ethical and social issues throughout this book. As you will see, these issues are not easy to resolve. The purpose of these discussions is to make you aware of issues and provoke your thoughts. Remember that the purpose of education is not only to develop skilled professionals but also to remind professionals of the impact of their work on the welfare of other people, and to make professionals socially responsible.

Storage

One of the greatest benefits of using IT is the ability to store vast amounts of data and information. Technically, storing a library of millions of volumes on optical discs is not inconceivable. In fact, some universities are moving to do just that.

Computer Equipment for Information Systems

Figure 1.6 illustrates the five basic components of the computer system within an IS:

- Input devices introduce data into the IS.
- The computer processes data through the IS.
- Output devices display information.
- Storage devices store data and information.
- Networking devices and communications lines transfer data and information over long distances.

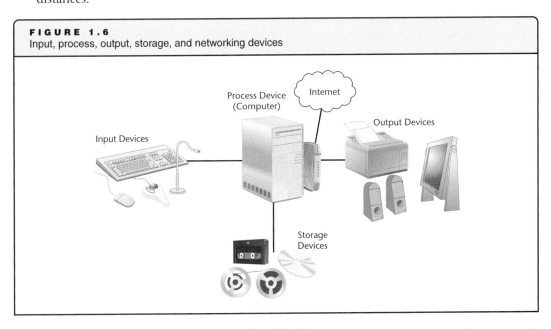

FIGURE 1.6
Input, process, output, storage, and networking devices

In addition to communication that takes place between computer components, communication occurs between computers over great distances (called **telecommunications**). Communications technology lets users access data and other electronic resources of many computers, all connected in a network. This way, a computer's power might be augmented with the power of an entire network.

There are many different types of information systems—for different types of organizations, for different functions within organizations, for different business needs, and at different management levels of an organization. Business enterprises differ in their objectives, structure, interests, and approaches. However, ISs can be generally categorized based on the level of a system's complexity and the type of functions it serves. ISs in business range from the basic transaction processing system that records events such as sales to sophisticated expert systems, such as computer programs that provide advice and reduce the need for the expensive services of a human expert. In recent years the capabilities of these applications have been combined and merged. It is less and less likely that you will find any of the following applications as stand-alone systems with a single capability. Managers and other professionals plan, control, and make decisions. As long as a system supports one or more of these activities, it may be referred to as a **management information system (MIS)**.

Cash registers are a ubiquitous type of transaction processing system.

Photodisc Collection/Getty Images

Transaction Processing Systems

Transaction processing systems (TPSs) are the most widely used information systems. The predominant function of TPSs is to record data collected at the boundaries of organizations, in other words, at the point where the organization transacts business with other parties. TPSs include cash registers, which record sales; automatic teller machines, which record cash withdrawals, deposits, and transfers; and purchase order systems, which record purchases. A typical example would be the purchase of gasoline at a pump, using a credit card. The purchase is recorded by the gasoline company and later at the credit card-processing bank. After these data are collected, the IS either automatically processes the data immediately or stores it for later access on demand.

Supply Chain Management Systems

The term "supply chain" refers to the sequence of activities involved in producing a product or service. In industries that produce goods, the activities include marketing, purchasing raw materials, manufacturing and assembly, packing and shipping, billing, collection, and after-the-sale services. In service industries, the sequence might include marketing, document management, and monitoring customer portfolios. Information systems that support these activities and are linked to become one large IS providing information on any stage of a business process are called **supply chain management (SCM) systems**.

Often, such systems are called **enterprise resource planning (ERP) systems**, because the information they provide supports planning of shipping resources such as personnel, funds, raw materials, and vehicles. However, ERP is a misnomer for the systems, because they mainly serve managers in monitoring and modifying business processes as they occur, and not only for planning. The term "supply chain," too, is somewhat misleading. Business processes do not always take the form of a sequence. There are processes that take place in parallel. This is true in manufacturing, where two or three teams work on different parts of a product, and in services, where two or three different people peruse a document online and add their input to it within a certain period of time rather than sequentially. In the production of goods and services, some modules of SCM systems provide support to the major processes. These components include human resources (HR) information systems and cost accounting systems.

SCM systems are the result of systems thinking and support systems thinking. They eliminate the need to reenter data that has already been captured somewhere else in the organization. An SCM is an **enterprise application** because the systems that support each business process are connected to each other to form one large IS. Technically, anyone with access to the system can know the status of every part of an order the business received: whether the raw materials have been purchased, which subassemblies are ready, how many units of the finished product have been shipped, and how much money has been billed or collected for this order. HR managers can tell which workers are involved in any of the processes of the order. Accountants can use their

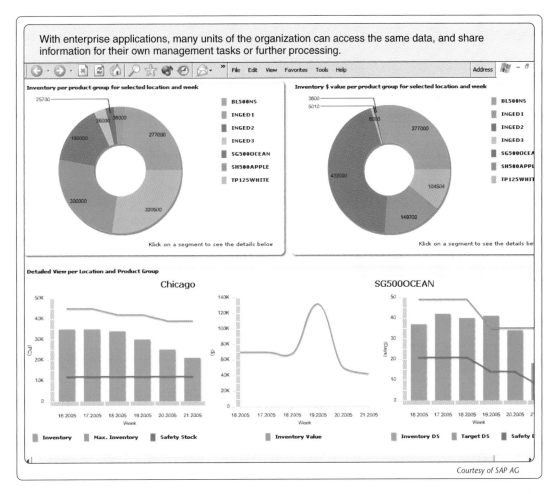

With enterprise applications, many units of the organization can access the same data, and share information for their own management tasks or further processing.

Courtesy of SAP AG

module of the system to know how much money has been spent on this order and what the breakdown of the cost is into labor, materials, and overhead expenditures.

Customer Relationship Management Systems

Customer relationship management (CRM) systems help manage an organization's relationships with its customers. The term refers to a large variety of information systems, from simple ones that help maintain customer records to sophisticated ones that dynamically analyze and detect buying patterns and predict when a specific customer is about to switch to a competitor. Many CRM systems are used by service representatives in combination with a telephone. When a customer telephones, the representative can view the entire history of the customer's relationship with the company: anything that the customer has purchased, deliveries made, unfulfilled orders, and other information that can help resolve a problem or help the customer find the good or service he or she is seeking. The main goals of CRM systems are to increase the quality of customer service, reduce the amount of labor involved in serving customers, and learn as much as possible about the preferences of individual customers.

CRM systems are often linked to Web applications that track online shopping and process online transactions. Using sophisticated applications, a company can learn what makes a customer balk just before submitting an online order, or what a customer prefers to see displayed on Web pages. Online retailers such as Amazon.com, Buy.com, and Target.com use applications that construct different Web pages for different customers, even when they search on the same keywords. The pages are constructed to optimally suit the individual customer's interests as inferred from previous visits and purchases. CRM systems provide important data that can be accumulated in large databases and processed into business intelligence.

Business Intelligence Systems

ISs whose purpose is to glean from raw data relationships and trends that might help organizations compete better are called **business intelligence (BI)** systems. Usually, these applications consist of sophisticated statistical models, sometimes general and sometimes tailored for an industry or an organization. The applications access large pools of data, usually transactional records stored in large databases called **data warehouses**. With proper analysis models BI systems might discover peculiar buying patterns of consumers, such as combinations of products purchased by a certain demographic group or on certain days; products that are sold at greater cycles than others; reasons for customer's churns, that is, customers leaving a service provider for a competitor; and other valuable business intelligence that helps managers quickly decide to change a strategy.

Customer relationship management systems help support customers and learn more about their preferences.

© Jon Feingersh/Masterfile

Decision Support and Expert Systems

Professionals often need to select one course of action from many alternatives. Because they have neither the time nor the resources to study and absorb long, detailed reports of data and information, organizations often build information systems specifically designed to help make decisions. These systems are called **decision support systems (DSSs)**. While DSSs rely on models and formulas to produce concise tables or a single number that determines a decision, **expert systems (ESs)** rely on artificial intelligence techniques to support knowledge-intensive decision-making processes.

Decision support systems help find the optimal course of action and answer "What if?" questions. "What if we purchase raw materials overseas?" "What if we merge our warehouses?" "What if we double our shifts and cut our staff?" These questions seek answers like, "This is how this action will impact our revenue, or our market share, or our costs." DSSs are programmed to process raw data, make comparisons, and generate information to help professionals glean the best alternatives for financial investment, marketing strategy, credit approval, and the like. However, it is important to understand that a DSS is only a decision aid, not an absolute alternative to human decision making.

Many environments are not sufficiently structured to let an IS use data to provide the one best answer. For instance, stock portfolio management takes place in a highly uncertain environment. No single method exists to determine which securities portfolio is best, that is, which one will yield the highest return. Medical care is another unstructured environment. There might be many methods of diagnosing a patient on the basis of his or her symptoms. Indeed, a patient with a particular set of symptoms might receive as many different diagnoses as the number of doctors he or she visits.

Using ESs saves a company the high cost of employing human experts. After gathering expertise from experts and building a program, the program can be distributed and used repeatedly. The expertise resides in the program in the form of a knowledge base consisting of facts and relationships among the facts. You learn about DSS and ES in detail in Chapter 10.

Geographic Information Systems

In some cases, the information decision makers need is related to a map. In such cases, special ISs called **geographic information systems (GISs)** can be used to tie data to physical locations. A GIS application accesses a database that contains data about a neighborhood, city, county, state, country, or even the entire world. By representing data on a map in different graphical forms, a user is able to understand promptly a situation taking place in that part of the world and act upon it. Examples of such information include population levels, the number of police officers deployed, probabilities of finding minerals, transportation routes, and vehicle allocation for transportation or distribution systems. Thus, when a supermarket chain considers

Stock And Lambert Strategic Profit works as an example of a DSS locations for expansion, executives look at a map that reflects not only geographic attributes but also demographic information such as population growth by age and income groups. GISs are often used to manage daily operations but also in planning and decision making. They also have been used to provide service via the Web, such as helping residents find locations of different services on a city map or plan travel routes. Some GISs that support operations use information from global positioning system (GPS) satellites, especially to show the current location of a vehicle or person on a map or to provide directions.

INFORMATION SYSTEMS IN BUSINESS FUNCTIONS

ISs serve various purposes throughout an organization in what are known as functional business areas—in-house services that support an organization's main business. Functional business areas include, but are not limited to, accounting, finance, marketing, and human resources. As mentioned before, in a growing number of organizations these systems are modules of a larger enterprise system, an SCM or ERP system. Chapter 3, "Business Functions and Supply Chains," discusses business functions and their systems in detail.

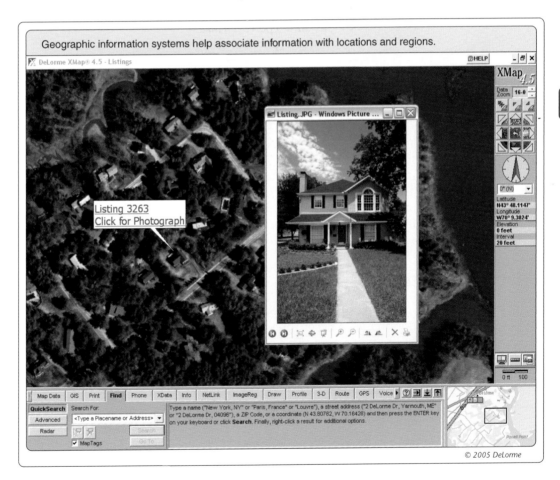

Geographic information systems help associate information with locations and regions.

© 2005 DeLorme

Accounting

In accounting, information systems help record business transactions, produce periodic financial statements, and create reports required by law, such as balance sheets and profit-and-loss statements. ISs also help create reports that might not be required by law, but that help managers understand changes in an organization's finances. Accounting ISs contain controls to ascertain adherence to standards, such as double entry.

Finance

While accounting systems focus on recording and reporting financial changes and states, the purpose of financial systems is to facilitate financial planning and business transactions. In finance, information systems help organize budgets, manage cash flow, analyze investments, and make decisions that could reduce interest payments and increase revenues from financial transactions.

Marketing

Marketing's purpose is to pinpoint the people and organizations most likely to purchase what the organization sells and to promote the appropriate products and services to those people and organizations. For instance, marketing information systems help analyze demand for various products in different regions and population groups in order to more accurately market the right product to the right consumers. Marketing ISs provide information that helps management decide how many sales representatives to assign to specific products in specific geographical areas. The systems identify trends in the demand for the company's products and services. They also help answer such questions as, "How can an advertising campaign affect our profit?" The Web has created excellent opportunities both to collect marketing data and to promote products and services by displaying information about them. That is why organizations conduct so much of their marketing efforts through ISs linked to the Web.

Human Resources

Human resource (HR) management systems mainly help in record-keeping and employee evaluation. Every organization must maintain accurate employee records. Human resource management systems maintain such records, including employees' pictures, employee marital status and tax information, and other data that other systems such as payroll might use.

Performance evaluation systems provide essential checklists that managers can use to assess their subordinates. These systems also offer a scoring utility to quantify workers' strengths and weaknesses.

HR management systems have evolved to serve many purposes: recruiting, selection, placement, benefits analysis, online benefits information for employees to access through an intranet, requirement projections (how many employees with certain skills will be required in so many months?), and other services.

WEB-EMPOWERED ENTERPRISES

 The most exciting intersection of IT and business in recent years is networked commerce—buying and selling goods and services via a telecommunications network—or as it is popularly called, **e-commerce**. The development of the Web and the opening of the Internet to commercial activities spawned a huge surge in business-to-business and business-to-consumer electronic trade. Now, every individual and small business can afford to use a network for business: the Internet.

The Internet is a vast network of computers connected across the globe that can share both information and processing. The Web is capable of displaying text, graphics, sounds, and moving images. It has enticed thousands of businesses to become involved in commercial, social, and educational initiatives. Almost every brick-and-mortar business has extended its operations to the Web. Chapter 8, "The Web-Enabled Enterprise," discusses Web technologies and how they are used in business activities. Because of its great impact on the use of information technology, the Web's impact on the use of information systems is discussed throughout the book.

CAREERS IN INFORMATION SYSTEMS

The IT trade is made up of people engaged in a wide variety of activities. According to a forecast by the U.S. Bureau of Labor Statistics, demand for IT professionals in the United States will continue to grow. Compared with demand in 2005, demand for network systems and data communications analysts is expected to increase 57 percent by 2012. Demand for software engineers will increase by 46 percent, for database administrators by 44 percent, for systems analysts by 39 percent, and for network and systems administrators by 37 percent. All of these occupations will continue to be among the top 25 percent of the best-paying jobs. The following sections review the responsibilities of IT professionals in typical areas of specialization and show parts of posted help wanted ads from Monster.com, the largest online source for employers seeking IT professionals.

Systems Analyst

Many IT professionals start their careers as programmers, or **programmer/analysts**, and then are promoted to **systems analysts**, positions that require a broad range of skills. A programmer/analyst is partly involved in the analysis of business needs and ISs, but the greater part of the job involves setting up business applications. A systems analyst is involved in designing new ISs and in updating and maintaining existing ISs. A big part of this job includes developing alternative system plans based on (1) analyzing system requirements provided by user input, (2) documenting development efforts and system features, and (3) providing adequate specifications for programmers.

To succeed, systems analysts must possess excellent communication skills to translate users' descriptions of business processes into system concepts. They must understand a wide range of business processes and ways in which IT can be applied to support them. Since analysts often deal with systems that serve more than one organizational unit, they must also understand organizational politics and be shrewd negotiators.

An excerpt from a help wanted ad for a systems analyst

- Assist in the development and enforcement of IT project standards and documentation
- Perform analyses on existing systems and work processes and recommend enhancements within existing environment
- Facilitate existing reporting processes while developing new and improved reports
- Programming experience with AS400/RPG, DB2, structured query language
- Experience with client/server environments, MS SQL Server, Windows 2000
- Experience with World Writer, Fastr, Crystal Reports and project management software
- Bachelor's degree in Information Systems or Computer Science or equivalent experience; 4+ years of manufacturing business experience
- Must be highly motivated, organized and detail oriented individual who takes direction and is a team player as well as being able to work independently and conscientiously pursues achievement of objectives
- Excellent oral and written communication skills, systems analysis, requirements specifications, system design development and system testing
- Good interpersonal skills
- Effective time management skills
- Ability to interface with all levels of management and employees
- Must be able to establish and maintain good relations to understand and readily adapt to changing demands and needs of management

Successful candidate will be enthusiastic, creative, hands-on and results-driven.

Most importantly, systems analysts must always keep in mind that they are agents of change, and that most people resist change. Unlike many other occupations, theirs often involves the creation of new systems or the modification of existing ones. Because new or modified systems often affect human activities and organizational cultures, systems analysts must be able to convince both line workers and managers that change will benefit them. Thus, these IS professionals must possess good persuasive and presentation skills.

Senior systems analysts often advance to become project leaders. In this capacity, they are put in charge of several analysts and programmers. They seek and allocate resources, such as personnel, hardware, and software, which are used in the development process, and they use project management methods to plan activities, determine milestones, and control use of resources.

Database Administrator

The **database administrator (DBA)** is responsible for the databases and data warehouses of an organization—a very sensitive and powerful position. Since access to information often connotes power, this person must be astute not only technologically but politically as well. He or she must evaluate requests for access to data from managers to determine who has a real "need to know." The DBA is responsible for developing or acquiring database applications and must carefully consider how data will be used. In addition, the DBA must adhere to federal, state, and corporate regulations to protect the privacy of customers and employees.

A growing number of organizations link their databases to the Web for use by employees, business partners, and customers. Attacks on corporate databases by hackers and computer viruses have made the DBA's job more difficult. In addition to optimizing databases and developing data management applications, this person must oversee the planning and implementation of sophisticated security measures to block unauthorized access but at the same time to allow easy and timely access to authorized users. The DBA is also highly involved in the implementation of SCM systems, because they access corporate databases.

An excerpt from a help wanted ad for a database administrator

The successful candidate will be able to do the following:
- Develop, implement, optimize and support database servers.
- Create views and stored procedures
- System backups
- Database consistency checks
- Index statistic updates
- Automated system monitors and scheduled tasks status
- Security
- Performance tuning/monitoring
- Analyze and optimize physical disk layout
- Analyze database and table growth and storage usage
- Create documentation of database system
- Create and maintain regular and ad-hoc reports
- Work with software developers to architect data models for efficient data access, reporting, and data validation
- Performance analysis & optimization of databases
- Physical disk & capacity planning for large databases
- Debugging and optimization of existing SQL queries and stored procedures

---

Network administrators plan and supervise the organization's internal networks and its connections to the Internet and other networks.

REUTERS/Pawel Kopczynski

Network Administrator

Among the many IT areas, the one that has seen the most exciting developments in recent years is networks and telecommunications. Not surprisingly, this area has also seen the greatest increase in corporate allocation of IT resources in many organizations. The emergence of new technologies, such as Voice over Internet Protocol and Wi-Fi, which are discussed in Chapter 6, is expected to sustain this trend for some years, allowing specialized professionals to be in great demand and to command high salaries.

The **network administrator** is responsible for acquiring, implementing, managing, maintaining, and troubleshooting networks throughout the organization and the links with the outside world. He or she is also often involved in selecting and implementing network security measures such as firewalls and access codes.

An excerpt from a help wanted ad for a network administrator

MAJOR RESPONSIBILITIES:
. Develop and implement ███████'s communications services program for cellular, voice, data and audio/video/web conferencing. This includes policies and feature specification.
. Manage multiple communications vendors.
. Develop metrics and a reporting framework to reduce costs, monitor SLA compliance and identify areas for inprovement.
. Manage adds, moves, and changes of communications services.
. Monthly company wide reporting on telcom expenses by department and top spenders.
. Management of telecommunications equipment inventory.
. Develop processes and procedures for ordering and provisioning voice and data networks, cellular phones, calling cards and other services.
. Assist in provisioning services as needed.
. Assist in creating and maintaining graphical and text-based documentation.
. Assist with GL coding and bill payment.
. Assist with budget development and management.
. Evaluation of new telecommuncations products and services.

REQUIRED SKILLS, KNOWLEDGE, AND EXPERIENCE:
· Minimum of 2 years experience in a telecommunications services management position.
· Excellent Excel and PowerPoint skills.
· Excellent organizational skills and attention to detail.
· Ability to multi-task and prioritize activities.
· Strong customer service skills with exceptional verbal and written communication skills.
· Successful track record managing communications services and projects.
· Operational experience with: Cisco AVVID and/or ohe PBXs, Cisco networking equipment, VOIP, TCP/IP is preferred.
· International experience is preferred.

Webmaster

The rapid spread of the Web, intranets, and extranets has increased the responsibility and stature of the organizational Webmaster. A **Webmaster** is responsible for creating and maintaining the organization's Web site and its intranet and extranet pages. Webmasters are increasingly involved in creatively deciding how to represent the organization on the Web. These decisions involve elements of marketing and graphic design. Since many organizations use the Web for commerce, Webmasters must also be well versed in Web transaction software, payment-processing software, and security software. The demand for Webmasters is expected to grow as long as corporate use of the Web continues to grow.

An excerpt from a help wanted ad for a Webmaster

The ideal candidate will have a Bachelor's degree in Computer Science or MIS and a minimum of 3 years Webmaster experience. Must have experience with graphic design, UI design, and web design; HTML, ASP, JSP coding using Visual Age or WSAD, knowledge of DHTML, CSS, JavaScript, XML, and Java illustration skills with Adobe Photoshop/Illustrator, content management, streaming audio, and multimedia.

Chief Security Officer

Because of the growing threat to information security, many organizations have created the position of **chief security officer (CSO)**, or chief information security officer (CISO). In most organizations the person in this position reports to the chief information officer (CIO) (see next section), but in some the two executives report to the same person, usually the chief executive officer (CEO). The rationale is that security should be a business issue, not an IT issue. A major challenge for CSOs is the misperception of other executives that IT security is an inhibitor rather than an enabler to operations.

Chief Information Officer and Chief Technology Officer

The fact that a corporation has a position titled **chief information officer (CIO)** reflects the importance that the company places on ISs as a strategic resource. The CIO, who is responsible for all aspects of an organization's ISs, is often, but not always, a corporate vice president. Some companies prefer to call this position **chief technology officer (CTO)**. However, you might find organizations where there are both a CIO and a CTO and one reports to the other. There is no universal agreement of what the responsibility of each should be. Yet, in most cases when you encounter both positions in one organization, the CTO reports to the CIO.

An excerpt from a help wanted ad for a chief technology officer

SKILL, KNOWLEDGE, AND ABILITY REQUIRED

15+ years experience within the IT industry with a large company that supports web-based, client server based, and mainframe based technologies

Knowledge and understanding of marketplace developments and trends related to the Information Technology (IT) function.
Knowledge of concepts and philosophies regarding the design and deployment of information technologies and associated architectural concepts, principles, and tools.
Knowledge of emerging technologies.
Knowledge of the existing and planned Information Architecture and Information Management Methodology.
Knowledge of major tasks, deliverables, formal methodologies and disciplines for delivering new or enhanced applications.
Knowledge of a variety of specific tools and toolkits for development and support of applications.
Knowledge of the existing and planned software technology and the global, regional and local software architecture and infrastructure components.
Knowledge of the existing and planned telecommunications platforms and the global, regional and local telecommunications architecture and infrastructure components.
Knowledge of the data center operating environment and the day-to-day operational requirements.
Knowledge of the asset and process management practices, requirements, and support services for the IT function.
Demonstrated leadership capabilities, including successful experience in strategic planning, complex project management, personnel management, and team leadership
Experience in managing large-scale transaction processing in addition to supporting information intensive businesses.

A person who holds the position of CIO must have both technical understanding of current and developing information technologies and business knowledge. As Figure 1.7 shows, the CIO plays an important role in integrating the IS strategic plan into the organization's overall strategic plan. He or she must not only keep abreast of technical developments but also have a keen understanding of how different technologies can improve business processes or aid in the creation of new products and services.

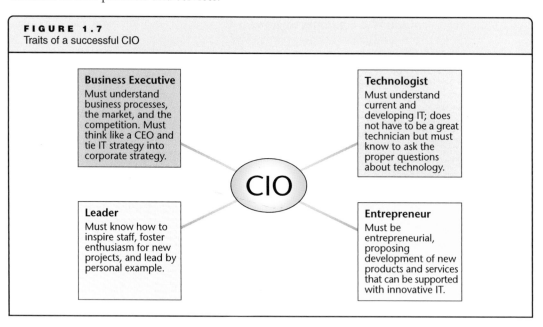

FIGURE 1.7
Traits of a successful CIO

Business Executive
Must understand business processes, the market, and the competition. Must think like a CEO and tie IT strategy into corporate strategy.

Technologist
Must understand current and developing IT; does not have to be a great technician but must know to ask the proper questions about technology.

Leader
Must know how to inspire staff, foster enthusiasm for new projects, and lead by personal example.

Entrepreneur
Must be entrepreneurial, proposing development of new products and services that can be supported with innovative IT.

CIO

- Computer-based information systems pervade almost every aspect of our lives. Their ability to help solve problems and make decisions makes them indispensable in business and management. Computer-based information systems take data as raw material, process the data, and produce information as output. While data sometimes can be useful as is, it usually must be manipulated to produce information, which is facts, statistics, and other items useful for reporting and decision making.

- A system is a set of components that work together to achieve a common goal. An information system (IS) consists of several components: hardware (the computer and its peripheral equipment), software (programs that run the computer), data, people, and procedures. The components' common goal is to produce the best information from available data.

- Often, a system performs a limited task that produces an end result, which must be combined with other products from other systems to reach an ultimate goal. Such a system is called a subsystem. Several subsystems might make up a system. Sometimes, systems are also classified as closed or open. A stand-alone system that has no contact with other systems is called a closed system. A system that interfaces with other systems is an open system.

- Data processing has four basic stages. In the input stage, data are collected and entered into the computer. The computer then performs the next stage, data processing, which is the manipulation of data into information using mathematical, statistical, and other tools. The subsequent stage, output, displays or presents the information. We often also want to maintain data and information for later use. This activity is called storage.

- Any information system that helps in management may be referred to as a management information system (MIS). MISs use recorded transactions and other data to produce information for problem solving and decision making.

- There are several different types of information systems. They include transaction processing systems (TPSs), supply chain management (SCM) systems, customer relationship management (CRM) systems, business intelligence (BI) systems, decision support systems (DSSs) and expert systems (ESs), and geographic information systems (GISs). Often, some or all of these systems are linked to each other or to other information systems.

- Enterprise application systems, such as SCM or ERP systems, are information systems that tie together the different functional areas of a business, such as order entry, inventory management, accounting and finance, and manufacturing. Such systems allow businesses to operate more efficiently by avoiding reentry and duplication of information. The systems can provide an up-to-the-minute picture of inventory, work-in-progress, and the status of an order to be fulfilled.

- ISs are used in many business functions, most commonly accounting, finance, marketing, and human resources. These systems aid in the daily operations of organizations by maintaining proper accounting information and producing reports, assisting in managing cash and investments, helping marketing professionals find the most likely buyers for their products and services, and keeping accurate employee records and assisting with their performance evaluations.

- The job prospects for IT professionals are bright. Among the typical careers in this field are systems analyst, database administrator, network administrator, Webmaster, chief security officer, chief information officer, and chief technology officer.

- IT has many advantages, but it also has created societal concerns. Issues such as privacy, free speech on the Web, spam, and Web annoyances are viewed by many people as serious ethical issues. And while IT professionals increasingly affect our lives through the systems they develop and maintain, they are not required to adhere to any code of ethics as other professionals are. These and related issues are discussed throughout the book.

EATS2GO REVISITED

Now that Chapter 1 has helped you understand how business uses data, information, and information systems, let's revisit Eats2Go. Juan, Kendra, and Dave are trying to improve their lunch business. How would you cope with their challenges?

What Would You Do?

1. Juan has been bogged down entering sales receipts into the business's computer programs at the end of the week. He has also been swamped at the end of the month, when he generates reports on overall sales, taxes, and expenses. He needs a better system. What would you do to increase the efficiency of the business transactions? Examine the business's inputs, processing, and outputs. Formulate a method to streamline the business transactions. What type of reports does Juan need?

2. Kendra noticed the varying sales of some menu items. What information about sales does she need to optimize orders of ingredients and the labor spent on food preparation?

3. Currently, Eats2Go does not collect information about the items that are ordered together by an individual customer. Do you think that information would be helpful to the owners? How might they generate and use such information?

4. Are SCM or CRM applicable to Eats2Go? If so, which one is more important to Eats2Go at the beginning of their business? Explain.

New Perspectives

1. What business opportunities can Eats2Go generate from the following changes in the food industry?

    - The U.S. Department of Agriculture recently adopted new standards for organic food labeling. Consumers now can determine exactly how a product has been produced from the label it carries. Food producers and retailers can apply for certification from the USDA. You have advised the team to apply for certification, which means they would have to label each wrapped meal. Advise them how a personal computer could help with this task.

    - The food wholesaler the business uses is setting up a Web site to allow its customers to order supplies online. How would this change Eats2Go's current operations? List both benefits and drawbacks.

2. The Chamber of Commerce has approached Eats2Go to provide food snacks at the city's organized events for Memorial Day, Fourth of July, and Labor Day. Advise Juan, Kendra, and Dave: what information do they need to decide whether to accept this offer? Do they currently have this information from the data they have collected? If they decide to accept this offer, what information will tell them whether they made the right decision?

KEY TERMS

business intelligence (BI), 20
chief information officer (CIO), 25
chief security officer (CSO), 25
chief technology officer (CTO), 25

closed system, 10
customer relationship management (CRM), 19
data, 7
data processing, 15
data warehouse, 20

database, 11
database administrator (DBA), 24
decision support system (DSS), 20
e-commerce, 22

enterprise application, 18
enterprise resource planning (ERP) system, 18
expert system (ES), 20
geographic information system (GIS), 20
information, 7
information map, 12
information system (IS), 11
information technology (IT), 13
input, 15

management information system (MIS), 18
network administrator, 24
open system, 10
output, 15
process, 8
programmer/analyst, 23
storage, 15
subsystem, 9
supply chain management (SCM) system, 18
synergy, 13

system, 9
systems analyst, 23
telecommunications, 17
transaction, 15
transaction processing system (TPS), 15
Webmaster, 25

REVIEW QUESTIONS

1. What does the word "processing" in data processing mean?

2. Give three examples in which raw data also serves as useful information.

3. Give three business examples (not mentioned in the text) of data that must be processed to provide useful information.

4. Give three examples of subsystems not operating in the context of IT. Why are these subsystems and not systems?

5. How do TPSs and DSSs differ?

6. What is a problem? Give an example of a business problem and discuss how a computer-based information system could solve it.

7. What is synergy? How is synergy accomplished when a person uses a computer?

8. "An information system consists of hardware and software." Why is this statement inadequate?

9. When does one need to make a decision?

10. How can a DSS help make decisions?

11. Note the word "support" in decision support systems. Why are these applications not called decision-*making* systems?

12. Who is considered a knowledge worker? Will you have a career as a knowledge worker? Explain.

13. What is the most prevalent type of information system? Why is this type of IS so ubiquitous?

14. TPSs are usually used at the boundaries of the organization. What are boundaries in this context? Give three examples of boundaries.

15. Among IT professionals, the greatest demand is for network administrators and analysts. Why?

DISCUSSION QUESTIONS

1. No longer the domain of technical personnel, information systems are the business of every professional. Why?

2. Assume that computers can recognize voices easily and detect their users' exact meaning when talking. Will the necessity for written language be reduced to zero? Why or why not?

3. Information systems cannot solve some business problems. Give three examples and explain why technology cannot help.

4. An increasing number of knowledge workers must know how to use information systems. Why?

5. Often, computer illiteracy is likened to reading illiteracy. Is this realistic? Is computer illiteracy as severe a handicap as reading illiteracy?

6. Think of two examples of fully Web-based businesses. What made the Web so attractive for these entrepreneurs?

7. We will soon stop talking of e-commerce and simply speak of commerce. Why?

8. Help wanted advertisements do not use the term "computer specialists"; rather, they use the term "information system professionals" or "information technology professionals." Why?

9. How do traditional commerce and Web-based commerce differ?

10. What changed the average citizen's life more, the industrial revolution or the information revolution? How and why?

11. Information technology might bring people together, but it also isolates them. Explain the latter claim and give an example.

12. Give two examples of phenomena that are a social concern because of information technology. Explain.

13. What irritates you about the Web? What would you do to minimize this irritation?

14. Do you foresee an IT-related societal or ethical concern that is not a current concern? Explain.

15. If you chose a career in IT apart from CIO or CTO, which position would you choose, and why?

APPLYING CONCEPTS

 1. Recall what you did yesterday from the moment you got up until the moment you went to bed. How many times did you use a computer or receive data or information from someone who used a computer? (Do not forget ATMs, cash registers, automated kiosks, etc.) Write a two-page essay on your daily experience with IT and on society's dependency on computers.

 2. Contact a business organization and ask permission to observe a business process. Pinpoint the segments in the process that a computer-based information system could aid. Write a report detailing your observations and suggestions.

3. Observe activities in a supermarket: shoppers looking down aisles for specific products; lines forming at the cash registers; workers sticking new prices to items on the shelves. Prepare a list of shoppers' and workers' activities that could be carried out with less use of human time and more accuracy if they were aided by IT. Explain how you would change those activities.

HANDS-ON ACTIVITIES

1. Scientists are researching a contagious disease. They found that, on average, each person who is infected transmits the disease to three other people within one year. Currently, there are 3,000 infected people in the country. Use Excel or another spreadsheet application to find out (1) how many people will contract the disease each year over the next decade, and (2) how many infected people will there be each year if no medication is administered. (Do not worry: there is a medication for this disease.) "Currently" means in the first year of your calculation. Calculate for the next nine years. Explain why this is a modeling problem. What is your model in the spreadsheet?

2. Use a résumé template in your word-processing program to type your résumé If you don't have a lot of direct work experience, remember to include all types of work, whether it's babysitting, camp counseling, mowing the lawn, or whatever.

3. Use your word-processing application to prepare a list: what information that you currently receive through other means could you receive through your computer? The list should include text, images, audio, and animated information. Would you prefer to receive this information on the computer or as you do now?

TEAM ACTIVITIES

1. Form a team with two other students. Each team member should play the role of a vice president in charge of a business function: human resources, accounting, marketing, finance, and so on. Each vice president should enumerate information he or she needs to perform his or her function. Now list information that two or more of the functions must share and data produced by one function that another function uses.

2. Team up with another two students. Brainstorm and try to think of a new business opportunity that you would like to pursue in which you will not need IT. You should be able to convince your professor that IT cannot improve the operations of this business.

1. Use Excel to create a simple financial spreadsheet for Eats2Go's business plan.

2. Use presentation software to create a presentation in support of Eats2Go's application to the bank for a business loan.

VIDEO QUESTIONS

1. The video segment mentions Jef Raskin. Who was he? What were some of his inventions? What are his theories about design?

2. Do you agree with Buxton's contention that devices should be designed by humanists rather than engineers? Why or why not?

FROM IDEAS TO APPLICATION: REAL CASES

The Personal Touch

FedEx is an organization that never sleeps and for which every minute counts. On the peak days between Christmas and New Years' Eve, it typically ships more than 8 million packages. On a normal day the company transports an average of 5.5 million packages, using over 600 aircraft and 71,000 trucks. Inevitably, some packages miss their delivery time, some miss their destination, and some are damaged. When that happens, FedEx's 4,000 customer service reps are the people customers call.

Prompt, efficient customer service is extremely important for staying in this highly competitive global shipping industry, let alone do so with a satisfactory profit. Incoming telephone calls at the FedEx customer service center in Fullerton, California, never stop, and FedEx reps never have an idle moment on shift. Sitting in front of computer monitors in a cluster of cubicles with headsets on, these agents barely have time to stretch their limbs.

A caller complains that her package hasn't arrived, which is a common complaint. Another asks if he can change his pickup time. A third caller is confused about signature: is he supposed to sign for the delivery or will the package just be dropped at his doorstep? The reps are confident and friendly. They welcome any question or complaint even if they have heard it a thousand times before. The words "I am sorry" are uttered often. They are careful not to give the customers a feeling of being rushed, but try to resolve complaints quickly. Time is money.

Several years ago FedEx installed software that reps at the call centers can use to provide faster service. Many of the callers are already registered in the company's database. One of the most frequent requests is to send a FedEx worker to pick up a package. Using the software, a rep can handle such a request in 20 seconds. All she needs to do is enter a name, which leads to a zip code, which in turn leads to a tracking number. That number uniquely identifies the package. Some complaints are more complex. For example, a FedEx driver misunderstood a note a caller had left for him and therefore misdelivered a package. A complaint like that takes no more than 10 minutes to resolve.

An experienced and efficient rep can handle about 10 callers in 45 minutes. Ideally, though, nobody would call. If FedEx had its way, at least six of the ten callers would use their computers to go to FedEx's Web site and solve their problem by themselves. Six of ten, because about 60 percent of FedEx's clients have a computer connected to the Internet. Like other companies, FedEx tries to save labor by directing callers to its Web site. Yet, many people prefer to use the phone and talk to a human helper.

Every time a customer decides to use the company's Web site instead of telephoning, the company saves up to $1.87. Efforts to divert callers to the site have been fruitful. In 2005, FedEx call centers received 470,000 calls per day, 83,000 fewer than in 2000. This difference in calls translates into a saving of $57.56 million per year. The company's Web site handles an average of 60 million requests to track packages per month. Operating the Web site does cost money. Each of these requests cost FedEx 3 cents, amounting to $21.6 million per year. However, if all these requests were made by phone, the cost would exceed $1.36 billion per year. As it is impossible to divert all callers to the Web site, the company must maintain call centers. The annual cost of these call centers is $326 million. This cost might decrease over the years, as more and more customers use the Web site, but there will probably always be call centers, because FedEx does not want to lose frustrated customers.

Many people are still uncomfortable doing business at a Web site. The cost of a customer who is frustrated by the company Web site is incalculable. Experience shows that people are willing to encounter one or two obstacles with the Web site, but then they stop trying.

Since its establishment in 1971 as Federal Express Corp., the company was keen on information technologies, but over the years it used an increasing number of disparate systems for different business purposes, such as air freight, ground freight, special logistic operations, and custom shipping of critical items. By 1999, customer information was scattered in computer systems implemented over 14 years. To periodically test service, executives pretend to be customers. They discovered that customers who used more than one FedEx business were not treated consistently. For example, when claiming damages customer had to fill out 37 fields on a claims form, such as tracking number, ship date, pickup location, and destination, even though FedEx systems already held data for 33 of those fields. The official change of "Federal Express" to "FedEx" started an important move: all the company units were to share the same information systems.

Meanwhile, FedEx's customer service centers were redesigned around a PC-based software desktop. If reps could pull up historical data on customers whenever they called—not just their shipping histories, but their preferences and even images of their paper bills—

FedEx could provide better, faster service, both to individual customers and to businesses that sold goods through catalogs.

In 2000, management purchased customer relationship management software called Clarify. A new policy was established: systems and customer service experts are equally responsible for the call centers. Using PCs, reps can pull up historical data on customers whenever customers call. Customer records that are immediately available to reps include shipping histories, preferences, and images of the paper bills. Customers are happier now than they were just a few years ago. So are the reps. Turnover of service reps has decreased 20 percent.

Productivity is important, but so is the reps' service quality. They must be polite, provide customers with correct appropriate information, and try not to give customers a reason to call again. Typically, callers are either determined to speak to a human or they know the help they need is too complex to be available at the company's Web site. Therefore, callers require more time than in the past. The company periodically evaluates the reps' performance based on clearly stated goals that take all these factors into consideration. Typically, 32 percent of the reps' performance rating is based on the quality of their response, and 17 percent on their efficiency. The other 51 percent is based on attendance, adherence to scheduled breaks, and compliance with regulations.

Interestingly, customers are not interested in friendliness, but in quick and accurate information. FedEx constantly follows customer reactions to different help styles. Managers discovered then when reps' time is not limited, they tend to speak with customers beyond the time required to solve the problem. Customers perceive them as too talkative, and they get a bad impression about FedEx. Thus, reps are encouraged to get off the phone as soon as the problem is resolved rather than try to be "nice."

The professionals who work for the vendor of Clarify, the CRM software, spend time with reps to see how well the software serves them. They discovered that reps often move quickly from one window of information to another, and that sometimes they took extra time to find a window that "disappeared." The software engineers decided to modify Clarify so it interacts with Java code. This enables the reps to switch between windows and different applications of Clarify quickly during a call without reentering customer data. For instance, if a customer needs directions to pick up a package, the rep can click the tab of the mapping application. Relying on the customer's account data, the application picks up the customer's zip code.

Combining it with the code of the pickup center, the software immediately produces directions, which the rep can read to the customer.

While great improvements have already been accomplished both in service speed and quality, FedEx executives continue to look for ways to improve. They refuse to discuss what their next step is because it might be copied immediately by competitors, but they do reveal that their goal is to bring call centers to the point where a rep never has to put a customer on hold.

Experts expect a single "nervous system" for all types of customer calls by 2010. Software will accept all customer calls from the customer's PC, phone, or handheld device. Special software involving artificial intelligence techniques will screen all incoming calls, evaluate the problem complexity, and decide whether to direct the calls to other software for resolution or to invite a human rep to intervene.

Source: Gage, D., "FedEx: Personal Touch," *Baseline* (www. baselinemag.com), January 13, 2005; www.fedex.com/us, 2005.

Thinking About the Case

1. What is CRM in general? Give examples of *different* CRM applications.

2. Enumerate and explain the various ways in which the CRM application discussed here (Clarify) saves costs or helps in other ways.

3. Which metrics would you use to measure *before* and *after* performance regarding the information technologies implemented in this case? Consider cost, service quality, cycle time, and any other performance factor and provide a specific metric (i.e., ratio, product, or absolute value).

4. As a customer, would you prefer more, or less, mechanized service in lieu of human help?

5. As an executive for FedEx or a similar company, what else would you implement using software and the Internet?

From Penny Arcade to Service in a Jiffy

In the world of commercial banking, Commerce Bank truly stands out. Whether it's the especially friendly bank tellers and branch managers who put on a mask for Halloween or customer service treats like free coin counters, Commerce is a retail banking operation that has bucked trends, foreseen consumer demand in response to new technology, and always thought about service from different angles.

Commerce was founded in 1973 in a Philadelphia suburb close to the headquarters of its parent company, Commerce Bancorp Inc. With over 320 branches in New Jersey, southeastern Pennsylvania, New York, and Delaware, the bank posted net profits of $254.6 million in 2004 on $1.32 billion in revenues.

From its early days, Commerce has put high emphasis on excellent customer service. Unlike the vast majority of commercial banks in the United States, all Commerce branches are open on Saturday and Sunday, with weekday operations from 7:30 a.m. to 8:00 p.m. Management sensed that what other banks were doing was not wise: they were closing branches and relying more heavily on ATMs and online banking to serve customers. Apparently, customers like the personal touch that live tellers in branch offices can give. Commerce enjoyed increasing revenues when other banks kept losing customers. However, friendly service requires ISs that support tellers in terms of speed and quality.

Commerce has a small IT staff. In 1999, the staff launched an application it calls WOW Answer Guide that uses a popular intraorganizational document-sharing program called Lotus Notes. Tellers can use this online help system from their stations to quickly find answers to questions without having to ask colleagues or supervisors or leave customers waiting. And online customers have access to the same help system on the bank's Web site.

Early on, Commerce eliminated the float period, the time between the moment a customer deposits a check and the moment the funds are available for withdrawal. To Commerce, the float period was a "stupid rule," and it designed its information systems to eliminate it early on. In 2003, the U.S. Congress passed an act popularly known as Rule 21, forcing banks to make funds available for withdrawal the day after a check is deposited. Most banks had to adjust their information systems to comply, but Commerce was ready.

Commerce's commitment to its customers requires the bank to consistently increase service quality and quantity. Identity verification has long been managed through a "signature upon screen" system, which enables tellers to view a customer's scanned signature immediately after they enter the person's account number. This expedites identity verification, and the teller can execute transactions without delay.

But the IT professionals also ensure that operations not seen by customers are efficient. Branch managers or head tellers in banks must "settle the branch" at the end of each work day. Settling means that every penny of a deposit or withdrawal is accounted for. Before Commerce's new Browser Teller System, settling a branch typically took about 40 minutes. With the new system the head teller settles the branch with four keystrokes.

Commerce's prioritization of customer service has yielded significant growth and pleased shareholders with positive bottom lines. For the third quarter of 2004, Commerce had increased revenues by 31 percent over the same period the previous year and profits were up 42 percent. Deposits were also up 34 percent, and the bank's total assets reached $28.4 billion, one-third higher than they were in the same quarter of 2003.

Commerce never tires of conceiving new ways to better use IT. In recent years, the IT budget has increased annually by 35 percent. Slightly less than half of that is devoted to increased operations, and the remaining 20 percent funds new efforts.

In the past decade, Commerce has upgraded its teller system three times and adopted an innovative cash-dispensing process at its most trafficked branches. The results have been dramatic. In the past, customers wishing to cash a check had to wait approximately 57 seconds, but check-cashing now requires just 10 seconds at the busiest Commerce locations, as tellers have been trained to use the new system. The average time for all types of transactions has been reduced to less than 11 seconds. Therefore, while each branch handles an average of 45,000 transactions per month, and some locations manage 90,000 transactions, customers do not have to wait in long lines. Despite the growing number of transactions per branch and the faster service, the bank did not have to increase the number of employees per branch.

While IT development behind the scenes has helped Commerce to increase its brand recognition, customer base, and profits, simpler alterations to customer engagement and banking options have especially raised the bank's profile. Tellers make a conscious effort to exude enthusiasm and smile when they interact with customers. Their desire for speedy processing and short lines is ingrained as a company hallmark.

While many commercial banks today are focusing on reducing employee-customer interaction (reinforcing banks' traditional reputation for bad service), Commerce has always stressed positive, personalized service that attracts customers. Research data indicates that people prefer to handle their banking needs in person, and branch banking remains the bread-and-butter segment of business operations for U.S. banks. Although retail operations require much more physical maintenance and personnel than automated teller machines (ATMs) and online banking, Commerce has built on the typical customer's preference for service from a face rather than a screen and turned this loyalty and satisfaction into profit growth. This relationship with the customer increased the number of new deposit accounts in the last six months of 2004 to 90,000 per month from 80,000 per month in the year before.

Commerce's efforts to emphasize personal service have even affected the way its ATMs are designed. The company has driven ATM manufacturers to build machines that are smaller than usual, so they don't obscure the view of Commerce branches' lobbies.

The bank also offers several conveniences that individually strike a positive note with customers and challenge competitors. These include no fees for checking or savings accounts with at least a $100 balance each month, an instant debit card that enables new customers to withdraw money from their just-opened account the next business day, and Penny Arcade.

Of all the Commerce sweeteners for customers, Penny Arcade is the most famous. The machine, located in every branch, counts coins at no fee. It cuts retail losses and has been instrumental in building brand recognition. This is especially true in the case of families, as parents bring children with their piggy banks, and the youngsters watch the coins being counted at a screen specifically designed for their height.

In spite of its emphasis on human interaction, Commerce Bank has not ignored online banking. On the contrary, it invites customers to bank online at its elaborate and friendly Web site. Except for depositing and cashing checks, customers can do almost anything from their PCs that they can do at a branch, from opening an account to reordering checks to transferring funds from one account to another. And if customers prefer to do any of that in Spanish, one click will switch them to a Spanish site that mirrors the English one.

Commerce's dependence on excellent customer service and innovative IT has consistently benefited the bank across the board. In the last year, average new deposit accounts per month increased, and Commerce is opening new branches in Connecticut and Washington, D.C. With Penny Arcade and its numerous amendments to traditional retail banking services, Commerce proves that a penny saved is indeed a penny earned.

Source: Fitzgerald, M., "How Commerce Bank Puts the Fast Food into Banking," *CIO Insight*, January 5, 2005; www. commerceonline.com, 2005.

Thinking About the Case

1. For many years other banks tried to close down branches and provide more services through ATMs and online banking. Why? Why did this approach fail?

2. What is the clearest evidence that IT makes Commerce Bank's operations more efficient?

3. What can you cite as evidence that IT helps improve customer service quality at Commerce Bank?

2

TWO

Strategic Uses of Information Systems

LEARNING OBJECTIVES

Executives know that information technology is not merely a resource to support day-to-day operations. Clever use of IT can significantly change an organization's long-term strategic position in national and global markets. Often, applying information systems to long-term planning completely changes the way a firm conducts its business. Some systems even change the product or service that a firm provides. Today, information systems are an accepted and integral part of strategic planning for nearly all organizations.

When you finish this chapter, you will be able to:

- Explain what business strategy and strategic moves are.

- Illustrate how information systems can give businesses a competitive advantage.

- Identify basic initiatives for gaining a competitive advantage.

- Explain what makes an information system a *strategic* information system.

- Identify fundamental requirements for developing strategic information systems.

- Explain circumstances and initiatives that make one IT strategy succeed and another fail.

EATS2GO:
Using Information Strategically

The information systems that Eats2Go had in place had succeeded so far: the business had been operating for a year, and it was profitable. Juan Moreno, Kendra Banks, and Dave Slater had begun to enjoy running their pushcart lunch business. Handling the food concessions for the city's major holiday celebrations had helped carry them through the summer, when there weren't as many students on campus. Now the three entrepreneurs were looking for ways to expand and increase their profits even more. An opportunity presented itself at a Chamber of Commerce meeting.

Looking at Expansion

Dave regularly attended Chamber of Commerce meetings to keep in touch with the local business community. He was always looking for new opportunities. After one meeting, the owner of Campus Town's outdoor shopping mall approached him with a proposal: the mall owner wanted to draw more foot traffic, and he thought that some small food vendors would provide a fun atmosphere and encourage shoppers to linger. He was thinking of a couple of pushcarts—would Eats2Go be interested? Dave checked with his partners, and they decided to expand their operations to the mall.

However, the increased sales from operating three carts meant that Juan, Kendra, and Dave needed to ramp up their production—and quickly. They were having trouble handling their increased cooking and food preparation load—they were in Juan's uncle's kitchen earlier and earlier to finish in time. They seriously needed to consider renting kitchen space for themselves. And they also needed to hire additional staff to help prepare the sandwiches and man the carts—it was simply too much for Juan, Kendra, and Dave to cover three carts by themselves.

A New Line of Business?

Customers began lining up at the outdoor mall lunch carts in droves. To keep their clientele happy, Eats2Go experimented with new chip varieties—handing them out to waiting customers and getting their immediate feedback. Kendra tried plantain chips and baked pita chips in different flavors, in addition to the all-natural potato chips they originally offered. Customers loved the new pita chips, and they could be made from wraps that hadn't been used the previous day, so their additional cost was minimal. With the great customer reception of the chip line, Juan, Kendra, and Dave were now considering producing and packaging the chips for sale to other retail establishments—in other words, becoming a food manufacturer. They would definitely need to move to new kitchen facilities, but they reasoned they could use the new kitchen space around the clock eventually, if needed. The additional chip revenue could help them cover the cost of the equipment and new space. They'd also need their own pots and pans, ovens, and packaging equipment. None of this would be cheap, so they'd need to watch expenses and revenues closely in their spreadsheets.

Charting a Strategy with Information Systems

Juan and Dave also investigated the option of using only organic ingredients, to appeal even more to the health-food market. They called organic suppliers and surfed the Web to gather data to plug into their spreadsheets. Doing this research helped them avoid what could have been a costly mistake—going organic would raise their prices 33 percent and would not be a good strategic move for them right now.

New Competition on the Block

After Juan, Kendra, and Dave had made these important decisions, they received some bad news. Word of Eats2Go's success had evidently spread—a local Subwich franchise had located a shop a few blocks away from Robbins Park to attract some of their business. The three partners were very worried about competing with a national franchise, which had much greater financial resources than they did.

To help retain loyal customers, they decided to implement a frequent buyer program, where current customers could get a free sandwich after the purchase of 10. The three partners registered repeat customers in their database and issued cards to be punched. They hoped this additional program would help them stay competitive with Subwich, but they knew they'd need to remain on their toes.

STRATEGY AND STRATEGIC MOVES

The word "strategy" originates from the Greek word *strategos*, meaning "general." In war, a strategy is a plan to gain an advantage over the enemy. Other disciplines, especially business, have borrowed the term. As you know from media coverage, corporate executives often discuss actions in ways that make business competition sound like war. Businesspeople must devise decisive courses of action to win—just as generals do. In business, a strategy is a plan designed to help an organization outperform its competitors. Unlike battle plans, however, business strategy often takes the form of creating new opportunities rather than beating rivals.

Although many information systems are built to solve problems, many others are built to seize opportunities. And, as anyone in business can tell you, identifying a problem is easier than creating an opportunity. Why? Because a problem already exists; it is an obstacle to a desired mode of operation and, as such, calls attention to itself. An opportunity, on the other hand, is less tangible. It takes a certain amount of imagination, creativity, and vision to identify an opportunity, or to create one and seize it. Information systems that help seize opportunities are often called **strategic information systems (SISs)**. They can be developed from scratch, or they can evolve from an organization's existing ISs.

In a free-market economy, it is difficult for a business to do well without some strategic planning. Although strategies vary, they tend to fall into some basic categories, such as developing a new product, identifying an unmet consumer need, changing a service to entice more customers or retain existing clients, or taking any other action that increases the organization's value through improved performance.

Many strategies do not, and cannot, involve information systems. But increasingly, corporations are able to implement certain strategies—such as maximizing sales and lowering costs—thanks to the innovative use of information systems. In other words, better information gives corporations a competitive advantage in the marketplace. A company achieves **strategic advantage** by using strategy to maximize its strengths, resulting in a **competitive advantage**. When a business uses a strategy with the intent to *create* a market for new products or services, it does not aim to compete with other organizations, because that market does not yet exist. Therefore, a strategic move is not always a competitive move. However, in a free-enterprise society, a market rarely remains the domain of one organization for long; thus, competition ensues almost immediately. So, we often use the terms "competitive advantage" and "strategic advantage" interchangeably.

You might have heard statements about using the Web strategically. Business competition is no longer limited to a particular country or even a region of the world. To increase the sale of goods and services, companies must regard the entire world as their market. Because thousands of corporations and hundreds of millions of consumers have access to the Web, augmenting business via the Web has become strategic: many companies that utilized the Web early on have enjoyed greater market shares, more experience with the Web as a business enabler, and larger

[Handwritten margin notes:] Competitive advantage comes from implementing management initiatives faster than the competition ✓

The advantage of being the first mover. This is a nonsensical statement.

> **POINT OF INTEREST**
>
> **Strategy? What Strategy?**
>
> A 2004 study by the professional groups Financial Executives International and Computer Sciences Corporation reported that fewer than half of U.S. and Canadian companies had written technology plans, and even fewer believed their plans were in line with the goals of their CEOs. However, planning does seem to pay off. Respondents from companies that had both a plan and good alignment with business goals said their organizations enjoyed a much higher rate of return on every dollar they invested in information technology.
>
> *Source*: Management By the Numbers, "How to Get Your Money's Worth," *Baseline* (www.baselinemag.com), March 1, 2004.

revenues than latecomers. Some companies developed information systems, or features of information systems, that are unique, such as Amazon's "one-click" online purchasing and Priceline's "name your own price" auctioning. Practically any Web-based system that gives a company competitive advantage is a strategic information system.

ACHIEVING A COMPETITIVE ADVANTAGE

Consider competitive advantage in terms of a for-profit company, whose major goal is to maximize profits by lowering costs and increasing revenue. A for-profit company achieves competitive advantage when its profits increase significantly, most commonly through increased market share. Figure 2.1 lists eight basic initiatives that can be used to gain competitive advantage, including offering a product or service that competitors cannot provide or providing the same product or service more attractively to customers. It is important to understand that the eight listed are the most common, but not the only, types of business strategy an organization can pursue. It is also important to understand that strategic moves often consist of a combination of two or more of these initiatives and other steps. The essence of strategy is innovation, so competitive advantage is often gained when an organization tries a strategy that no one has tried before. e.g. or implementing a strategy successful in one industry in another industry.

FIGURE 2.1
Eight basic ways to gain competitive advantage

Initiative	Benefit
Reduce costs	A company can gain advantage if it can sell more units at a lower price while providing quality and maintaining or increasing its profit margin.
Raise barriers to market entrants	A company can gain advantage if it deters potential entrants into the market, enjoying less competition and more market potential.
Establish high switching costs	A company can gain advantage if it creates high switching costs, making it economically infeasible for customers to buy from competitors.
Create new products or services	A company can gain advantage if it offers a unique product or service.
Differentiate products or services	A company can gain advantage if it can attract customers by convincing them its product differs from the competition's.
Enhance products or services	A company can gain advantage if its product or service is better than anyone else's.
Establish alliances	Companies from different industries can help each other gain advantage by offering combined packages of goods or services at special prices.
Lock in suppliers or buyers	A company can gain advantage if it can lock in either suppliers or buyers, making it economically impractical for suppliers or buyers to deal with competitors.

For example, Dell was the first PC manufacturer to use the Web to take customer orders. Competitors have long imitated the practice, but Dell, first to gain a Web audience, gained more experience than other PC makers on this e-commerce vehicle and still sells more computers via the Web than its competitors. Figure 2.2 indicates that a company can use many strategies together to gain competitive advantage.

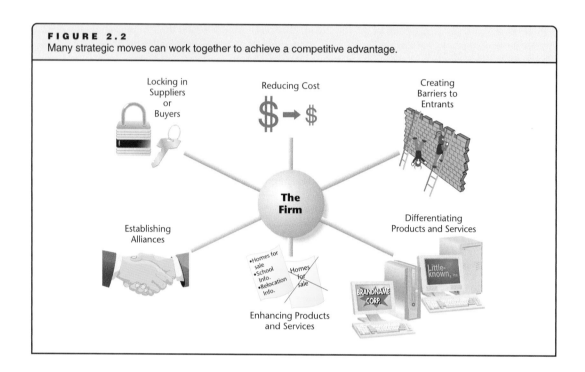

FIGURE 2.2
Many strategic moves can work together to achieve a competitive advantage.

Initiative #1: Reduce Costs

Customers like to pay as little as possible while still receiving the quality of service or product they need. One way to increase market share is to lower prices, and the best way to lower prices is to **reduce costs**. For instance, if carried out successfully, massive automation of any business process gives an organization competitive advantage. The reason is simple: automation makes an organization more productive, and any cost savings can be transferred to customers through lower prices. We saw this happen in the auto industry. In the 1970s, Japanese automakers brought robots to their production and assembly lines and reduced costs—and subsequently prices—quickly and dramatically. The robots weld, paint, and assemble parts at a far lower cost than manual labor. Until their competitors began to employ robots, the Japanese had a clear competitive advantage because they were able to sell high-quality cars for less than their competitors.

In the service sector, the Web has created an opportunity to automate what until recently was considered an activity that only humans could perform: customer service. An enormous trend toward automating online customer service began with companies such as FedEx, which initially gave customers an opportunity to track their parcels' status by logging on to a dedicated, private network and database. The same approach is now implemented through the Web. Many sites today include answers to FAQs (frequently asked questions). Others have special programs that can respond to customer questions. Online service gives businesses two major benefits: it changes service from being labor intensive to technology intensive, which is much less expensive; and it provides customers easy access to a service 7 days a week, 24 hours a day. It not only cuts the costs of expensive human labor but also of telephone and mailing charges. Companies that are first to adopt advanced systems that reduce labor enjoy competitive advantage for as long as their competitors lag behind.

Initiative #2: Raise Barriers to Market Entrants

The smaller the number of companies competing within an industry, the better off each company is. Therefore, an organization might gain competitive advantage by making it difficult, or impossible, for other organizations to produce the product or service it provides. Using expertise or technology that is unavailable to competitors or prohibitively expensive is one way to bar new entrants.

Companies **raise barriers to entrants** in a number of ways. Obtaining legal protection of intellectual property such as an invention or artistic work bars competitors from freely using it. Microsoft and other software powerhouses have gained tremendous strategic advantages by copyrighting and patenting software. On the Web, there are numerous examples of such protection. Priceline.com holds a patent for online reverse ("name your own price") auctioning, which has prevented competitors from entering its business space. Amazon.com secured a patent for one-click online purchasing, which enables customers to enter shipping and credit-card information once, so all subsequent orders do not have to go through a verification Web page. Although the software is quite simple, Amazon obtained a patent for it in 1999 that won't expire until 2017. Amazon successfully sued Barnes & Noble (B&N) when it implemented the same technology on BN.com. Now B&N pays Amazon for its use. More recently, Amazon obtained a patent for its techniques used to decide what types of items a user might like to buy in the future. Exclusive use of the methods might give the company additional strategic advantage in online shopping. Protecting any invention, including hardware and software, with patents and copyrights provides an excellent barrier to potential entrants

Another barrier to potential new market entrants is the high expense of entering that market. The pension fund management industry is a prime illustration. State Street Corporation is one of its most successful examples. In the 1980s, State Street committed massive amounts of money to developing ISs that helped make the company a leader in managing pension funds and international bank accounts. The huge capital allocation required to build a system to compete successfully with State Street keeps potential entrants out of the market. Instead, other pension management corporations rent State Street's technology and expertise. In fact, State Street derives about 70 percent of its revenues from selling its IS services. This company is an interesting example of an entire business refocusing around its ISs.

Initiative #3: Establish High Switching Costs

Switching costs are expenses incurred when a customer stops buying a product or service from one business and starts buying it from another. Switching costs can be explicit (such as charges the seller levies on a customer for switching) or implicit (such as the indirect costs in time and money spent adjusting to a new product that does the same job as the old).

Often, explicit switching costs are fixed, nonrecurring costs, such as a penalty a buyer must pay for terminating a deal early. In the cellular telephone service industry, you can usually get an attractive deal, but if you cancel the service before a full year or more has passed, you have to pay a hefty penalty. So although another company's service might be more attractive, you might decide to wait the full contract period because the penalty outweighs the benefits of the new company's service. When you do decide to switch, you might discover that the telephone is not suitable for service with any other telephone company. The cost of the telephone itself, then, is another disincentive to switch.

A perfect example of indirect switching expenses is the time and money required to learn new software. Once a company trains its personnel to use one word-processing or spreadsheet program, a competing software company must offer a very enticing deal to make switching worthwhile. The same principle holds for many other applications, such as database management systems and Web page editors and graphical software. Consider Microsoft's popular MS Office suite; you can purchase the significantly less expensive Sun Microsystems' StarOffice, a software suite that is equivalent to MS Office. Better yet, you can download free of charge the entire suite of OpenOffice.org. Yet, few organizations or consumers who are accustomed to MS Office are willing to switch to StarOffice or OpenOffice.org.

Manufacturers of laser and ink-jet printers sell their printers at cost or below cost. However, once you purchase a printer, you must replace a depleted ink or toner cartridge with one that the printer manufacturer sells, or take a risk with nonoriginal cartridges. As a cartridge customer, you face high costs if you consider switching to another brand. Even if comparable cartridges from another manufacturer are less expensive, you cannot use them; and if you decide to use those cartridges, you will lose your investment in the printer, because you must buy a new one. Thus, establishing high switching costs often locks in customers. Locking in customers by any means is a way to accomplish a strategic advantage, and is discussed later.

Initiative #4: Create New Products or Services

Clearly, **creating a new and unique product or service** that many organizations and individuals need gives an organization a great competitive advantage. Unfortunately, the advantage lasts only until other organizations in the industry start offering an identical or similar product or service for a comparable or lower price.

Examples of this scenario abound in the software industry. For instance, Lotus Development Corporation became the major player early on in the electronic spreadsheet market after it introduced its Lotus 1-2-3 program. When two competitors tried to market similar products, Lotus sued for copyright infringement and won the court case, sustaining its market dominance for several years. However, with time, Microsoft established its Excel spreadsheet application as the world leader, not only by aggressive marketing but also by including better features in its application.

Another example of a company creating a new service is eBay, the firm that dominates online auctions. The organization was the first to offer this service, which became very popular within only a few months. While other firms now offer a similar service (e.g., Amazon.com and Yahoo! Auctions), the fact that eBay was the first to offer it gave eBay a huge advantage: it quickly acquired a large number of sellers and bidders, a network that is so critical to creating a "mass" of clients, which in turn is the main draw for additional clients. It also gave eBay a great advantage in experience and allowed it to open a gap that was difficult for competitors to close, even for giants such as Amazon.com. eBay is an example of an entire business that would be impossible without the Web and the information technologies that support the firm's service.

eBay's success demonstrates the strategic advantage of the **first mover**, an organization that is the first to offer a new product or service. By the time other organizations start offering the same product or service, the first mover has usually created some assets that cannot be had by the competitors: a superior brand name, a better technology or method for delivery, or a **critical mass**. A critical mass is a body of clients that is large enough to attract many other clients. In many cases, first movers simply enjoy longer experience, which in itself is an advantage over competitors.

XM and Sirius, satellite-based radio services, have changed radio broadcasting. Their broadcasts release radio services from the constraints of territorial boundaries and so far have avoided national content regulation. This is an example of a new service that is fast garnering an increasing client base. Some observers predict that in a decade or so, the number of listeners to this type of broadcast will surpass the number of listeners to traditional radio stations. Many radio personalities and radio stations now offer programs on satellite radio, hoping to participate in its strategic advantage The two pioneers in this market, XM and Sirius, are reaping the rewards of first movers.

Being a first mover is not always a guarantee of long-term success, however. One example of how a first-mover strategic advantage can be lost within just a few months is in the Web browser arena. Netscape Corporation (now part of AOL) dominated the Web browser market, which was new in 1994. By allowing individual users to download its browser for free, it cornered up to 95 percent of the market. The wide use of the browser by individuals moved commercial organizations to purchase the product and other software compatible with the browser. Netscape's dominance quickly diminished when Microsoft aggressively marketed its own browser, which many perceived as at least as good as Netscape's. Microsoft provided Internet Explorer free of charge to anyone and then bundled it into the Microsoft Windows operating system software

cf p.38
CONTRADICTION?

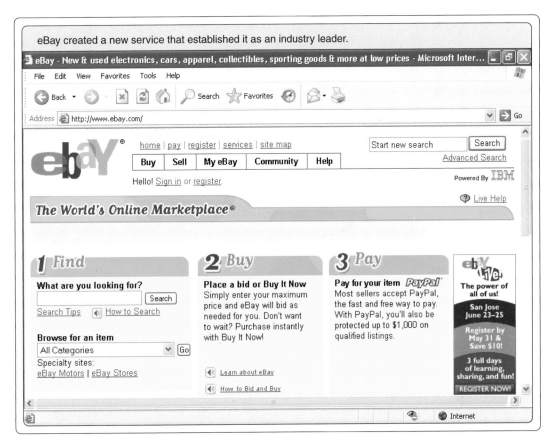

eBay created a new service that established it as an industry leader.

distributed with almost all PCs. Even after the court-ordered unbundling, its browser still dominated. This dominance in turn has been threatened by free browsers such as Mozilla's Firefox and Avant Force's Avant Browser, which offer similar or better features, more flexibility, and fewer security vulnerabilities.

Other first movers have lost market share because they neglected to improve the service they pioneered. Few Web surfers remember Infoseek, the first commercial search engine. Google, which entered the search engine arena in 1998, improved the quality and speed of Web searches, offering a clutter-free home page. The strategy of its two young entrepreneurs was simple: provide the best search engine, and refrain from commercializing it for a while. Over a period of about three years Google established itself as the best search engine. In time, it started to capitalize on this prominence by selling sponsored links (the right side of the results of a user's search). Most importantly, the organization never stopped improving its search algorithms and periodically has offered new services. The strategy has succeeded so much that "google it" has become synonymous with "search for it on the Web."

Initiative #5: Differentiate Products or Services

A company can achieve a competitive advantage by persuading consumers that its product or service is better than its competitors', even if it is not. Called product **differentiation**, this advantage is usually achieved through advertising. Brand-name success is a perfect example of product differentiation. Think of Levi's Jeans, Chanel and Lucky perfumes, and Gap clothes. The customer buys the brand-name product, perceiving it to be superior to similar products. In fact, some products *are* the same, but units sold under a prestigious brand name sell for higher prices. You often see this phenomenon in the food, clothing, drug, and cosmetics markets.

Product and service differentiation impacts not only consumers but also businesses. For example, IBM's Global Services division has created a great brand name for itself as an IT consulting firm. Interestingly, while IBM lost the corporate world's perception that only IBM computers are reliable enough to support business operations ("Nobody ever got fired for buying IBM"), it has gradually differentiated itself as a reliable and knowledgeable consulting organization.

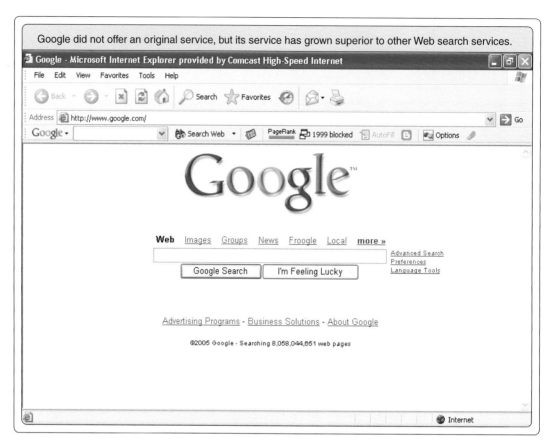

Google did not offer an original service, but its service has grown superior to other Web search services.

Initiative #6: Enhance Products or Services

Instead of differentiating a product or service, an organization might actually add to the product or service to increase its value to the consumer; this is called **enhancing existing products or services**. For example, car manufacturers might entice customers by offering a longer warranty period for their cars, and real-estate agents might attract more business by providing useful financing information to potential buyers.

POINT OF INTEREST

Still Room for Improvement

Using Web technologies as a strategic weapon reaps dividends. Keynote Systems, Inc., a consulting firm, conducted a survey of 2,000 customers responding to questions about the Web sites of 16 leading travel and airline companies. Online travel agencies Expedia, Orbitz, and Travelocity were ranked more highly than any airline site except Southwest Airlines. One of the most important criteria for any transactional Web site is conversion, turning a Web shopper into a paying customer. Customers tend to shop more at sites where they enjoy the experience. Southwest and JetBlue outranked much larger airlines both in terms of conversion and customer experience.

Source: McGann, R., "Online Travel Companies Edge Airline Web Sites," *ClickZ Stats* (www.clickz.com/stats), March 3, 2005.

Since the Internet opened its portals to commercial enterprises in the early 1990s, an increasing number of companies have supplemented their products and services. Their Web sites provide up-to-date information that helps customers utilize their purchased products better or receive additional services. Companies that pioneered such Internet use reaped great rewards. For example, Charles Schwab gained a competitive advantage over other, older brokerage companies such as Merrill Lynch by opening a site for online stock transactions. Nearly half its revenue now comes from this site. All brokerage houses followed and allow customers to trade through a Web site.

Understand the Notion of Strategic Information Systems

Although devising strategic moves is mainly the responsibility of senior management, let us remember Napoleon's words: "Every soldier carries a marshal's baton in his knapsack." To paraphrase: every junior manager is a potential senior manager. Thus, it is incumbent on every professional to try to think strategically for his or her organization. In fact, employees at the lowest levels have proposed some of the most brilliant strategic ideas. In today's highly competitive market, strategy might determine an organization's rise or fall.

An increasing number of strategic moves are either possible only with the aid of ISs or have ISs at the center of their strategy—that is, technology provides the product, service, or method that gains the organization strategic advantage. The potential for new business models on the Web is still great. Thus, professionals must understand how to use technology in strategic moves. Understanding how strategic information systems are conceived and implemented might help you suggest good ideas for such systems in your organization and facilitate your promotion up the organizational ladder.

Other companies use the Internet to maintain their competitive edge by continually adding to and enhancing their online services. Dell is not the only company that sells computers online, for example. Other, smaller companies provide a similar service and sell comparable products, with more flexibility in "building your own computer online," often at lower prices. However, Dell maintains the popularity of its site through continuous enhancement of the services it offers. For example, it offers a buying guide center that clearly explains what to look for in various types of products and explains topics of interest such as software security.

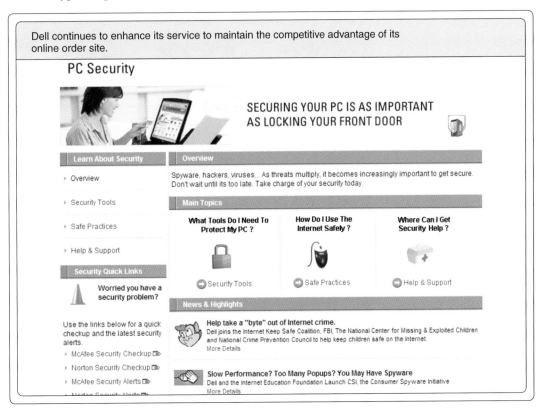

Dell continues to enhance its service to maintain the competitive advantage of its online order site.

Initiative #7: Establish Alliances

Companies can gain competitive advantage by combining services to make them more attractive (and usually less expensive) than purchasing services separately. These **alliances** provide two draws for customers: combined service is cheaper, and one-stop shopping is more convenient. The travel industry is very aggressive in this area. For example, airlines collaborate with hotel chains and car-rental firms to offer travel and lodging packages and with credit-card companies that offer discount ticket purchases from particular airlines or the products of particular manufacturers. Credit-card companies commonly offer frequent flier miles for every dollar spent. In all these cases, alliances create competitive advantages.

As Figure 2.3 indicates, by creating an alliance, organizations enjoy synergy: the combined profit for the allies from the sale of a package of goods or services exceeds the profits earned when each acts individually. Sometimes, the alliances are formed by more than two organizations. Consider the benefits you receive when you agree to accept a major credit card: discounts from several hotel chains, restaurant chains, flower delivery chains, and other stores, as well as free insurance when renting a car, and frequent flier miles, to name a few. Similarly, travel Web sites such as Orbitz offer you the opportunity to reserve lodging and car rental at discounts while you make your airline reservations. The company has also established alliances with hotel chains and car rental companies.

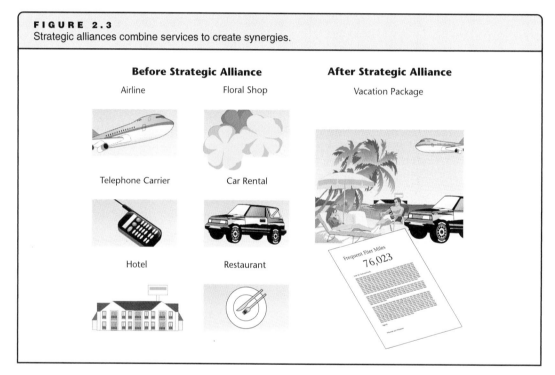

FIGURE 2.3
Strategic alliances combine services to create synergies.

What is the common denominator among these companies? They each have an information system that tracks all these transactions and discounts. A package of attractive propositions entices clients who need these services (and most businesses do). Would this offer be feasible without an IS to track transactions and discounts? Probably not.

Growing Web use for e-commerce has pushed organizations to create alliances that would be unimaginable a few years ago. Consider the alliance between Hewlett-Packard and FedEx. HP is a leading manufacturer of computers and computer equipment. FedEx is a shipping company. HP maintains inventory of its products at FedEx facilities. When customers order items from HP via its Web site, HP routes the order, via the Web, to FedEx. FedEx packages the items and ships them to customers. This arrangement lets HP ship ordered items within hours rather than days. The alliance gives HP an advantage that other computer equipment makers do not share. Again, it is a clever IS that enables this strategy.

On the Web, an obvious example of alliances is an **affiliate program**. Anyone can place links to commercial sites on his or her personal Web site. When a visitor clicks through to a commercial site and makes a purchase, the first site's owner is paid a fee. Some online retailers have thousands of affiliates. The early adopters of such programs, Amazon.com, Buy.com, Priceline.com, and other large e-retailers, enjoyed a competitive advantage in gaining new customers. It is easy for any Web site holder to become an affiliate of Amazon.com.

Another example is the collaboration between Amazon.com and other retailers who leverage Amazon's technology. Target Corp. is one of America's largest retailers. To extend its operation to the Web, it formed a strategic alliance with the giant online retailer. If you go to Target's site, you will notice the words "Powered by Amazon.com." Amazon provides Target with its proprietary search engine, order-fulfillment and customer-service systems, and the patented one-click shopping application, which lets customers pay for merchandise selected from the Target, Marshall Field's, and Mervyns' sites from one electronic shopping cart (Marshall Field's and Mervyns are Target subsidiaries). In return, Amazon collects a percentage of all sales from Target's retail sites, as well as annual fixed fees. Have we mentioned referrals? Next to the logos of Target and its subsidiaries, you also find Amazon's logo, which serves as a link to Amazon's site (where you also see the Target logo prominently displayed).

The Web has generated strategic alliances that would probably never be created offline. Can you imagine Wal-Mart inviting Sears to sell Sears' merchandise from Wal-Mart stores? This is exactly what Amazon does. Its site has links to sales of other companies, and not just companies such as Target, with which it has a special relationship. When you search for an item on Amazon, you might find links not only to its own products but also to those of competitors, such as Circuit City, the consumer electronics chain. If this sounds strange, consider the rationale: Amazon wants customers to compare its price and its competitors' price for the same item and see that Amazon's is lower, mainly because Amazon manages its warehouses more efficiently than any other retailer in the world. Even if customers decide to purchase from the competitor through the Amazon site, Amazon receives a commission from the seller.

Initiative #8: Lock in Suppliers or Buyers

Organizations can achieve competitive advantage if they are powerful enough to **lock in** either suppliers to their mode of operation or buyers to their product. Possessing bargaining power—the leverage to influence buyers and suppliers—is the key to this approach. As such, companies so large that suppliers and buyers must listen to their demands use this tactic nearly exclusively.

A firm gains bargaining power with a supplier either when the firm has few competitors or when the firm is a major competitor in its industry. In the former case, the fewer the companies that make up a supplier's customer base, the more important each company is to the supplier; in the latter case, the more important a specific company is to a supplier's success, the greater bargaining power that company has over that supplier.

The most common leverage in bargaining is purchase volume. Companies that spend billions of dollars purchasing parts and services have the power to force their suppliers to conform to their methods of operation, and even to shift some costs onto suppliers as part of the business arrangement. Consider Wal-Mart, the world's largest retailer. Not only does the company use its great bargaining power to pressure suppliers to lower prices, but it also requires them to use information systems that are compatible with its own automated processes. The suppliers must use ISs that tell them when to ship products to Wal-Mart so that the giant retailer is never left understocked or overstocked. In recent years this power allowed the company to require its suppliers to use radio frequency identification (RFID) devices in packaging, to allow more accurate tracking of ordered, shelved, and sold items. This great bargaining power and tight control of inventory enables Wal-Mart to enjoy great cost savings, which it passes on to customers, which keep growing in numbers thanks to the competitive prices. Many suppliers are locked in with Wal-Mart because of the sheer volume of business they have with the company: some sell a third to one-half of everything they produce to this single retailer, and some, such as the giant consumer products maker Procter & Gamble, have a "Vice President, Wal-Mart" as a member of the senior management.

One way to lock in *buyers* in a free market is to create the impression that an organization's product is significantly better than the competitors', or to enjoy a situation in which customers fear high switching costs. In the software arena, enterprise applications are a good example. This type of software helps organizations manage a wide array of operations: purchasing, manufacturing, human resources, finance, and so forth. The software is expensive, costing millions of dollars. After a company purchases the software from a firm, it is locked in to that firm's services: training, implementation, updates, and so forth. Thus, companies that sell enterprise software, such as SAP, Oracle, and Invensys, make great efforts to improve both their software and support services to maintain leadership in this market.

Another way to lock in clients is to **create a standard**. The software industry has pursued this strategy vigorously, especially in the Internet arena. For example, Microsoft's decision to give away its Web browser by letting both individuals and organizations download it free from its site was not altruistic. Microsoft executives knew that the greater the number of Internet Explorer (IE) users, the greater the user base. The greater the user base, the more likely organizations were to purchase Microsoft's proprietary software to help manage their Web sites. Also, once individual users committed to IE as their main browser, they were likely to purchase Microsoft software that enhanced the browser's capabilities.

Similarly, Adobe gives away its Acrobat Reader software, an application that lets Web surfers open and manipulate documents created using different computers running different operating systems, such as various versions of Windows, the Mac operating system, and UNIX. When the Reader user base became large enough, organizations and individuals found it economically justifiable to purchase and use the full Acrobat application (the application used to create the documents) and related applications. Using this strategy put Adobe's PDF (portable data format) standard in an unrivaled position.

Another company, Macromedia Inc., developed software called Flash to create Web page animations. It offers the Flash player for download free of charge but sells the development tool. Like Adobe, Macromedia has created a symbiotic situation to augment its market: the more individuals download the player, the more businesses are willing to purchase the development tool. The more companies engage Flash modules in their Web pages, the more individuals download the player, without which they cannot enjoy those animations.

CREATING AND MAINTAINING STRATEGIC INFORMATION SYSTEMS

There might be many opportunities to accomplish a competitive edge with IT, especially in industries that are using older software, such as the insurance industry. Insurance companies were among the early adopters of IT and have not changed much of their software. This is why some observers say the entire industry is inefficient. Once an insurance company adopts innovative software applications, it might gain competitive advantage. This might remind you of the airline industry. Most airlines still use antiquated hardware and software. As you'll learn later in the chapter, when JetBlue was established, it adopted the latest technologies, and this was a major reason for its great competitive advantage.

Companies can implement some of the strategic initiatives described in the previous section by using information systems. As we mentioned at the beginning of the chapter, a strategic information system (SIS) is any information system that can help an organization achieve a long-term competitive advantage. An SIS can be created from scratch, developed by modifying an existing system, or "discovered" by realizing that a system already in place can be used to strategic advantage. While companies continue to explore new ways of devising SISs, some successful SISs are the result of less lofty endeavors: the intention to improve mundane operations using IT has occasionally yielded a system with strategic qualities.

Strategic information systems combine two types of ideas: ideas for making potentially winning business decisions and ideas for harnessing information technology to implement the decisions. For an information system to be an SIS, two conditions must exist. First, the information system must serve an organizational goal rather than simply provide information; and second, the organization's IS unit must work with managers of other functional units (including marketing, finance, purchasing, human resources, and so on) to pursue the organizational goal.

Creating an SIS

To develop an SIS, top management must be involved from initial consideration through development and implementation. In other words, the SIS must be part of the overall organizational strategic plan. There is always the danger that a new SIS might be considered the IS unit's exclusive property. However, to succeed, the project must be a corporate effort, involving all managers who use the system.

Figure 2.4 presents questions that management should ask to determine whether to develop a new SIS. Executives meet to try to identify areas in which information can support a strategic goal. Only after completing the activities outlined in Figure 2.4 will management be able to conceptualize an SIS that seizes an opportunity.

FIGURE 2.4
Questions to answer in a strategic information system idea-generating meeting

1. **What would be the most effective way to gain an advantage?**

2. **Would more accessible or timely information to our employees, customers, or suppliers help establish a significant advantage? If so...**

3. **Can an information system be developed that provides more accessible and timely information?**

4. **Will the development effort be economically justified?**

   ◆ Can existing competitors afford to fund the development of a similar system?
   ◆ How long will it take the competitors to build their own, similar system?
   ◆ Can we make our system a moving target to the competition by constantly enhancing it, so that it always retains its superiority?

5. **What is the risk of not developing such a system?**

6. **Are alternative means of achieving the same goals available, and if so, how do they compare with the advantages and disadvantages of a new SIS?**

[handwritten margin notes: DECISION / APPROACH / DATA / RISK & READINESS]

A word of caution regarding Question 4 in Figure 2.4, the issue of economic justification of an SIS: an increasing number of researchers and practitioners conclude that estimating the financial benefits of information systems is extremely difficult. This difficulty is especially true of SISs. The purpose of these systems is not simply to reduce costs or increase output per employee; many create a whole new service or product. Some completely change the way an organization does business. Because so many fundamental business changes are involved, measuring the financial impact is difficult, if not impossible, even after implementation, let alone before. For example, if a bank is considering offering a full range of financial services via the Web, how can management know whether the move justifies the great cost of the special software? It is extremely difficult to estimate the success of such a bold approach in terms of how many new customers the bank would gain.

Reengineering and Organizational Change

Sometimes, to implement an SIS and achieve competitive advantage, organizations must rethink the entire way they operate. While brainstorming about strategic plans, management should ask: "If we established this business unit again, from scratch, what processes would we implement and how?" The answer often leads to the decision to eliminate one set of operations and build others from the ground up. Changes such as these are called **reengineering**. Reengineering often involves adoption of new machinery and elimination of management layers. Frequently, information technology plays an important role in this process.

Reengineering's goal is not to gain small incremental cost savings, but to achieve great efficiency leaps—of 100 percent and even 1000 percent. With that degree of improvement, a company often gains competitive advantage. Interestingly, a company that undertakes reengineering along with implementing a new SIS cannot always tell whether the SIS was successful. The reengineering process makes it impossible to determine how much each change contributed to the organization's improved position.

Implementation of an SIS requires a business to revamp processes—to undergo organizational change—to gain an advantage. For example, when General Motors Corp. (GM) decided to manufacture a new car that would compete with Japanese cars, it chose a different production process from that of its other cars. Management first identified goals that could make the new car successful in terms of how to build it and also how to deliver and service it. Realizing that none of its existing divisions could meet these goals because of their organizational structures, their cultures, and their inadequate ISs, management established Saturn as an independent company with a completely separate operation.

Part of GM's initiative was to recognize the importance of Saturn dealerships in gaining competitive advantage. Through satellite communications, the new company gave dealers access to factory information. Clients could find out if, and exactly when, different cars with different features would be available.

Another feature of Saturn's SIS was improved customer service. Saturn embeds an electronic computer chip in the chassis of each car. The chip maintains a record of the car's technical details and the owner's name. When the car is serviced after the sale, new information is added to the chip. At their first service visit, many Saturn owners were surprised to be greeted by name as they rolled down their windows. While the quality of the car itself has been important to Saturn's success, the new SIS also played an important role. This technology was later copied by other automakers.

Competitive Advantage as a Moving Target

As you might have guessed, competitive advantage is not often long lasting. In time, competitors imitate the leader, and the advantage diminishes. So, the quest for innovative strategies must be dynamic. Corporations must continuously contemplate new ways to use information technology to their advantage. In a way, companies' jockeying for the latest competitive advantage is a lot like an arms race. Side A develops an advanced weapon, then side B develops a similar weapon that terminates the advantage of side A, and so on.

In an environment where most information technology is available to all, SISs originally developed to create a strategic advantage quickly become an expected standard business practice. A prime example is the banking industry, where surveys indicate that increased IS expenditures did not yield long-range strategic advantages. The few banks that provided services such as ATMs and online banking once had a powerful strategic advantage, but now almost every bank provides these services.

A system can only help a company sustain competitive advantage if the company continuously modifies and enhances it, creating a moving target for competitors. American Airlines' Sabre—the online reservation system for travel agents—is a classic example. The innovative IS was redesigned in the late 1970s to expedite airline reservations and sell travel agencies a new service. But over the years, the company spun off an office automation package for travel agencies called Agency Data Systems. The reservation system now encompasses hotel reservations, car rentals, train schedules, theater tickets, and limousine rentals. It later added a feature that let travelers use Sabre from their own computers. The system has been so successful that in its early years American earned more from it than from its airline operations. The organizational unit that developed and operated the software became a separate IT powerhouse at AMR Corp., the parent company of American Airlines, and now operates as Sabre Inc., an AMR subsidiary. It is the leading provider of technology for the travel industry. Travelocity, Inc., the popular Web-based travel site, is a subsidiary of Sabre, and, naturally, uses Sabre's software. Chances are you are using Sabre technology when you make airline reservations through other Web sites, as well.

We return again to Amazon as an example of how ISs help companies maintain competitive advantage. Management believes that it must add new features to its Web site to attract buyers over and over again. The company continuously improves its Web pages' look and the online services it provides. Amazon has moved from merely selling books through the Web to providing best-seller lists, readers' reviews, authors' interviews; selling almost any consumer product imaginable; and posting consumer wish lists, product reviews by customers, and other "cool stuff." The constant improvements help the company maintain its dominant position in online retailing.

JETBLUE: A SUCCESS STORY

We usually expect entrepreneurs to enter a new and profitable industry, not an old, money-losing one. However, with the proper technology and management methods, it seems that some energetic people can gain strategic advantage where others have been hurting. The U.S. airline industry has seen mainly bad times since the industry's deregulation in the 1970s. Things got worse in the beginning of the third millennium, and even worse after the terrible events of September 11, 2001. In 2001, the industry lost $7.7 billion, but JetBlue had a profit of $38.5 million on revenue of $320.4 million. It continued to be profitable in 2002, 2003, and 2004 along with only one other airline, Southwest Airlines, while all other U.S. carriers had losses. Its revenues grew from $998.4 in 2003 to $1.27 billion in 2004.

JetBlue was established in February 2000 by David Neeleman, who serves as its CEO. Two decades earlier, in 1984, Neeleman cofounded Morris Air, a small airline in Salt Lake City, Utah, which was the first airline to offer ticketless travel, a program that was developed inside the company. With a college student he developed Open Skies, a computer program that integrates electronic ticketing, Internet reservations, and revenue management. Revenue management tools help an airline plan the most profitable routes and ticket pricing. Morris Air was sold to Southwest Airlines, which enthusiastically adopted the e-ticket idea. Neeleman became an executive at Southwest but left in frustration, because he believed that an airline could achieve much more efficiency with information technology. Now headquartered in Forest Hills, New York, JetBlue has gained a great strategic advantage over larger and older airlines. The company's success is the result of understanding customers' priorities and gaining great efficiencies through automating whatever IT can automate. Management also learned to break away from practices that inhibit efficiency and agility.

In a highly competitive industry that traditionally has had a narrow profit margin, JetBlue managed to gain strategic advantage by *reducing cost* and therefore reducing the price to the customer; and *improving a service*, especially in terms of on-time departures and arrivals.

Massive Automation

We usually think of manufacturing organizations when mentioning automation, but great benefits can also be gained by automating services. JetBlue uses Open Skies, the software that Neeleman developed. It is a combination reservation system and accounting system, and supports customer service and sales tracking. The company avoids travel agents. Booking a flight through a travel agent costs airlines $20 per ticket. JetBlue saves office space rent and electricity by using reservation agents who work from home (telecommuting is discussed in Chapter 6) and use VoIP (Voice over Internet Protocol, also discussed in Chapter 6) for telephoning. The company pays a flat fee of $25 per telephone line per month for these telecommuting agents. This reduces its handling cost per ticket to $4.50.

Because all tickets are electronic, there is no paper handling or expense. JetBlue encourages customers to purchase their tickets online, and more than 79 percent of them do so, saving the company much labor. The cost of handling a ticket ordered via the Web is reduced to only 50 cents, as opposed to $4.50 paid to a reservation agent, and a far cry from the $20 a booking through a travel agent.

JetBlue automates other aspects of running an airline as well. Its maintenance workers use a maintenance information system from Dash Group to log all airplane parts and their time cycles, that is, when the parts must be replaced and where they can be found. The system reduces manual tracking costs.

Flight planning to maximize yield—the number of seats occupied on a flight—is executed on a flight-planning application from Bornemann Associates. It reduces planning costs and makes operations more efficient. JetBlue also uses an application that its team of 58 IT professionals developed in-house, called Blue Performance. It tracks operational data that is updated flight by flight. The company's intranet enables its 2,800 employees to access the performance data. Managers have up-to-the-minute metrics, so critical in airline operations, which enable them to respond immediately to problems.

 When on the ground, employees use wireless devices to report and respond to any irregular event, from weather delays to passenger injuries. The response is quick, and the events are recorded in a database for later analysis.

When training pilots and other employees, no paper records are kept. An aviation training management system provides a database to track each employee's training record. It is easy to update and efficient for record retrieval.

Away from Tradition

The company decided not to use the hub-and-spokes method of routing its airplanes, a method used by all major airlines. Instead of having its airplanes land in one or two hubs and undergo maintenance there before taking off for the next leg of a route, it simply uses the most profitable routes between any two cities. All flights are point to point—no hubs, no spokes.

JetBlue was the first airline to establish paperless cockpits. The Federal Aviation Authority (FAA) mandates that pilots and other air crew members have access to flight manuals. The manuals are the documents showing information about each flight, including route, weight, and how the weight is spread on board, fuel quantity, and even details such as how many pets are on board. Other airlines update their manuals and then print them after every update. All JetBlue flight manuals are centrally maintained, and the pilots and first officers access and update the manuals on laptop computers that they carry into the cockpit. As soon as the data have been entered, employees have access to the information.

The laptops enable the pilots and first officers to calculate the weight and balance of their plane with a few keystrokes instead of relying on dispatchers at headquarters to do the calculations for them. JetBlue saves paper and time by having employees enter flight data. The company subscribes to SharePoint, a Web-based portal that enables electronic updates to flight manuals. This cuts 15 to 20 minutes from preflight preparations for every flight. The result is a savings of about 4,800 hours per year and planes that take off and land on time.

JetBlue continues to harness IT to maintain the strategic gap between it and its competitors. Management planned a paperless frequent flier program, cockpit-monitoring cameras transmitting through satellites so that ground crews can monitor activity, and biometric applications in airport terminals. Biometrics use physical characteristics of people, such as fingerprints and retina scans, for authentication and access to physical places and online information systems. Biometrics are more secure than access codes. The IT team is also developing a new reservation system that will have features no other airline reservation system has.

Enhanced Service

Much of the technology that helps JetBlue employees provide better service is invisible to the customers, but it also has some more obvious winning features. JetBlue offers leather seats and individual real-time television on all its airplanes. Other airlines do not offer such seats on economy class, and offer only recorded television programs. The real-time TV service is offered under a contract with DirecTV.

Its use of IT technologies also placed the airline at the top of the list for on-schedule departures and arrivals, a service that is very important, especially to business travelers. Perhaps even better, JetBlue ranks at the top as having the fewest mishandled bags. Thanks to constant updates to the Open Skies system, the company has managed to maintain check-in time at less than one minute. When passengers arrive at JetBlue's terminal at JFK airport, they are directed by a large LCD display with a computer-generated voice telling them which window is available to serve them. Usually, checking baggage takes 45 seconds. When passengers arrive at their destination, they do not have to wait for their suitcases. Their electronically tagged suitcases wait for them at the baggage claim area.

For JetBlue, information technology is at least as important as fuel.

Because of heightened security awareness, management decided to install hidden video cameras in the cabin and monitors in the cockpit. Technicians used the DirecTV wires to add the cameras and monitors. Customers are more comfortable knowing of this extra step to enhance their safety.

Impressive Performance

The most important metric in the airline industry is cost per available seat-mile (CASM), which is how much it costs to fly a passenger one mile of the journey. JetBlue has been able to maintain the lowest or next to lowest CASM in its first three years of operations. While its competitors' CASM is 11 cents or higher, JetBlue's CASM is less than 7 cents. While its competitors fill only 71 percent of seats, JetBlue fills 78 percent.

Late Mover Advantage

Some observers cite the fact that JetBlue is a late competitor as an important factor in its success. The company is not burdened with antiquated information systems, or as IT professionals like to call them, legacy systems. This allowed its CIO, Jeff Cohen, to implement the latest available technologies: fast databases, VoIP, a slick Web site, laptop computers with the latest algorithms for fast calculation of routes and loads in the cockpit, and other technologies. This situation illustrates the strategic advantage of the late mover.

JetBlue executives quip that while other airlines run on fuel, theirs runs on information technology. Cohen said that up to 40 percent of the software the company was using was beta or new software. Beta software is software that the developer gives to potential adopters for trial use. Talk about being on the cutting—and possibly bleeding—edge! Yet, competitors have taken notice. Delta Airlines established a subsidiary called Delta Song. The organization mimics many of JetBlue's innovations, including live TV. Similarly, United Airlines created a nimble subsidiary airline called Ted to compete with JetBlue.

[Handwritten margin note: PERHAPS THIS WORKED BECAUSE THIS WAS A STRESSED AND TRADITIONAL INDUSTRY.]

FORD ON THE WEB: A FAILURE STORY

Sometimes what seems to be a great, forward-looking strategic move ends up as a colossal failure. It might be because of lack of attention to details or simply because the innovator could not predict the response of customers or business partners. Such was the great initiative of Jacques Nasser, the former CEO of Ford Motor Company, the second largest U.S. automaker.

The Ideas

When Nasser was appointed CEO of Ford in 1999, he regarded himself as an agent of change. He was eager to push the company into the Web, which was then at the height of its hype as a commercial vehicle. "We are now measuring speed in gigahertz, not horsepower," he said at the 2000 North American International Auto Show in Detroit. The concept cars sported, among other innovations, mobile Internet access. Ford Motor Co., he said, would put the Internet on wheels.

Ford launched Wingcast telematics, devices that would be installed in the company's vehicles and enable drivers and passengers to access the Web. To this end the company formed an alliance with Qualcomm Inc., a telecommunications company, and Yahoo!

Ford created a joint venture with General Motors Corp. and DaimlerChrysler to establish Covisint, a Web site that serves as an electronic market for parts suppliers who can bid online on requests for proposals posted by the automakers. Although not announced this way, the automakers' hope was that suppliers would fiercely compete in an open bidding process and cut their prices dramatically, so the auto companies could enjoy cost cuts. This was the business-to-business (B2B) part of Nassers's grand plan.

The business-to-consumer (B2C) idea was bolder: Ford wanted to push vehicle sales to the Web. Nasser wanted to bypass dealerships and retail the vehicles online directly to consumers. Consumers would go to the Web site, take a virtual test-drive, see images of a vehicle in all its available colors, order a vehicle, pay for it online, and then have it driven to their door. Ford would not only provide a great service but also save the dealer fees. The company called the site FordDirect.com. A special organizational unit, ConsumerConnect, was established to build the Web site and handle the direct sales.

Hitting the Wall

Apparently, buyers were not as enthusiastic about having Web access in their vehicles as Nasser predicted. In June 2001, Ford eliminated the Wingcast project. The B2B effort, Covisint, works, and now includes more automakers, such as the French company Renault and the Japanese company Nissan. The B2C initiative failed.

The failure was not the result of faulty technology. There are excellent Web technologies that would support retail through the Web. There is no reason why a car cannot be selected, paid for, and delivered (with the help of companies that specialize with such delivery from the manufacturer to the buyer) via the Web. The company failed because it did not carefully consider state laws and its relationships with dealers.

Many state laws do not permit cutting an agent out of the sale. State franchising laws did not allow Ford to bypass its dealers. Also, since Ford would still rely on dealers to sell cars to people who do not have access to the Internet or who like to sit in a physical car and test-drive it, it could not cut the relationship all at once. Ford still needed the collaboration of the dealers, if it could overcome the legal hurdles, in order for direct sales to take off.

The Retreat

The circumstances convinced Ford to abandon its plan to sell directly to consumers. The ConsumerConnect unit was disbanded. FordDirect.com is now operated jointly by Ford and its 3,900 Ford and Lincoln Mercury dealerships. The site helps consumers find the vehicles they want, but they then have to find a dealer close to their homes who can deliver the vehicle. Like any car dealer, the site also offers used cars for sale, which is not what Ford would like to do. The price tag of this failed experiment was reported to be a hefty portion of the $1 billion Ford spent on its Internet initiative under Nasser's leadership.

Size Matters

At what point do the public and the courts start to consider a successful strategy as a predatory, unfair business practice that makes competition from other businesses impossible, even if their products are better? For instance, should a firm that takes bold entrepreneurial steps to become a business leader be curbed when it succeeds in becoming powerful? Several court cases against Microsoft, the software industry leader, have focused on these questions. However, the questions are not simply legal issues. They are also important because they impact the economy and, as a result, society.

- **Historical Background.** In the 1970s, Microsoft was a small software company headed by its young president, Bill Gates, who established the company at age 19. The company was fortunate to find and buy an operating system from a small company in Seattle, Washington, for $50,000. An operating system (OS) is the software program that "mediates" between any computer program and the computer. Every application is developed with a particular operating system, or several operating systems, in mind. To a great extent, the operating system determines which applications a computer can run. Therefore, it is an extremely important program. We discuss operating systems and other types of software in Chapter 5, "Business Software.")

  So, people who purchased a computer had to consider the OS to determine which applications they could run on their computer. After Microsoft bought the operating system, it entered into a contract with IBM, the most powerful computer manufacturer at that time. IBM needed an operating system for its new creation, the IBM PC, and they chose Microsoft's DOS (Disk Operating System). While Microsoft did not make much money on the IBM deal, its executives realized the strategic potential of contracting with "the big guy."

  Indeed, the strategy paid off. Soon, Compaq (now part of Hewlett-Packard) and many other manufacturers started to market IBM PC clones, cheaper computers that performed as well as IBM PCs and that could run the same operating system and applications. Because Microsoft's contract with IBM allowed it to sell DOS to other parties, it made a fortune selling DOS to Compaq and others. Later, Microsoft developed Windows, an improved operating system, and the success story repeated itself. To this day, the majority of buyers of personal computers also buy a copy of some version of Windows.

  One major key to gaining a decent share of the new Internet market was the widespread use of Web browsers. In the mid-1990s, more than 80 percent

of Web surfers used Netscape's browsers. Netscape (now part of AOL) was a young, entrepreneurial company selling innovative products. Microsoft decided to increase its own browser's market share of about 15 percent to a leading position. If a great number of people used its browser, Microsoft could expect hefty sales of related software, such as server management applications.

- **Controversial Practices.** No one would deny that Microsoft's attempt to compete in the browser market was legitimate. While Netscape gave its browsers away to individuals and educational institutions but charged for-profit organizations, Microsoft gave its browser to everyone free of charge. Also, the company took advantage of Windows dominance; it started bundling its browser with Windows, practically forcing any PC maker who wanted to sell the machines with the operating system installed to also install Internet Explorer (IE). The great majority of new PC owners used IE without even trying any other browser.

  Within two years, a majority of Web surfers were using IE. But Netscape, the U.S. Department of Justice, and many individuals considered Microsoft's tactics unfair. Microsoft used its muscle in the operating system market to compel sellers of personal computers to include a copy of Internet Explorer with Windows. Furthermore, the browser was inseparable from the newer Windows version, Windows 98. Since sellers had to include Windows on every machine, and because it is practically the only operating system most buyers would accept, sellers had no choice but to succumb to the pressure. The U.S. Department of Justice and the Attorneys General of several states filed lawsuits claiming Microsoft violated fair trade practices. Subsequently, legal authorities in other countries, such as the European Union (EU) and Taiwan, also either probed the company or sued it. In 2004, the EU's antitrust office fined Microsoft 497 million euros ($665 million) for abusively wielding Windows' monopoly and for locking competitors out of the software market. Meanwhile, as competition in the digital audio and video media increased, Microsoft bundled its Media Player software with the Windows OS. In 2002, the U.S. Department of Justice settled with Microsoft on this issue, requiring the company only to enable users to hide Media Player and set another application as the default player. The EU demanded that Microsoft sell Windows without Media Player.

It also demanded that the company allow all software developers access to information about Windows, so that they could develop applications that would compete well with Microsoft's own applications. The EU claimed that developers of nonproprietary software (software that is not owned by anyone and can be used free of charge) were denied access to the Windows information altogether. If the company did not stop these practices, the EU threatened it with additional fines reaching 5 percent of the company's daily worldwide sales revenue until the company complied with the EU's demands.

Contrary to public perception, the United States, the European Union, and many other countries do not outlaw monopolies. They only forbid unfair use of monopolistic power. Because anyone may compete in any market, it would be unfair to punish an entrepreneur for marketing unique products and mustering market power of any magnitude. Of concern in the eyes of U.S. law, for example, are two issues: (1) have any unfair practices helped the company gain monopolistic power, and (2) does the monopolistic situation serve customers well, or does it hurt them?

- **Up Side, Down Side.** Microsoft argues that although it could charge higher prices for Windows, it has not, because it wants to make Windows affordable to all. Microsoft also argues that, unlike typical monopolists, it invests huge amounts of money in research and development, which eventually benefit society in the form of better and less-expensive products. Microsoft's rivals in the software industry claim that Microsoft's practices stifle true competition. Both claims are difficult to measure. Some observers argue that allowing the same company to develop operating systems and many applications is good for consumers: the applications are compatible with each other; all use the same interface of menus and icons. Others suggest that Microsoft should be broken into two organizations, one that develops operating systems and another that develops only applications and competes fairly in that market. And some organizations and individuals simply fear the great power that a single person, Bill Gates, holds in an industry that so greatly impacts our economy and society. What is your opinion? What would you do about this issue?

Ford's management can find some solace in the continued operation of FordDirect.com. Although the grand plan did not materialize, the site is the origin point of 10,000 sales transactions per month. Ford reported that it sold 100,000 vehicles through the Web site in 2001, and that 60 percent of those transactions would not even have started had the site not existed. The monthly sales through the Web site have increased since. In April 2005 the site generated sales of 22,500 new vehicles.

Some observers say that Ford's focus on the Internet was at times greater than on making automobiles. While other automakers were making modest profits in the period from 2000 to 2001, Ford had losses. Nasser was forced to leave the company.

THE BLEEDING EDGE

As you might often hear, huge rewards go to whomever first implements a new idea. Innovators might enjoy a strategic advantage until competitors discover the benefits of a new business idea or a new technology. However, taking such steps before competitors have tested a system involves great risk. In some cases, failure results from rushing implementation without adequately testing a market. But even with careful planning, pioneers sometimes get burned.

For example, several supermarket chains tried self-checkout stations in the mid-1990s. Consumers were expected to ring up their own purchases. By and large, investment in such devices failed not because the technology was bad, but because many consumers either preferred the human touch, or because they did not want to learn how to correct mistakes when the devices did not pick up the price of an item or picked it up twice. Recently, machines that are more user friendly and less error prone have been installed by several chains, and consumers have been more willing to use them.

While it is tempting to take the lead, the risk of business failure is quite high. Several organizations have experienced disasters with new business ideas, which are only magnified when implementing new technology. When failure occurs because an organization tries to be on the technological leading edge, observers call it the **bleeding edge**. The pioneering organization "bleeds" cash on a technology that increases costs instead of profits. Adopting a new technology involves great risk: there is no experience from which to learn, no guarantees that the technology will work well, and no certainty that customers and employees will welcome it.

Being on the bleeding edge often means that implementation costs are significantly more than anticipated, that the new technology does not work as well as expected, or that the parties who were supposed to benefit—employees, customers, or suppliers—do not like using it. Thus, instead of leading, the organization ends up bleeding, that is, suffering from high cost and lost market share. For this reason, some organizations decide to let competitors test new technology before they adopt it. They risk losing the initial rewards they might reap, but if a competitor succeeds, they can quickly adopt the technology and even try to use it better than the pioneering organization.

Microsoft generally takes this approach. It seizes an existing idea, improves it, and promotes the result with its great marketing power. For instance, the company did not invent word processing, but Word is the most popular word-processing application today. The company did not invent the electronic spreadsheet, but Excel is the most popular spreadsheet application. And Microsoft was not the first to introduce a PC database management application, but it sells the highly popular Access. The company joined the Internet rush late, but it developed and gave away Internet Explorer, a Web browser that competed with the highly popular Netscape Navigator and now dominates the market (in part because it was given free to everyone, including for-profit businesses). You might call this approach competing by emulating and improving, rather than competing by being on the leading edge.

Sometimes, companies wait quite a long time to ensure that a technology has matured before they start using it, even at the risk of diminishing their strategic position. Although data warehousing—the organization and summarization of huge amounts of transactional records for later analysis—has been around since the mid-1990s, The Home Depot, Inc., decided only in 2002 to build a data warehouse. Home Depot is the world's largest home improvement retailer. It started the project years after its main rival in the United States, Lowe's, had implemented a well-functioning data warehouse, which it used effectively for strategic decision making.

- Some ISs have become strategic tools as a result of strategic planning; others have evolved into strategic tools. To compete in the market, executives need to define strategic goals and determine whether new or improved ISs can support these goals. Rather than waiting complacently until a problem occurs, businesses actively look for opportunities to improve their position with information systems.

- An IS that helps gain strategic advantage is called a strategic information system (SIS). To assure optimal utilization of IT for competitive advantage, executives must participate in generating ideas and champion new, innovative uses of information systems. In recent years, many of these ideas involved using the Internet.

- A company achieves strategic advantage by using strategy to maximize its strengths, resulting in a competitive advantage.

- Strategic advantage is often achieved by one or a combination of the following initiatives. Cost reduction enables a business to sell more units of its products or services while maintaining or increasing its profit margin. Raising barriers to potential entrants to the industry lets an organization maintain a sizable market share by developing systems that are prohibitively expensive for competitors to emulate. By establishing high switching costs, a business can make buying from competitors unattractive to clients. Developing totally new products and services can create an entirely new market for an organization, which can also enjoy the advantage of being a first mover for that product and market. And if the organization cannot create new products or services, it can still enjoy competitive advantage by differentiating its products so that customers view them as better than a competitor's products. Organizations also attain advantage by enhancing existing products or services. Many new services are the fruits

- of alliances between companies: each contributes its own expertise to package services that entice customers with an overall value greater than that offered by the separate services individually. Locking in clients or suppliers, that is, creating conditions that make dealing with competitors infeasible, is a powerful strategy to gain advantage.

- In the software industry, creating standards often creates strategic advantage. A standard is an application used by a significant share of the users. To this end, many companies go as far as giving software away. When the standard has been established, the company enjoys a large sales volume of compatible and add-on software. Microsoft, the software giant, has been found guilty of using unfair trade practices in trying to establish standards and squash competitors.

- Reengineering is the process of designing a business process from scratch to achieve hundreds of percentage points in improvement rates. Almost always, reengineering involves implementing new ISs.

- Strategic advantages from information systems are often short lived, because competitors quickly emulate the systems for their own benefit. Therefore, looking for new opportunities must be an ongoing process.

- To maintain a strategic advantage, organizations must develop new features to keep the system on the leading edge. But they must be mindful of the bleeding edge, the undesirable results (such as huge ongoing costs and loss of customers) of being the first to use new technology with the hope of establishing a competitive advantage. Early adopters find themselves on the bleeding edge when the new technology is not yet fully reliable or when customers are uncomfortable with it.

EATS2GO REVISITED

As you saw in the continuing story of Eats2Go, the three young entrepreneurs have gained experience, used information systems to research options, and instituted changes to remain profitable and expand their business. They also face some new opportunities and challenges for the strategic direction of their business. The next section explores some of their strategic initiatives to see whether you think they can make improvements.

What Would You Do?

1. Through their alliance with the shopping mall owner, Eats2Go has increased its business to three lunch carts. From the case at the beginning of the chapter, identify some strategic moves the three have already made to help them compete. Have any of their partners operated strategically? How? Be sure to consider these ways to gain a competitive advantage:

   - Reduce costs.

   - Raise barriers to entrants.

   - Establish high switching costs.

   - Create new products and services.

   - Differentiate products and services.

   - Enhance products or services.

   - Establish alliances.

   - Lock in suppliers or buyers.

2. Review the decision that Juan, Kendra, and Dave made not to pursue organic labels for their food. Was this decision correct, in your opinion? What further information could they use to monitor the organic food market in the future?

New Perspectives

1. Operating from a new kitchen space and becoming a chip manufacturer offers Juan, Kendra, and Dave the opportunity to rethink completely their food preparation processes—to reengineer. Think of some options the three can pursue in redesigning their food preparation for both their lunch business and chip manufacturing. Consider how the changes can help them compete effectively.

2. With the Subwich franchise as a new competitor to the pushcart lunch business, Juan, Kendra, and Dave need to monitor costs and profits closely, and they need to keep making changes to remain competitive. They already have a loyal customer base. How can they use their existing information systems to compete effectively against Subwich? Suggest at least three ways to help them compete. Would a Web site help them at all? Why or why not?

KEY TERMS

affiliate program, 46
alliance, 45
bleeding edge, 56
competitive advantage, 38
creating new and unique products or services, 42
creating a standard, 48
critical mass, 42

differentiation, 43
enhancing existing products or services, 44
first mover, 42
late mover, 53
locking in clients or suppliers, 47
raising barriers to entrants, 41

reducing costs, 40
reengineering, 49
strategic advantage, 38
strategic information system (SIS), 38
switching costs, 41

1. In what respect does business strategy resemble military strategy?

2. What should an information system achieve for an organization in order to be considered a strategic information system?

3. What strategic goal can an IS attain that does not involve wresting market share from competitors?

4. What conditions must exist in an organization planning an SIS?

5. Sometimes it is difficult to convince top management to commit funds to develop and implement an SIS. Why?

6. An SIS often offers a corporation short-lived advantages. How so?

7. What is reengineering? What does it have to do with IT?

8. Software developers have made great efforts to "create a standard." What does creating a standard mean in the software industry, and why are companies doing it?

9. What should an organization do to sustain the strategic benefits of an IS?

10. Adobe encourages PC users to download its Acrobat Reader free of charge. Macromedia encourages people to download its Flash player free of charge. How does this eventually help them strategically? If they give the application away, how does their generosity help them make money?

11. Referring to the list of strategic moves (see Figure 2.2), classify the initiatives of JetBlue.

12. What were the reasons for the failure of FordDirect.com?

13. The executives of well-established airlines are not less smart than those at JetBlue, and yet, their larger airlines have not done what JetBlue has done. Why?

14. What does the term "first mover" mean?

15. Can a *late mover* have any strategic advantage with IT? What is the risk that a late mover takes?

16. What does the term "bleeding edge" mean?

1. Can an off-the-shelf computer program be used as an SIS? Why or why not?

2. The organizations that eventually use the systems, not consulting firms, develop more successful SISs. What might be the reasons for this?

3. You head a small company. You have an idea for software that can give your company an advantage over competitors. Since you do not have a staff that can develop and implement the software, you decide to approach a software company. Other than the technical requirements, what should you desire of the software company?

4. Some argue that an SIS gives a company an unfair advantage and might even cause the demise of smaller, weaker companies that cannot afford to build similar systems. Is this good or bad for customers? Explain your opinion.

5. Why has the Web been the arena of so much competition in recent years?

6. ISs play a major role in almost every reengineering project. Why?

7. Accounting and payroll ISs have never become SISs. Why? What other types of ISs are unlikely to ever gain their owners strategic advantage?

8. Ford's CEO envisioned a future in which consumers log on to an automaker's Web site, design their cars online, wait for the cars to be manufactured (design transformed into electronic blueprints), and have the car delivered to their door. Do you think we will see this in practice within the next decade? Why, or why not?

9. Give two examples of other products or services whose delivery time could be cut from days to minutes with the aid of IT.

10. What is the role of ISs in alliances such as airlines and credit-card issuers? Why would such alliances be practically infeasible without IT?

11. JetBlue uses new software that has not been tested by other companies. If you were a CIO, would you use software that is still in beta (untested with live data) in your organization?

12. You are an executive for a large organization that provides services to state and federal agencies. A software development firm approached you with an offer to implement new software that might give your organization a strategic advantage by reducing the service delivery cycle by several days. What would you do to avoid putting your organization on the "bleeding edge" while still considering the new software?

13. When a software developer creates a *de facto* standard (i.e., not the official standard, but something so widely used that it becomes a standard), it has monopolistic power. Should governments intervene to prevent this practice? Explain your opinion.

14. Suppose you are a venture capitalist considering a proposal to invest millions of dollars in a new online business. What questions would you ask the enthusiastic young people who have approached you for funds?

15. What are the potential risks of a single organization controlling much of the market of essential software?

APPLYING CONCEPTS

1. Use a literature search program to find a news story on a strategic information system. Write a short report that explains: (a) the industry in which the business competes, (b) the function(s) of the system, and (c) how the system gives the company strategic advantage. For (c), identify the type of strategic move that the organization made from the list provided in Figure 2.1. Suggest how the company might improve the system to maintain its advantage in the future, when competitors mimic the system. Alternatively, find a story on a new business model. In your write-up explain (a) the term "business model," (b) the particular business model you found, and (c) how information systems support this business model.

2. Prepare a brief essay that includes an example of each of the following strategic moves: raising barriers to entrants (*Hint*: intellectual property), establishing high switching costs, creating a new product or service (*Hint*: the Web), and establishing alliances. The examples do not necessarily have to involve IT. Do not use examples already presented in the text. You may use examples from actual events or your own suggestions, but the examples must be practical.

3. A publishing company is contemplating publishing electronic books on small CDs. To read the discs, users will need a device called an electronic book reader. At least two firms have developed e-book technologies that the publisher can adopt. The publisher hires you as a strategic consultant. Write a report explaining the strategic moves you suggest. What would you advise the company to do: try to develop its own e-book reader or purchase a license for existing technology? Who should be the initial target audience for the product? What should be the company's major goal in the first two or three years: profit, market share, user base, technological improvement, or perhaps having the largest salesforce in this industry? Should the company give anything away? Prepare a detailed report enumerating and explaining your suggestions.

4. You are a software-marketing expert. A new software development firm has hired you to advise it on pricing and marketing strategies of its new application. After some research, you conclude that the firm can be successful either by selling at a high unit price (in which case, probably only businesses would purchase licenses to use the application), or at a very low price, which would be attractive to many individuals and companies. You estimate that by the end of the sixth year of the marketing effort competing software will be offered, which will bring the number of units sold to zero. For alternative A, the price would be $400 per license, and you expect 500 adopters in the first year and an annual growth of adopters of 70 percent. For alternative B, the price would be $30, and you expect 600,000 adopters in the first year and an annual growth of adopters of 4 percent. Use a spreadsheet application to calculate revenue, and tell the firm which strategy is expected to bring in greater revenue. Enter the prices and number of first-year adopters for each alternative only once, each in a single cell, and use absolute referencing to those cells.

1. Use PowerPoint or other presentation software to present the ideas you generated in Question 1 or 2 of "Applying Concepts." Use the program's best features to make a convincing and visually pleasing presentation.

2. Do a library or Web search of business journals and magazines such as the *Wall Street Journal, BusinessWeek, Forbes,* or *Fortune.* Find a story on a business's strategic use of data, information, or information systems. (*Note:* The writer might not have identified the strategic use, but you might find that the use served strategic goals.) Prepare a report explaining the opportunity seized. Did the organization create a new product or service, improve one, or manage to capture a significantly greater market share of an existing product or service? How did the data, information, or information system play a major role in the strategic move?

3. Consider the information provided in the "Ethical & Societal Issues" box of this chapter. Prepare two extensive lists, pros and cons. The pros should aim to convince an audience why Microsoft, or a similar company, should be left alone to practice its business maneuvers. The cons should aim to convince an audience why governments should intervene in how corporations such as Microsoft behave and explain what such interventions are meant to accomplish.

1. Brainstorm with your team to answer the question: "Which information technology over the past two years has epitomized a unique product or service that was 'ahead of the curve' for a significant amount of time?" This might be a physical product using IT or an online service that was, or still is, unique. List the reasons each of the team members liked this product or service so much.

2. Some information technologies had a certain original purpose but were creatively used to serve additional purposes. For example, companies have used caller ID to retrieve customer records as soon as a customer telephones. This saves labor and increases service quality. You and your teammates are consultants who work with many businesses. Offering your clients original ideas will increase your success. Select an information technology or IT feature that can be leveraged in ways not originally conceived. How can your clients (in manufacturing, service, or any other business sector) use this feature to gain strategic advantage? Prepare a rationale.

3. Someone suggested that you and your teammates establish the first Web cemetery for pets. Obviously, you cannot bury any pets there, but there might be other services you can offer. Prepare a written plan that describes what you would offer, what you would charge for different features, and how you can sustain your strategic position if traditional pet cemeteries go online. (*Note:* There might be some online pet cemeteries. Assume there are none.)

1. Clear the cookies from your computer. Visit Amazon.com or another e-commerce site listed in this chapter. Browse the site and click on items you might buy and add them to your cart. Don't actually make a purchase. Open the cookie file on your computer. How many cookies did the site put on your computer?

2. How can Excel's goal seek function be used in strategic planning? Give an example.

1. Do some research to determine how big the potential market for this product is. Who are its competitors (think about products that are designed to do similar things (e.g., prevent auto theft) but may not be a direct competitor)?

2. Name 3 companies whose products or services might be potential strategic alliances with this product.

FROM IDEAS TO APPLICATION: REAL CASES

IT Makes Cents

Does Avis Walton mind receiving orders from a machine when he works? No, he actually thinks it is "cool." Avis works as a "picker" for 99 Cents Only Stores. Walton spends his workday in a 750,000 square-foot distribution center in Katy, near Houston, Texas, riding an electric vehicle. He wears an earbud that streams instructions from a central information system. The female voice gives him a row number, then a section number, and then a bin number. He scans the tag on the bin's front with a wireless hand-held computer to confirm that he is at the right bin. The voice then orders him to pick so many cases. He gets off the vehicle, picks up the boxes, and places them on a pallet. He confirms the pick into a microphone. The voice now sends him to his next assignment.

He and his 15 fellow pickers are used to the electronic voice. It is generated by a computer that runs the distribution center's warehouse-management software. It instructs them which items to pick for individual stores. It also calculates the most efficient routes while ensuring that the carts do not crash into each other. The "lady" tells the pickers which bins need to be replenished and where to find the items to replenish those bins. Pickers place the boxes on a three-story conveyor. Laser scanners quickly scan box tags and route the boxes to 20 different lanes, ensuring that each box is on the proper path to a pallet waiting below for specific stores. The system also plans loading to utilize maximum space on each truck.

99 Cents Only Stores is America's oldest chain of one-price stores. The chain consists of 220 stores in California, Nevada, Arizona, and Texas. The business was started as single store in Los Angeles in 1984. David Gold, age 71, still comes to the office daily at 4 a.m. The company never had a year in which it lost money. Between 1996, when it went public, and 2003, its stock price climbed from $3.12 to $36.22. There are several other chains of fixed-price stores in the United States, and competition is fierce. The chain does better than its competitors in every measure important in the retail industry: sales per square foot and net profit margin on revenue. In 2003, profit margin was 8.3 percent while profit at Wal-Mart was 3.1 percent and at Kroger Co., the supermarket chain, a mere 2.1 percent (but typical for supermarkets). Gold, who recently stepped down as the company's CEO, remains active as the Chairman of the Board, and his two sons and son-in-law run the company. The Gold family owns about 35 percent of the company.

Despite sales revenues of $862.5 million in 2003, the amount of spending on IT is relatively small, only $5 million in 2003. The company's 2004 profit was slightly less, $836 million, but still the proportion of IT spending was small. However, Robert Adams, vice president of IS, selects IT projects carefully. Each store has a wireless local area network (WLAN) and connection to the Internet. All district managers carry cell phones, which they can also use as walkie-talkies. When Adams moved from another company to work for the chain, he was afraid he would not get the budget he might need for new systems because the management would be cheap and not see the need for technology. The contrary happened. Because the company is family-run, decisions are made quickly. He does not need to go through formal meetings. Therefore, the time between request and implementation is very short.

The fixed-price-store industry, popularly known as dollar stores, has been slow to adopt state-of-the-art technology. Only recently such chains started adopting modern systems, and 99 Cents seems to be ahead of them. Some software companies, such as HighJump Software, design systems that can specifically support the operations of these chains. IT has enabled 99 Cents to differentiate itself from similar chains. The store areas of competitors are typically 4,000 to 6,000 square feet, and each store has annual revenue of $1 million. A 99 Cents store is 19,000 square feet and has annual revenue of $4.8 million. The targeted audience, too, is different. While other stores target neighborhoods with low to medium incomes, David Gold observed that rich people, too, like to save money. His company's most profitable store is located close to Beverly Hills, has an area of 18,000 square feet, and earns an average of $10 million annually.

If you have shopped more than once at the same dollar store, you probably noticed that an item you purchased the first time is no longer available on a subsequent visit. This is typical, because dollar stores purchase not by item but by price. When purchasing officers spot an opportunity to buy a lot of a discontinued product, they offer a very low price and purchase it. It is difficult for these chains to reorder the same items at the same low price. 99 Cents succeeds in reordering 60 percent of its inventory. The rest are one-time-only close-outs.

Gold and his executives have a simple goal, which is to establish the shortest path between an inexpensive item and a paying customer. This drives all the decisions on which IT to pursue. And IT plays a major role in identifying suitable merchandise, efficiently receiving it at the distribution centers, and then distributing it to the stores while avoiding overstocks or understocks. Interestingly, Gold is not fond of computers. He rarely uses his own office PC. He does not have anything against IT, he says, he just dislikes big spending on IT if the information it produces is not used. He is also annoyed by the average IT professional, who keeps himself above the nontechnical masses. Adams, he says, is different. Adams is personable, a perfect choice for the company, Gold says.

Adams has an 18-person IT team to which he delegates much authority. However, he is a demanding boss who leads by example. David Gold was impressed when Adams wrote the entire code for the company's point-of-sale systems. He still writes code when needed. He and his team write code whenever it is cheaper to purchase ready-made software and modify it than spend the resources to develop the software from scratch in-house. Since 40 percent of its merchandise consists of one-time-only inventory that will never be purchased again, 99 Cents Only requires systems that can accept new items on the fly. Adams' team ensures that the ISs are flexible. If the decision is to develop software in-house, Adams spends much time with the project team. He still regards himself as a software developer and refuses to pay another company much money for modifications or for new software.

Until 2004, the company had a single distribution center in Commerce City, California. In mid-2004 management decided to expand to Texas and build another distribution center there. It purchased facilities and equipment from supermarket giant Albertson's Inc. Albertson's had invested $80 million in the facility in 1995. 99 Cents paid Albertson's $23 million for it. Adams had only four months to equip the warehouse with the proper IT so it could start operations. This time it did not make business sense to develop code in-house. Adams contacted HighJump Software, a subsidiary of 3M, which sells warehouse management software.

HighJump's software, called Warehouse Advantage, supports all the activities that occur from the time products enter the warehouse to the moment they leave. A Voxware computer receives the picking profile from Warehouse Advantage and tells workers what to pick and where to find it. At the retail stores, employees can use a Web-based system to access information about the status of incoming shipments. Management uses Advantage Dashboard for a high-level view of facility and worker performance expressed as metrics and graphs. Managers receive real-time inventory levels and order volumes of various products. The new

systems are proving themselves. Picking accuracy, that is, picking and shipping the right item, is 90 percent at the California distribution center. At the Texas center it is 99 percent. Picking speed at Texas is 20 percent greater than at the California center. The system works so well that Adams decided to implement it in California.

With all his enthusiasm for IT, Adams avoids implementing cutting-edge technologies. He says the company is too small and traditional to sustain "bleeding edge" technologies. The strategic advantage he believes 99 Cents has is in the business intelligence with which the company integrates proven technologies into it operations. He says he prioritizes IT projects by how much obvious return on investment he sees in them. When it is obvious a certain technology will gain his company efficiency, he implements it. Often, his team completes only a part of a project, so it can start a new project that helps the company more. Adams says reprioritizing allows the company to get the greatest benefits from all IT projects. What is not completed now can be completed after that other, more important project is completed.

All dollar store customers like bargains, but the customers of 99 Cents Only visit their favorite stores more often and buy more. And they probably do not know that ever-better IT ensures that they can find those great, inexpensive items on the shelves almost as soon as 99 Cents Only can find them.

Source: Rae-Supree, J., "99 Cents Only Stores' Efficient IT Infrastructure," *CIO Insight*, January 1 2004; HighJump Software (www.highjumpsoftware.com), 2005; www.hoover.com, 2005.

Thinking About the Case

1. Is 99 Cents Only on the leading edge of IT? Is it on the bleeding edge?

2. What characteristics of the dollar store industry make it so important to increase efficiency?

3. The company has performed better than its competitors. In terms of the eight initiatives discussed in this chapter, which initiative or initiatives has gained it the competitive advantage?

4. 99 Cents Only must modify its information systems frequently. Why?

5. Often, CIOs are frustrated with the time it takes senior management to support their strategic initiatives and with the difficulty of earmarking funds for such initiatives. How is 99 Cents Only different in this respect?

Where There's Demand There's a Business

While many twenty-somethings in the late 1990s focused their efforts on creating the hottest new dot-com and launching the next huge IPO (initial public offering) of stock, others drew inspiration for their success from unfulfilled practical desires involving a decades-old piece of technology. The story of one San Franciscan who worked as a freelance cameraman for a local TV station illustrates what can happen when imagination, strategic planning, and IT development mix.

Babak Farahi noticed that the station where he worked consistently rejected viewers' requests for tapes of their children, friends, or pets that had appeared on the station's news broadcast the day before. But, he thought, if there is a demand for such television snippets, why not sell them? So the 24-year-old set up four VCRs in his parents' home, recorded the news every day, and persuaded the TV station's receptionists to refer viewers to him when calling to request a copy. The plan worked. His clients included small businesses, especially restaurants, and, of course, many parents who wanted copies of their children's TV appearance.

The cameraman did not grow complacent with his success. He took his business to a whole new realm after something caught his eye while waiting for a flight at San Francisco International Airport. He noticed that the TV monitor in the waiting area had printed text at the bottom of the screen. Could he expand his business by creating a closed-caption database of company products and names for sale to clients interested in monitoring press coverage of their business? This database would actively store televised references to companies without having to wait for specific companies to request the service. Since the captions were stored in digital form, he could use them to do an electronic search for words, and therefore for business names.

Further research uncovered two important findings essential for his new idea to thrive. First, Congress had recently passed a law that would soon mandate that broadcasters and cable operators provide closed captioning for each show with text at the bottom of the screen. This meant that companies could know if they were mentioned in a national news show on CNN or on a local channel in Baton Rouge. The less satisfying discovery was that there was no closed-caption database software. So the cameraman shut down his video recording business, committed himself fully to the new venture, and hired a couple of programmers to build the hardware and software for closed-caption text capture and searching.

Within a year, a new company was born, Multivision. Based in Oakland, California, Multivision

enables companies to automatically receive TV clips with closed captions that mention their companies via the Internet. Clients can receive all TV mentions or ones that are specific to certain fields, like a show, a network, or a time of day. Multivision has eight offices throughout the United States and records over 75 percent of the 210 TV markets in the country. The company's toughest competitor is the industry leader, Video Monitoring Services (VMS), which has existed 16 years longer than Multivision but introduced closed-caption searches three years after Multivision. In other words, VMS imitated the idea and supported it with its huge financial resources and brand recognition.

Multivision's sales were projected to reach $17 million in 2005, ensuring it the second largest share in a $100 million market. Multivision's future plans include expansion into international markets, where voice-recognition and image-recognition software could deliver the same service even in markets without closed captioning. On the domestic front, the company aims to focus more on niche broadcasters, with the channels offered growing faster than ever. Digital Showroom, a proprietary application of Multivision, allows customers to monitor their broadcast coverage, watch the actual video of what aired, analyze the different media outlets, and present the results to their perspective marketing teams, so they can take the best advantage of the media exposure. Multivision's coverage includes more than 1,000 television stations, almost 25,000 hours of daily coverage, and is the industry's most specialized archive.

The goal, says Babak Farahi, is to watch every television station in the country for certain keywords, such as the name of a company. Clients can buy "buzz reports" to determine how much media exposure they received. In 2005, Multivision covered the United States' 160 television markets, which serve 98 percent of American viewers as well as 20 countries on 5 continents. Ongoing television and radio feeds from England, Ireland, South Africa, Australia, Malaysia, Singapore, Spain, Poland, Canada, and other countries are available through Multivision's proprietary and industry-leading content database. Video can be made available for viewing online through Multivision's Digital Showroom. The company now monitors and indexes broadcast content more than any other organization. Farahi says this satisfies his clients' ever-growing need to monitor as much broadcast content in as many markets as possible to effectively manage their brand, product, and messaging objectives.

Source: Shubert, S., *Business 2.0*, April 20, 2005; www.lostremote.com, May 20, 2005; www.multivisioninc.com, 2005; www.tmcnet.com, May 16, 2005.

Thinking About the Case

1. What was Farahi's original idea?

2. What does this idea have to do with IT? Why is IT so important in implementing this idea?

3. Was Farahi's idea aimed at an existing market, or did he create a new market? Explain.

4. Was Multivision a first mover? If so, did its moves guarantee it market dominance? Explain.

5. Multivision could not find an appropriate software application to serve its purpose in indexing and archiving video, so it developed its own. How does developing its own software serve its strategic advantage?

3

THREE

Business Functions and Supply Chains

LEARNING OBJECTIVES

In an economy that produces and consumes so much information, professionals must know how to use information systems in virtually every business activity. Managers must have an overall understanding of all elements of a system, so that they know what options are available to control quality, costs, and resources. Modern information systems encompass whole business cycles, often called supply chains.

When you finish this chapter, you will be able to:

- Identify various business functions and the role of ISs in these functions.

- Explain how ISs in the basic business functions relate to each other.

- Articulate what supply chains are and how information technology supports management of supply chains.

- Enumerate the purposes of customer relationship management systems.

- Explain the notion of enterprise resource planning systems.

EATS2GO:
Continued Growth and Specialization

Something had to give: Eats2Go's business expansion to more carts and to chip manufacturing had worked so well that Juan Moreno was drowning in piles of sales receipts. He had hired a part-time assistant to help him input the receipts to the business's spreadsheet program, but that solution was no longer enough. The labor-intensive process simply had to go. Luckily, Juan, Kendra Banks, and Dave Slater found a solution in a handheld personal digital assistant (PDA) with wireless mobile printer software. The sales staff manning the carts keyed the customer's menu selections into the PDAs and printed a receipt. Later, the information was downloaded from the PDAs to the business's main accounting system. The time saved by automating the sales transactions allowed Juan to concentrate on bigger issues the partners faced: tracking sales, costs, and profitability.

As part of his monthly sales analysis, Juan printed sales reports segregated by each of the three carts. When he did so, he noticed that sales from the Robbins Park pushcart were dropping. Their Subwich competitor was drawing customers from the Robbins Park cart. Also, Juan noticed that business was even worse during colder months and bad weather. The partners needed to turn the situation around.

A New Opportunity Appears

Earlier Juan, Kendra, and Dave had decided to find their own kitchen space to handle their increased food volume. When they were looking for rental space, they ran across a vacant storefront in Campus Town. Instead of simply renting kitchen space, they decided they'd open a small restaurant with its own kitchen. That way, they could meet their Subwich competitor head on, offering dinners as well as lunches and not worrying about the change of seasons or weather. They could also use the restaurant's kitchen for chip manufacturing when the restaurant was closed.

To handle the increased workload for the restaurant, the three entrepreneurs hired a full-time chef and kitchen staff. Kendra and the chef developed streamlined cooking procedures for both the meal and chip operations and then trained the staff in the procedures. That freed Kendra to work on new restaurant recipes.

Advertising Needs and Promotions

To announce the opening of their new restaurant, Dave used a desktop publishing program to create flyers for their grand opening that could be handed out to pushcart customers or on campus. The flyers included a feedback form, and those who returned the forms received discount coupons for a free beverage with the purchase of a sandwich. They hoped these special offers would attract new customers. Juan also suggested they produce radio commercials, reasoning that radio offered an affordable means of reaching their customers—college students, shoppers, and commuters. They'd need professional help with that media project.

Moving Forward

Eats2Go had come a long way since its start, but the entrepreneurs still had decisions to make and changes to undergo. With the opening of the restaurant, the partners needed to revamp their computer systems to handle credit-card purchases. Eats2Go also needed to automate and expand its employee systems. Juan had written checks by hand when the business only had a small staff payroll to deal with. But the new chef and kitchen staff now made that system impractical. Finally, Kendra thought that their food inventory and preparation systems might benefit from automation. She had tracked her inventory closely, but with the expansion, it was getting more and more difficult to keep up. Juan and Dave agreed that an inventory control system would be a good move, so they bought the QuickBooks program. This software could help them not only with inventory control but also with online credit verifications, sales and expenses, payroll and accounting, and other needed functions, such as tracking sales taxes, invoicing, and check printing. With this more comprehensive system, the three entrepreneurs believed they had made a great leap forward. It was clear to them that a well-run information system was an integral part of their business, simplifying their business as activities became more complex. They'd need to remain informed about technology as they looked to the future.

EFFECTIVENESS AND EFFICIENCY

The telephones at the offices of Capital One Financial Corp., a leading credit-card issuer, ring more than a million times per week. Cardholders call to ask about their balance or to ensure that the company received their recent payment. While callers almost immediately hear a human voice at the other end, computers actually do the initial work. The computers use the caller's telephone number to search the company's huge databases. Inferring from previous calls and numerous recorded credit-card transactions of the caller, the computers predict the reason for calling. Based on the assumed reason, the computers channel the call to one of 50 employees who can best handle the situation. Important information about the caller is brought up on the employee's computer monitor. Although callers usually do not contact the company to make purchases, the computer also brings up information about what the caller might want to purchase. As soon as the customer service representative provides the caller with satisfactory answers, he or she also offers the cardholder special sales. Many callers do indeed purchase the offered merchandise. All of these steps—accepting the call, reviewing and analyzing the data, routing the call, and recommending merchandise—take the computers a mere tenth of a second.

It is often said that the use of information technology makes our work more effective, more efficient, or both. What do these terms mean? **Effectiveness** defines the degree to which a goal is achieved. Thus, a system is more or less effective depending on (1) how much of its goal it achieves, and (2) the degree to which it achieves better outcomes than other systems do.

Efficiency is determined by the relationship between resources expended and the benefits gained in achieving a goal. Expressed mathematically,

$$\text{Efficiency} = \frac{\text{Benefits}}{\text{Costs}}$$

One system is more efficient than another if its operating costs are lower for the same or better quality product, or if its product's quality is greater for the same or lower costs. The term "productivity" is commonly used as a synonym for efficiency. However, **productivity** specifically refers to the efficiency of *human* resources. Productivity improves when fewer workers are required to produce the same amount of output, or, alternatively, when the same number of workers produces a greater amount of output. This is why IT professionals often speak of "productivity tools," which are software applications that help workers produce more in less time. The closer the result of an effort is to the ultimate goal, the more effective the effort. The fewer the resources spent on achieving a goal, the more efficient the effort.

Suppose your goal is to design a new car that reaches a speed of 60 miles per hour in 5 seconds. If you manage to build it, then you produce the product effectively. If the car does not meet the requirement, your effort is ineffective. If your competitor makes a car with the same features and performance, but uses fewer people and fewer other resources, then your competitor is not only as effective as you but also more efficient. ISs contribute to both the effectiveness and efficiency of businesses, especially when positioned in specific business functions, such as accounting, finance, and engineering, and when used to help companies achieve their goals more quickly by facilitating collaborative work.

One way to look at business functions and their supporting systems is to follow typical business cycles, which often begin with marketing and sales activities (see Figure 3.1). Serving customers better and faster, as well as learning more about their experiences and preferences, is facilitated by **customer relationship management (CRM)** systems. When customers place orders, the orders are executed in the supply chain. Customer relationship management continues after delivery of the ordered goods in the forms of customer service and more marketing. When an organization enjoys the support of CRM and supply chain management (SCM) systems, it can plan its resources well. Combined, these systems are often referred to as enterprise resource planning (ERP) systems.

RIS

FIGURE 3.1
Business activities consist of customer relationship management, supply chain management, and supporting functions.

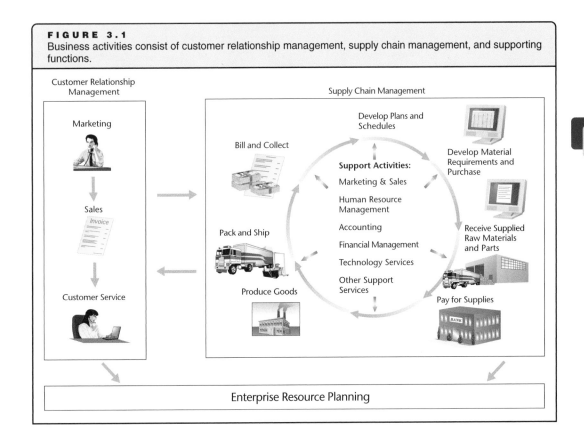

Figure 3.2 shows some of the most common business activities and their interdependence. For example, cost accounting systems are linked to payroll, benefits, and purchasing systems to accumulate the cost of products manufactured by a company; and information from purchasing systems flows to both cost accounting and financial reporting systems. The following discussion addresses the role of information systems, one business function at a time.

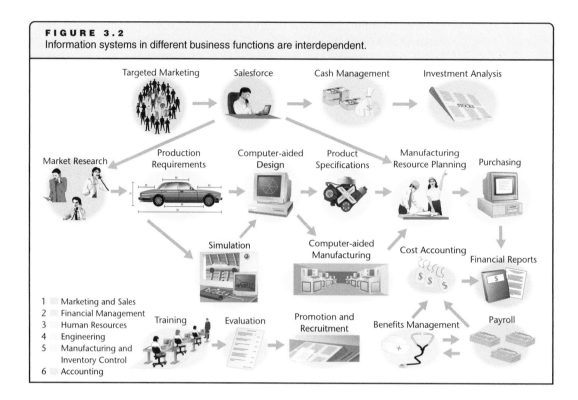

FIGURE 3.2
Information systems in different business functions are interdependent.

Targeted Marketing   Salesforce   Cash Management   Investment Analysis

Market Research   Production Requirements   Computer-aided Design   Product Specifications   Manufacturing Resource Planning   Purchasing

Simulation   Computer-aided Manufacturing   Cost Accounting   Financial Reports

1 Marketing and Sales
2 Financial Management
3 Human Resources
4 Engineering
5 Manufacturing and Inventory Control
6 Accounting

Training   Evaluation   Promotion and Recruitment   Benefits Management   Payroll

ACCOUNTING

The purpose of accounting is to track every financial transaction within a company, from a few cents to multimillion dollar purchases, from salaries and benefits to the sale of every item. Without tracking the costs of labor, materials, and purchased services using a cost-accounting system, a company might discover too late that it sells products below what it costs to make them. Without a system of accounts receivable, managers might not know who owes the company how much money and when it is due. Without an accounts payable system, managers cannot know how much money the company owes each supplier and when payment is due. Without a system that records and helps plan cash flow, managers cannot keep enough cash in the bank to make payments on schedule. At the year's end, the company cannot present a picture of its financial situation—called a balance sheet—and a profit-and-loss report, unless it maintains a general ledger to record every transaction with a financial impact. General ledger, accounts receivable, accounts payable, and cash-flow books conveniently lend themselves to computerization and can easily generate balance sheets and profit-and-loss statements from records (see Figure 3.3).

Typically, accounting ISs receive records of routine business transactions—such as the purchase of raw materials or services, or the sale of manufactured goods—from transaction processing systems (TPSs). Such a system automatically routes every purchase of raw materials or services to the accounts payable system, which uses it to produce checks or transfer funds to a vendor's bank account. Whenever a sale is recorded, the transaction is routed to the accounts receivable system (which generates invoices) and other destinations. Totals of accounts receivable and accounts payable can be automatically transferred to a balance sheet. Data from the general ledger can be automatically compiled to generate a cash-flow report or a profit-and-loss report for the past quarter or year. Accounting ISs can generate any of these reports on demand, as well as at scheduled times.

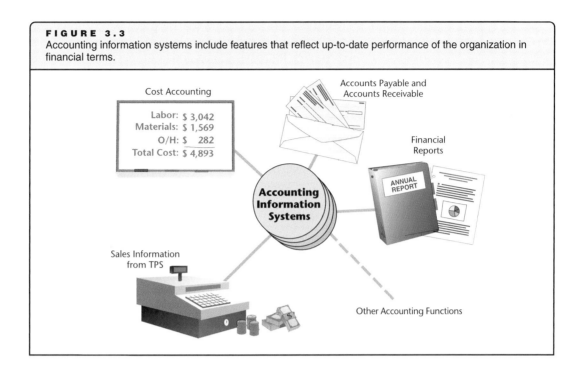

FIGURE 3.3
Accounting information systems include features that reflect up-to-date performance of the organization in financial terms.

Know About Business Functions and Supply Chains

Today's professionals are expected to be knowledgeable not only in their specific line of work but also in other areas, specifically information technology. In today's market, many employers look for generalists rather than specialists and focus on the techno-manager, a manager well-versed in information technology.

Because many ISs serve multiple functions and interface with other systems, it is extremely important for a professional to be familiar with the way ISs facilitate work in areas outside his or her expertise. If you work for a commercial organization, you are bound to be part of a supply chain or work for a unit that supports a supply chain. Knowledge of systems in different business areas helps you cooperate with your peers and coordinate efforts that cross departmental boundaries. Because professionals often have opportunities to be promoted to positions in other disciplines, the more you know, the better your chances of being "cross-promoted."

When a company develops and manufactures a new product that has never been available on the market, how can it determine a price that covers costs and generates a decent profit? It must maintain a system that tracks the costs of labor, materials, consulting fees, and every other expense related to the product's development and manufacture. Cost-accounting systems, used to accumulate data about costs involved in producing specific products, make excellent use of IT to compile pricing data. ISs also help allocate costs to specific work orders. A work order is an authorization to perform work for a specific purpose. When interfaced with payroll and purchasing ISs, a cost-accounting system automatically captures records of every penny spent (and originally recorded in the payroll and purchasing systems) and routes expenses to the appropriate work order. Because work orders are associated with specific products and services, the company now knows how much each product or service costs.

Accounting ISs are also used extensively for managerial purposes, assisting in organizing quarterly and annual budgets for departments, divisions, and entire corporations. The same systems help managers control their budgets by tracking income and expense in real time and comparing them with the amounts predicted in the budget. Budget applications are designed with proper controls, so that the system does not allow spending funds for a specific purpose beyond the amount that was budgeted for that purpose.

FINANCE

A firm's health is often measured by its finances, and ISs can significantly improve financial management (see Figure 3.4). The goal of financial managers, including controllers and treasurers, is to manage an organization's money as efficiently as possible. They achieve this goal by (1) collecting payables as soon as possible, (2) making payments at the latest time allowed by contract or law, (3) ensuring that sufficient funds are available for day-to-day operations, and (4) taking advantage of opportunities to accrue the highest yield on funds not used for current activities. These goals can be best met by careful cash management and investment analysis.

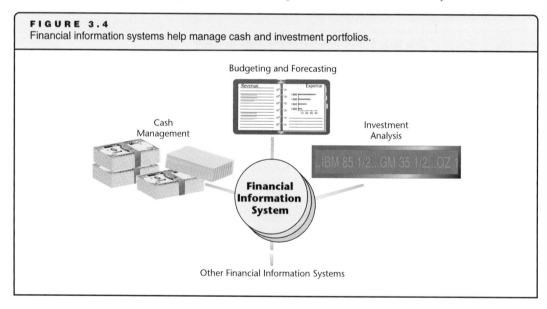

FIGURE 3.4
Financial information systems help manage cash and investment portfolios.

Cash Management

Financial information systems help managers track a company's finances. These systems record every payment and cash receipt to reflect cash movement, employ budgeting software to track plans for company finances, and include capital investment systems to manage investments, thus balancing the need to accrue interest on idle money against the need to have cash available. The information on expected cash receipts comes from sales contracts, and the information on cash outlays comes from purchasing contracts, as well as payroll and benefits schedules. Systems that deal specifically with cash are often called **cash management systems (CMSs)**. One common use for a CMS is to execute cash transactions in which financial institutions transfer huge amounts of money using **electronic funds transfer (EFT)**. EFT is the electronic transfer of cash from an account in one bank to an account in another bank. More than three-quarters of all payments of the U.S. government are made using EFT systems.

Investment Analysis and Service

Every investor's goal is to buy an asset and later sell it for more than it cost. When investing in securities, such as stocks and bonds, it is important to know the prices of securities in real time, that is, *right now*. The ability of financial ISs to record millions of securities prices and their changes over long time periods, coupled with the ability to manipulate numbers using software, puts powerful analysis tools in investment managers' hands. Within seconds, an investment analyst can use a financial IS and chart prices of a specific stock or bond over a given period and then build models to estimate what might happen to securities prices in the future.

Even the smallest investment firm can provide clients with an inexpensive online service for buying and selling securities, providing on-demand statements listing the stocks they own (called a portfolio), periodic yield, and the portfolio's current value. Clients serve themselves through the Web sites of brokerage firms to place buy and sell orders. Execution of orders takes only a few seconds.

Nearly instantaneously, ISs provide subscriber brokers and their clients with financial news, stock prices, commodity prices, and currency exchange rates from multiple locations across the world. Consider what happens when a foreign currency's exchange rate fluctuates a fraction of a percent. A brokerage house can make a profit of several thousand dollars within two minutes of buying and selling several million dollars' worth of the foreign currency.

Financial managers need to consider many factors before they invest in a security. Some of the most important factors these managers must consider are (1) risk, measured as the variability (degree of change) of the paper's past yield; (2) expected return; and (3) liquidity, a measure of how fast an investment can be turned into cash. Special programs help calculate these factors and present the results either in tables or graphs to allow timely decision making.

ENGINEERING

The time between generating an idea for a product and completing a prototype that can be mass-manufactured is known as engineering lead time, or **time to market**. Engineering includes **brainstorming** (the process of a group of colleagues meeting and working collaboratively to generate creative solutions and new ideas), developing a concept, creating mock-ups, building prototypes, testing, and other activities that require investments of time, labor, and money. Minimizing lead time is key to maintaining a competitive edge: it leaves competitors insufficient time to introduce their own products first. ISs can contribute significantly to this effort. Over the past decade, automakers have used engineering and other ISs to reduce the time from product concept to market from seven to two years.

IT's greatest contribution to engineering is in the area of **computer-aided design (CAD)** and **rapid prototyping** (creating one-of-a-kind products to test design in three dimensions). Engineers can use computers to modify designs quickly and store drawings electronically. With collaborative software, they perform much of this process over the Internet: engineers can conduct remote conferences while viewing and developing plans and drawings together. The electronic drawings are then available to make rapid prototypes.

Rapid prototyping allows a model of a product to be produced within hours, rather than days or weeks. The model required is often a mock-up to show only the physical look and dimensions of a product, without the electronics or other components that are part of the full product. First, an image of the object is created on a computer. The computer is connected to a special machine that creates a physical, three-dimensional model by laying down hundreds or thousands of thin layers of liquid plastic or special resin. The model can be examined by engineers and marketing managers in the organization, or shown to clients.

When the prototypes are satisfactory, the electronic drawings and material specifications can be transferred from the CAD systems to **computer-aided manufacturing (CAM)** systems. CAM systems process the data to instruct machines, including robots, how to manufacture the parts and assemble the product (see Figure 3.5).

Computer-aided design systems significantly shorten the time needed to produce drawings and complete the design of new products.

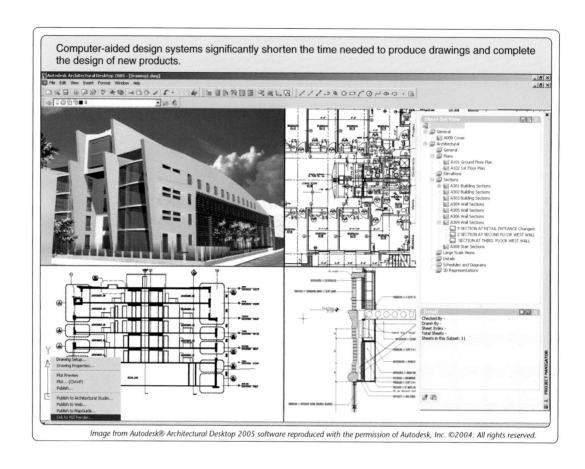

FIGURE 3.5
Engineering information systems aid engineers in designing new products and simulating how they operate.

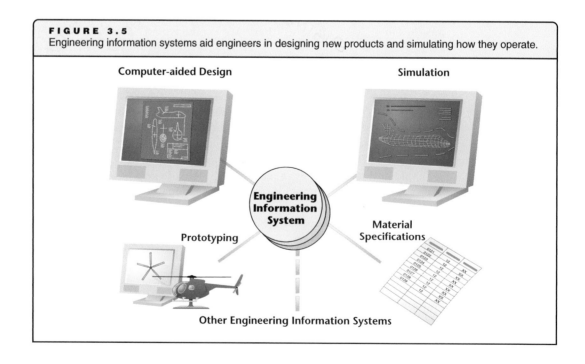

Until several years ago, automakers needed four to five years to turn a concept into vehicles rolling out for sale. Now, thanks to CAD, CAM, rapid prototyping, and collaborative engineering software, the lead time has been reduced to less than two years. The digital design of vehicles saves not only time but also the cost of cars crashed in tests. All the tests are performed with sophisticated software rather than with real cars.

Rapid prototyping shortens time to market. The white plastic model here is for an automotive differential housing.

Courtesy of Stratasys, Inc.

SUPPLY CHAIN MANAGEMENT

In its fundamental form, a **supply chain** consists of three phases: procurement of raw materials, processing the materials into intermediate and finished goods, and delivery of the goods to customers. Processing raw materials into goods is manufacturing. **Supply chain management (SCM)** consists of monitoring, controlling, and facilitating supply chains, as depicted in the right side of Figure 3.1. Supply chain management (SCM) systems are information technologies that support SCM. SCM systems have been instrumental in reducing manufacturing costs, including the costs of managing resources and controlling inventory (see Figure 3.6). In retail, the manufacturing phase does not exist, so the term "supply chain" refers only to purchasing of finished goods and the delivery to customers of those goods. In the service industries the term is practically meaningless.

As is clear from the previous discussion, much of the data required for manufacturing processes can flow directly from CAD systems to CAM systems, as well as inventory control systems and other systems that support planning and execution of manufacturing. While CAM systems participate in physical activities such as cutting and welding, other information systems help to plan and monitor manufacturing.

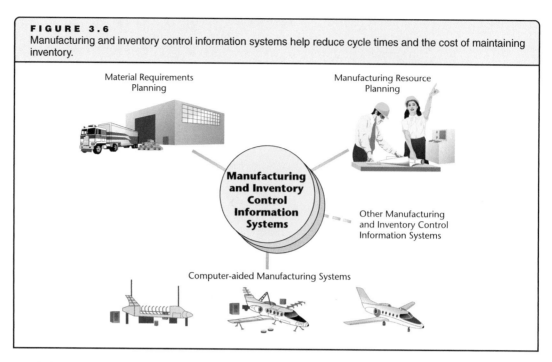

FIGURE 3.6
Manufacturing and inventory control information systems help reduce cycle times and the cost of maintaining inventory.

Information technology helps in the following manufacturing activities:

- Scheduling plant activities while optimizing the combined use of all resources—machines, personnel, tooling, and raw and interim materials.

- Planning material requirements based on current and forecasted demand.

- Reallocating materials rapidly from one order to another to satisfy due dates.

- Letting users manage inventories in real time, taking into consideration demand and the responsiveness of all work centers.

- Grouping work orders by characteristics of items ordered, such as color and width of products.

- Considering the qualifications of each resource (such as qualified labor, set-up crews, and specialized tools) to accomplish its task. For instance, people and raw materials can be moved from one assembly line to another to respond to machine breakdown or customer emergency, and design changes can be implemented quickly to respond to changes in customer wishes.

Material Requirements Planning and Purchasing

One area of manufacturing that has experienced the greatest improvement from IS is inventory control, or **material requirements planning (MRP)**. Traditional inventory control techniques operated according to the basic principle that future inventory needs are based on past use: once used up, inventory was replaced. By contrast, replenishment in MRP is based on *future* need, calculated by MRP software from demand forecasts. MRP programs take customer demand as their initial input. The main input to MRP programs is the number of product units needed and the time at which they are needed; the programs then work back to calculate the amounts of resources required to produce subparts and assemblies. The programs use long-range forecasts to put long-lead material on order.

Other important input to MRP applications includes a list of all raw materials and subcomponent demands (called the **bill of materials**, or **BOM**) and the economic order quantity of different raw materials. The **economic order quantity (EOQ)** of a specific raw material is the optimal quantity that allows a business to minimize overstocking and save cost, without risking understocking and missing production deadlines. A special program calculates EOQ for each item. It considers several factors: the item's cost, the discount schedule for large quantities, the cost of warehousing ordered parts, the cost of alternative uses of the money (such as the interest

MRP systems help reduce inventory cost while ensuring availability.

© AP/Wide World Photos

Computer-aided manufacturing systems control robots.

© REUTERS/Rebecca Cook/Landov

the money could earn had it not been spent on inventory), and other factors affecting the cost of ordering the item. Some MRP applications are tied to a purchasing IS, to produce purchase orders automatically when the quantity on hand reaches a reorder level. The purchase order includes the economic order quantity.

Manufacturing Resource Planning

Manufacturing resource planning (MRP II) combines material requirements planning (MRP) with other manufacturing-related activities to plan the entire manufacturing process, not just inventory. MRP II systems can quickly modify schedules to accommodate orders, track production in real time, and fix quality slippage. The most important input of MRP II systems is the **master production schedule (MPS)**, which specifies how production capacity is to be used to meet customer demands and maintain inventories. Virtually every report an MRP II package generates starts with, or is based on, the MPS. Purchases of materials and internal control of manufacturing work flow, for example, start with the MPS, so the MPS directly affects operational costs and asset use.

MRP II systems help balance production economies, customer demands, manufacturing capacity, and inventory levels over a planning horizon of several months. Successful MRP II systems have made a significant contribution to **just-in-time (JIT)** manufacturing, where suppliers ship parts directly to assembly lines, saving the cost of warehousing raw materials, parts, and subassemblies.

Ideally, the ISs of manufacturing organizations and their suppliers would be linked in a way that makes them subsystems of one large system. The MRP II application of an organization that manufactures a final product would plan and dictate the items required, their quantities, and the exact times they are needed at the assembly lines. Suppliers would ship items directly to assembly lines just before they are incorporated into the final product (hence the term *just-in-time manufacturing*). Manufacturing organizations have not yet reached the point where JIT is accomplished with every product, but they have made great progress toward this ideal.

The Internet facilitates such system linking. Companies that were quick to link their systems to their suppliers' systems attained strategic advantages. One such company is Cisco Systems, a world leader in design and manufacturing of telecommunications devices. The company used to maintain many manufacturing plants. In 2001, it had sold all but two. The company's ISs are linked through the Internet to the ISs of its suppliers, some of whom purchased the very plants that Cisco sold. Through these systems managers can track orders. They can tell Cisco clients the exact status of their orders and the time of delivery. Cisco managers keep track of the products they order and know at what phase of manufacturing and delivery each item is—as if *they* were running the manufacturing plants. More than 80 percent of what Cisco orders never passes through the company's facilities; the manufacturers ship the products directly to Cisco's clients.

Monitoring and Control

Information systems have been designed to control manufacturing processes, not just monitor them. Controlling processes is important to ensure quality. For example, Ford Motor Company implemented software that it calls Project Execution, which combines bar-coding and wireless technology to ensure quality. Since each vehicle is assembled on a chassis, each chassis is tagged with a unique bar code. A bar-code sensor is installed in each stop of the assembly line. The sensor transmits wireless signals to computers and electronically controlled gates. The purpose of the system is to ensure that no assembly steps are skipped, and that each vehicle passes a series of performance and quality tests along the way. If a step is missed, the gate does not let the vehicle leave the plant.

Shipping

When the process of manufacturing products is complete, the next link in the supply chain is shipping. Shipping is performed either by the manufacturer or by a hired shipping company. The variables that affect the cost and speed of shipping are numerous: length of routes, sequence of loading and unloading, type of shipped materials (e.g., perishable, hazardous, or fragile), fuel prices, road tolls, terrain and restricted roads, and many more. Therefore, the use of sophisticated software to optimize shipping time and the cost of labor and equipment use helps companies stay competitive. Figure 3.7 shows an example of such software.

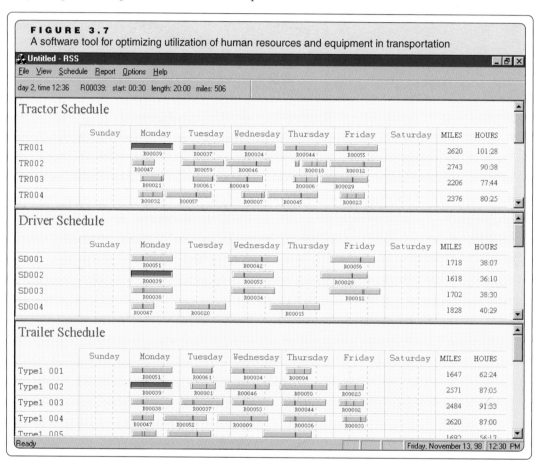

FIGURE 3.7
A software tool for optimizing utilization of human resources and equipment in transportation

Today's trucks are equipped with computers and satellite communication hardware and software. You might have seen small antennas on trucks. The antenna receives real-time orders from a central shipping office, especially when routing changes are necessary, and transmits information about the truck, such as current location, the previous point of loading or unloading, and the next point of loading or unloading. Truckers rarely reach a shipping office. These systems allow them to be on the road doing productive work all the time, thanks to constant communication with the office.

Supply chain management software in transportation helps load trucks, ships, and airplanes in an optimal manner both in terms of space utilization and sequence of unloading. Figure 3.8 provides a visual description of an optimal loading of boxes on a truck before its dispatch.

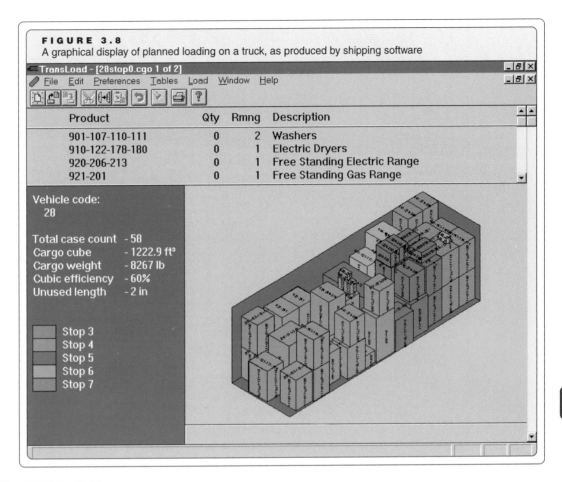

RFID in SCM

The most important development in hardware to support SCM has been a technology called **radio frequency identification (RFID)**. We discuss the technology itself in Chapter 6. RFID tags contain circuitry that allows recording of information about a product. When attached to a product, it contains an **electronic product code (EPC)**, which replaces the universal product code (UPC) with much more information. The tag can include the date of manufacturing, the plant in which the product was made, lot number, expiration date, destination, and many other details that help track its movement and sale. The information can be read and also revised by special RFID transceivers (transmitter-receiver devices). Figure 3.9 shows an example of how RFID is used in a supply chain. Items with rewritable tags can contain maintenance history of products, which helps optimize maintenance of the items.

The same technology can also be used for other purposes: detection of items that should be recalled because of hazardous components, detection of counterfeit products, and accurate condemnation of expired items, such as drugs and auto parts. When a pattern of defects is discovered in a product, RFID helps pinpoint the plant at which it was produced and the particular lot from which it came. Only products from that lot are recalled and replaced or fixed. It does not take too long to find out the particular manufacturing phase in which the defect was caused. When the expiration date of an item arrives, a transceiver detects that fact and alerts personnel to remove it from a shelf. Packaging of drugs and other items contain RFID tags with unique identifiers. Transceivers can detect whether the products are genuine.

Trucks are equipped with a satellite antenna and in-cabin computer to communicate up-to-the-minute status of shipping assignments.

© Getty Images

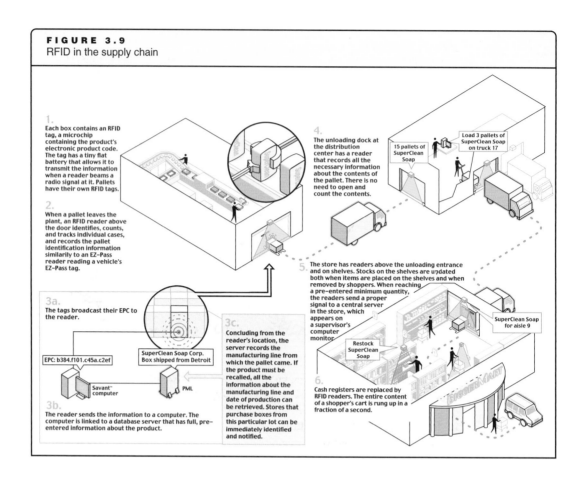

FIGURE 3.9
RFID in the supply chain

1.
Each box contains an RFID tag, a microchip containing the product's electronic product code. The tag has a tiny flat battery that allows it to transmit the information when a reader beams a radio signal at it. Pallets have their own RFID tags.

2.
When a pallet leaves the plant, an RFID reader above the door identifies, counts, and tracks individual cases, and records the pallet identification information similarly to an EZ-Pass reader reading a vehicle's EZ-Pass tag.

3a.
The tags broadcast their EPC to the reader.

EPC: b384.f101.c45a.c2ef

SuperClean Soap Corp. Box shipped from Detroit

Savant™ computer

PML

3b.
The reader sends the information to a computer. The computer is linked to a database server that has full, pre-entered information about the product.

3c.
Concluding from the reader's location, the server records the manufacturing line from which the pallet came. If the product must be recalled, all the information about the manufacturing line and date of production can be retrieved. Stores that purchase boxes from this particular lot can be immediately identified and notified.

4.
The unloading dock at the distribution center has a reader that records all the necessary information about the contents of the pallet. There is no need to open and count the contents.

15 pallets of SuperClean Soap

Load 3 pallets of SuperClean Soap on truck 17

5.
The store has readers above the unloading entrance and on shelves. Stocks on the shelves are updated both when items are placed on the shelves and when removed by shoppers. When reaching a pre-entered minimum quantity, the readers send a proper signal to a central server in the store, which appears on a supervisor's computer monitor.

Restock SuperClean Soap

SuperClean Soap for aisle 9

6.
Cash registers are replaced by RFID readers. The entire content of a shopper's cart is rung up in a fraction of a second.

CUSTOMER RELATIONSHIP MANAGEMENT

No commercial organization can survive without selling its products or services. Thus, businesses seek to provide products that consumers want and to entice them to buy what the business produces. They exert marketing efforts to pinpoint demographic groups that are most likely to buy products, to determine features that consumers desire most, and to provide the most efficient and effective ways to execute a sale when a consumer shows interest in the product or service. Because these efforts depend mainly on the analysis of huge amounts of data, ISs have become key tools to conceiving and executing marketing strategies. When marketing succeeds, ISs support the sales effort; to entice customers to continue to purchase, ISs support customer service (see Figure 3.10).

FIGURE 3.10
Customer relationship management systems help marketing, sales, and customer service departments target interested customers, learn from their experiences, and serve them better.

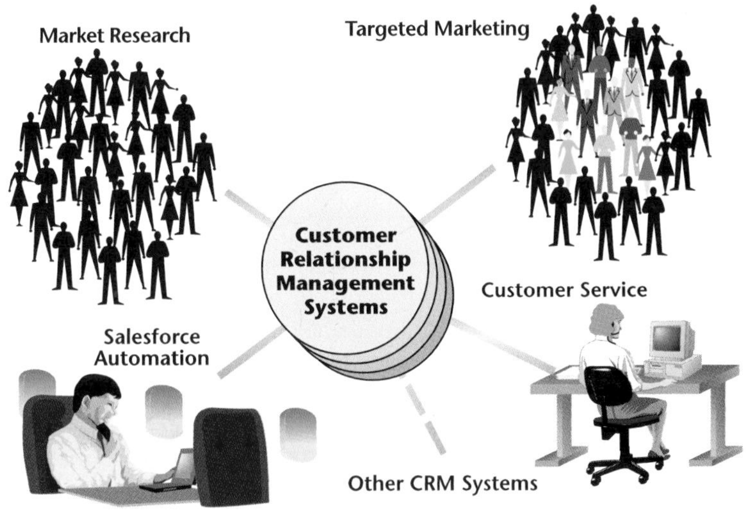

Customer relationship management (CRM) systems are designed to support any and all relationships with customers. Mostly, they support three areas: marketing, sales, and customer service. Modern CRM systems can help capture the entire customer experience with an organization, from response to an online advertisement to automatic replenishment of products, to proactive service. With growing competition and so many options available to consumers, keeping customers satisfied is extremely important. Many executives will tell you that their companies do not make money (and might even lose money) on a first sale to a new customer because of the great investment in marketing. Thus, they constantly strive to improve customer service and periodically contact anyone who has ever purchased something from them to ensure repeat sales and to encourage customer loyalty. Any information technology that supports these efforts is considered a CRM system, but in recent years the effort has been to combine applications that support all three areas—marketing, sales, and customer service—to better understand what customers want, to ensure timely shipping, and to be able to collect payment sooner.

CRM systems also provide an organization with an important element: all employees of the company who directly or indirectly serve a customer are "on the same page." Through their individual computers, all can have immediate access to the status of an order for an item or a resolution of a buyer's complaint, or to any other information that has to do with the customer. All who serve the customer are well-informed and receive the information from the same source. This is especially important in a long, complex sales cycle, because it minimizes response time and improves the quality of service for customers.

Market Research

Few organizations can sell their products and services without promotion; fewer still can promote successfully without market research. Market research systems help to find the populations and regions that are most likely to purchase a new product or service. They also help analyze how a new product fares in its first several months on the market.

Through interviews with consumers and retailers, market researchers collect information on what consumers like and dislike about products. When the researchers collect sufficient data, the marketing department uses statistical models to predict sales volumes of different products and of different designs of the same product. This critical information aids in planning manufacturing capacities and production lines. It is also extremely important for budgeting purposes.

Targeted Marketing

To save resources, businesses use IT to promote to people most likely to purchase their products. This activity is often referred to as **targeted marketing**. Great advances in database technology enable even the smallest and poorest business to use targeted marketing. The principle of targeted marketing is to define the prospective customer as accurately as possible and then to direct promotional dollars to those people most likely to purchase your product. Perhaps the best evidence of how much companies use ISs for targeted marketing is the use of the Internet for mass communication of unsolicited promotional e-mail, a practice called spamming. Many people loathe spamming, but it is certainly the least expensive method of advertising. Another controversial, but apparently effective method is pop-up advertising, in which a small window pops up either in front of or behind a Web browser's window.

To define their target markets, businesses collect data everywhere they can: from sales transactions and warranty cards, or by purchasing databases with information about organizations and individuals. Using database management systems (DBMSs), special programs to build and manipulate data pools, a company can sort and categorize consumers by age, gender, income, previous purchase of a related product, or any combination of these facts and other demographic information. The company then selects those whose characteristics match the company's customer profile and spends its promotional dollars to try to sell to those select customers.

POINT OF INTEREST

The Tune That Heals

To contact a prospective customer, telemarketers use special computer programs that automatically dial telephone numbers. Only if someone picks up the phone does a salesperson (or a recording) start the sales pitch. If the computer detects the famous 3-tone sound preceding "The number you have dialed is no longer in service," the computer deletes the record from its database. The digital file of this tune is available on the Web for free downloading. The filename is sit.wav. (SIT stands for Special Information Tone.) To reduce the number of uninvited sales calls, record the tune at the beginning of the outgoing message on your answering machine.

The great amount of personal information that corporations collect and purchase lets them prepare electronic dossiers on the interests, tastes, and buying habits of individuals. The information they possess lets them target "a market of one," namely, an individual rather than a group. Online purchase transactions and online product registrations by consumers provide a wealth of information to corporations. Vendors sort the information to send promotional material via ground mail or e-mail only to those customers whose profiles indicate potential interest.

Telemarketing (marketing over the telephone) makes extensive use of IT. The telemarketer uses a PC connected to a large database. The database contains records of potential or existing customers. With a retrieved record displayed on the screen, a marketer dials the number by pressing a single key or clicking the mouse. The telemarketer speaks to the potential buyer while looking at that person's purchasing record with the organization or even other organizations. Universities and charitable organizations use the same method to solicit donations.

Computer telephony integration (CTI) is a technique enabling a computer to use the digital signal coming through a telephone line as input in a computer system. It has been used often in marketing, sales, and customer service. For example, some mail-order firms use caller ID to better serve their customers. Caller ID was originally intended to identify the telephone number from which a person calls, but mail-order businesses quickly found a new use for the gadget. They connect it to their customer database. When you call to order, a simple program searches for your number, retrieves your record, and displays it on a PC monitor. You might be surprised when the person who receives your call greets you by name and later asks if you want to use the same credit-card number you used in your last purchase.

Techniques such as data mining take advantage of large data warehouses to find trends and shopping habits of various demographic groups. For example, the software discovers clusters of products that people tend to purchase together, and then the marketing experts promote the products as a combination, and might suggest displaying them together on store shelves. You will learn more about data mining in Chapter 11.

With the proliferation of set-top boxes for digital televisions, several software companies, such as Visible World, Navic Networks, and OpenTV, have developed applications that may allow television networks to transition from the wasteful and expensive 30-second commercial to more personal advertising. Relying on information provided by households through these interactive boxes, they can select and transmit to each subscriber commercials only for products in which the subscriber is interested. For example, you will not receive commercials about pet food if you do not have pets but will receive commercials about gardening if this is your hobby.

Mobile Web browsing allows advertisers to target on-the-go customers for products or services.

Courtesy of Bitstream, Inc.

Use of information technology for targeted marketing has taken sophisticated forms on the Web. More than just targeting a certain demographic group, Web technologies enable retailers to *personalize* marketing when shopping and buying are conducted online. Special software on online retailers' servers keeps track of every visit consumers make and captures their "click streams" (the sequence of selections they make) and the amount of time they spend viewing each page. The retailer's software combines this information with information from online purchases to personalize the pages whenever consumers revisit the site. The reconstructed page introduces information about the products that the individual visitor is most likely to purchase. For example, two people with different purchasing records at Amazon.com who revisit the company's home page will find that they are looking at slightly different versions of the page. Amazon's software custom-composes the elements for each person according to his or her inferred interests in products. The ones that the software concludes might be of the highest interest are displayed or linked on the page.

Customer Service

Web-based customer service provides automated customer support 24 hours per day, 365 days per year. At the same time, it saves companies the cost of labor required when humans provide the same service. For example, letting customers pay their bills electronically not only provides convenience but also saves (both customers and companies) the cost of postage and paper and saves the company the time required for dealing with paper documents. Online billing costs only a small fraction of paper billing. The business research firm Gartner Group estimates the average invoice-to-payment cycle at 41 days, while online invoice and payment shortens the period by at least six days. Customers appreciate the discounts that many companies offer for accepting statements and paying bills online.

CRM systems help service representatives support customers and learn more about their preferences.

© Andersen Ross/Getty Images

Online customer service applications have become increasingly sophisticated. They help track past purchases and payments, update online answers to frequently asked questions (FAQs) about products and services, and analyze customers' contacts with the company to maintain and update an electronic customer profile. The FAQ pages of many companies have been replaced with options for open-ended questions; instead of looking up a question that is similar to what you would ask, you can simply type in your question. Employing artificial intelligence software, the site will "understand" your question and provide a short list of links where you can find an answer.

Salesforce Automation

Salesforce automation equips traveling salespeople with information technology to facilitate their productivity. Typically, salespeople are equipped with notebook computers that store promotional information for prospective customers, software for manipulating this information, and computerized forms. Many salespeople carry laptop computers or personal digital assistants (PDAs) with all the information they need and that allow them to connect to their organizational information systems through the Internet. Salesforce automation can increase sales productivity significantly, making sales presentations more efficient and letting field representatives close deals on the spot, using preformatted contracts and forms.

Information technology lets salespeople present different options for products and services on the computer, rather than asking prospective customers to wait until the main office faxes or mails the information. At the end of the day or the week, salespeople can upload sales information to a computer at the main office, where it is raw input to the order-processing department, the manufacturing unit, or the shipping and invoicing departments.

Using PDAs that can establish a wireless connection to the Internet enables salespeople to check prices, check availability of the items in which a customer is interested, and place an order away from the office. The salespeople can then spend much more time on the road, increasing time spent with prospective customers.

Salesforce automation increases marketing and sales productivity.

© Pinto/Gulliver/Corbis

Consumer Privacy

Consider the following scenario: you agree to give some financial information about yourself to one organization in exchange for credit. At a later date, you provide some medical information to another organization. In the meantime, your credit-card company has enough information from your purchasing activity to know your culinary and fashion tastes better than you do. Finally, without your knowledge or consent, yet another organization gathers all this information and puts it in one big record that is practically a detailed personal dossier. Whenever you use your credit card, you provide information about you. Whenever you interact with an organization online, you provide information about you. Do you ever stop to think where the information goes?

Organizations collect huge amounts of personal information. Every time you pay with your credit card you leave a personal record; the few details of your purchase are often used to update an already hefty dossier about your buying habits. Every time you provide personal information at a Web site, you either help open a new dossier with an organization or help other organizations update their dossier about you. In their zeal to market more effectively, businesses often violate consumer privacy.

- **What Is Privacy?** In the context of information, privacy is your right to control information about yourself. For example, you keep your privacy if you keep to yourself your college grades, medical background, or the name of the person with whom you had dinner last evening. Someone who receives such information without your permission is violating your privacy.

- **Business Arguments.** Business leaders argue that they must collect and use personal data. Without personal data, they would have to waste time and money to target likely buyers. They need to know the purchasing and payment habits of individuals because these details create credit histories that help make prudent decisions on consumer risks. This ability to purchase and manipulate large amounts of consumer information makes the business world more democratic than it used to be. Small companies now have the same chances of targeting prospective buyers with good credit as big companies, creating more opportunities and more competition, which eventually benefit consumers.

- **Consumer Arguments.** Consumers usually accept that they must divulge some private information to receive services, but many do not accept

the mass violation of privacy. They resent unsolicited mail and e-mail sent by companies who know much about them although they have never provided personal details to these companies. They hate telephone calls from salespeople who obtained their records from companies that were supposed to keep their records confidential. And they are frightened by the "dossier phenomenon": it might be the greatest concern to consumers.

- **Losing Control.** In many cases, you volunteer information in return for some benefits, such as coupons or sweepstakes participation. In others, you simply cannot receive the service or product unless you agree to give certain personal details. In such cases, you give implicit or explicit informed consent to obtain information about yourself. However, once you provide information, you have little control over it. With some newer technology, such as RFID, you might not even be aware of who and when information is collected about you. You have just stepped out of a supermarket with a cartful of groceries. All are RFID-tagged. The supermarket systems recorded your visit and detailed what you purchased. Can you be sure that nobody else has the proper device to read and record what you purchased?

- **The Eight Commandments of Personal Data Collection and Maintenance.** In a free, market-oriented society, not allowing organizations to collect personal data is inconceivable. What can businesses do to help protect privacy? They can try to adhere to these rules to avoid misuse:

  Purpose. Companies should inform people who provide information of the specific, exclusive purpose for which the company maintains its data, and only use the data for another purpose with the subjects' consent. For example, this practice could protect psychiatric patients from having their insurance companies sell information about their treatments.

  Relevance. Companies should record and use only data necessary to fulfill their own purposes. For example, an applicant's credit record should not contain his or her political views because that information is irrelevant in credit considerations and would only be useful if sold.

  Accuracy. Companies should ensure that the personal records they maintain are accurate. For example, many loan applicants have had terrible experiences because some of the data maintained by credit companies is erroneous. Careful data entry and periodic verification can enhance accuracy.

Currency. Companies should make sure that all data about an individual is current. If currency cannot be guaranteed, then data should be discarded periodically. Outdated information can create horribly negative repercussions. For example, a person who might have been unemployable due to past illness might not be able to get a job, even though he or she might be healthy now.

Security. Companies should limit access to data to only those who need to know. In addition to passwords, audit trails (which identify every employee who accesses a personal record and for what purpose) are also very effective tools for ensuring security.

Time Limitation. Companies should retain data only for the time period necessary.

Scrutiny. Companies should establish procedures to let individuals review their records and correct inaccuracies.

Sole Recording. When using a recording technology, a company should ensure that no other party can take advantage of the technology to record the same information. For example, if a

supermarket records an individual's purchases using RFID technology, it must ensure that the RFID tags embedded in the packaging are disabled as soon as the customer leaves the store.

Of course, many consumers will still feel that their privacy is invaded even if every business adopts these "commandments." How can you protect your privacy? Do not furnish your name, Social Security (or any other identifying) number, address, or any other private information if you do not know how it will be used. If you do provide detailed information, indicate that you do not wish the data to be shared with any other organization or individual. You can usually check a box to this effect on paper or online forms. To avoid junk mail or junk e-mail, again check the proper box on online forms. Do not fill out any online or paper forms with detailed data unless an opt-out option is available. Of course, many services we receive depend on our willingness to provide personal data, so at least some organizations must have personal information, but you can be selective. Always carefully weigh what you gain against the privacy you might lose.

HUMAN RESOURCE MANAGEMENT

Human resource management (HRM) has become more complex due to the fast growth in specialized occupations, the need to train and promote highly skilled employees, and the growing variety of benefits programs. Human resource management can be classified into five main activities: (1) employee record management, (2) promotion and recruitment, (3) training, (4) evaluation, and (5) compensation and benefits management (see Figure 3.11).

Employee Record Management

ISs facilitate employee record management. Human resource departments must keep personnel records to satisfy both external regulations (such as federal and state laws) and internal regulations, as well as for payroll and tax calculation and deposit, promotion consideration, and periodic reporting. Many HR ISs are now completely digitized (including employees' pictures), which dramatically reduces the space needed to store records, the time needed to retrieve them, and the costs of both.

Promotion and Recruitment

To select the best-qualified person for a position, a human resource manager can search a database of applicants and existing employees' records for set criteria, such as a specific type and length of education, particular experience, specific talents, and required licenses or certifications. Automating the selection process significantly minimizes time and money spent on recruitment but does require that a current database be maintained.

Intranets (intraorganizational networks that support Web applications) help HR managers post position vacancy announcements for employees to peruse and consider from their own PCs. This system is especially efficient in large organizations that employ thousands of workers, and even more so at multisite organizations.

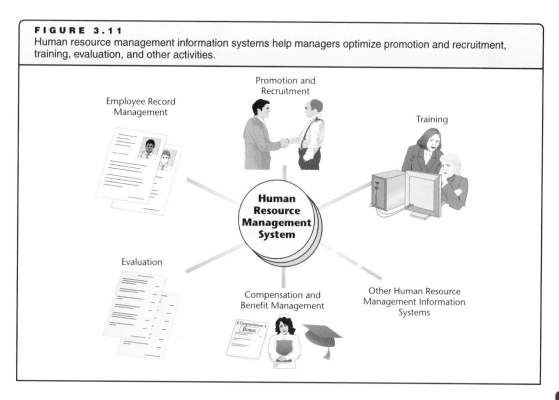

FIGURE 3.11
Human resource management information systems help managers optimize promotion and recruitment, training, evaluation, and other activities.

Text and pictures can be combined to store and retrieve employee records.

Many companies refuse to receive paper applications and résumés. Some accept such documents via e-mail, but others accept only forms that are filled out and submitted online. Using keywords, recruiting officers can then use special software to scour a database for the most-qualified candidates. HR consultants say that this process reduces the time spent on a typical search from several hours to several minutes. Some software companies sell automated recruiting and selection software to support such activities. For example, PeopleAdmin, Inc. offers software by the same name. HR managers save the cost of publishing help wanted ads and can start reviewing résumés as soon as applicants respond online instead of waiting the typical 6–8 days from advertising.

Some companies use the entire Web as a database for their search, which means they include in the search many people who have never applied for a job with them but have posted their résumés. Consider Humana, Inc., a large health-care organization. The company uses software that searches the Web for résumés and then matches qualified candidates with job openings. The company then uses a tracking system to e-mail candidates while updating the corporate HR databases with their résumés. Adopting this approach cut the cost of processing a qualifying résumé from $128 to a mere 6 cents. Overall, the new process saves Humana $8.3 million annually and more effectively forecasts the fit of candidates tracked through the recruiting system. Across industries, as companies move from traditional recruiting to recruiting through the Web, the cost per hire drops from $5,000–12,000 to $2,000–5,000, depending on the set of skills required and the level of the position.

Training

One important function of human resource departments is improving employee skills. In both the manufacturing and service sectors, multimedia software training is rapidly replacing training programs involving classrooms and teachers. Such applications include interactive, three-dimensional simulated environments. Some applications contain full-blown virtual reality components. For example, one such application trains workers to handle wrought iron that must be hammered manually. The worker wears special goggles and holds a hammer in one hand and a piece of metal in the other, over an anvil. The worker "sees" the metal piece through the goggles, "hears" the hitting sound through earphones, and receives a programmed, realistic jolt every time he "hits" the metal. This safely prepares the worker for the dangerous work instead of putting him at risk for injury before he has enough experience to do the actual work. Although the initial investment in multimedia training systems might be high, human resource managers find the systems very effective. Surgeons train using similar systems to operate on virtual patients rather than risk injuries to human patients.

Training software emulates situations in which an employee must act and includes tests and modules to evaluate a trainee's performance. In addition to the savings in trainers' time, there are other benefits. The trainee is more comfortable because he or she controls the speed at which the sessions run. The software lets the trainee go back to a certain point in the session if a concept is missed. Also, the software can emulate hazardous situations, thereby testing employee performance in a safe environment. And if training in a real environment involves destruction of equipment or consumption of materials, virtual reality training applications accomplish the same results in skill enhancement without destruction or waste.

Developments in IT enable organizations to reduce training costs dramatically. Consider CVS, one of the largest U.S. drugstore chains. The company has more than 17,000 employees it calls technicians, whom it trains continually. The technicians must pass exams to be promoted. In 2000, the company installed PCs at its 400 training sites where technicians can take courses, review, and take exams during breaks or after work. The average cost per trainee was $50. Then, the company put the training materials on CD-ROMs. More than 80 percent of the trainees took the CDs home, so they could learn at their convenience. This approach reduced the average cost per employee to $15. The company also moved the training materials and exams to a central Web site so employees can personalize learning: using a Web browser, they can find the materials they need, bookmark selected Web pages, leave the training session when they wish, and come back to finish it later. When they do finish a training session, they can take certification tests. Their completed tests are then fed into a database at corporate headquarters so that managers can track who is ready to be promoted. The move to the Web reduced the average training cost per employee to $5.

Evaluation

Supervisors must periodically evaluate the technical ability, communications skills, professional conduct, and general behavior of employees. While objective factors are involved in evaluation—such as attendance rates and punctuality—employee evaluation is often very subjective. Assessing performance and effort levels, and their relative weights of importance, varies significantly, depending on who is evaluating. A supervisor might forget to include some factors altogether or might inappropriately weigh a particular aspect of performance. Subjectivity is particularly problematic when several employees are being considered for a promotion, and their evaluations are compared to determine the strongest candidate. By helping to standardize the evaluation process across employees and departments, evaluation software adds a certain measure of objectivity and consistency.

In an evaluation, a supervisor provides feedback to an employee, records the evaluation for official records and future comparison, and accepts input from the employee. Software helps managers standardize their employee evaluations by providing step-by-step guides to writing performance reviews, a checklist of performance areas to include in the evaluation (with the option to add or remove topics), scales to indicate how strong the employee is in each area, and the ability to select the relative importance each factor should hold in the overall evaluation. Performance areas include written and oral communication, job knowledge, and management skills, with each topic broken down into basic elements to assist the supervisor in creating an accurate evaluation. A typical application guides the user through all necessary factors and includes a help guide. When the evaluator finishes entering data, the application automatically computes a subtotal for each category and a weighted grade, which can then be electronically stored as part of the employee's record.

Compensation and Benefits Management

ISs help HR officers manage compensation (salaries, hourly pay, commissions, and bonuses) efficiently and effectively. Programs can easily calculate weekly, monthly, and hourly pay according to annual salaries and can include federal, state, and local tax tables to assist in complying with compensation regulations. This same system can also automatically generate paychecks or direct deposits, which are the electronic transfer of funds from the firm's bank account to the employee's.

Special software helps the HR department manage benefits, such as health insurance, life insurance, retirement plans, and sick and leave days, which are determined by seniority, amounts individuals pay into programs, and other factors. To optimize benefits, some companies use special software, incorporating expert systems (ISs that emulate human expertise) that determine the optimal health and retirement plans for each employee based on factors such as marital status, age, occupation, and other data.

Using intranets, many organizations allow their employees to access the benefits database directly and make changes to their preferences, such as selecting another health-care insurance program, or adding a family member as a beneficiary in a life insurance plan. When the company engages a third party for managing pension funds or other benefits, employees can go directly to the Web site of that company, not involving their own company resources at all. By making the changes directly from their PCs, employees reduce the amount of work of the HR staff and decrease the company's overhead costs.

INTERORGANIZATIONAL SUPPLY CHAIN MANAGEMENT SYSTEMS

U.S. Department of Commerce statistics show that over the past two decades inventory as a percentage of U.S. gross domestic product (GDP) decreased by about half. During that period, the total GDP more than tripled while the dollar value of inventory did not even double. This means that the U.S. GDP grew while less and less money was tied to inventory. The smaller the inventory, the more money can be spent on other resources. Much of this trend can be attributed to the use of ISs, especially SCM systems.

According to IBM, companies that implemented SCM systems have reduced inventory levels by 10–50 percent, improved the rate of accurate deliveries by 95–99 percent, reduced unscheduled work stoppages to 0–5 percent, reduced cycle time (from order to collection) by 10–20 percent, and reduced transportation costs by 10–15 percent.

Several enterprise applications, such as ERP systems, also serve as SCM systems. As Figure 3.12 illustrates, many such systems enable managers not only to monitor what goes on at their own units or organization but also to follow what goes on at the facilities of their suppliers and contractors. For example, at any given point in time managers can know the status of the following: an order now being handled by a contractor, by order number; the phase of manufacturing the produced units have reached; and the date of delivery, including any delays and their length. When purchasing parts, managers use the systems for issuing electronic purchase orders, and they can follow the fulfillment process at the supplier's facilities, such as when the parts were packed, when they were loaded on trucks, and when they are estimated to arrive at the managers' floor or the floor of another business partner who needed the parts.

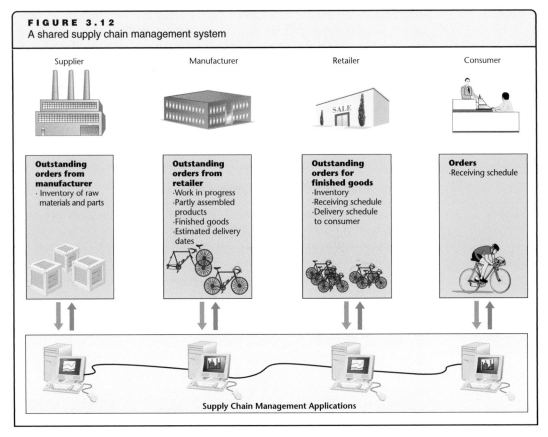

FIGURE 3.12
A shared supply chain management system

SCM applications streamline operations throughout the chain, from suppliers to customers, lowering inventories, decreasing production costs, and improving responsiveness to suppliers and clients. Harnessing the global network, managers can supervise an entire supply chain regardless of the location of the activity—at their own facilities or another organization's, at the same location or thousands of miles away. Older SCM systems connected two organizations. New ones connect several. For example, a distributor can reorder products from Organization A and simultaneously alert Organization B, the supplier of Organization A. The systems let all parties—suppliers, manufacturers, distributors, and customers—see the same information. A change made by any organization that affects an order can affect a corresponding change in scheduling and operations in the other organization's activities.

Companies that have adopted SCM systems have seen improvement in three major areas: reduction in inventory, reduction in cycle time (the time it takes to complete a business process), and, as a result, reduction in production cost. Companies can reduce their inventory by communicating to their suppliers through a shared SCM system the exact number of units of each item they need and the exact time they need them. In ideal situations, they do not need to stockpile any inventory, saving warehouse costs. The management consulting firm Aberdeen Group estimates that companies using SCM systems through the Internet reduce purchase order processing cycles by 70–80 percent and pay 5–10 percent less for the items they purchase.

The Importance of Trust

SCM systems accomplish the greatest efficiencies when all businesses in the chain link their systems and share all the information that is pertinent to planning production and shipment. For example, Chevron, the giant gas and oil company, used to pump oil and deliver as much as it could to gas stations without accurate information about their future needs. Therefore, in many cases its clients, the gas stations, ran out of gas and had to wait for a delivery, or when the tanker delivered it often had to leave some of the oil in the tank because the gas station tanks reached their full capacity. To avoid unplanned shortages, the company often had to purchase oil in the "spot market" and pay more for it than if it had pumped the oil from its own wells. Both situations cost the company millions of dollars. To avoid such situations, the company linked the gas stations' transaction information systems to its ISs, so that the company can plan drilling and refining based on the gas stations' demand. The increased efficiency saves Chevron much money.

However, not all organizations are willing to collaborate with their business partners. One reason is the fear that when Organization A purchases from Organization B and has access to Organization B's demand figures, it might disclose the information to competitors in an attempt to stir more competition and enjoy favorable prices. Another fear is that if Organization B realizes that at a certain point in time Organization A is in dire need of its raw materials, Organization B might take advantage of the situation and negotiate higher prices.

The first type of fear can be found in initial reluctance of suppliers to share information with large buyers such as Wal-Mart. Only the bargaining power of Wal-Mart and its insistence on sharing such information convinced suppliers to link their systems with those of Wal-Mart. The second type of fear is still there between General Motors and its main tire supplier, Goodyear. Goodyear could enjoy lower inventories if it had GM's demand schedule for tires. It could then calibrate its own order for raw materials, such as rubber, and its manufacturing capacity to suit those of GM, save money, and pass at least some of the savings to its client in the form of cheaper products. It could always replenish its client's inventory of tires before GM ran out of them. Better yet, it could deliver the tires directly to the assembly lines just when they are needed, saving both GM and itself warehousing costs. Yet, GM is guarding its production schedule as confidential.

Thus, effective supply chain management between companies is not only a matter of appropriate technology but also a matter of trust and culture change. So far, most of the successful collaborations have been between a large company and its business partners, whereby the company uses its power to dictate collaboration. However, some large companies have tied their SCM systems out of mutual understanding that this would benefit both companies, even if the shared information reveals some unpleasant facts. For example, Procter & Gamble Inc., the giant supplier of household products, has had its systems connected to those of Wal-Mart since 1987, when the term "supply chain management" was not even in use. By providing its retail information to P&G, Wal-Mart ensures that it never runs out of P&G products. A culture of sharing—you show me some of your information and I show you some of mine—is essential for the success of both companies and creates a sense of mutual dependence and true partnership.

SCM systems can be taken a step beyond the sale. The systems can be used for after-the-sale services. For example, Beckman Coulter Inc., in Fullerton, California, makes blood analyzers and other medical devices. After it sells a machine, the company uses the Internet to link the machine from the client's facility to a computer in its Fullerton factory. Software on the computer runs 7 days per week, 24 hours per day to monitor the sold machine. When a problem occurs, the computer alerts a Beckman technician, who can repair the machine before it stops working. Beckman estimates that the system saves it $1 million annually, because malfunctions are captured at an early stage, which avoids the higher cost of fixing a more damaged machine. The added benefit is increased customer satisfaction.

The Musical Chairs of Inventory

Recall the wonderful trend cited in the beginning of this section: the dollar value of inventory for U.S. businesses was growing at about 60 percent of the growth of GDP. However, much of the trend took place in the 1981–1991 period. In the 1992–2004 period, inventory as a percentage of GDP stayed fairly similar at about 3.5 percent. Apparently, while large corporations have the resources to install and run SCM systems to cut their own inventory, the ratio of inventory to revenue in small enterprises is growing because they do not use such systems. And sometimes, the companies that suffer the inventory ripple effect are not small. They might be powerful, and they even might own their own SCM system, but their system might not be linked to their buyers' systems, so they cannot plan their own production to reduce inventory.

For an example, let us return to the relationship between General Motors and Goodyear. The world's largest auto manufacturer improved "inventory turns" 55.2 percent between 1996 and 2001. Inventory turns is the number of times a business sells (or turns over) its inventory per year. It is calculated by dividing the sales revenue by the average value of inventory. The greater the inventory turns number, the better. During the same period, Goodyear, GM's tire supplier, experienced a 21 percent decrease in inventory turns. The likely conclusion is that GM avoided purchasing tires from Goodyear until it needed them at the assembly line, but Goodyear did not have enough information on when, exactly, those tires would be required, and therefore kept overstocks. Had the SCM systems of the companies been linked, Goodyear could reduce inventory and see its inventory turns rise rather than fall. It is also reasonable to assume that thanks to the cost savings Goodyear would be able to sell tires to GM at a lower price. GM and other companies have created a situation where each company tries to "sit" with a lean inventory while, inadvertently, leaving another "standing" with an overstock. In order for all involved in a supply chain to enjoy efficiencies, the musical chairs, or "hot potato" situation, must stop.

Collaborative Logistics

The Web enables organizations from totally different industries to streamline operations through collaboration. In recent years an increasing number of businesses found a new way to cut shipping costs: they combine freight with other businesses, sharing their own trucks or the vehicles of trucking companies. The collaboration reduces partially empty trucks, or empty trucks between stops. To this end, the companies connect their SCM systems to the site of a company that specializes in optimization of logistics, such as Nistevo Corporation. The company manages the site and uses sophisticated software to calculate the shortest routes between departure and arrival points and the best combination of loads from two or more companies to share trucks and routes. The SCM systems of subscribing companies provide daily data into the shared system. The IS takes into consideration the type of freight to ensure safety and adherence to regulations. For example, the software is designed not to combine chemicals with food. Therefore, typical allies of food manufacturers have been paper manufacturers, for instance. The cost savings have been impressive.

The spice maker McCormick & Co., Inc. has reduced freight costs by 5–15 percent, while General Mills has realized savings of up to 7 percent of its overall logistics costs. Manufacturers of household paper products such as Georgia-Pacific and International Paper Co. share about 80 long-distance routes with General Mills on a regular basis, cutting freight costs for those shipments 5–20 percent. Because the success of collaborative shipping is so impressive, some experts expect competitors to share trucks, leaving competition to some other areas of their operations, such as development and manufacturing processes.

Another area where some companies have explored collaboration is warehousing. The principle here is the same: try to maximize the use of warehouse space, and if you cannot use all of it, allow other businesses to use the extra space. The way to accomplish this, again, goes through the Web: a third party specializing in warehousing optimization combines warehousing needs and availability from member companies to offer optimal solutions.

ENTERPRISE RESOURCE PLANNING

 A growing number of organizations elect to replace old, disparate ISs with enterprise applications that support all or most of the business activities we have described. As mentioned before, these systems are often referred to as **enterprise resource planning (ERP)** systems, although they are used not only for planning but also for managing daily operations. Designers of ERP systems take a systems approach to an enterprise. For example, the Manufacturing Resource Planning component of the system uses the information recorded on a sale to retrieve product specifications; the data is used to generate purchasing information such as items, quantities, and the timetable for suppliers to deliver for the purchasing department. As products are manufactured, the system tracks the stages of the work in progress. When items are ready to be shipped, the shipping department can retrieve information on the items for its operations. The system keeps shipping information such as content and destination, along with billing information, to help produce shipping and billing documentation. The system also records financial transactions involved in such activities, such as payment made from a bank account. The accounting component records the transactions. In addition, ERP systems also provide human resource modules for payroll, employee benefits management, and employee evaluation software. CRM components are also available and are tied to other components through orders applications and sales records.

ERP packages are quite complex. Because they are not tailored to the needs of specific clients, they often require adjustment and fine-tuning for specific organizations. Therefore, their installation and testing involve experts who are usually employees of the software vendor or professionals who are certified for such work by the vendor. The most visible software companies specializing in ERP systems are SAP and Oracle.

ERP applications are expensive. Some modules of these systems cost several million dollars. Buyers usually must allocate several more million dollars to pay for installation and modifications. Installation often takes many months to complete. Implementation of ERP systems can fail because of formidable challenges: the gap between system capabilities and business needs, lack of expertise on the consultant's part, and mismanagement of the implementation project. The business research firm Standish Group found that only 10 percent of ERP implementation projects are completed as planned, on time, and within budget. Fifty-five percent are completed late or over budget (which usually means loss of business and revenue), and the other 35 percent of such projects are canceled because of difficulties. At Hewlett-Packard, one of the world's largest computer and IT equipment makers, a $400 million loss in the third quarter of 2004 was blamed on poorly managed migration to a new ERP system.

■ Effectiveness is the degree to which a task is accomplished. The better a person performs a job, the more effective he or she is. Efficiency is measured as the ratio of output to input. The more output with the same input, or the less input for the same output used in a process, the more efficient the process. ISs can help companies attain more effective and efficient business processes. Productivity is the measure of people's efficiency. When people use ISs, their productivity increases.

■ ISs have been integrated into almost every functional business area. In accounting and payroll, because of the routine and structured nature of accounting tasks, the systems automatically post transactions in the books and automate the generation of reports for management and for legal requirements.

■ Financial ISs help managers track cash available for transactions, while ensuring that available money is invested in short- or long-term programs to yield the highest interest possible. Investment analysis ISs help build portfolios based on historical performance and other characteristics of securities.

■ Computer-aided design (CAD) systems help engineers design new products and save and modify drawings electronically. Computer-aided manufacturing (CAM) systems direct machines in manufacturing parts and assembling products.

■ Supply chain management systems optimize workload, speed, and cost in the supply chains: procurement of raw materials, manufacturing, and shipping of goods. ISs, especially MRP and MRP II systems, facilitate production scheduling and material requirements planning, and shorten lead time between idea and product. Shipping ISs help speed up delivery and cut costs. RFID technology helps promote and operate supply chain management (SCM) systems. Radio frequency identification (RFID) tags carry product information that can be tracked and updated.

■ Customer relationship management (CRM) includes the entire cycle of relationships with customers, from marketing through sales to customer service. CRM ISs collect information about shoppers and customers and help target the most likely buyers of a product or service. Online customer service systems help customers help themselves via the Web 24 hours per day, 7 days per week, and save the company labor and telephone expenses. Salesforce automation allows traveling salespeople to spend more time with customers and less time in the office.

■ Human resource management systems expedite staff selection and record keeping. An increasing amount of recruiting is done via the Web. Managers often use evaluation software to help assess their subordinates' performance. Employees can use expert systems to choose health care and other benefits programs that best suit their situation.

■ Companies can link their SCM systems to monitor the status of orders at their own facilities but also at those of their business partners, usually their suppliers. Such cooperation can create further efficiencies, but it requires a high degree of trust between organizations.

■ Rather than use disparate ISs for business functions, many organizations opt to install a single system that encompasses all their business processes, or at least the major ones. They employ enterprise resource planning (ERP) systems to support their supply chain management and customer relationship management.

EATS2GO REVISITED

Eats2Go has grown in the last two years from a single pushcart to a business with many sites, different products, and more customers. The partners have noticed that their activities are becoming more specialized as the business grows and that they need information systems to support those activities. Help them sort through their systems.

What Would You Do?

1. Using the classifications in this chapter, identify the business functions within Eats2Go. Which information systems do Juan, Kendra, and Dave use now to streamline their operations? What other applications could they use?

2. Do you think that Eats2Go should invest in an ERP system at this time? Why or why not? If not, which types of information systems mentioned in this chapter would be appropriate short of an ERP system?

New Perspectives

1. A large snack-food manufacturer has noticed that Kendra's chip line is very successful. The manufacturer is now proposing that Eats2Go license its chip business—the partners would get a percentage of the profits from the expanded sales and the manufacturer would have a new healthful chip line to round out its snack-food product line. What information could the three entrepreneurs use to help them decide whether this opportunity would be a good idea? Suggest how they could obtain this information.

KEY TERMS

bill of material (BOM), 78
brainstorming, 78
cash management system (CMS), 74
computer-aided design (CAD), 75
computer-aided manufacturing (CAM), 75
customer relationship management (CRM), 71
economic order quantity (EOQ), 78
effectiveness, 70

efficiency, 70
electronic funds transfer (EFT) , 74
electronic product code (EPC), 81
enterprise resource planning (ERP), 95
just-in-time (JIT), 79
manufacturing resource planning (MRP II), 79
master production schedule (MPS), 79

material requirements planning (MRP), 78
productivity, 78
radio frequency identification (RFID), 81
rapid prototyping, 75
supply chain, 77
supply chain management (SCM), 77
targeted marketing, 84
time to market, 75

1. What is a supply chain? What is the purpose of supply chain management systems?

2. What is the purpose of cost accounting ISs?

3. What is the relationship between CAD and CAM systems?

4. What are the concerns in cash management, and how do cash management ISs help financial managers?

5. What is time to market? How have ISs affected time to market?

6. In brief, what is the purpose of customer relationship management systems?

7. What are the typical components of ERP systems?

8. Although technologically the full linking of the SCM systems of suppliers and buyers is feasible, many buyers are reluctant to do so. Why?

9. Why do the ERP installation and testing of systems require that experts be involved? Why does the implementation of so many ERP systems face severe challenges or totally fail?

10. What is EOQ? Which two problems do ISs that calculate EOQ help minimize?

11. What is JIT? How do MRP and MRP II systems help achieve JIT?

12. For the human resource managers of some organizations the entire Web is a database of job candidates. How so?

13. What information technologies play a crucial role in marketing?

14. Many sales reps have no offices, yet their productivity is great. Explain how that is possible.

15. What is RFID, and what role does it play in SCM?

16. In the supply chain, shipping software helps mainly in two ways. What are they?

1. You established a small shop that manufactures a single product that you sell by mail. You purchase raw materials from several vendors and employ five full-time employees. For which business functions would you certainly use software?

2. Which of the ISs you listed for Question 1 would you link to each other, and for what purpose?

3. Why is it so important to have a quick response of online investment ISs? Give two examples of how such systems are critical.

4. Some experts say that ISs have great potential in manufacturing. Explain why. (*Hint*: business process reengineering.)

5. Over the past decade, banks and investment firms have offered many services that would be impossible without ISs. Describe three such services and explain how IT makes them possible.

6. CAD systems replace older, manual tools in engineering, but they also contribute by maintaining all information in electronic form. How does this facilitate the work of draftspeople and engineers? How do such systems help the transition from engineering a product to manufacturing it?

7. ISs in both the manufacturing and service sectors often help to *optimize*. Give two examples of what they optimize.

8. The Web has significantly cut the cost of collecting data about shoppers and buyers. Explain how.

9. Sellers of consumer products argue that targeted marketing serves not only them but also their consumers. How so?

10. If you had to evaluate your own subordinates, would you prefer to evaluate them in written, open-ended form, or would you prefer to use employee evaluation software? Why?

11. As an employee, would you prefer that your supervisor evaluate you with the aid of employee evaluation software or without it? Why?

12. Try to remember the last time you gave someone your personal data. What was the reason for asking for the data?

13. Some consumer advocates argue that organizations should pay every individual whenever they sell data about him or her to another organization. (They suggest 5 or 10 cents per sale.) Do you agree? Why?

14. Examine the list of precautions suggested in "Ethical & Societal Issues" for ensuring minimum invasion of privacy when businesses use personal data. Which steps can be taken without, or with minimal added cost? Which steps would impose financial burdens on businesses? Why?

15. RFID tags are increasingly embedded in almost every type of good, from soda six-packs to clothing items. Consumer advocates fear that the technology might cause massive violation of privacy. Describe at least two ways in which this can happen. What controls or limitations would you impose on RFID tags and use to minimize the fears of invasion of privacy?

APPLYING CONCEPTS

1. Choose three distinct but related business functions (e.g., inventory control, purchasing, payroll, accounting, etc.). Write a short paper describing how interfacing the information systems of these three functions can improve an organization's performance.

2. Select a business process (possibly at a local firm) not mentioned in this chapter. Write an essay explaining how IS technology could make the process (1) more efficient and (2) more effective.

3. Write a three-page essay titled "Factory of the Future." Your factory of the future will not require anybody in the manufacturing organization to enter any data into information systems. All the necessary information will come from customers at one end and suppliers at the other end. There will also be no need to type in any data for payments and collections. Explain how all this will work.

HANDS-ON ACTIVITIES

Many companies use e-mail to advertise their products. Your company is trying to sell a new product and is advised to use e-mail. The profit on each unit sold is $200. Developing the attractive e-mail message, use of 2,750,000 e-mail addresses, and sending the message would cost $25,000. Experience shows that 5 percent of the initial recipients forward such messages to friends and family. Experience also shows that 2 percent of all recipients actually click the Web address included in the message and visit the commercial site. Of these visitors, 0.5 percent end up purchasing the advertised item.

Using Microsoft Excel or another spreadsheet, answer the following questions: (1) Would you generate a profit if you used this advertising opportunity? (2) Would you profit if you could e-mail only 1,000,000 people?

TEAM ACTIVITIES

1. Form a team and design an IS for a small business that sells manufactured parts to other businesses. The system must handle customer order processing, sales, salesperson commissions, billing, and accounts receivable. Prepare a report describing the system's different components and their points of interface. What files are necessary? How will the business use data in each file? If you have command of Microsoft Access, create the tables for the above objects, and populate each one with three to five records.

2. Assume that you and your teammates are about to start a Web-based business for sporting goods. You wish to e-mail information to potential customers. Determine the demographic characteristics of your target audience. Search the Web for companies that sell consumer data that can serve you. Prepare a report about three such companies: their names, services, and prices (if available).

1. Create a database with at least 5 records that could be used by a company such as Capital One Financial Corp.

2. Research systems shipping companies can use to track products throughout the shipping process. List at least two such systems and summarize how they work.

1. What practices used by Krispy Kreme might Eats2Go be able to adopt for their business?

2. Use PowerPoint or another presentation program to create a figure showing what you think the supply chain looks like for Krispy Kreme.

FROM IDEAS TO APPLICATION: REAL CASES

A Match Made in Heaven

This is the tale of how IT made a difference in the merger of two banks that could not be more different, enabling the new company to capitalize on the strengths of each. One bank, First Union Corp. of Charlotte, North Carolina, strove to shift labor onto its customers. Under an initiative called Future Bank, customers were greeted at the door and directed to ATMs or telephone kiosks. The kiosks were plugged into 10 regional call centers. Customers used them to open accounts, apply for loans, request money transfers, or stop payments. Banks rewarded employees when a customer purchased a new service to which the employees referred them. First Union used special software that tracked which employees earned which commission upon successful referral.

Wachovia, headquartered in Winston-Salem, North Carolina, had a different approach. At Wachovia, tellers spent much time with customers. They executed all service transactions, including account openings and inquiries. Loan officers, mortgage specialists, and investment bankers—not tellers or people answering over a telephone—sold these more profitable services. Management placed a heavy emphasis on customer service. They sent "shoppers" to branches to rate the quality of service, and branch managers and tellers were rewarded based on the ratings of these evaluators.

With its emphasis on sales, First Union generated $2 million of new consumer and small-business loans per branch per quarter from its 2,200 branches. Wachovia had only 700 branches and generated less than $500,000 in new loans per branch per quarter. However, generating business is only half the job; retaining customers is equally important. Wachovia, with its personal touch, excelled at keeping customers happy. Among the 20 largest U.S. banks, *Consumer Reports* ranked Wachovia fourth in customer satisfaction. First Union was ranked the lowest.

In April 2001 First Union purchased Wachovia for $13 billion in stock. Apparently, executives at both banks saw an opportunity to combine the great sales savvy of First Union with the high customer retention rate of Wachovia. Although Wachovia was the smaller party to the merger, the combined organization was named Wachovia to maintain the brand name of customer satisfaction. Now, the incentives systems of the banks would have to be restructured, so that employees were rewarded not only for gaining customers but also for ensuring they stay with the company.

An early task was to overhaul the system developed at First Union to reward tellers for successfully referring clients to investment advisers. The incentive and compensation programs used a 19-year-old spreadsheet program to record referrals and calculate commissions and bonuses. The program was difficult to modify, and it was impossible to use for modeling. Modeling would allow "if-then" analysis that shows which combination of incentives works best overall. That meant incentive programs could not be changed to meet competitive threats or executive orders. The system was also prone to errors because it relied on manual entry. It was estimated that overcharges due to manual errors cost First Union nearly $7.5 million per year. One manager equated the system to a large old calculator. It was clear that the system had to be tied directly to the system that recorded new transactions, such as opening a new account, or purchase of certificates of deposit.

The bank considered applications from Oracle and SAP, as well as from companies that specialize in enterprise incentive management (EIM) applications, such as Synygy, Incentive Systems, and Callidus Software. The bank selected Callidus' TrueComp system, mainly for its successful track record in the banking and insurance industries. TrueComp enabled the new Wachovia to automate and effectively manage its compensation programs. The system tracks 31 different incentive plans, including customer satisfaction, investment referrals, loan referrals, and credit-card sign-ups, and credits new business to more than 25,000 eligible employees. It is integrated into a bank sales application, SOLD. Whenever a new product is sold or a new account is opened, the details, including the name of the employee entitled to a reward, are recorded in TrueComp. Having the applications integrated eliminates most manual errors, a saving that alone would justify the investment in the new software. In addition to accuracy, TrueComp allows flexible modeling. Analyzing past incentive schemes and their results, executives can determine the best way to reach business goals.

For example, if the bank stops giving tellers incentives for referrals to investment advisers, will generation of new business suffer? Such analysis can tell executives whether they are spending more money on incentives than they are gaining from the newly generated business. Modeling can also answer questions such as what might happen if the bank cancels incentives for referrals, but raises incentives based on teller or branch customer satisfaction ratings. The great benefit of integrating the applications into one system is that the bank can more accurately control and report costs and better align incentive programs with company goals.

Since 2001, the volume of new loans per branch has grown from a quarterly average of $499,000 to $2.3 million. This is a larger figure than First Union's volume before the merger: $2 million per branch. And, the emphasis on customer service has been retained: on a seven-point scale, Wachovia's customer satisfaction score, as measured by Gallup surveys, rose from 5.59 in 1999 to 6.57 in the third quarter of 2004.

Source: Duvall, M., "Wachovia: Best Incentives," *Baseline* (www.baseline.com), January 13, 2005; LeFevre, J., "Callidus Software Helps Wachovia to Optimize Its Incentive Compensation," Callidus Press Release, November 16, 2004.

Thinking About the Case

1. This case demonstrates how important it is to link two information systems that use the same information for two different purposes. What are those two systems?

2. What information does the bank have now that it did not have before the systems were linked?

3. More than one party is eventually compensated when an employee successfully refers a customer to an investment consultant in the bank. List all the parties and explain how the new system helps ensure proper calculation and recording.

Who Are Our Employees?

Employees are the most important resource of any organization, and as such, must be managed well. Executives at Canada Post knew that, and also realized that they did not have the proper tools to manage human resources effectively.

Canada Post, the national postal service, is Canada's seventh largest employer, with 70,000 employees. As in the United States, it is facing increasing competition from private carriers such as FedEx and UPS. Competition has eroded profits. It was clear that competitors had much better information systems than Canada Post. Its own system was not integrated or flexible enough to cope with a fast-changing industry. Jamie Esler, a general manager in Canada Post's human resource department, admitted growth rates were slowing down.

The HR department owned "legacy" ISs that could not communicate with each other. Managers found the outdated ISs difficult to use. To ease difficulties, the company outsourced some HR management (HRM) functions to other companies. However, this did not help keep the company competitive. Scheduling

payroll was a constant challenge. So were other tasks, such as selecting employees with certain qualifications for certain positions. Executives wanted to be able to answer questions such as: How much does employee turnover cost us annually? How can we make a better use of employee skills to increase efficiencies? They could not answer such questions. They realized they had to take drastic measures. The HR ISs were so inefficient that investment in a new integrated HR software package would certainly pay for itself within a short period of time.

Management approached SAP, a leading vendor of enterprise applications. SAP was to implement a new HRM system. One important component of the new system would be the human capital management (HCM) system. That was several years ago. HRM looks completely different now.

Now, managers at Canada Post's HR department track employee skills, training priorities, workforce scheduling, and a long list of other employee-related issues. The company stopped its contracts with vendors to whom it had outsourced HRM function, and by so doing saved millions of dollars annually. All HRM functions are integrated through the new system: payroll, training, employee evaluation, promotion, and others.

Canada Post is using HCM as a strategic tool to build stronger teams. Employees can take online remote training sessions. Their scores are recorded, and when they complete courses, their new skills are automatically recorded in the HCM database. When an HR manager looks for certain skills for a new position, it takes only seconds to "fish" the records of qualified employees. In the long run, executives hope the integrated system can help build a cadre of new leaders for the company by staffing according to desired technical and leadership skill as they are reflected in the HCM system.

The integrated system relies on a single repository of employee information to help managers analyze human resources needs. HCM supports workforce planning (forecasting growth or downsizing), acquisition (recruitment and procurement of part-time or temporary help), management (training, performance management, and succession planning), and optimization (putting the right people in the right jobs at the right time). This helps managers at Canada Post make intelligent decisions about employees and what they should be doing both in the near and farther future.

The new system helps not only managers but also employees. Through an intranet (an organization's internal communication network using Web technologies), employees can access the company's HR portal. They can view their own data, such as their medical benefits, vacation time, e-learning opportunities, and recent performance reviews. This cuts HRM costs because employees can do much by serving themselves rather than turning to the HR department for help. It also increases an important intangible benefit: employee satisfaction.

Thinking About the Case

1. Give three examples of HRM activities that require access to an employee record. How could an organization benefit from integrating these activities so they can be done using a single IS?

2. The new system at Canada Post has additional benefits to better managing people. What are they?

3. The HCM system helps plan human resources. Give an example of how you, as an HR executive, would use the system for HR planning at a manufacturing plant.

Source: D'Agostino, D., "Human Interest," *CIO Insight*, January 5, 2005; www.canadapost.ca, 2005.

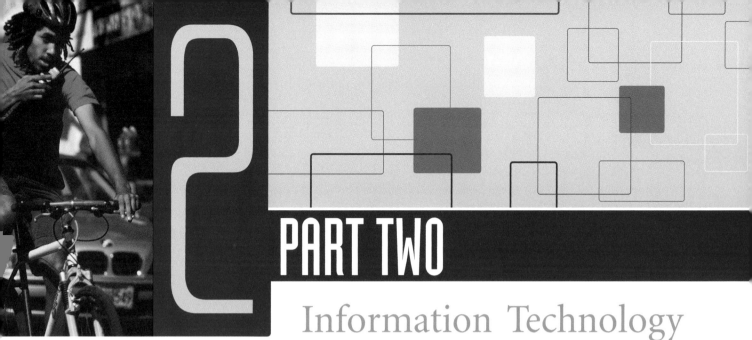

© Getty Images

CASE II: QUICKBIZ MESSENGERS

Andrew Langston looked out of his office window and smiled when he saw another of his bike messengers pedal in from a delivery. Had it really been a decade since he began QuickBiz Messengers? He'd come a long way from his early days in the business, when he got a phone call, hopped on his bike, and made the deliveries himself.

During college, Andrew competed in the cycling club's races at his Eastern university. A friend told him that he worked part time for the local bicycle delivery service to keep in shape, so Andrew decided to sign up, too. He could use a little extra cash. That was how he'd learned the ropes of the messenger delivery business. His employer had been operating for a long time in the big city's central business district, and working there gave Andrew a taste of a different career option. After graduation, Andrew had moved back to Seattle, his hometown, and started QuickBiz. It was the best way he could think to combine his love of cycling with the need to earn a living. Besides, at the time, Seattle had only a handful of small messenger services.

It was slow going at first. With such a small business and few funds, he had to watch every penny. But timing had helped him survive. With the business boom in the 1990s, the pace of business transactions skyrocketed. Firms of all sizes needed additional services to carry out their day-to-day transactions, so deliveries needed to increase, too. "Instant service" became the watchwords of business in the Information Age. Meanwhile, traffic on Seattle's streets had grown heavier and heavier. Delays throughout the metropolitan area became a frustrating fact of life. Andrew found he could zip by the cars in downtown traffic as if they were parked. He loved pumping his way up the hills and coasting down to deliver his packages safe and sound—and always on time. He was proud that he'd built his business on his reputation for reliability. Now, here he was, president of a company with nearly 90 employees making deliveries by both bicycle and car. He'd met each challenge with the determination he'd had when he was racing. And as with his bicycle, he tried to keep his business running smoothly, although it didn't always run the way a well-oiled machine should.

Bumps in the Road

There was the time that a quickly opened door of a parked car had flattened one of his first messengers and landed him in the emergency room. With no way to communicate except a pager, Andrew didn't know where his messenger was until he regained consciousness and had the nurses call him. Andrew spent the afternoon worrying, calling local police stations, and trying to placate his customer about her missing delivery. Also, he remembered the time high winds had whipped up huge waves, which washed over the I-90 floating bridge. No traffic— including his car messengers—could get through for a day. QuickBiz had no system for traffic alerts then, so some messengers were stranded in the backup. Cellular phones and e-mailed delivery notices had certainly helped him maintain better contact in the field. Now if a messenger didn't arrive on time, he knew it sooner and could check the problem out directly.

Early Expansion and Growth

QuickBiz had expanded rapidly over its first few years as demand grew for its services. Businesses found it cheaper to use a delivery service than to waste their own employees' time running across town to make deliveries. The price for the service was another advantage—customers could get same-day delivery at prices much lower than the large package delivery services could offer. So, QuickBiz definitely had a niche to fill in Seattle's business community.

As QuickBiz grew, Andrew gradually added staff to his payroll—both messengers and dispatchers—to handle repeat customers and routine route deliveries. The company served a variety of businesses: law firms needing contracts signed or papers filed, architects sending plans to their clients, medical and pharmaceutical suppliers who needed rush deliveries, public relations firms sending their copy to poster and sign suppliers, and other businesses needing quick deliveries to satellite offices, suppliers, or clients.

Andrew set up routes within the main business district to handle his regular customers' needs. He also accepted requests for special deliveries from drop-off or call-in business. Standard delivery was 2-hour service, with premium rates for faster service. If a business only needed same-day service, then it could opt for the economy rate. QuickBiz made deliveries year-round, in any kind of weather, which in Seattle usually meant rain or occasional snow. Regular service operated Monday through Friday, from 7 a.m. to 7 p.m. During the high-technology boom, QuickBiz also added premium service delivery on Saturdays.

Moving Beyond Bikes

After a few years of building QuickBiz's clientele, Andrew noticed that revenues began to plateau. His competitors were offering the same type of service, and there was only so much business to go around. He needed to think of some way to separate his business from the pack—and soon.

In looking over the customer feedback his messengers entered into their report forms, Andrew saw patterns emerging. Messengers said several of his customers that had satellite offices outside downtown and in nearby towns in the Puget Sound area had requested expanded routes. He also had repeated inquiries to serve several art galleries in the area. Handling fragile art glass and other one-of-a-kind, irreplaceable items definitely called for a safer delivery method than bicycles. So, Andrew had investigated the feasibility of adding car and truck deliveries to his business and decided to make the move.

Maintaining a fleet and drivers took the business to an entirely new level, but it also allowed QuickBiz to deliver a wider and more profitable range of services—deliveries no longer had to fit in a backpack or bike basket. Ultimately, adding automobile service allowed QuickBiz to double its size. It now made about 700 deliveries per day and generated revenue of roughly $1.5 million annually.

With the addition of auto service, Andrew needed to develop new pricing scales and schedules. He used his financial information system to calculate all the costs that went into a delivery—such as car and truck purchases and maintenance, fuel costs, and driver salaries. Then he added a profit margin. Next, he used a mapping system to compute delivery route mileage based on the zip codes of sending and receiving parties. To cover the new territories, he added even more employees, especially to the central office staff to handle customer orders and other business functions. Finally, he set special rates for "white glove" service for the galleries and medical centers.

Customers Come First

Still, even with the expansion, the key to QuickBiz's success remained its service quality. Andrew insisted each of his employees provide the same on-time deliveries and courteous service that he had when he biked the routes himself. Messengers were on the front lines, and they represented the company to customers, so their attitudes and hard work were critical to QuickBiz. Over the years, he'd had some run-ins with messengers over slack work habits, and a few had quit or just didn't work out and were let go. Andrew had documented problems in employees' computerized personnel files when necessary. But overall, he considered his employees part of an extended family and valued their loyalty. Ongoing training for messengers and dispatchers was important to maintain service levels. Above all, he wanted all his employees to enjoy the work they did.

Increasing Reliance on Information Systems

Throughout his expansions, Andrew had turned to information systems to increase his efficiency and handle growing amounts of data. Information technology had helped him in so many areas:

- Automating payroll and accounting services.
- Streamlining customer paperwork.
- Tracking equipment maintenance and supplies.
- Routing deliveries.
- Maintaining customer and messenger contact.

- Providing customized services on the Web.
- Handling customer and employee database files.

In fact, for a business that many considered low-tech, QuickBiz has relied on very high-tech computer hardware and software.

Handheld computers had rescued quite a few new messengers who became lost in Seattle's maze of streets. They'd found their way by bringing maps up on their handheld's screen. So, information technology was certainly critical to his employees. A couple of years ago the company even added a Web site offering online ordering to handle increased customer demands. Customers were pleased with the new option. For his own work, there were the useful databases—without which Andrew wouldn't know who his customers were or what their needs were. He'd also lose track of his employees and their productivity. The company had certainly followed the digital wave. Looking back, he knew he wouldn't be able to sustain his business without these technologies.

Back to Business

Andrew's thoughts were interrupted by Leslie Chen, his administrative assistant, who was knocking at the door.

"Andrew? Sorry to bother you. Time for our meeting with the tire supplier. They want to discuss our upcoming needs for the year."

"Maybe we can get a volume price break on our fleet this year," noted Andrew. "We added two new trucks, you know." He had used the same tire supplier since the addition of the firm's first motor vehicle. His business relationship was strong and long lasting. He'd heard that the supplier had offered some quantity price breaks to other businesses, so he was going to pull the entire purchasing history of the supplier and use the information to squeeze out better discounts this year. Every dollar saved was a dollar he could put to use somewhere else.

While the processing speed of mainframes is often not higher than that of the fastest PCs, they often have multiple processors and their memories are significantly larger, measured in terabytes. By some estimates, 40–50 percent of the world's business data reside on mainframes.

Midrange Computers

Midrange computers are smaller than mainframes and less powerful. They are usually used as a shared resource, serving hundreds of users that connect to them from personal computers. Therefore, they act as servers, computers used to communicate to other computers, both through the Internet and locally within organizations. The IBM AS/400, HP 9000, and HP Alpha families of computers are the best-known midrange computers. Like mainframe computers, midrange computers often use multiple processors.

Microcomputers

Microcomputers is the collective name for all personal computers (PCs), notebook computers, and handheld computers. More powerful microcomputers are sometimes called **workstations**. Workstations are typically used for computer-aided design (CAD), computer-aided manufacturing (CAM), complex simulation, and scientific applications. As the performance of PCs steadily improves, computers that in the past were classified as midrange computers are now marketed as PC servers, and the lines between computer categories continue to blur.

The power of microcomputers in terms of speed and memory capacity doubles about every two years. Most PCs now sold to individuals and businesses cost less than $1,000. However, a growing number of microcomputers are not PCs, but notebooks, handheld, and tablet computers. Many cell phones now also serve as handheld computers. Some global positioning system (GPS) devices double as navigation tools and handheld computers. We are witnessing the merging of several technologies into a single device, mostly into mobile devices.

Handheld computers are popular devices for people who spend much time out of the office.

© Marc Romanelli/Getty Images

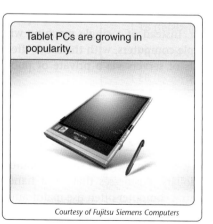

Tablet PCs are growing in popularity.

Courtesy of Fujitsu Siemens Computers

Computers on the Go: Notebook, Handheld, and Tablet Computers

In today's mobile society, computers are increasingly used outside the office. Notebook or handheld computers are used to record and retrieve data for people on the go. The **notebook computer** (also called a laptop) is a compact, light, personal computer powered by a rechargeable battery. They can operate for up to eight hours without recharging their batteries. Many notebooks have accessories that enable the user to communicate with other computers and even send and receive faxes. All new notebook computers are constructed with internal circuitry that enables them to connect to networks and the Internet without wires or cables. (Wireless technology is covered in Chapter 6.) So far, notebooks have trailed PCs in terms of speed, memory, and hard disk capacity.

One highly popular class of computing machinery is the handheld computer, also known as the **personal digital assistant (PDA)**. Handheld computers appeared on the market in the early 1990s but became popular only toward the end of the decade. These devices are small enough to fit in the palm of your hand, and typically a **stylus** (a penlike pointing and drawing device) is used to enter data through a touch screen, although some handhelds also have a small keyboard or can plug into a folding portable keyboard. With a special device called a projection keyboard, a virtual keyboard is projected on a surface and lets the users "type" as if they used a full-size keyboard. A special sensor detects the location of each key and its "depression" by the user. A growing number of PDAs are merged with mobile phones.

Another recent development in computers is the **tablet computer**, often called a tablet PC. It is a full-power PC in the form of a thick writing tablet. It looks like a notebook computer without a keyboard, although it can be connected to a keyboard and a mouse. Instead of a mouse, the user uses a stylus. The user can handwrite text, which automatically turns into typed text (as with some of the smaller handheld computers). The stylus is also used to click icons and select items from menus. The tablet PC is enthusiastically received among salespeople and hospital staffs. Forms now can be filled out directly on screen, eliminating hours of paperwork for sales representatives and nurses.

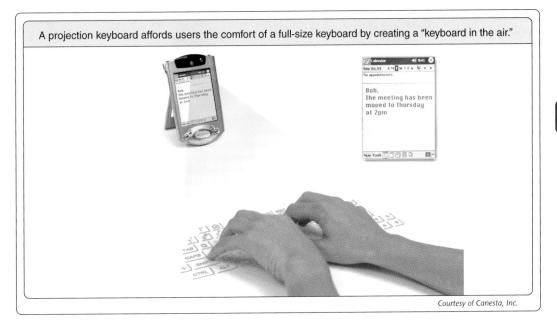

A projection keyboard affords users the comfort of a full-size keyboard by creating a "keyboard in the air."

Courtesy of Canesta, Inc.

Converging Technologies

In recent years there has been a trend of **technology convergence**, building several technologies into a single piece of hardware. This is true especially in handheld units. A unit might be called a cell phone, or a digital camera, but it is also a computer and several other things. Consider the MM-A800, manufactured by Samsung. It is a cell phone and a digital camera. It is also a television set, because it can play television shows. It is a digital sound recorder and has a speech recognition mechanism and software that can transcribe what you speak to it. It also can scan and store business cards, and it plays MP3 music files. Another handheld product, iQue3600 from Garmin, is a PDA, a GPS device with speech directions, and MP3 player. In homes, personal computers can be turned into entertainment centers that transmit sound and television broadcast to other computers or to sound systems and TV sets. Expect to see a growing convergence of digital technologies both in mobile units and in home devices.

A PEEK INSIDE THE COMPUTER

 It is not necessary to look under a car's hood to drive it, but it is important to know enough about how a car is built to know which car to buy. Similarly, professionals must know enough about the major components of a computer to understand what computing power and capabilities they buy or recommend for buying. The following discussion introduces the computer's most common parts and peripheral equipment and describes in some detail how these devices work.

The Central Processing Unit

The CPU is the computer's brain, where all processing takes place. The CPU consists of two units: the **control unit** and the **arithmetic logic unit (ALU)**. These units store and process data. The CPU is a silicon chip with multiple circuits. It carries signals that execute all processing within a computer. Because the chip is so small, it is often called a **microprocessor**, or simply a processor. Modern processors, such as the Intel Pentium 4, are capable of performing more than one task at a time (multitasking). For example, they can carry out a calculation in a spreadsheet and process a graphical design simultaneously. In this respect, a CPU actually acts as a dual processor, and if it is capable of running more than two processes at a time, it functions like a multiprocessor. Processing more than one program, or processing several parts of a program, at the same time is often called **multithreading**, whereby each process is a thread.

POINT OF INTEREST

Chip Ahoy

A popular microprocessor used in many PCs is the Pentium 4, developed by Intel Corp. It has 125 million transistors and a maximum clock rate of 3.8 GHz. Engineers from IBM, Sony, and Toshiba developed a microprocessor called Cell, which has 234 million transistors and a clock rate greater than 4 GHz. Cell compresses several computing engines, called cores, with each core acting like an individual CPU. While Pentium 4 can carry out two simultaneous processes, Cell can carry out eight. For home computers this means that the user can play a video game, watch television, and operate a spreadsheet or word processor literally at the same time.

Source: MSNBC News (www.msnbc.msn.com), February 7, 2005.

Microprocessors

Microprocessors are made of silicon embedded with transistors. A transistor is a semiconductor, a component that can serve as either a conductor or an insulator, depending on the voltage of electricity that tries to flow through it. This property is excellent for computer communications, because it provides a means to represent binary code's two states: a 1 (voltage conducted) or a 0 (voltage not conducted). Thus, transistors can sense binary signals that are actually encoded instructions telling the computer to conduct different operations.

Engineers continue to install more and more transistors on microsprocessors.

Courtesy of Intel Corporation

The greater the number of transistors that can be embedded in the chip—which means the greater the number of circuits—the more powerful the microprocessor. Current processors can contain several hundred million circuits. Current technology enables chip makers to print circuits on silicon that is 0.1 micron thick, one thousand times thinner than a human hair. New processor-making technologies let engineers increase the processing speed of computers while enabling computers to use less energy and give off less heat.

The Machine Cycle

When a program starts running in a computer, the CPU performs a routine sequence, illustrated in Figure 4.3 for a simple arithmetic function. First, the control unit, one of the two parts of the CPU, fetches an instruction from a program in primary memory and decodes it, that is, interprets what should be done. The control unit transmits this code to the other part of the CPU, the arithmetic logic unit (ALU), which executes the instruction. Usually, the operation's result is needed for further operations. Therefore, the control unit takes the result and stores it in primary memory. The control unit then fetches the next instruction, decodes it, and puts it in the ALU, which executes the instruction. The control unit stores the result in primary memory, and so on, until the entire program is executed, or something happens that stops the cycle. Anything that stops the cycle is called an interrupt. It might be an instruction in the program itself, a power failure, or any other event that stops the CPU.

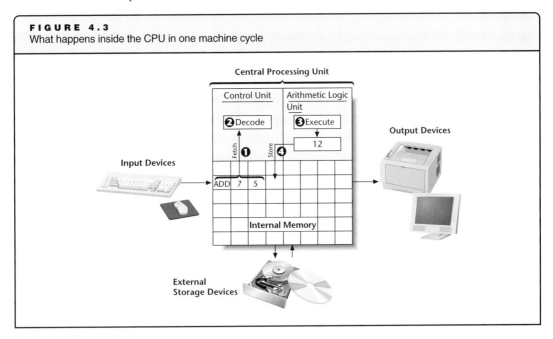

FIGURE 4.3
What happens inside the CPU in one machine cycle

As you can see, the CPU performs four functions in every cycle: fetch, decode, execute, and store. Each cycle is called a **machine cycle**. CPUs can perform billions of machine cycles per second. The rate of repetitive cycles is called frequency, or **clock rate**. One cycle per second is 1 hertz. Computer frequencies are measured in megahertz (MHz, millions of hertz), or gigahertz (GHz, billions of hertz). During the time it takes your eye to blink (about 0.2 second), a computer can execute hundreds of millions of instructions. Therefore, timing of computer operations is measured in very small fractions of a second (see Figure 4.4).

FIGURE 4.4
Computer time

1 millisecond = 1/1,000 (0.001) second

1 microsecond = 1/1,000,000 (0.000001) second

1 nanosecond = 1/1,000,000,000 (0.000000001) second

1 picosecond = 1/1,000,000,000,000 (0.000000000001) second

The sequence of CPU operations must be paced so that different tasks do not collide. To this end, the control unit uses special circuitry called a **system clock**, which synchronizes all tasks. The system clock is programmed to run operations at the maximum rate allowable.

The Word
The **data word** (or "word" for short) is the maximum number of bits that the control unit can fetch from primary memory in one machine cycle. The word's size is determined by the size of the CPU circuitry that holds information for processing. Obviously, the larger the word, the more instructions or data can be retrieved per second. Therefore, all other things being equal, the larger the word, the faster the computer. Current microcomputers have words of 32 and 64 bits.

The Arithmetic Logic Unit Operations
The ALU is the part of the CPU where all arithmetic and logic operations take place. Arithmetic operations include addition, subtraction, multiplication, division, exponentiation, logarithmic calculations, trigonometric computations, and other complex mathematical tasks. Logic operations

compare numbers and strings of characters. For example, comparisons such as greater than, less than, and equal to are logic operations. The ALU also compares character strings that are not quantitative. For example, when you try to find a word in the text of a word-processing document, the ALU compares all words in the text to that specific word until it finds an identical word.

Why You Should...

Understand Some Technical Details

Business majors and other non-IT professionals often ask: "Why do I have to study computer hardware?" The answer is threefold. You must know enough about hardware to be able to communicate your needs to IT professionals who can provide you with the devices you need for your work; if you are in a position to choose among various options and make a decision on certain hardware pieces, you must be sufficiently knowledgeable about hardware to make informed decisions; and since you are or will be a professional, you will have to purchase hardware for your personal use. Keeping abreast of development in hardware will make you an informed consumer. You will be able to optimize your purchases.

In addition, knowledge of new technologies might give you ideas about how to develop new products and services to improve your organization's competitive position. Throughout history, necessity has been the mother of invention, but this is not so with information technology. Time and again inventions have been available long before business puts them to use. Professionals who realize that a certain development can give their companies an advantage will be rewarded for their vision.

Computer Power

What makes one computer more powerful than another? There are two major factors to consider: processing speed and memory capacity. A computer's speed is determined mainly by (1) the CPU clock rate (measured in MHz or GHz), and (2) the amount of information the CPU can process per cycle (determined by the size of the data word and the capacity of internal communication lines, referred to as *buses*).

All other things being equal, the greater the clock rate, the faster the machine, because it can fetch, decode, execute, and store more instructions per second. Also, all other things being equal, the larger the data word, the faster the computer. A larger word means that in each trip to the primary memory, the control unit can retrieve more bits to process. Therefore, the CPU can execute a program faster.

You might have seen advertisements promoting a "64-bit computer." This means the data word's capacity is 64 bits. You must be cautious with regard to word size. A larger word does not always mean a faster computer, because the speed at which the bits move between the CPU and other components depends on the capacity of internal communication lines. The system bus—also called simply the **bus**—which is the electronic lines or traces used for communication inside the computer, might have a width of only 32 bits, while the word might contain 64 bits. The number of bits is also referred to as the width of the bus.

Buses have their own clock rate. The bus that computer makers usually mention in ads is the front side bus, which is the bus connecting the CPU to the memory. A typical front side bus clock rate is 800 MHz. The combination of bus width and clock rate determines throughput. **Throughput** is the number of bits per second that the bus can accommodate. Only considering both factors, CPU clock rate (so many GHz) and bus throughput, enables you to compare properly the speeds of different computers.

Computer speed is also measured in **MIPS**, millions of instructions per second, which is an inaccurate measure, because instructions have various levels of complexity. However, computer speed expressed in MIPS is often used to indicate overall processing speed because all factors that determine speed are considered: clock rate, data word size, and bus throughput, as well as other speed factors that we do not discuss here. Computer speeds expressed in MIPS have been used to indicate the dramatic reduction in the cost of computing; observers often divide the MIPS by the cost of a computer and marvel how the cost of computer power has decreased dramatically, from MIPS per dollar to MIPS per cent. In recent years, computer makers have also used the term "transactions per minute" (TPM), referring mainly to database transactions, but this ratio, too, is not an absolute measurement.

INPUT DEVICES

Computers must receive input to produce desired output. Input devices include all machines and other apparatuses used to enter instructions and data into the computer. Popular input devices include the keyboard, mouse, trackball, microphone, and various types of scanners. The most common input device is the keyboard.

Keyboard

The keyboard contains keys that users press to enter data and instructions into primary memory and instruct programs to run. All keyboards include the basic letters of the alphabet, numbers, and punctuation marks, plus several function keys numbered F1, F2, and so on, that can be activated to execute preprogrammed functions, such as copying a highlighted sentence in a text file created with a word processor. With the growing use of the Web and use of computers to play music and video clips, keyboard manufacturers have added keys that facilitate Web browser commands such as Back and Forward, and music keys such as Volume, and Play/Pause. On some keyboards you can bring up your e-mail application by pressing the Mail key or the calculator by pressing the Calculator key.

QWERTY and Dvorak Keyboards
The standard keyboard layout is called QWERTY, an acronym based on the top row of letter keys from left to right. Interestingly, the QWERTY keyboard was originally designed to slow down typing, because early mechanical typewriters jammed when users typed too fast. Today's electrical devices make this layout counterproductive. Other keyboard designs facilitate faster typing. On the Dvorak keyboard, the most frequently used keys are in the home, or central, row. Using this keyboard can increase typing speed by 95 percent. Some operating systems, such as Windows, let users map QWERTY keys into a Dvorak layout. Most computer users are reluctant to retrain themselves for the Dvorak map.

Many people prefer to use ergonomic keyboards.

Courtesy of Microsoft Corporation

Ergonomic Keyboards
One of the most prevalent computer-related work injuries is carpal tunnel syndrome, the pain or numbness caused by holding the forearms in an unnatural position for long periods. The repetitive motion of typing exacerbates this problem, causing repetitive-stress injuries (RSIs). In response, ergonomic keyboards are gaining popularity. **Ergonomics** is the study of the comfort and safety of human beings in their working environment. Ergonomic keyboards are split in the middle, and the two parts are twisted outward to better fit the natural position of the forearms.

Mouse, Trackball, and Trackpad

A **mouse** is an input device that controls an on-screen pointer to facilitate the point-and-click approach to executing different operations. It is most commonly used with a keyboard, although some programs use it exclusively. Mice have one to five buttons that let the user place the pointer anywhere on the screen, highlight portions of the screen, and select items from a menu.

When the user moves the mouse on the surface of a desk or a pad, the computer detects the movements, translates them into digital coordinates on the screen, and moves the pointer to imitate the mouse's movement. The buttons are used for clicking, locking, and dragging displayed information. A **trackball** is similar to a mouse, but the ball moves within the device,

Using wireless devices is especially convenient in computer-based presentations.

Courtesy of InFocus

rather than over a surface. With a **trackpad**, a user controls the cursor by moving his or her finger along a touch-sensitive pad. Many notebook computers have built-in trackpads. Many mice and trackballs have a built-in wheel that scrolls pages displayed on the monitor.

Mice, trackballs, and keyboards are also available as wireless units that use infrared or radio technology. These units give users more flexibility, especially in software-based presentations, in which the presenter may move around with the mouse in his or her palm.

Touch Screen

Sometimes a single device, such as a **touch screen**, may serve both as an input and output device. A touch screen lets the computer user choose operations by touching the options on the computer screen. Some common public applications use touch screens to provide advice to tourists, select lottery numbers, and ring in grocery items at self-serve supermarket checkouts. Because a keyboard is impractical for handheld computers, the screen serves as both a display and input device. The user enters commands and data by touching a stylus on icons and menu items. With other touch screens, especially GPS units, you can execute commands by touching the screen with your fingers.

Source Data Input Devices

In some businesses, the speed of data entry is a top priority. These businesses use machine reading devices, such as bar-code scanners, known as **source data input devices**. They copy data directly from the source, such as a bar code or magnetic ink characters, without human intervention. They can also record data directly from other sources, including checks and credit cards. Source data input technologies are widely used in banking, credit-card processing, and shipping.

Source Data Technology
Mark-recognition devices are essential to successful source data entry. Special devices use *optical mark recognition* to detect the positions of marks on source documents, such as standardized test response forms. *Optical bar recognition* senses data encoded in the series of thick and thin black bars in bar codes.

Another less accurate technology used for source data entry is *optical character recognition* (*OCR*). Unlike optical mark recognition, OCR technology is often used to try to interpret handwritten and printed texts not originally designed for source data entry. A special scanner scans the page and translates each character into a digitized representation. A special program then tries to correlate the images with characters and stores interpreted text for further processing. Postal services around the world have experimented with OCR to replace human eyes and hands in the tedious job of mail sorting.

Note that OCR is not optical mark sensing. In optical mark sensing, the scanner senses a mark's *position*, not what the mark actually is. The mark's position determines the input. Because the mark's position rather than its shape determines the input data, mark sensing is far more accurate than OCR.

OCR has recently been integrated into mobile devices. For example, Samsung sells a cellular phone that can help save time entering information into the phone's address book. When you use the phone's digital camera to photograph a business card, the built-in character recognition software captures the information from the picture and enters it into the address book.

Banking

In the United States, commercial banks and the Federal Reserve Bank process about 200 million checks daily. Entering check data manually would make the process extremely expensive and slow. The bank identification number, account number, and check number are printed in special magnetic ink at the bottom of each check, as shown in Figure 4.5. A special device called a magnetic-ink reader uses **magnetic-ink character recognition** (**MICR**, pronounced MIKE-er) to detect these numbers. A person at the bank enters the amount of the check, also in magnetic ink. The bank then records its check deposits by placing a large number of checks in a MICR device, which records check amounts and accounts from which the money is drawn.

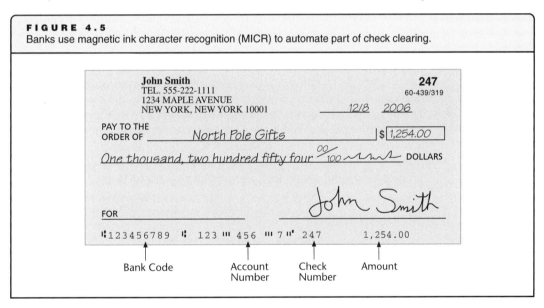

FIGURE 4.5
Banks use magnetic ink character recognition (MICR) to automate part of check clearing.

Credit Cards

Credit cards, too, facilitate source data entry. Card number and holder information are coded on the magnetic strip on the card's back. When you charge a purchase with your credit card, the card is passed through the reader at the point of sale (POS) to record the account number and your name and address. The total amount charged is either keyed manually or recorded automatically from the cash register (often from a bar code on the item purchased).

Shipping and Inventory Control

You might have noticed that every package you receive through shipping companies such as UPS and FedEx has a bar code on it. Bar codes use the optical bar recognition techniques described earlier to represent information for both inventory control and shipment tracking. Before the package leaves the shipping facility it is scanned, and the information is channeled into a computer that stores information such as the recipient's name and address. Whenever the item reaches a station, the bar code is scanned again. That information is combined with the identification information of the station. So, anyone with access to the shipping company's database can see exactly where the item has been and when, right up to the point of delivery. You can track an item by logging on to the shipping company's Web site and entering the item's tracking number. Since quick delivery is essential, source data input is extremely important in the shipping industry, because it is highly accurate and saves much labor and time. As discussed in Chapter 3, in time bar codes will be replaced with RFID tags for both shipping and inventory control.

Imaging

A growing number of organizations are **imaging**, or image processing, their documents. Doing so allows not only the storage of enormous amounts of data in less space than paper but also much more efficient retrieval and filing. By scanning and storing images, many companies have already reduced millions of paper documents to digitized pictures. They use the technology to store shipping documents, insurance policies and claims, personnel files, checks, and many other document types. The images are stored in large databases from which they can be retrieved and displayed on computer monitors. This technology is particularly useful when documents include signatures and graphics.

Once scanned, the original document can be destroyed because an exact copy can be generated on demand. Since it is in electronic form, it can be indexed. Indexing enables you to search a document by keywords and numbers. This reduces the average time of searching a document from several hours to about 5 seconds. In the United States, checking account holders receive one or two sheets of imaged canceled checks from their banks instead of a stack of their original checks. Customers who do their banking online can retrieve these images at any time. This system saves banks millions of dollars in paper, space, and handling costs. The images are often stored on DVDs. Because imaging reduces the amount of paper in organizations, some of the most enthusiastic adopters of imaging are companies in paper-intensive fields: law, retail, insurance, banking, health care, and shipping.

Imaging technologies continue to progress. American Express, a financial services group with assets worth $232 billion, makes extensive use of imaging. For some years the group imaged documents at a rate of 25 pages per minute. Adopting new machines and software from the British company Captiva, the group now images about at a rate of 190 pages per minute. The indexing process was reduced from 45 seconds per document to 12 seconds per document. This allowed American Express to record 3,000 client folders per hour. The number of employees involved in imaging was reduced from 95 to 45, and at an average salary of $30,000 per year, the immediate savings in the first year was about $1.5 million.

Speech Recognition

In some work environments, using manual input devices is either impossible or inconvenient. In other situations, such as customer service, using a computer to respond automatically to spoken customer queries can save labor costs. Instructing machines by speech can help in these instances. Speech recognition is fast becoming a staple of business. **Speech recognition**—also called voice recognition—is the process of translating human speech into computer-readable data and instructions. Although speech recognition systems vary in sophistication, all receive voice input from a microphone and process it with software.

Among the most advanced commercial speech recognition application is ViaVoice from IBM. The Mac OS and Windows XP operating systems include a voice recognition feature. The customer service departments of many companies use voice recognition of simple commands for telephone callers, who can utter answers to questions and receive recorded responses.

Some observers think speech-operated computers might increase already high noise levels in offices and add distraction. Imagine an office where everyone who currently types in their cubicles suddenly talked to computers. Also, speech recognition could become the source of pranks; people walking by could shout commands to other workers' computers.

Computers May Be Hazardous to Your Health

According to the U.S. National Institute of Occupational Safety and Health (NIOSH), about 75 million Americans—more than half the workforce—have jobs that require them to sit in front of a computer for many hours daily. An increasing number of studies show that working with computers threatens workers with a variety of hazards. These risks include repetitive-stress injuries (RSIs) due to long periods of repeated motions. According to the U.S. Bureau of Labor Statistics, RSIs cost American businesses an estimated $33 billion annually in workers' compensation claims. The U.S. Department of Labor estimates that about two-thirds of the reported injuries are due to working with computers. As work with computers has grown, RSIs have grown, too, to the extent that some scientists call these injuries an epidemic.

The most common computer-related type of RSI is carpal tunnel syndrome. It is the result of repetitive use of a keyboard. The injury causes pain in the forearms due to swelling and pressure on the median nerve passing through the wrist. Carpal tunnel syndrome may cause permanent disability. In rare cases workers lost their ability to return to work due to this injury.

Our eyes, too, are strained from computer work. Studies found that a programmer's eyes make as many as 30,000 movements in a workday. These are movements up, down, and to the sides, which strain the eye muscles. However, other studies found that while staring at a computer monitor people blink at one-sixth of the frequency that they blink normally. Blinking is important for moisturizing the eyeball, which helps kill harmful germs and eases eye strain. A study by NIOSH found that short breaks from work with computers that involve keyboards and video displays reduce eye soreness, visual blurring, and upper-body discomfort, while quantity and quality of work were not compromised. The agency estimates than more than half of those 75 million Americans who stare at computer displays for long hours develop a health problem called computer vision syndrome (CVS), which is any combination of headaches, loss of focus, burning eyes, double vision, or blurred vision. The American Optometric Association reports that about 14 percent of patients schedule eye exams because of CVS.

The argument has been made that it is an employer's moral obligation to educate employees about such risks and to provide an environment that minimizes them. Both factors, the economic and ethical, have moved many employers to try to reduce the increasing "injuries of the Information Age." They do so by purchasing and installing ergonomic equipment, training employees how to use computers in a way that minimizes injuries, and enforcing periodic breaks from repetitive activities such as typing. The breaks help prevent both RSIs and eye strain. The Occupational Safety and Health Administration (OSHA), an arm of the U.S. Department of Labor, maintains a Web site, www.osha.gov/SLTC/computerworkstation, that provides useful tips on safe computer work. As a professional it is likely you will spend much of your workday sitting in front of a computer. Read the tips and apply them to maintain your good health.

OUTPUT DEVICES

Output devices include all electronic and electromechanical devices that deliver results of computer processing. We receive most information in visual form, either on screen or on paper. Therefore, this discussion focuses on the most popular output devices: monitors and printers. Output also includes audio signals, received through speakers and earphones, or downloaded to digital audio players. Soon we might also be able to enjoy smell output using digital technology.

Monitors

The most common output device is the computer monitor, which looks like and uses technology similar to a television screen. There are two major types of monitors: cathode-ray tube (CRT) and flat-panel display. Images on a monitor are made up of small dots called **pixels** (*pic*ture *el*ements, with the addition of an *x* for easier pronunciation).

In a **CRT (cathode-ray tube)** monitor, the inner side of the screen has a layer of tiny phosphoric dots, which make up the pixels. These dots respond to electronic beams by displaying different colored light. An electron gun receives instructions from the computer and sweeps the rows of pixels, spraying a ray of electrons. When electrons hit a pixel, the pixel emits light for a limited time. The electronic gun bombards some pixels and skips others, creating a picture on the screen.

Hardly any new CRT monitors are made now. The only advantage of CRT monitors over flat-panel monitors is their speed of rendering a new picture. This is why people who often play computer games (popularly called "gamers") as well as artists who create digital video prefer this technology. However, the rendition speed gap between CRTs and flat monitors is closing fast. It is likely that within a few years we will rarely see CRT monitors in offices or homes.

Flat-panel monitors have gained popularity as monitors for personal computers and handheld computers after years of their use in notebook computers. Their price has decreased tenfold over the past several years. The advantages of flat-panel monitors are their slim profile, their sharper images, and their lower consumption of power. The most common type of flat-panel monitor is the **liquid crystal display (LCD)**, but any type of high definition television (HDTV) set can be connected to a computer (if it has the proper socket) and serve as a computer monitor.

In LCD, a conductive film-covered screen is filled with a liquid crystal, whose molecules can align in different planes when charged with a certain electrical voltage. The proper voltage applied to segments of the screen disrupts the crystal's regular structure in those areas, causing it to block light. Light continues to pass through the rest of the liquid. This combination of light and dark areas produces images of characters and pictures.

LCD displays have largely replaced CRTs in organizations and households.

Courtesy of Acer America, Inc.

The price of a monitor depends primarily on its size, measured as the diagonal length of the screen. Common sizes are 15 to 21 inches. Other price factors include brightness (the brighter the better), contrast ratio (the higher the better), and pixel pitch (how close the pixels are to each other; the closer the better).

The greater the number of pixels per unit area on the screen, the sharper the picture. Picture sharpness is called **resolution**. It is expressed as the number of pixels that fit the width and height of a complete screen image. Monitors come in several resolutions. The resolution required for clear text is 640 × 350. If you multiply these numbers, you get the total number of pixels on the screen. Common resolutions are 1024 × 768, 1280 × 1024, 1600 × 1200, and 1920 × 1200.

Good color monitors can display more than 16 million colors and hues. The number of colors and the overall quality of pictures also depends on the quality of the video card used inside the computer. The video card contains memory and circuitry to manipulate and display two- and three-dimensional images.

Printers

Printers can be classified into two basic types based on the technology they use to create images on paper: nonimpact and impact.

Nonimpact Printers

The printer most commonly used today in businesses is the laser printer, which is a **nonimpact printer** because it creates images on a page without mechanically impacting the paper. Nonimpact printers include laser, ink-jet, electrostatic, and electrothermal printers. Laser printers are also page printers, because they print one whole page at a time. Laser and ink-jet printers produce very high-quality output, including color. Laser printing technology can create typeset quality equal to what you see in magazines and textbooks. All nonimpact printers have fewer moving parts than impact printers and are, therefore, significantly quieter. They are also much faster. The excellent quality of their output makes laser printers the choice of many individual and corporate users for desktop publishing.

Two qualities to check when purchasing a laser or ink-jet printer are speed, measured in pages per minute (PPM), and density, measured in dots per inch (DPI). The higher the density, the sharper the output. Desktop printers produce output at 300, 600, and 1200 DPI or more. The speed of desktop laser printers is 4 to 25 PPM. Color laser printing is somewhat slower, because of the time it takes the printer to compose the image. Larger, commercial laser printers reach speeds of more than 400 PPM. The low prices of laser and ink-jet printers might be misleading. Over the life of the printer, the buyer will pay much more money for the cartridges than for the printer. For example, a color laser printer that costs $500 typically requires four cartridges, each costing about $130. Just a single set of new cartridges costs more than a new printer. This might lead some buyers to actually throw away such printers and buy new ones instead of replacing the cartridges. If a new printer is to be used for high-volume printing, the initial larger expenditure on a laser printer makes business sense because the per-page cost of laser cartridges is lower than the per-page cost of ink-jet cartridges.

Impact Printers

Printers are considered **impact printers** if they reproduce an image on a page using mechanical impact. Of this type, the only printers you might still encounter are dot-matrix printers. The print head of **dot-matrix printers** consists of a matrix of little pins. When certain pins strike the ribbon against the paper, they mark the shape of a character or another form on the paper. Thus, each character is made up of tiny dots, and so are other images. Dot-matrix printers produce low-quality output but are still in use in many businesses.

STORAGE MEDIA

To maintain programs, data, and information for later use, data must be stored on a nonvolatile medium, that is, a medium that retains data even when not connected to electric power. Often, we also want to move stored data to a computer that is not part of a network, and we need to back up important programs and data as well. For these purposes, we use external storage media, that is, storage media outside the computer's memory. The terms "storage media" and "storage devices" are often used interchangeably.

External storage devices come in different forms and use different materials, each with strengths and weaknesses. Important properties to consider are capacity, access speed, and access mode. As always, cost must be considered, too. Capacity is the amount of data the medium can hold per area of its surface, access speed is the amount of data that can be stored or retrieved per time unit, and access mode refers to the organization of data on the medium, either random or sequential.

POINT OF INTEREST

Squeezing More Bytes

IBM is developing a new storage technology called Millipede, which allows computers to store data at a density of a trillion bytes per square inch, about 20 times denser than magnetic disks available today. The technology, called nanotechnology, uses 4,000 very fine silicon tips that punch holes onto a thin film of plastic. The tiny holes represent bits. The technology is called nanotechnology, because it is at the level of atoms. A storage device the size of a postage stamp will hold more than 1 trillion bits. This is the size of 600,000 digital camera pictures.

Storage devices differ in the technology they use to maintain data (such as magnetic or optical) and in their physical structure (disks, tapes, or other forms). Physical structure might limit ways in which data can be organized on the medium. While disks allow any type of organization, tapes allow only sequential organization. This section first discusses modes of access, then looks at specific media and technologies, and then considers the trade-offs that managers must consider when evaluating what type of storage media is best for a particular business.

Modes of Access

There are two basic types of access modes in data storage: sequential and direct (random) access (see Figure 4.6). In **sequential storage**, data is organized one record after another. With sequential storage (the only option for magnetic or optical tapes), to read data from anywhere on the tape, you have to read through all the data before that point on the tape. Retrieving files from sequential devices is slower and less convenient than on devices that utilize direct access. In **direct access**, records are not organized sequentially, but by the physical address on the device, and can be accessed directly without going through other records. Devices that allow direct access storage are often called DASD (DAZ-dee), short for direct access storage device. They include magnetic and optical disks as well as **flash drives**, small storage devices that connect to a computer via a **universal serial bus (USB)** receptacle.

Because storage and retrieval are slow on sequential storage devices (mainly due to the time it takes a robot to mount them on tape drives) and because they are inexpensive, tapes are suitable for backup purposes. Direct access storage media are the only practical way to organize and query databases.

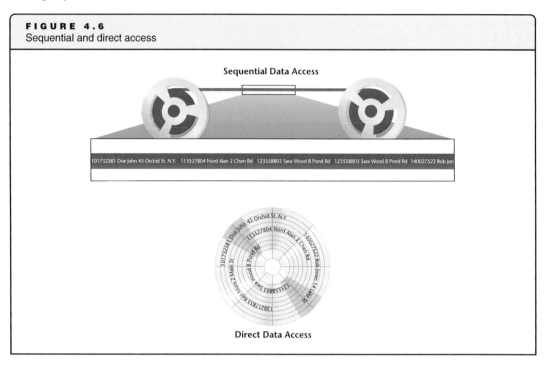

FIGURE 4.6
Sequential and direct access

Sequential Data Access

101732581 Doe John 45 Orchid St. N.Y.   113527804 Nord Alan 2 Chen Rd   123558803 Sara Wood 8 Pond Rd   123558803 Sara Wood 8 Pond Rd   140027522 Bob Jon

Direct Data Access

Magnetic Tapes

DLT tape is an inexpensive way to back up data.

Courtesy of Quantum Corp.

Magnetic tapes similar to those used in tape recorders and VCRs are also used to store computer data. While some tape drives still use open reel tapes, most now use tape cartridges. Many of these cartridges look, in general, like the tapes used in audio tape players. However, one of the most popular types of tape cartridges is the Digital Linear Tape (DLT). Quantum, a storage media manufacturer, offers tape cartridges with a capacity of 3.5 TB (terabytes) that access data at a rate of 250 MB per second. The cost of storage is measured in how much money is spent on each byte of storage capacity. Tapes provide the lowest cost in terms of bytes per dollar. In terms of storage capacity, tape storage costs about 1/20th of magnetic disk storage.

Backing up all or a designated part of data from its original storage medium is often done regularly. The entire hard disk of a PC can be backed up, or, in organizations, large amounts of data are backed up in case a hard disk crashes or a disaster occurs that makes the original data irretrievable. Backing up can be done manually or automatically, with the help of software. When the backup is done for an organization, often the organization makes use of a storage area network, a dedicated area where tapes (and possibly disks) are connected through communication lines to organizational ISs for the sole purpose of data backup. Such networks are discussed later in this chapter.

Some organizations use magnetic tapes to automatically create two backups of all data. AOK, Germany's largest health insurance company with more than 25 million policyholders, uses 128 300-GB tape drives to store 44 TB of data. The amount of data grows at a rate of 6 percent per year. The data is backed up through a dispersed network of parallel tape drives. The company is well prepared for any disaster that might destroy data.

For PCs, the most popular cartridges are connected to the computer via its USB port. All PCs and other microcomputers are manufactured with several of these ports, which are used to connect many different peripheral devices, including external storage media.

USB ports enable users to connect a variety of equipment to a computer, such as external tape cartridges.

© Gary Herrington;   Courtesy of Certance LLC

Tapes are inexpensive but they have two major flaws. It takes a long time to copy from a tape. This is a serious concern when terabytes of data must be recopied to a disk from a tape. Tapes are also unreliable after about 5 years. To extend this period, a magnetic tape must be reeled back and forth every few months to maintain an even tension. Uneven tension, which always develops over time, renders the stored data inaccurate. Some of the data might become unreadable.

Magnetic Disks

The most widely used storage medium is the **magnetic disk**. Magnetic disks include hard disks and floppy disks. As with information on magnetic tape, information on magnetic disks is coded in magnetized spots on the disk's surface. The 3.5-inch floppy disks are now being replaced by portable media such as writeable CDs and portable flash memory drives that connect to USB ports.

PCs always come with at least one hard disk built in. (Hard disks are often mistakenly called hard drives. The disk is the storage medium itself; the drive is the mechanism that stores data to it and retrieves data from it. However "hard disk" and "hard drive" are commonly used to mean the combination of the two, because the drive and disk are sold and installed as one unit.) A **hard disk** is a stack of several rigid aluminum platters installed in the same box that holds the CPU and other computer components, or attached externally to the computer, usually through a USB port. An external hard disk is portable; it easily can be connected to or disconnected from the computer without opening the computer box. External hard disks are usually more expensive than internal disks with the same capacity. Hard disks are capable of storing up to 500 GB of data. The cost of storing 1 GB has decreased to less than one dollar.

Spending on storage devices accounts for about 30 percent of all IT expenditure of corporations. In recent years the most important impetus for acquisition of hard disks has been the construction of data warehouses, large databases that maintain mainly consumer purchase records. For example, Wal-Mart, the world's largest retailer, maintains close to 500 TB of consumer data.

Optical Discs

Optical discs are recorded by treating the disc surface so it reflects light in two different ways. A special detecting device detects the two different reflections, which represent ones and zeros of digital coding. There are two basic categories of optical discs: **compact discs**, or **CDs**, and

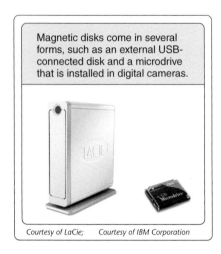

Magnetic disks come in several forms, such as an external USB-connected disk and a microdrive that is installed in digital cameras.

Courtesy of LaCie; Courtesy of IBM Corporation

Advanced DVDs can hold up to 50 GB of data.

Kyodo/Landov

digital video discs, or DVDs (sometimes called digital versatile discs). There are several types of CDs—CD-ROM (Compact Disc, Read Only Memory), CD-R (recordable), and CD-RW (rewritable). Recordable DVDs come in a variety of recording options. The main advantage of optical discs is their storage capacity and portability. CDs are also less expensive than hard disks in terms of bytes per dollar. Standard DVDs can store 4.7 GB per side for a total of 9.4 GB. More advanced DVDs, using techniques called blue laser and double storage, can reach capacities of 50 GB. However, the disadvantage of all optical discs is that the speed of storage and retrieval is currently slower than that of hard disks.

You might have noticed CD drive speeds listed in the form of 52X, 60X, or another X-number. Years ago, the original data retrieval (transfer) rate of CD drives was 150,000 bits per second. This number represents single speed, or "1X." Thus, 60X means 60 × 150,000 = 9,000,000 bits per second. The greater the data retrieval rate, the more desirable the drive. Note that writable CDs usually have different reading and writing speeds. Reading is often faster than writing. So, you might find that a CD drive reads at 60X but writes at only 24X.

Corporations use DVDs to store massive amounts of information, both for long-term storage and for operational use. They place manuals, drawings, and other large amounts of information that used to fill many books and file cabinets on a single or a few DVDs. Consider that the 32 volumes of *Encyclopaedia Britannica*—over 75,000 articles, including images and sounds—are stored on a single DVD, along with a dictionary and an atlas. In fact, the DVD contains both versions of the *Encyclopaedia*, the Student and Elementary editions.

Optical Tape

Optical tape uses the same technology as optical discs to store and retrieve data. The only difference is that the bits are organized sequentially as they are on magnetic tape. Like magnetic tapes, optical tapes are made as reels or cassettes. Their storage capacity is enormous. A reel 14 inches in diameter stores over 1 terabyte (1 trillion bytes). A cassette stores about 9 gigabytes. Currently, the main use of optical tapes is in digital video camcorders. There is relatively little use of the technology in corporations.

Flash Memory

Flash memory is becoming popular for both primary memory (memory inside the computer) and external storage. Flash memory is a memory chip that can be rewritten and hold its content without electric power. Flash memory consumes very little power and does not need a constant power supply to retain data when disconnected. It offers fast access times and is relatively immune to shock or vibration. These qualities make flash memory an excellent choice for portable devices such as MP3 players, or as independent portable storage. Unlike other types of memory, erasing data can only be done in blocks of bytes, not individual bytes, and hence the name: a whole block of bytes is erased in a flash.

As an independent memory device, flash memory takes two main forms: as a memory card (often used in digital cameras and other portable devices), and as a USB drive, sometimes called a thumb drive or USB flash drive. Many computers and some monitors and printers include multiple built-in card readers that accommodate the most popular flash memory cards, such as SD (Secure Digital) and CF (Compact Flash). USB drives are about the size of an adult's thumb, and act as portable storage. (The name "drive" is a misnomer; there are no moving parts or disks in flash memory.) They plug into the computer through a USB port. As USB ports come standard in all microcomputers, it is easy to use a thumb drive to save data or transfer data between computers. There is usually no need to set up any software once the USB drive is plugged in. The

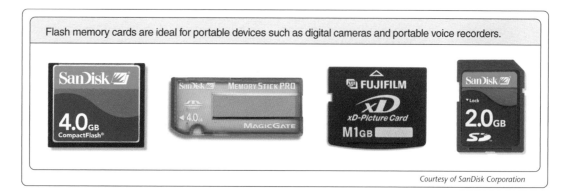

Flash memory cards are ideal for portable devices such as digital cameras and portable voice recorders.

Courtesy of SanDisk Corporation

Flash memory connects through USB ports to any computer. It often holds several gigabytes of data.

Courtesy of Kingston Technology Company, Inc.

Many computers and some monitors have built-in USB ports and flash card slots. Two USB ports and four card readers are built into this LCD monitor.

device is recognized as an additional external storage device. USB drives come in storage capacities of up to several gigabytes, and their cost is decreasing rapidly.

Transfer rate (speed of storage and retrieval) of flash memory in USB flash drives and memory cards is usually indicated in the same manner as that of optical discs: so many Xs. A memory card of 80X is considered fast. Cards of the same storage capacity are significantly different in price due to transfer rate.

Flash memory is often called solid state memory. In addition to its use in USB flash drives and memory cards, it is used in solid state disks. A **solid state disk (SSD)** is an alternative to magnetic disks. Again, the word "disk" is a misnomer, because this type of storage involves no disk. SSDs are attached to computers in a similar way to magnetic disks. The fact that there is no need to wait for a disk to rotate in order to locate data—time that is called latency—makes SSDs up to 250 times faster than magnetic disks, especially if the SSD comes with its own CPU. The function of such CPUs is specifically to speed up data processing. SSDs are used by organizations to store frequently used software to prevent data processing "bottlenecks."

DAS, NAS, and SAN

Organizations increasingly rely on storage systems that allow multiple users to share the same storage media over a network. In **direct access storage (DAS)** the disk or array of disks is directly connected to a server. The storage devices might also be tapes, especially if the storage is for backup. Other computers on the network must access the server to use the disks or tapes. DAS is relatively easy to deploy and manage, and involves relatively low cost. However, speed of access to data might be compromised because the server also processes other software, such as e-mail and databases. Also, if the server is down, the other computers cannot access the storage devices. DAS might be suitable for localized file sharing, which is typical in small businesses. It is not easily scalable, because each additional server and its storage devices must be managed separately. Scalability is the ability to add more hardware or software to accommodate changing business needs.

Two other arrangements place the storage devices on the organization's network so that they can be accessed directly by all other computers. These approaches are known as network-attached storage (NAS) and storage area network (SAN).

Network-attached storage (NAS) is a device especially designed for networked storage. It comprises both the storage media, such as hard disks, and management software, which is fully dedicated to serving (accessing) files over the network. NAS relieves the server of handling storage, so the server can process other applications, such as e-mail and databases. Disks can store many terabytes of data in a small, centralized space, and managing such a large storage in one place saves money. NAS is highly scalable. While in DAS each server runs its own operating system, NAS can communicate with servers running various operating systems, and therefore allow much flexibility when adding computers and other devices to the network.

Storage area network (SAN) is a network fully devoted to storage and transfer of data between servers and storage devices. The storage devices are part of this dedicated network, which is managed separately from the organization's local area network. (Networks are covered in Chapter 6.) A SAN may combine DAS and NAS devices. The communication lines in this network are high-speed optical fibers. The data transfer standards used in a SAN are different from those used by a NAS and generally support higher speeds. NAS identifies data by files, or, as professionals say, at the file level. SAN identifies much larger quantities of data, called data blocks, and therefore can transfer and back up much larger amounts of data at a time. This is important when high speed of data transfer is important, such as in online business transactions that involve a large number of records in a stored database. A large number of users can simultaneously access data without delays. SANs are highly scalable. For these reasons, SANs are used by organizations that conduct business on the Web and require high-volume transaction processing. However, SANs are relatively expensive and their management is complex. In recent years, the technical differences between NAS and SAN have blurred.

DAS, NAS, and SAN often include **RAID** (redundant array of independent disks), whereby data is replicated on different disks to enhance processing speed and fault-tolerance. Fault-tolerance is the ability of the system to sustain failure of a disk, because the same data also appears on another disk.

Several companies specialize in NAS and SAN systems and the software that manages them, including Network Appliance, EMC, Hewlett-Packard, and IBM. For example, Network Appliance offers FAS3050, a storage system with up to 336 disk drives and a storage capacity of 84 terabytes. It can be attached as a device in a SAN or a NAS.

Business Considerations in Evaluating Storage Media

Before spending money on storage devices, managers must consider several factors: the purpose of data storage, the amount of data to be stored, the required speed of data storage and retrieval, how portable the device needs to be, and, as always, cost.

Use of Stored Data

The first consideration before adopting storage media is how the data will be used, mainly, whether it will be used for current operations or as backup. If it is to be used for backup only, and not processing, magnetic tape or CDs would be a proper choice. Magnetic tape is less costly and holds more data per reel or cassette than a single CD; this should be a consideration, too. If the users need to access individual records quickly, then magnetic hard disks are the best choice. Thus, a business that allows customers to retrieve their records online should use fast magnetic disks. If the information is archival, such as encyclopedias or maps used by library patrons, the library should place the information on CDs or DVDs, because the user needs fast, direct retrieval of specific information (records), and might not tolerate sequential search on a tape.

Amount of Data Stored

When storage volume is the most important factor, managers must first consider price per megabit or megabyte, that is, the ratio of dollars spent to storage capacity. If the medium is to be used solely for backup, their low cost makes magnetic tapes and CD-Rs an ideal choice. If the medium is to be used for fast retrieval, fast magnetic disks would be the best choice. If much data must be stored, especially large files such as pictures, sound, and video, but the speed of finding a particular file or record is not so important, a DVD is a good choice, but its current high cost must be considered.

For some purposes, the absolute capacity of the device, not the density, is important. When a set of very large software applications and/or data must be stored on a single device, a device with a large capacity must be selected. For example, if a sales rep must be able to demonstrate applications totaling 4 GB, it might be more economical to store the data on five CDs, but this would be impractical because the rep would either have to first copy the content of all the CDs onto every PC where she makes a demonstration (which for security reasons might be prohibited by the hosting party), or she would have to swap the CDs throughout the demonstration. A small portable hard disk or USB flash drive of at least 4 GB would be a more practical option, albeit significantly more expensive.

Speed

The speed of magnetic disks is often measured in rotations per minute (RPM). Current disks come with speeds of 5,400, 7,200, 10,000, and 15,000 RPM. For disks of the same size, the greater the RPM the shorter the data transfer time and usually the better the performance overall. While the great capacity and low cost of CDs are appealing, the transfer rate of magnetic hard disks is still significantly better than that of CDs and their faster relatives, DVDs. If very high speed is required, SSD is currently the best choice, although its price is significantly higher than that of magnetic disks.

Unit Space and Portability

Sometimes the cost of a gigabyte stored is not the most important consideration, but the physical size of the storage medium is. A portable hard disk drive might be economical and fast, but it is more practical for a traveling salesperson to carry a CD rather than an external hard disk. And even though a CD is significantly less expensive than a USB flash drive, the salesperson might find it more convenient to carry a 4 GB USB drive than carrying several CDs. CDs do not fit in shirt pockets, while a USB flash drive can be attached to a key chain or clipped to a shirt pocket. Thus, even if storage cost is not as attractive as that of CDs, portability and the fact that USB ports are ubiquitous in PCs might push one toward selecting a USB flash drive.

Cost

Once managers agree on the best type of data storage device for a particular business use, they need to consider cost. The approach is simple: obtain the largest size of storage for the smallest amount of money. In other words, for each proposed device, consider the ratio of cents per gigabyte of capacity. The lower the ratio, the more favorable the product. It is easy to find the ratio. If a 300 GB hard disk costs $200, the ratio is $200/300 GB, or about 67 cents per gigabyte. If a 4 GB thumb drive costs $120, the cost per gigabyte is $120/4 GB, or $30. Thus, if the convenience and portability of a thumb drive is important to you, you will pay significantly more per byte of storage capacity.

Reliability and Life Expectancy

Although this is usually not the highest priority, businesses must also consider the storage medium's reliability and life expectancy. For instance, optical discs are more reliable and durable than magnetic disks. Magnetically stored data remains reliable for about 10 years, whereas CDs and DVDs are expected to store data reliably for 50 to 100 years (although they have not been around long enough to prove that).

Trade-Offs

As you can see, several factors must be considered when purchasing storage media, and often you must trade one quality of the device for another. For example, while USB drives are convenient and fast, they are also expensive and unacceptable for storing large amounts of transactional data, or even backing up large amounts of data, because of their relatively small capacity. Figure 4.7 summarizes characteristics of the most popular storage media. Obviously, terms such as "moderate cost" and "high capacity" are relative. Storage capacities and speeds of almost all storage media have increased over the years, and costs have decreased. Thus, the specific capacities, retrieval speeds, and costs change all the time. The table is presented for general comparison and reference, whereby "high" and "low" for each medium are relative to the other media.

FIGURE 4.7
Characteristics of storage media for business purposes

Medium	Storage Density (bits/ square inch, or physical size)	Recording and Retrieval Speed	Cost ($/GB)	Ideal for...	Capacity per Device	Limitations
Magnetic hard disk 	High	Very High	High	Immediate transactions	Very high	Bulky, heavy
Magnetic tape 	High	Slow	Very low	Backup	Very high	Not suitable for immediate processing
Optical tape 	Very High	High	Low	Backup	Very High	Limited market
Recordable CDs 	Very High	Medium	Very low	Backup, distribution of software	Low	Low capacity per device
Flash memory 	High	High	High	Backup, portability	Medium	Expensive

CONSIDERATIONS IN PURCHASING HARDWARE

Decisions about purchasing computers are usually made by an organization's IS professionals or with the help of a consulting firm. But surveys show a new trend: involving end users in the decision-making process. More and more companies realize that effective use of computers depends on whether their employees are satisfied with the computers and other equipment installed in their workplace.

Before deciding what to purchase, consider the following variables:

- The equipment's power: its speed, its memory size, and the capacity of its storage devices, such as the hard disk installed in the computer.

- Expansion slots: computers should have enough slots to add circuitry cards for additional purposes, such as graphic cards and wireless cards on their motherboards (the main board on which the CPU and other circuitry are installed). These expansion slots are called PCI (Peripheral Component Interconnect) sockets. Some graphics cards need AGP (Accelerated Graphics Port) sockets for future improvement of graphics performance. It might also help to have slots for additional memory cards so the amount of concurrent programs and data run on the computer can grow.

- The number and type of external **ports**, or sockets used to connect a computer to external devices: printers, hard disks, scanners, remote keyboards and pointers, and communications devices. More ports give more flexibility. Because so many external devices—hard disks, printers, scanners, thumb drives, digital cameras, and many others—connect to the computer through a USB port, the greater the number of USB ports the more external devices can be added at the same time. Built-in multiple card readers for flash memory makes it convenient to read data from the cards instead of connecting the device that houses them, such as digital cameras.

- The monitor type and resolution: higher resolution is more pleasing and less straining to the eyes. Larger monitors allow opening of many software applications simultaneously and require less scrolling.

- Ergonomics: ergonomic equipment does not strain the back, arms, and eyes. For example, working with the keyboard must be comfortable. Traditional keyboards cause muscle pain when used for long sessions. Consider purchasing an ergonomic keyboard. Consider a trackball, instead of a mouse; it requires only moving fingers rather than the forearm.

- Compatibility: IT managers must ensure that new systems will integrate with existing hardware, software, and networks. A new computer might have a different operating system or internal architecture, and if it is to be used to host an important application, care must be taken to ensure that the application will run on the new machine. For example, commercial software vendors guarantee that their applications will run on a list of processors and operating systems. Microsoft SQL Server 2000 is guaranteed to run on Intel processors of at least 166 MHz running a Windows 2000 (or later) operating system: it is not compatible with older processors. Managers must consider **backward compatibility**, in which newer hardware is compatible with older hardware. (The same term applies to software.) For example, USB 2.0 devices are backward-compatible with USB 1.1 ports (although the communications speed then deteriorates to the speed of the older port). Compatibility between hardware and networks is also important. Newer handheld devices such as bar-code scanners might use a newer communication standard and no longer communicate with an existing warehouse network, because the new devices are not backward-compatible with the older-standard transceivers.

- The hardware footprint: if space is scarce, you might want to consider the size of the computer and its peripheral equipment. The footprint is the area that a computer occupies. A smaller footprint leaves more desk space for other devices. This is one of the major reasons for adopting flat-panel monitors when they first appeared on the market.

- The reliability of the vendor, the warranty policy, and the support given after the warranty expires: ask if the vendor provides a Web site and 24-hour help via telephone. Try to assess how soon the equipment will be obsolete, a difficult task given the reality of fast development in computer equipment.

- Power consumption and noise: computers that consume less power help save money on electricity and usually also give off less heat. Computers use fans to cool down the circuitry. Quiet fans will make the work environment more pleasant.

- Cost: all of the factors just discussed must be weighed against cost. Careful study might yield hardware with excellent performance for an affordable price. Perusing print and Web-based trade journals is extremely helpful. Many periodicals provide tables evaluating comparable hardware, based on laboratory tests by impartial technicians. You do not have to be an IT professional to understand their evaluations.

Figure 4.8 summarizes the factors discussed in this chapter that you should consider when purchasing hardware. When comparing computers from different vendors, it is useful to establish a 10-point scale and score each category to indicate how well each computer addresses each important item. Your organization's or even your department's internal needs may require you to add some factors. The equipment receiving the highest score is the best in the evaluator's opinion.

Scalability and Updating Hardware

IT purchasing managers try to extend the life of their hardware purchases by ensuring that any equipment they buy is scalable. The principle of **scalability** implies that resources—in this case, hardware—can be expanded or upgraded, to provide increased power as demands increase. For instance, many servers are designed to use multiple processors—4, 8, or 16 is not uncommon. If the server is initially installed with only a small number of processors, say two, then processors can be added over the years to increase capacity. This way the machine will not have to be discarded too soon, and this helps protect the organization's initial investment. The same can be done for memory, storage, and other components.

FIGURE 4.8
Example of a hardware evaluation form

Factor	What to look for	Score
Power		
Speed	Greater frequency and word size	———
RAM capacity	Larger	———
Expandability	Greater number of board slots for additional devices and memory	———
Ports	Greater number of ports for printer, external hard disk, communication devices, and other peripherals	———
Ergonomics	Greater comfort and safety	———
Compatiblity		
with hardware	Compatibility with many other computers and peripheral devices from the same and other manufacturers	———
with software	Compatibility with many software packages currently used and potentially to be used	———
Footprint	Smaller area	———
Support	Availability of telephone and online support for troubleshooting	———
	Supply of information on new upgrades	———
Warranty	Longer warranty period	———
Cost	Lower cost	———

However, some hardware is not scalable. Businesses tend to update their software, especially operating systems (such as Windows) when a new version is available, but many still maintain old hardware. While they avoid the cost of purchasing new hardware, this might actually cost the companies in lost productivity: newer software cannot run as fast or as reliably on the old machines. Often, excellent features of newer software are not available if it runs on older machines.

Hardware should be discarded and new hardware should be installed to avoid performance gaps between software and hardware. One rough formula to help determine when to replace hardware is the ratio of the average age of hardware pieces to the average age of the operating systems running on the machines. If the ratio is less than one, it might be time to replace some or all of the hardware.

If you are concerned that the equipment's useful life might be short because more powerful computers might be available within months, you can lease your system instead of buying it. Many vendors offer leasing programs. However, note that vendors are also aware of how quickly hardware becomes obsolete and price the leases accordingly; thus, you might find that the lease payment often covers the purchase price within a mere 18–24 months. Yet, many firms prefer leasing their PCs and notebook computers to purchasing them.

As you will see throughout this book, hardware components are combined in many different configurations to help businesses streamline operations and attain strategic goals. But hardware is rarely the first consideration in acquiring a new IS. When planning a new IS, managers should first determine their business needs and then consider which software can support those needs. Only then should they select the hardware that supports the software. The next chapter focuses on software.

■ More and more professionals outside the IT field find themselves in the decision-making role regarding the purchase and use of computer hardware. Therefore, understanding hardware is important.

■ For ease of reference, computers are classified into several categories according to their power. The most powerful are supercomputers, used mainly by research institutions for complex scientific calculations. Somewhat less powerful are mainframe computers; many organizations still use them to process large databases and perform other tasks that require speed and large primary memory. Midrange computers are less powerful than mainframe computers and are often used as servers. Microcomputers include PCs and smaller computers, such as notebook, handheld, and tablet computers.

■ Regardless of their size and power, all computers must have several components to function. The "brain" of every computer is its central processing unit (CPU), which consists of circuitry on a piece of silicon wafer and controls four basic operations: (1) it fetches instructions from memory, (2) it decodes them, (3) it executes them, and (4) it stores the results in memory.

■ The rate at which the CPU does all this is the computer's clock rate.

■ A computer's word is the number of bits that can move through its CPU in one machine cycle.

■ Speed and memory size are the main determinants of a computer's power.

■ The larger part of a computer's memory, RAM (random access memory), is volatile; that is, it keeps data only as long as electrical power is supplied. ROM (read-only memory) is nonvolatile. Unlike data in RAM, data stored in ROM stays in ROM when you turn the computer off. Similarly, all secondary storage media, such as magnetic disks, optical discs, and flash cards, are nonvolatile.

■ Imaging devices help process large amounts of text and graphic data and have made the work of banks and other industries more productive.

■ When evaluating external storage, factors to consider are the medium's density, its transfer rate, the capacity, portability, and the form of data organization that it allows. The latter determines the mode of access (sequential or direct).

■ On tapes, data can only be organized and retrieved sequentially, therefore tapes are good for backup but not for transactions. Direct access storage devices, such as RAM, magnetic disks, and optical discs, allow random organization and retrieval. Direct organization provides faster storage and retrieval of records that must be accessed individually and quickly, such as records in airline reservation systems. Only direct access devices are suitable for processing databases.

■ When purchasing computers, managers should consider computer power and other factors in addition to cost. Managers should consider expandability of RAM, the availability of sockets (ports) for connecting peripheral equipment, and compatibility with existing hardware and software.

■ Like many new technologies, information technology may pose health risks to users. The most common problems computer users experience are carpal tunnel syndrome and repetitive-stress injuries caused by the repetitive use of the keyboard over long time periods. Today, manufacturers of computer equipment pay more attention to health hazards and try to design devices ergonomically.

QUICKBIZ MESSENGERS REVISITED

QuickBiz's business has expanded from a one-person bicycle messenger service to a company with bicycles, cars, and trucks, as well as main office staff. As it expanded, the firm has upgraded its information systems to streamline its processes and handle its increasing customer load. Let's examine some of the changes it has made.

What Would You Do?

1. QuickBiz has used many different types of input and output devices throughout its history. How many can you find? Create a two-column chart and list them under the headings Input and Output. Can you think of any other devices or technologies they haven't thought of yet that might help them?

2. Consider QuickBiz's change in storage media. It moved from magnetic tape backup to rewritable CDs. Go online to investigate the costs and capacities of current tape and CD storage systems. How do they compare? Do you think

Andrew and Sarah were wise to change systems? Why or why not?

New Perspectives

1. Review Andrew and Sarah's decision to buy a server and handheld computers. What advantages does source data technology give to the messengers themselves? To the central office staff?

2. Seattle had a 6.8-scale earthquake. QuickBiz's main office suffered some damage during the quake. Its main information system was down for 2 days. Luckily, QuickBiz messengers could still make deliveries and save data on their handheld computers. But that crisis got Andrew thinking that his business needed additional safeguards. Discuss with your classmates and list some ways that QuickBiz can make sure its data and its main information system can be backed up in case of a disaster.

KEY TERMS

arithmetic logic unit
    (ALU), 116
backward compatibility, 133
bit, 112
bus, 118
byte, 112
CRT (cathode-ray tube), 123
central processing unit
    (CPU), 112
clock rate, 117
compact disc (CD), 127
control unit, 116
data word, 117
digital video disc (DVD), 128
direct access, 125

direct access storage
    (DAS), 129
dot-matrix printer, 125
ergonomics, 119
external memory, 112
flash drive, 126
flash memory, 128
flat-panel monitor, 124
hard disk, 127
hardware, 111
imaging, 122
impact printer, 125
input device, 111
internal memory, 112
liquid crystal display
    (LCD), 124

machine cycle, 117
magnetic disk, 127
magnetic-ink character recog-
    nition (MICR), 121
magnetic tape, 126
mainframe computer, 113
microcomputer, 114
microprocessor, 116
midrange computer, 114
MIPS, 118
motherboard, 112
mouse, 119
multiprocessing, 113
multithreading, 116
network-attached storage
    (NAS), 129

nonimpact printer, 124
notebook computer, 114
optical disc , 127
output device, 112
parallel processing, 113
personal digital assistant
   (PDA), 114
pixel, 123
port, 132
RAID, 130
RAM (random access
   memory), 112

ROM (read-only memory), 112
resolution, 124
scalability, 133
sequential storage, 125
solid state disk (SSD), 129
source data input device, 120
speech recognition, 122
storage area network (SAN), 130
stylus, 114
supercomputer, 113
system clock, 117

tablet computer, 114
technology convergence, 115
throughput, 118
touch screen, 120
trackball, 119
trackpad, 120
universal serial bus (USB), 126
USB drive, 128
workstation, 114

REVIEW QUESTIONS

1. You have decided to buy parts and build your own personal computer. At the minimum, what are the components that you would need for this device to be considered a computer?

2. Modern CPUs are capable of multithreading. What is multithreading?

3. Most people never get to see a supercomputer, let alone use one. Why? What are the most frequent uses of this type of computer?

4. Why are computers designed to work in binary form rather than by using multiple value signals? Try to use the analogy of colors to explain your answer.

5. News about the death of mainframe computers has been greatly exaggerated. How so?

6. IT professionals often speak of the merging of technologies. Think of handheld computers and cell phones. Give an example of such merging.

7. When a computer is offered for sale, one of its advertised characteristics is something such as "4 GHz." What does that mean, and what does it measure?

8. Why are computers said to be processing data digitally?

9. What is the difference between volatile and non-volatile memory? Give one example of volatile memory and one example of nonvolatile memory.

10. What are the main qualities to look for in an LCD monitor?

11. Among the external storage devices discussed in this chapter, all but one store data on the surface of some material, and one in circuitry. Which one?

12. What is DVD technology? How does it differ from CD technology?

13. What does footprint mean in hardware? When is a footprint important in the office?

14. What are the most important features to consider before purchasing a PC?

15. On a continental tour, a traveling salesperson makes software-based presentations at every place he stops. He has ensured that there is a PC and projecting equipment at every site he visits. Every so often, he needs to change the content of his presentation. He wants to carry as little as possible. What data storage device would you recommend he carry?

DISCUSSION QUESTIONS

1. Computers fail significantly less frequently than copy machines and printers. Why?

2. Comment on this statement: large computers, such as mainframes and supercomputers, have no future.

3. Because information technology advances so rapidly, managers find it difficult to make informed decisions regarding computer and

peripheral equipment purchases. What factors cause this difficulty?

4. End users' role in making hardware purchasing decisions is growing. Analyze the technological and operational reasons for this trend.

5. Would you replace a PC with a handheld computer for your studies or work? Why or why not?

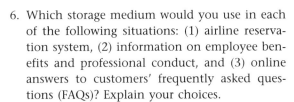

6. Which storage medium would you use in each of the following situations: (1) airline reservation system, (2) information on employee benefits and professional conduct, and (3) online answers to customers' frequently asked questions (FAQs)? Explain your choices.

7. What health hazards are associated with computer use? What can be done to alleviate each type of health risk? Should the government pass laws to protect employees against such hazards?

8. The miniaturization and merging of technologies into highly portable devices has caused some annoyances. Give some examples.

9. Comment on the following statement: the useful life of a PC is about 2 years, therefore, it is not important whether the vendor is still in business in 2 or 3 years.

10. About 18–24 months into the life of a PC, a new PC becomes available that is twice as powerful. As a result, many IS managers opt to lease, rather than buy, PCs for employees. What factors would you consider in deciding whether to buy or to lease?

11. Thanks to DVD and other advanced technologies, a PC can combine the functions of a computer, telephone, fax machine, and television set. Would you give up your home telephone and television set if you could use your PC to make calls and watch television? Why or why not?

12. Sometimes useful information might be lost, not because the medium on which it was stored deteriorated or was damaged, but because no device was available to retrieve the information. How could that happen? Can you give examples?

13. You might have heard of the electronic book, a handheld device that allows readers to read a book from a CD. What are the advantages and disadvantages of such devices when compared with traditional books? Think in terms of portability, text clarity, searching for specific words or pages, and so on. What would you prefer: an electronic book or a paper book? Why?

14. Observers say that personal computers are fast becoming a commodity. What does the term "commodity" mean? How could this development impact businesses and homes?

15. A mechanic once recommended that the author of this book not purchase a car that has too many computer chips, because if those chips fail, they must be replaced; mechanics cannot fix them. Would you take the mechanic's advice? Why or why not?

16. Try to count how many hours per week you use a personal computer: at your home, in the PC lab, in the library, or elsewhere. Have you become a "computer junkie" in the Information Age? Do you, or does society in general, have an alternative to IT dependence?

17. What do you expect will be the most popular storage devices for personal use in 5 years? What will be the most popular nonportable storage devices for corporate use in 5 years? Why?

18. Almost daily a new electronic device, often one that combines several technologies, is offered for sale. People sometimes refer to some of these devices as "gadgets," hints that they might be nice to have but not really useful. How do *you* delineate the difference between a gadget and helpful device?

APPLYING CONCEPTS

1. Recommend one of the three hardware configurations described in the following table for each of the scenarios listed. Assume that all of the hardware configurations cost the same. Explain your choices.

Features	Computer Configuration		
	A	B	C
RAM	512 MB	1 GB	512 MB
External storage			
Hard disk	200 GB	120 GB	60 GB
Thumb drive (USB 2.0)	256 MB	512 MB	256 MB
Speed (clock rate)	1.7 GHz	3.06 GHz	5 GHz
Printer	Laser	Ink-jet	Laser
	1200 DPI	600 DPI	600 DPI
	20 PPM	12 PPM	16 PPM

a. The employees of this firm do a lot of graphic design work. Graphics require large programs. Printouts must be high quality.

b. This firm uses the computer mainly for word processing. The biggest application occupies 24 MB.

c. Employees of this firm use scientific programs that run for many hours.

d. It is imperative that employees be able to print reports quickly with reasonable print quality. They almost always print their reports from portable storage devices.

2. Assume you can choose among magnetic tapes, magnetic hard disks, recordable optical discs (CD-R: write once, read many), and flash memory USB drives. Consider each scenario independently of the others. For each of the following purposes, explain which one of the media you would choose and why. Start by saying which medium you have chosen. Then explain why.

a. You need to store thousands of employee records for several years. This is only a backup procedure. The information will never be processed from the backup medium.

b. The storage medium is used as part of an airline reservation system.

c. Your business sells machines that must be maintained well by your clients. You wish to provide them with a digital version of the maintenance manual. The manual includes an index (like one at the end of a book) with links to the proper pages.

d. You are a sales manager who travels often. You must store a large PowerPoint presentation that you show to prospective customers in their office. You do not carry a laptop computer, but there is a PC wherever you go. You do not want to carry CDs, because you found that the graphic-rich presentation moves too slowly from CDs.

e. You have a business on the Web. You maintain your own server and site. You provide much textual and graphical information from the site. Customers can search products and make purchases.

f. You want to store all the paintings of impressionist painters for use by your local library patrons. Patrons can search by artist name, artist nationality, or by the painting's topic. The library would like multiple copies of what you store, and to be able to loan them to patrons for viewing at home.

g. You use the medium for a large database that your employees manipulate frequently.

h. You work for the IRS, and you need to archive the tax records of millions of taxpayers for several years. The archiving is done after all processing of tax filings are complete and after all refunds and payments have been made. IRS employees must occasionally go back and retrieve specific records from these files, and when they need a record, they want to access it directly.

3. Search the Web for remote-control devices to use with presentation applications such as PowerPoint. (Go to Web sites of online PC vendors such as cdw.com and pcconnection.com.) Examine the pictures of five different units. Summarize your thoughts about the ergonomics of these devices.

HANDS-ON ACTIVITIES

1. Your company is about to open a new branch. You were selected to equip the new office with 20 personal computers, 10 notebook computers, and 5 laser printers. Management has asked that you purchase all the equipment from a single online vendor. Each PC must be purchased complete with a 19-inch LCD monitor. After interviewing employees about their typical computing needs, you developed the following scale:

PCs: Every 1 MHz of clock rate receives 1 point; every 1 MB of RAM receives 10 points; every 1 GB of hard disk storage receives 1 point. For CD-RW, each 1X of reading speed receives 1 point (writing and rewriting speeds are not essential, but the capabilities are required).

LCD monitors: Every 1:100 of contrast ratio gets 10 points; every 10 cd/m^2 of brightness receives 1 point. Other features are not essential.

Laptops: The same scoring as for PCs.

Printers: Every 1 PPM receives 100 points; every 1 DPI receives 1 point.

Research three online vendor sites for this equipment. Prepare a spreadsheet table with three columns, one for each vendor, and enter the information you found about each piece of equipment for each vendor. Enter a formula to add up the total number of points at the bottom of each column. Do not consider any factor that is not mentioned here. Find the vendor whose total points per dollar is the highest.

2. Try to forget the shapes of PCs, monitors, keyboards, and mice. Use a word-processing application to write a two-page description of your own ideas for an ergonomic workstation. Explain what about today's PCs and peripheral equipment does not fit human hands, eyes, and ears, and how you would like to change these devices'

features and shapes for more comfortable and effective use. Be as revolutionary as your imagination lets you.

3. Use a spreadsheet application to prepare a table that clearly shows (both in text and numbers) how to calculate the following: a music CD contains 750 million bits. How long does it take to play all the music on it assuming it plays at 1X? If the CD contains data, how long would it take to retrieve all the data from it into a computer's RAM, if you used a 60X CD drive?

TEAM ACTIVITIES

1. Your team has received $2,500 to purchase a computer system. Assume you have no equipment; everything needs to be purchased. Use the evaluation form in Figure 4.8. Visit the Web sites of three computer hardware vendors, and write down specifications of three sets of equipment. Include in each set a computer, a keyboard and mouse (or trackball), a compatible 19- or 21-inch LCD monitor, and a black-and-white laser printer. Your team should evaluate the features of each configuration, on a scale of 1 to 10 (1 = worst; 10 = best), and total the points. Which configuration (and, therefore, vendor)

would you recommend to your fellow students? If you cannot spend your entire $2,500, any surplus should be considered a benefit. Be ready to explain your recommendation.

2. As in Activity 1, assume you have $2,500 available. You are to purchase your ideal PC, monitor, and printer, while utilizing all or almost all of your budget. Shop the Web for these devices, list them (item name, vendor, and capabilities) and their prices, and rationalize why this is the ideal system for your needs and desires.

COMPANION CD QUESTIONS

1. Compare similar computers from three different manufacturers. Use a spreadsheet to list each component, its specifications, and its price. Which computer is the better value?

2. Convert the following binary number into a decimal: 10011101.

VIDEO QUESTIONS

1. A friend has asked you to help him decide what computer to buy. Make a list of questions you would ask to help him decide what computer to buy. Indicate how the answers to each question will help you decide what hardware to recommend.

2. What components are on the computer you use most often? Be specific about sizes and speeds.

In another cost-saving and efficiency-driving move, Crittenden has ventured onto the leading edge of technology by further empowering Rock County's current 1,000 desktop machines through implementation of a thin-client desktop strategy. A thin client is any personal computer that uses resources of a server rather than its own. Thus, the machine each employee uses will be much cheaper because it needs only a small hard disk. All applications and data will reside on the servers to which these personal computers are linked, and all files saved by county workers will be saved on the servers or SAN disks. If access to more software and files is required, the same desktops can still be used; instead of upgrading them, the power of the servers can be upgraded, or the servers themselves, rather than 1,000 desktop computers, can be replaced.

Source: "Case Study: Streamlining Government," www.hp.com, June 1, 2005.

Thinking About the Case

1. Why is centralization of resources—storage devices, application servers, and printers—so important in the particular case of Rock County?

2. A SAN enables Rock County to use storage devices more efficiently. Do further research on the difference in storage allocation between DAS and SAN. How does the SAN enable more efficient storage than the previous DAS arrangement at the county?

3. Centralized printing can increase productivity only if offices are not dispersed over a large area. Why?

4. What was the major change that reduced the cost of maintenance by the IT Department?

S FIVE

Business Software

LEARNING OBJECTIVES

Hardware, as powerful as it might be, is useless without software. Software consists of instructions that tell the computer and its peripheral devices what to do and how to do it. These instructions are called programs or applications. Many IT professionals refer to computer programs as "systems" because they are composed of components working to achieve a common goal. As a professional, you must be able to make educated decisions regarding software selection. To do so, you must understand the factors involved in developing, selecting, and using software.

When you finish this chapter, you will be able to:

- Explain the difference between application software and system software.

- Enumerate the different generations of programming languages and explain how they differ.

- Cite the latest major developments in application and system software.

- Clarify the differences between proprietary software and open source software.

- List characteristics that are important in evaluating packaged software applications for business use.

- Understand the problem of software piracy and how it affects businesses and consumers.

QUICKBIZ MESSENGERS:
Software Steers a Path to Stability

Growth adds complexity. But the efficiency Andrew Langston found in information systems had helped him manage QuickBiz's complexity repeatedly through the years.

General Software Needs

When Andrew considered buying a new PC-based server system, he wanted to be sure that it could handle his needs. So, he listed the main business functions for which he needed software support:

- General word-processing software for letters and memos.
- Financial accounting and reporting software for tracking sales, invoicing, and paying taxes and license fees.
- Human resource information software to track full-time and part-time workers' time sheets and to generate their W-2 and 1099 income tax forms.
- Database management system software for recording employee and client information.
- Basic desktop publishing software for direct-mail pieces to send to prospective clients.

Andrew chose a software suite to handle most of the business functions because the pieces would work together well and share a common database. He also was able to purchase the financial, human resource, and desktop publishing software off the shelf.

Finding Efficient Routes

Andrew and his long-time messengers knew Seattle like the backs of their hands. They set their own best routes. Now that QuickBiz had more than 90 employees—some not native to the area—Andrew noticed that a few deliveries were delayed because messengers had taken the wrong route. Customers complained, and the problem needed to be solved to maintain QuickBiz's reputation.

Luckily, Andrew ran across an article in *InformationWeek* on a new routing program. The software could be loaded with a map and, given start and end points, could generate the shortest route and logical delivery territories. He was surprised how well the software could organize the routes to save time, fuel, and—most importantly—money. It worked particularly well for the longer routes he'd added when service was extended beyond downtown.

The software was also tied into global positioning system (GPS) satellites so that messengers could get instant route information beamed to them as they worked. The software was installed on both the dispatchers' system and the messengers' handheld computers.

Staffing Challenges

Andrew also had trouble tracking his employees' availability for work. Sarah Truesdale and Leslie Chen had to make frequent manual changes to the schedule to ensure that routes had adequate coverage. Scheduling became increasingly complicated as the company grew and hired more part-time workers. Because many of those workers were college students, their availability changed from semester to semester, thus the entire schedule was revamped two or three times a year. Also, when someone called in sick, they had to scramble to line up a replacement. It was time to automate.

Sarah told Andrew about scheduling software that her friend, a nurse at a local hospital, had used at work. The employer simply input employees' available hours, and the program generated a schedule. Making changes was streamlined, too—the software could identify on-call employees or revise a worker's schedule quickly. Master schedules were posted at the end of the week for next week's work, and changes were generated as needed.

Andrew had always enjoyed the closeness of his small company. Employees worked hard to do their jobs well. To foster pride in efficiency, Andrew began a new program to track the number of deliveries and shortest delivery times for each messenger. The program also tracked any feedback he received—customer compliments and complaints or speeding tickets. He called the messengers together to alert them that beginning with next month's deliveries, he'd begin tracking their productivity under his new incentive program. At the end of the month, the two employees—a bicycle courier and an auto or truck courier—with the most deliveries, lowest delivery times per mile, fewest complaints, and most compliments would receive a bonus.

Andrew also evaluated the delivery territories to determine which were most profitable. He generated sales reports by region from the customer database. From those reports, he noticed that the Saturday delivery service in the downtown area wasn't generating enough revenue to cover its cost. Therefore, he decided to research this particular service further and see if its elimination could cause loss of regular services. He also adjusted the number of couriers to add more service to his most profitable routes. Those changes would help boost the bottom line and keep QuickBiz rolling smoothly.

SOFTWARE: INSTRUCTIONS TO THE COMPUTER

Productivity is important not only for success but also for survival. When executives talk about productivity tools, they really mean computer programs, commonly known as software **applications**. Word processors, electronic spreadsheets, Web browsers, project management tools, collaborative work programs, and many other types of productivity tools are software that runs on computers and enables workers to produce more products and services in a given amount of time. This chapter discusses the differences between system software and application software, programming languages that are used to write software, and the types of software tools currently available.

Software is a series of instructions to a computer to execute any and all processes, such as displaying text, mathematically manipulating numbers, or copying or deleting documents. Computers only understand instructions made up of electrical signals alternating between two states, which eventually close or open tiny electrical circuits. Different sequences of signals represent different instructions to the computer. In the early days of computers, programming a computer meant actually changing the computer's wiring by opening and closing switches or moving plugs from one circuit to another. Because programs today consist of instructions that require no hardware reconfiguration, the skill of composing software programs is independent of building or directly manipulating hardware.

There are two major categories of software: application software and system software. **Application software** enables users to complete a particular application or task, such as word processing, investment analysis, data manipulation, or project management. **System software** enables application software to run on a computer and manages the interaction between the CPU, memory, storage, input/output devices, and other computer components. Both types of software are discussed later in the chapter.

PROGRAMMING LANGUAGES AND SOFTWARE DEVELOPMENT TOOLS

Programs are needed for absolutely every operation a computer conducts. An operation can be as simple as adding 1 + 2, typing a word, or emitting a beep, or as involved as calculating the trajectory of a spacecraft bound for Mars. The process of writing programs is **programming**.

Remember, the *only* language that computer hardware understands is a series of electrical signals that represent bits and bytes, which together provide computer hardware with instructions to carry out operations. But writing programs in that language—which is called **machine language**—requires a programmer to literally create long strings of ones and zeroes to represent different characters and symbols, work that is no longer required thanks to programming languages and other software development tools. **Assembly languages** made programming somewhat easier because they aggregated common commands into "words," although many of those "words" are not English-like. Higher-level **programming languages** enable the use of English-like statements to accomplish a goal, and those statements are translated by special software into the machine language. Software development tools are even easier to use because they require practically no knowledge of programming languages to develop software. Programmers have at their disposal literally thousands of different programming languages, such as Visual Basic, Java, and C++. Programmers and nonprogrammers alike can use software tools such as Web page development tools, which provide menus, icons, and palettes that the developer can select or click to create intricate Web pages, forms, and animation. To develop the software development tools themselves, as well as to develop highly specialized software, programmers still have to write code in programming languages.

Figure 5.1 shows how programming languages have evolved dramatically over the years. Their different stages of development are known as generations. First- and second-generation languages were quite inefficient tools for code writing. They required lengthy written code for even the simplest instructions. In third- and fourth-generation languages, shorter, more human-friendly commands replaced lengthy code. Ultimately, it would be nice to be able to program using the daily grammar of your native language—English, Spanish, Hebrew, or any other language. But even then, the so-called natural language would have to be translated by another program into machine language.

FIGURE 5.1
The evolution of programming languages

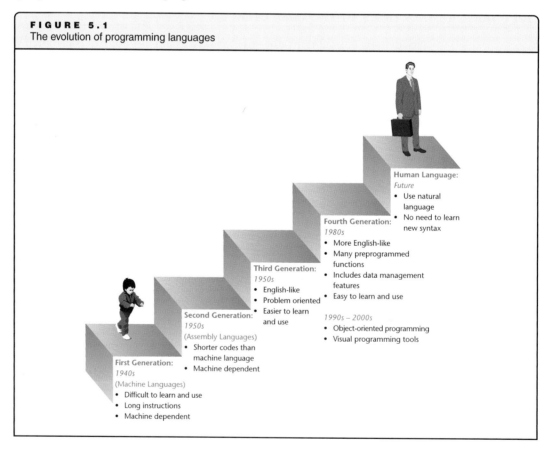

Third-generation languages (3GLs) are considered "procedural" because the programmer has to detail a logical procedure that solves the problem at hand. Third-generation languages reduce the programmer's time in producing code. One 3GL statement is equivalent to 5–10 assembly language statements. Some common procedural languages include FORTRAN, COBOL, BASIC, RPG, Pascal, and C.

Fourth-generation languages (4GLs) make application development even easier. They are built around database management systems that allow the programmer to create database structures, populate them with data, and manipulate the data. Many routine procedures are preprogrammed and can be recalled by including a single word in the code. A single 4GL statement is equivalent to several 3GL statements, and therefore to several tens of assembler statements.

4GL commands are more English-like than 3GL procedural languages' commands. In fact, 4GLs are significantly less procedural than 3GLs. With 4GL commands, the programmer often only needs to type what is to be done, but doesn't need to specify how the procedure accomplishes the task. For example, if one column in a database is AGE, the programmer can simply use the preprogrammed command LIST AVERAGE(AGE) to display on the screen the average age, which is calculated from the age values in all the records. Similarly, there are preprogrammed functions for total, standard deviation, count, median, and many more. The list of preprogrammed functions in electronic spreadsheets such as Microsoft Excel has become so comprehensive, that some people refer to them as 4GLs.

4GLs speed up the programming process. They are relatively easy to use by people who are not professional programmers, and therefore enable non-IT employees in many companies to produce applications on their own. The produced code is usually easy to change, which reduces the cost of software maintenance. Because 4GLs are very English-like, debugging—locating and fixing programming errors—is relatively easy.

POINT OF INTEREST

Software Leader

The United States is home to more software engineers than any other country: 2.35 million Americans develop software for a living. This is more than four times as many software developers in India, and almost seven times as many as software engineers in China.

Source: IDC, 2004.

Higher-level programming languages have their advantages, but also some disadvantages (see Figure 5.2). Therefore, programming languages are chosen based not only on programming productivity but also on the amount of control over the resulting software that is desired.

Visual Programming

 To accelerate their work, programmers can use one of several visual programming languages, such as Microsoft Visual Basic, Borland Delphi, Micro Focus COBOL, ASNA Visual RPG, and Visual C++. These languages let programmers create field windows, scroll-down menus, click buttons, and other objects by simply choosing the proper icon from a palette. They can then use a flexible tool to shape and color these objects. (Note that here the term "object" is used loosely, not with its special meaning in the context of object-oriented languages, as discussed in the next section.) Seeing exactly and immediately how boxes and menus look on-screen reduces the chance of bugs and lets programmers finish their jobs faster than if they had to write code. The appropriate code is written automatically for them when they click on elements. However, the programmer can always go back to the code and add or change statements for operations that cannot easily be accomplished by using the visual aids. Thus, knowledge of the programming language is still required.

FIGURE 5.2
Advantages and disadvantages of higher-level programming languages

Advantages of Higher-Level Programming

◆ Ease of learning the language

◆ Ease of programming

◆ Significantly shorter code

◆ Ease of debugging

◆ Ease of maintenance (for example, modification of a procedure)

Disadvantages of Higher-Level Programming

◆ Less control over hardware

◆ Less efficient memory use

◆ Program runs more slowly

Visual Basic programmers see how the elements they develop (left) will look in the final application (right).

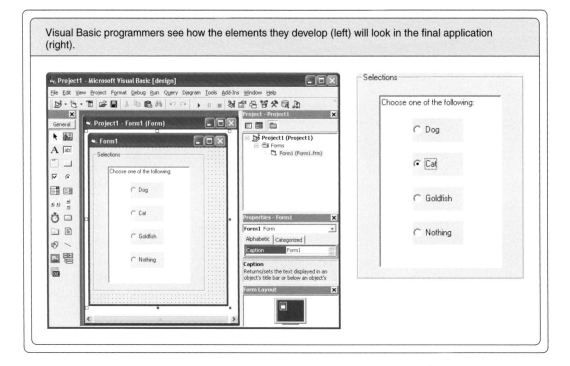

Object-Oriented Programming

An increasing amount of software is developed using **object-oriented programming (OOP) languages**. These languages use a modular approach, which offers two great advantages: ease of maintenance and efficiency in applications development (see Figure 5.3). In traditional programming, programmers receive specifications of how a program should process data and how it should interact with users, and then they write code. If business changes and the program must be modified, the programmer must change the code. In traditional programming, data and the operations to manipulate the data are kept separate from each other. In object-oriented programming, on the other hand, operations are linked to the data. For example, if the operation is to calculate an employee's gross pay, taxes, and net pay, selecting and clicking on the record triggers the calculation. Routine, frequent operations are kept with the data to be processed. Thus, OOP's primary emphasis is not on the procedure for performing a task, but on the objects involved in the task.

FIGURE 5.3
Advantages of object-oriented programming (OOP) over procedural languages

OOP Advantages

- ◆ Requires less code than other languages

- ◆ Requires less time than programming in other languages

- ◆ Enhances program modularity and reusability

- ◆ Makes code maintenance easier

- ◆ Enhances ability to create user-friendly interface

- ◆ Is appropriate for graphic- and sound-enhanced applications

---

What Is an Object in OOP?

Figure 5.4 illustrates how an object in OOP encapsulates a data set with the code used to operate on it. Data elements in the object are called "data members." They might be records, whole files, or another type of data structure. Data members have attributes that define the nature of the data, such as Social Security number, last name, and hourly rate. The code elements of the object are called "member functions" or "methods." These procedures operate on the data, such as calculating an employee's gross pay for the week. In object-oriented software, there is no direct access to data members of an object; they can be accessed only through the methods, which are part of the object. In our example, the object includes three methods: Weekly Pay, Overtime Pay, and Age. Weekly Pay calculates each employee's gross and net pay, Overtime Pay calculates each employee's overtime gross pay, and Age computes all employees' average age.

FIGURE 5.4
The object EMPLOYEE

E M P L O Y E E

Attributes

    Social Security Number

    Last Name

    First Name

    Address

    Date of Birth

    Hourly Rate

Methods

    Weekly Pay

    Overtime Pay

    Age

Ease of Maintenance and Development

Programmers spend 60–85 percent of their time maintaining software. Maintenance is mainly modifying programs to meet new business needs but also debugging of errors that were not detected in the testing of the developed code. In object-oriented programming, software developers treat objects as parts, or standardized modules that work together and can be used and reused. Instead of creating large, complex, tightly intertwined programs, programmers create objects. Objects are developed in standard ways and have standard behaviors and interfaces. These modules enable software to be assembled rapidly rather than written laboriously.

OOP also makes creating programs easier for nonprogrammers. The inexperienced developer does not need to know how an object does what it does, only *what* it does. Thus, the developer can select and combine appropriate objects from an object library, which is a repository of developed objects, to build a desired application.

Object-Oriented Programming Languages

Object-oriented programming languages have been around for many years, but they have only recently generated significant interest. The most popular OOP languages are Smalltalk, C++, Object Pascal, and Java. Smalltalk, developed by Xerox, was the first object-oriented programming language. C++ has become the major commercial OOP language because it combines traditional C programming with object-oriented capabilities. Java is a popular object-oriented language designed to be platform independent, that is, to run on any computer regardless of the CPU or operating system. Another popular language, Visual Basic, enables the programmer to use graphical objects, but does not fulfill all the requirements of a true OOP language. For example, moving an icon to another application does not move the code associated with it. Some OOP languages are designed specifically for use in developing graphical user interfaces (GUIs). Elements of GUIs include windows, icons, scroll boxes, and other graphical images that help the user interact with the program with minimum effort. One of the earliest uses of Smalltalk was to develop GUIs.

Software Tools for the Web

Because an increasing amount of software is developed for Web sites, special software languages and tools have been developed for these tasks. Programming languages include Java, JavaScript, J2EE (Java 2 Platform, Enterprise Edition), and PHP. Web page development packages include FrontPage, Dreamweaver, and GoLive. The main advantage of Java, J2EE, and JavaScript is that the code produced—often called **applets**—can be executed well regardless of the operating system that the computer uses. Therefore, the same applet will be executed the same way on a computer running Windows or one running Mac OS X. This is a great benefit especially when the applets are developed to be posted at a Web site.

Web page development packages expedite development of Web page elements. Like other visual tools, they provide menus, icons, and other features from which the developer can select. Therefore, developers have to write code only when a feature is not readily available. When using ready options, such as fill-in forms and animation effects, the code is automatically added. Since much of the code is in nonproprietary languages such as HTML and XML (which we discuss in Chapter 8), a programmer can start work with one development tool, such as FrontPage, and continue the work with another, such as Dreamweaver. Both tools recognize the code. Developers alternate if they find one tool is easier to use for quick development of icons, for example, whereas the other offers a more appealing way to develop animations.

Why You Should...

Be Software Savvy

As a professional, you should regard software as a tool to further your productivity and education. Software can automate many processes that professionals must accomplish. Even simple software such as electronic spreadsheets can be used to build decision-support applications. Software vendors offer a huge variety of programs. While it is doubtful that any individual can become knowledgeable about all available software, knowledge of the types of software and particular applications lets you make informed comparisons and suggestions for improving your organization's software portfolio and your own library of personal software.

LANGUAGE TRANSLATION: COMPILERS AND INTERPRETERS

Recall that computers understand only machine language. Just as assembly languages need assemblers, procedural languages need special programs to translate **source code**, which is the program as originally written, into **object code**, which is the same program in machine language. (Unfortunately, the word "object" is used for several different contexts. In the context of this section it has nothing to do with object-oriented languages.) There are two types of language translators: compilers and interpreters. Compilers translate the higher-level code into an equivalent machine language code but do not execute the code; the translated code must be run to see if there are any programming errors. Interpreters translate each program statement and execute it.

A **compiler** (see Figure 5.5) scans the entire source code, looking for errors in the form (syntax) and execution of the code. If it finds an error, it does not create the object code; instead, it generates an error message or a list of error messages. If the compiler finds no syntactic or execution errors, it translates source code into object code, which the computer can execute. At this point, the programmer can save the object code. From now on, the user can simply run only the object code. This saves translation time.

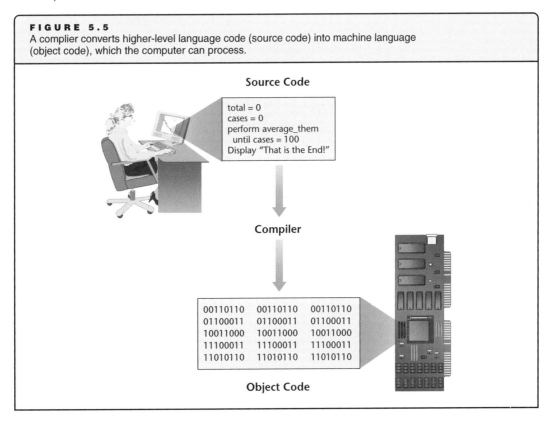

FIGURE 5.5
A complier converts higher-level language code (source code) into machine language (object code), which the computer can process.

Source Code

```
total = 0
cases = 0
perform average_them
    until cases = 100
Display "That is the End!"
```

Compiler

```
00110110   00110110   00110110
01100011   01100011   01100011
10011000   10011000   10011000
11100011   11100011   11100011
11010110   11010110   11010110
```

Object Code

An **interpreter** checks one statement at a time. If the first statement is free of syntactic and execution errors, it interprets the statement into object code and makes the computer execute it. If the statement is erroneous, the interpreter issues an error message. In some environments, the programmer can immediately correct the statement. The computer then executes the corrected statement, and the interpreter moves on to check the next statement. Error-free statements are executed immediately.

Code written in interpreted programming languages can run only on machines whose disks store the interpreter. In contrast, compiled code is ready to run because it is in machine language and does not need to be translated. Most Visual Basic and Java translators are interpreters. Translators of FORTRAN, COBOL, C, C++, and most other 3GLs are compilers.

When you purchase an application, whether a computer game or a business program, you purchase a compiled version of the code, that is, the object code. There are two reasons for this. First, most users do not have the compiler for the source code. Second, the vendor does not wish buyers to modify the code. If the program is sufficiently modified, the modified copies may be sold without violating intellectual property laws such as patents and copyrights. Source code can be modified by anyone who knows the programming language in which it was written; modifying object code is very difficult.

APPLICATION SOFTWARE

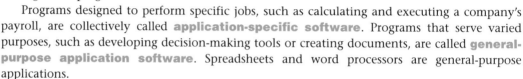

As noted earlier, an application is a program developed to address a specific need. An application can also be software that lets nonprogrammers develop such programs. Most programs that professionals use are application programs, such as word-processing programs, spreadsheet programs, payroll programs, investment analysis programs, and work-scheduling and project management programs.

Programs designed to perform specific jobs, such as calculating and executing a company's payroll, are collectively called **application-specific software**. Programs that serve varied purposes, such as developing decision-making tools or creating documents, are called **general-purpose application software**. Spreadsheets and word processors are general-purpose applications.

General-purpose applications are available as **packaged software**; that is, they come ready to install from an external storage medium such as a CD or a file downloaded from a vendor's Web site. Application-specific software is not always so readily available. Managers must decide whether an off-the-shelf software package fits all needs. If it does, the company can simply purchase it. But if off-the-shelf or other ready-made software cannot address an organization's specified needs, managers must have a program developed, either within the organization or by another organization specializing in that type of software. We discuss alternative ways to acquire ready-made software in Chapter 13, "Choices in Systems Acquisition."

Office Productivity Applications

The purpose of *all* software is to make the work of people more productive. However, applications that help employees in their routine office work often are called simply "productivity tools." They include word processors, spreadsheets, presentation tools, file and database management software, graphics programs, desktop publishing tools, and project management applications, as well as many others for more specialized purposes. Web browsers are also included in this group, because they help so many employees to find and communicate information in their daily work. Often, the tools are called desktop productivity tools, because they were developed to support home and office users on their personal computers.

While *word processors* are used mainly to type letters, articles, and other text documents, they also automate otherwise laborious tasks such as creating tables of contents and indexes. Some enable users to plan the binding and look of books up to the point of handing files to a high-quality printer for the production of the physical book. Examples of word processors include Microsoft Word, Corel WordPerfect, and Lotus WordPro.

Spreadsheets such as Microsoft Excel no longer limit users to entering numbers and performing basic arithmetic calculations. They include a long list of complex mathematical, statistical, financial, and other functions that users can integrate into analysis models. These functions are so powerful that statisticians often use them. Executives can build their own decision-support models with this robust tool. Spreadsheets also provide a large array of preformatted charts from which the user can select for presentation purposes.

Presentation tools such as Microsoft PowerPoint enable professionals and salespeople to quickly develop impressive presentations. One does not need to be a graphics expert, because the tools provide wide selections of font types and sizes and allow the users to embed almost any art that they find (with permission!) or have created in graphics programs. Animations, sound, and video clips can be integrated into presentations.

File management and data management tools enable the creation and manipulation of local or shared databases. Popular database management systems such as Microsoft Access are relatively easy to learn and create simple databases. They often include features that professional developers can use to create more complex databases.

Graphics programs make it easy to create intricate graphics and manipulate digital photographs. They are often used to create graphics to be placed on Web pages. The large selection of these tools includes Adobe's Illustrator and Photoshop, Corel Paint Shop, and MGI PhotoSuite, as well as the free IrfanView.

Desktop publishing tools, such as Microsoft Publisher and Home Publishing, and Corel Ventura, enable both expert and novice to easily create professional looking pamphlets, newsletters, cards, calendars, and many other items for publication on paper or as Web pages. More professional tools, such as Quark, by a company of the same name, have significantly increased the productivity of the publishing industry.

Project management tools help managers of any type of project—such as building construction, product development, and software development—to plan projects and track their progress. Project managers enter information such as tasks and their expected completion dates, milestones, and resources required for each task: labor hours, materials, and services. The software alerts planners when they enter illogical information such as scheduling a worker to work 120 hours in one week, and when tasks violate interdependencies. The latter happens when, for instance, planners schedule the start of Phase D before the completion of Phase C, though they had previously indicated that Phase D depends on the completion of Phase C.

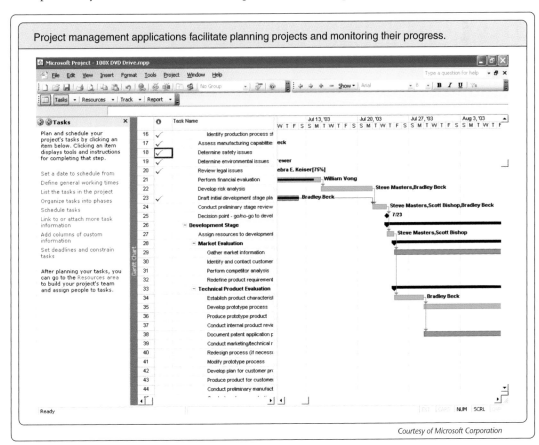

Project management applications facilitate planning projects and monitoring their progress.

Courtesy of Microsoft Corporation

Software developers often create **suites** of productivity tools. For example, most versions of Microsoft Office suite include a word processor (Word), spreadsheet (Excel), presentation application (PowerPoint), database management system (Access), and an e-mail application (Outlook). Other examples of suites are IBM Lotus SmartSuite, Sun StarOffice, and the free OfficeOne. When productivity tools are integrated into a software suite, the documents created can be interdependent using technologies such as object linking and embedding (OLE). You can create tables in a spreadsheet, copy them into a word-processed document or a presentation, and ensure that when you modify the tables in the spreadsheet they also change in the document or presentation. You can also embed links to Web sites in your documents. Linking among documents involves hypermedia technologies, and embedding information such as sound and video clips in documents uses multimedia technologies. These technologies are discussed in the next section.

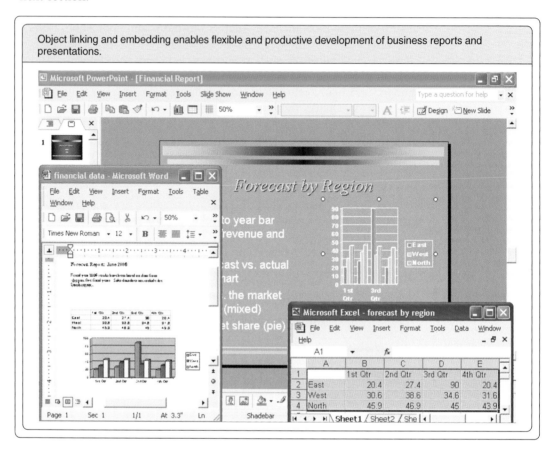

Object linking and embedding enables flexible and productive development of business reports and presentations.

Hypermedia and Multimedia

Hypermedia is a feature that enables a user to access additional information by clicking on selected text or graphics. It is the Web's most essential ingredient. When first conceived, the concept was limited to text and was called hypertext. Now, hypermedia is very common, used widely on software stored on CDs, and essential to Web-based documents, as well documents, charts, and presentations created using productivity tools. Any text or icon that can be clicked to jump to another place in a document or open a new document is called a link, whether on the Web or not. Often, we say that a word or icon is "clickable." Hypermedia enables linking text, pictures, sounds, animations, and video.

Hypermedia features are enabled by **Web page authoring tools**. They are also part of other applications, such as some word processors and presentation tools. You can fairly easily create a PowerPoint presentation with marked text or an icon that calls up a picture, a sound, or an animation, or one that takes you to another slide. Programs that can handle many different types of data are called **multimedia software**. Multimedia is a powerful means of communicating, because it does not limit the method of communication. A natural extension of the computer's capabilities, it provides flexibility that lets people work the way they think, integrating all types and forms of information. Multimedia is tightly associated with hypermedia, because it often uses embedded links. These links are the essence of hypermedia, to communicate pictures, sounds, and video as part of the same message in a way that is similar to an educational lecture or a product manual. Here are just a few examples of the uses of multimedia.

Multimedia in Education

One of the most common uses of multimedia is in education. A student taking a lesson using multimedia can view a scenario in one window and view text in another while listening to a recording of his or her professor. The student might then be asked to answer questions interactively, providing responses in another window on the screen. And the same program might be designed to provide the student with feedback on her performance. With voice recognition software, multimedia programs used in language training can ask a student to pronounce certain words and evaluate a student's performance.

Multimedia in Training

In many industries, multimedia is commonly used to simulate real-world situations for training exercises. For example, multimedia products that use video and voice and allow users to respond to questions about various situations have been used to teach workers for an electric utility company how to solve high-voltage wire problems. If they attempted to solve the same cases in the field, their lives would be jeopardized. Flight simulators use extensive multimedia software to simulate takeoff, landing, and other flight situations in training pilots before they fly real airplanes.

Multimedia in Research

Another common use of multimedia is in compiling and integrating data from research. For instance, a researcher might use multimedia programs to view written articles and television news footage and to listen to radio clips.

Multimedia in Business

Multimedia can be very useful in business situations as well. Consider this example: one manager writes a document that includes digitized photographs or video clips and possibly a "live" spreadsheet, which lets the user enter numbers and execute calculations. The manager sends the document to a colleague for review; the colleague tacks on a video and voice clip requesting clarification of a certain point. The compound document can be filed electronically, retrieved, altered, and communicated as appropriate, without ever being transformed into a paper document. In fact, multimedia by its very nature cannot be transferred to a paper document. Many Web sites include multimedia because of its interactive nature.

Groupware

Multimedia technologies are integrated with Web technologies to create groupware. **Groupware** applications are programs that enable workers to collaborate in real time over the Web. They not only eliminate the need to travel and sit in the same physical room but also facilitate expression of ideas by demonstrating them through the combination of text, images, drawings, sound, animation, and video. Consider this example of a young company that cleverly uses groupware.

Kidrobot sells mainly vinyl toys. Unlike similar companies that spend thousands of dollars on special software, Kidrobot employees design new toys using an off-the-shelf application called Adobe Illustrator. They create six views of each new toy with exploded views of detailed areas such as eyelashes. The manufacturer of the newly designed toys is located in China. For a subscription fee of $100 per month the designers place the illustrations online using Basecamp, a project management application that helps people remotely collaborate on projects. The Chinese engineers use the files to create the vinyl dolls. The company was established in 2002. By 2005, its revenues reached $5.5 million.

Virtual Reality

Virtual reality (VR) applications mimic sensory reality using software. They create the illusion of experiencing situations through simulated sight, hearing, and touch, such as flying in an airplane or forging a piece of hot metal. A user can sense virtual reality in several ways. The most sophisticated VR devices provide two important elements: immersion and interaction. They include goggles, gloves, earphones, and sometimes a moving base on which the user stands; all of these devices sense

Virtual reality applications are used not only for game playing but also as serious business tools.

© The Cover Story/CORBIS

movement, respond to signals, and provide feedback to the user. In immersion an individual senses that she or he is surrounded by the simulated environment. Interaction lets individuals simulate change in the environment by moving their hands or fingers. Users receive a three-dimensional visual sensation and hear stereophonic sound. With interactive gloves, the user can use hand motions to change the direction to "move" within the virtual environment. For instance, a VR system might be designed so the user experiences being a race car driver. In this case, when the user's hand makes a grabbing motion, sensors in the VR glove cause the hand in the VR image to "grab" the stick shift. The distinction between multimedia and VR can be hazy. Experts usually assert that only systems that include sensing helmets, gloves, and the like, which truly surround the user with a sense of a real experience, are VR. However, many people refer to sophisticated multimedia applications that run on PCs as VR as well.

Business use of VR is growing. VR business applications can decrease the cost of planning buildings, machines, and vehicles. They already help marketing efforts to lure buyers to try new products. For instance, architects can use VR to let a potential buyer "tour" a house that has not yet been built. The buyer can then request changes in the floor plan and other features before construction begins. Volvo, the Swedish car and truck maker, invites prospective buyers to test-drive its latest models in VR. Companies such as Raytheon and Fluor Daniel use VR to help design new manufacturing plants.

3-D Geographic Software

Similar to virtual reality but for somewhat different purposes, programmers develop three-dimensional models of geographic areas and whole cities. An increasing number of applications are being developed to create 3-D models of existing city blocks down to every hydrant and shrub. The raw materials are land and aerial photographs that cover the targeted area. The digital photographs are "sewn" together to allow a continuous "walk" or "travel" in a city street or on a university campus. This helps with navigation, whereby one can recognize buildings and landmarks by their similarity to the software images. This type of information can be delivered through the Web. When tied with a global positioning system (GPS), the software helps people who have never been to a place to navigate easily. In the near future, 3-D software such as this will help property rental companies manage their assets. For example, a manager will be able to click on an apartment on the 12th floor of a building and check information about the unit and let a potential renter have a view from the windows or balcony. Maintenance staffs will be able to virtually go into the walls and check pipes and electrical wiring, and fire companies will be able to navigate quickly and locate hydrants on their way to put out fires.

GeoSim, a company that specializes in such software, has developed "virtual cities" including Philadelphia. One can virtually walk in the streets, drive a car, or fly above a city. Similar software was developed for university campuses, notably that of University of Pennsylvania. Such software helps city planners and service agencies, as well as tourism and travel agencies. Some of this software is demonstrated at www.geosimcities.com.

SYSTEM SOFTWARE

System software includes programs that are designed to carry out general routine operations, such as the interface between user and computer, loading a file, copying a file, or deleting a file, as well as managing memory resources and operating peripheral equipment such as monitors and printers. The purpose of system software is to manage computer resources and perform routine tasks that are not specific to any application. On one hand, system software is developed to work in partnership with as many applications as possible; on the other, applications can work with system software only if they are developed to be compatible with that software. The following discussion covers major types of system programs. Note that compilers and interpreters, which were discussed earlier, are also classified as system software.

3-D city models help city planners maintain existing facilities and plan new blocks and parks.

Courtesy of GeoSim Systems Ltd.

Operating Systems

The **operating system (OS)** is the single most important program that runs on a computer and the most important type of system software. As Figure 5.6 illustrates, operating systems perform basic tasks, such as recognizing input from the keyboard and mouse, sending output to the computer display, keeping track of files and directories (groups of files) on disks, and sending documents to the printer. Without an operating system, no application can run on a computer. An operating system is developed for a certain microprocessor or multiple microprocessors. Programmers know which operations each microprocessor can perform and how it performs them. The OS must address technical details such as CPU circuitry and memory addresses. Therefore, OSs are usually developed with the aid of low-level programming languages, such as assembly languages or C.

The OS is sometimes called the "traffic cop" or the "boss" of computer resources. Indeed, it is charged with control functions such as optimally allocating memory locations for an application program, copying the application from an external storage medium into memory, passing control to the CPU for execution of program instructions, and sending processing results to output devices. Operating systems are also often referred to as "platforms," because they are the platform on which all other applications "ride" when interacting with the hardware.

From User to OS to CPU

Figure 5.7 shows the OS's position in the logical operation of a computer. The user interacts with the user interface using menus, icons, and commands the application provides. The application converts some of the user's input into commands the OS understands, and the OS commands the CPU to carry out the operation. (Some commands are not delivered to the OS but directly from the application to the hardware.) The OS ensures that applications can use the CPU, memory, input and output devices, and the file system. The file system is software that stores, organizes, and retrieves files.

For example, assume that you are using a word processor. You select a paragraph you wish to copy and paste. You select Copy from the menu. The word processor converts your choice into an appropriate command for the OS, which then instructs the CPU to copy the paragraph. A

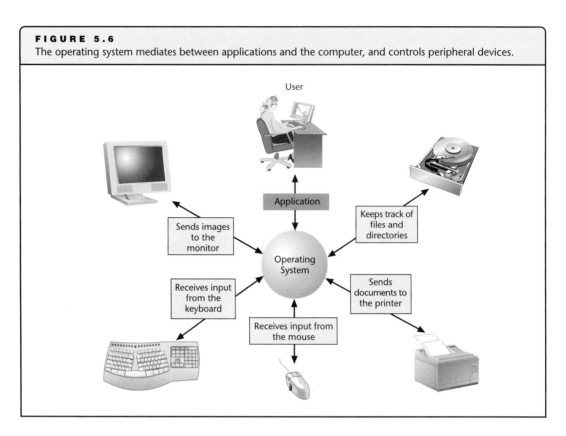

FIGURE 5.6
The operating system mediates between applications and the computer, and controls peripheral devices.

User

Application

Operating System

Sends images to the monitor

Keeps track of files and directories

Receives input from the keyboard

Sends documents to the printer

Receives input from the mouse

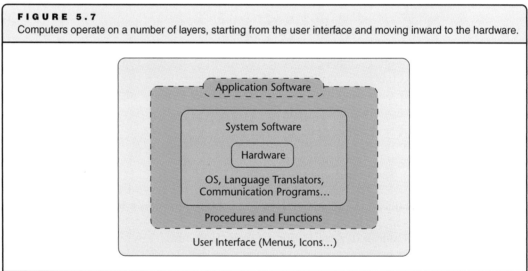

FIGURE 5.7
Computers operate on a number of layers, starting from the user interface and moving inward to the hardware.

Application Software

System Software

Hardware

OS, Language Translators, Communication Programs...

Procedures and Functions

User Interface (Menus, Icons...)

similar action takes place when you select Paste from the menu. Assume that you are using an electronic spreadsheet on your computer. You select a portion of a column of numbers that you want to copy and paste. The spreadsheet's menu might not look the same as the word processor's menu. However, when you select Copy, the operating system receives a command from the application that is identical to the one it received when you used the word processor. And when you paste, the Paste command that the OS receives from the spreadsheet is the same one it received from the word processor. Thus, developers of these two applications did not need to program the copy and paste operations; they only needed to know how their programs must call up these operations from the OS.

In addition to performing input and output services and controlling the CPU, many OSs perform accounting and statistical jobs, including recording times when a user logs on and logs off, the number of seconds the operator used the CPU in every session, and the number of pages a user printed. Some OSs also perform **utilities** such as hardware diagnostics, disk check, file comparison, file sorting, and the like. However, not all OSs provide all the utilities that might be necessary, in which case special utility programs must be used. Modern operating systems, especially those designed for networked computers, often include a number of security functions such as the ability to set user passwords and restrict access to files and computer resources.

Operating System Functions

Operating systems provide several services, the most important of which is system management. System management refers to the efficient allocation of hardware resources to applications and includes tasks such as prompting the user for certain actions, allocating RAM locations for software and data, instructing the CPU to run or stop, allocating CPU time to different programs running at the same time, and instructing coprocessors and peripheral equipment.

User Interface An important part of the OS is the user interface; older OSs prompted the user to enter commands; later OSs provided graphical user interfaces (GUIs), which makes the use of the computer intuitive and easier to learn. The interface takes the form of easy-to-understand frames, icons, and menus. Users find it helpful to have most of the interface features identical regardless of the application they use, unless the application requires an interface element for a unique feature.

Memory Allocation One of the most important functions of an operating system is memory management, especially RAM. RAM, you might remember, is the memory where data and program code must reside before being executed. Ideally, an entire application and all the data it processes reside in RAM until processing ends. However, large applications and data pools might exceed the computer's RAM capacity. One way the OS deals with insufficient RAM is to use **virtual memory**, which lets the user proceed as if significantly more RAM were available than really exists. Virtual memory uses the hard disk as an extension of RAM. A special module of the OS continually detects which parts of the application program are used frequently. The OS keeps these parts in RAM while leaving on the disk the least frequently used parts. Professionals call this activity "page swapping"—"pages" are program parts of equal size that the OS swaps between RAM and the disk, and the space on disk used as memory is called "swap space."

Plug and Play A good operating system should also facilitate fairly simple changes to hardware configuration. When a new device, such as an external hard disk or a DVD burner, an external communication device, or a joystick, is attached to a computer, the operating system's job is to recognize the new attachment and its function. If the OS can do so (without your intervention) immediately after you attach the device, it is a **plug-and-play (PnP)** OS, and the device, too, is referred to as a plug-and-play device. To do so, the operating system must have access to the attached device's driver. A **driver** is the software that enables the OS to control a device, either one installed inside the computer box (such as a second video card) or an external device such as a flash memory drive. Thus, a true PnP OS, such as Windows XP, includes the drivers for many devices, or at least is fully compatible with a driver that is installed either from a disc or after it is downloaded from the Web. In recent years almost all external devices have been built to attach to a computer through a USB port. (USB ports were discussed in Chapter 4.)

Increasing Services from OSs The trend in OS development is to incorporate more and more services that used to be provided by separate software. These services include database management, networking, and security. For instance, users now expect an OS to perform such security measures as tracking account numbers and passwords, controlling access to files and programs, and protecting the computer against viruses. OSs also check for access codes to ensure only authorized users can access the computer. Windows XP and NetWare provide networking functions previously handled by separate programs.

Current Operating Systems As mentioned earlier, operating systems are designed to work with a particular microprocessor; consequently, there are different OSs for different computers and types of microprocessors. While there are operating systems for supercomputers, mainframe computers, midrange computers, and handheld computers, most people use a PC operating system. Popular operating systems for microcomputers include Windows XP Home and Professional, and Linux for computers built around microprocessors designed by Intel, AMD, and other companies; and Mac

OS for the Macintosh, which for many years has used Motorola's PowerPC microprocessors. (In 2005, Apple Computer decided to use Intel microprocessors instead.) Older Microsoft operating systems for Intel-based computers include the veteran DOS, Windows 98, Windows 2000, and Windows NT. Some operating systems are designed especially for computers used as servers in networks. For example, NetWare and Windows Server 2003 are popular network operating systems that are compatible with clients running DOS, all versions of Windows, and Mac OS. Figure 5.8 provides a list of popular operating systems.

FIGURE 5.8
Popular operating systems

Name	OS Developer	Runs on...
Linux	Linus Torvalds and other individuals and companies	PCs, mainly servers
Mac OS X	Apple Computer	Macintosh PCs
MS-DOS	Microsoft	PCs
NetWare	Novell	Usually network servers
OS/400	IBM	IBM iSeries (the renamed AS/400) midrange computers
OS390 (formerly MVS)	IBM	IBM mainframes
Palm OS	Palm	Handheld computers (PDA)
Solaris	Sun Microsystems	Sun and other computers
UNIX	AT&T (originally) and other software companies	Various versions for IBM, Macintosh, Sun, and other computers
Windows 95, 98, Me, NT, 2000, XP, 2003	Microsoft	PCs
Windows CE	Microsoft	Handheld computers (PDAs)

POINT OF INTEREST

OS Trends

According to Microsoft Corporation, 600 million PCs ran Windows operating systems in 2004. A study by the Yankee Group in the same year found that 11 percent of the businesses that were using Windows planned to switch to Linux. Linux is especially popular with small- and medium-size companies, those whose annual revenue is less than $1 billion per year.

Source: Microsoft Corporation, 2005; Yankee Group, 2005.

One OS that has grown in popularity is Linux, which can be obtained free of charge. Linux is based on UNIX, an operating system developed by AT&T in 1969 to run on minicomputers, and for 10 years was distributed free of charge. Different companies and individuals modified UNIX, developing variations of the OS such as Linux (developed by Linus Torvalds) and Solaris (developed by Sun Microsystems). Linux and other "open source" software is discussed in the next section.

One of the most important qualities of an OS is its *stability*. A stable OS does not cause the computer to freeze or produce error messages. It is expected to continue to function even if the user makes a mistake, in which case it should gracefully notify the user what happened and give an opportunity to resolve the problem, rather than stop functioning. Windows 95, Windows 98, and Windows Me were notoriously unstable. Although mishaps do occur with Windows NT,

2000, XP, and Server 2003, they are significantly more stable. OSs based on UNIX are known to be highly stable, and their stability is the main reason for their popularity, especially for running servers. Mac OS X versions are based on UNIX. Linux is also considered to be very stable.

Other System Software

While operating systems are the most prevalent type of system software, there are other types of system programs: compilers and interpreters (which we discussed), communications software, and utilities. Some people also include in this class database management systems, which are discussed in Chapter 7.

Communications software supports transmission and reception of data across computer networks. We discuss networking and telecommunications in Chapter 6. Utilities include programs that enhance the performance of computers, such as Symantec's Norton SystemWorks, which checks PCs for inefficiencies and fixes them. Utilities also include antivirus programs, firewalls, and other programs that detect and remove unwanted files and applications, such as cookies and spyware, or block data from being transmitted into or out of a networked computer. We discuss these topics in Chapters 8 and 14.

OPEN SOURCE SOFTWARE

The great majority of business and individual software is proprietary, that is, software that is developed and sold for profit. The developers of **proprietary software** do not make the source code of their software public. The developer retains the rights to the software. In most cases you do not actually own the copies of applications that you purchase; you only purchase licenses to use those applications. In contrast to proprietary software, there are programmers who freely contribute to the development of a growing number of computer programs not for profit. The developers of **open source software** can obtain the source code free of charge, usually on the Web. Anyone who can contribute features is invited to do so. Anyone who wishes to download the latest version can do so free of charge. An open source program can be developed by a random group of programmers, rather than by a single company. Programmers share an application's basic code, find its weaknesses, debug it, and contribute new pieces. This process might yield better results than the traditional "closed" process of proprietary software, because so many talented programmers continuously try to show their prowess in improving the program. Some historians find the beginning of the open source "movement" in people such as Richard Stallman and his comrades in the Free Software Foundation, who believe that software should be as free as the air we breathe and never sold for money.

The advantages of open source software over proprietary software are clear: the software has fewer bugs because thousands of independent programmers review the code, and it can offer more innovative features by incorporating ideas from a diverse set of experts from different countries and cultures who collaborate. The motive for developing and improving open source software is not monetary, but rather the satisfaction of solving programming problems and the recognition of one's contribution. Programmers who improve such software do it for fame and recognition by their peers the world over. They collaborate mainly via the Internet. They post patches of code that improve current code, or add extensions and plug-ins to enhance functionality of an application. These extensions are free for all to download and use. The major disadvantage is that development and support depend on the continued effort of an army of volunteers.

There are hundreds of useful open source applications. They include the popular Web browser Mozilla Firefox, the e-mail application Thunderbird, the relational database management server MySQL, and the powerful programming language PERL (Practical Extraction and Report Language). OpenOffice.org, which can be freely downloaded at www.openoffice.org, provides a complete alternative to Microsoft's Office suite of productivity applications.

OpenOffice.org, an office suite; Firefox, a Web browser; and Thunderbird, an e-mail application, are just a few of hundreds of useful and popular open source applications.

Firefox

Thunderbird

Courtesy of The Mozilla Foundation

Courtesy of OpenOffice.org

Tux the penguin is the unofficial trademark of Linux. Linux has made inroads into the corporate world, where it is used mainly to run servers.

Courtesy of Larry Ewing and The GIMP

Note that not all free software is also open source. For example, Microsoft Internet Explorer browser can be downloaded and used free of charge, but the source code and documentation of the software are proprietary. On the other hand, the source code and documentation for Firefox is open: programmers from the world over can access the source code and improve it.

Linux is the best known open source operating system. A Finnish graduate student named Linus Torvalds developed it for his own use, but he has never claimed rights to the software. Hundreds of programmers have contributed code to Linux. Over time, Linux evolved into many different variants, some of which are sold by companies such as Red Hat, Mandrake-Soft, and SuSE. These companies mainly added interface features and support services to code that is free to the public. Linux has become the OS of choice of many Internet service providers to run their Internet servers. The major disadvantage of using Linux is the limited number of applications that can run on it, compared with the Windows platform.

Reputable software companies including IBM, Intel, Hewlett-Packard (HP), and Dell have committed to supporting Linux by developing applications that run on it. A growing number of corporations have adopted it, including DaimlerChrysler, Tommy Hilfiger, and practically every major brokerage house on Wall Street. Linux is popular not only because it is stable, but because it is versatile: it can run on mainframe computers, PCs, handhelds, and electronic devices. The oil company Amerada Hess uses Linux on a supercomputer to help find oil and gas deposits. Pixar Animation Studios uses Linux machines to render digital animated characters. The brokerage firm Morgan Stanley replaced 4,000 servers that ran Microsoft Windows and Sun Solaris with cheaper machines that run Linux and saved $100 million. TiVo, the television recording device, runs on Linux. So do many game consoles and television sets that are connected to the Internet.

Many governments, both local and national, have decided to move to open source software. They do so mostly to save money but also to improve operations. Many adopters of Linux, for instance, have reported a tenfold improvement in the speed of their software-based operations when they moved from a commercial OS to Linux. Forty-two percent of Argentine companies use Linux. The governments of Brazil, Peru, and Chile mandated that all public administration agencies use only open source software when available. The Brazilian government switched more than 300,000 of its computers from Windows to Linux.

POINT OF INTEREST

Free Software Nation

In an attempt to save millions of dollars, the president of Brazil instructed the government and state-owned companies to switch from proprietary operating systems to free operating systems, such as Linux. The major loser from this move is Microsoft. President Luiz Inacio Lula da Silva also decreed that any company or research institute that receives government funding to develop software must license it as open source, that is, the software's source code must be accessible to all, free of charge. This is part of a general effort to make IT and Internet access more affordable to this large nation of 183 million people. In 2005, only 10 percent of Brazilians had access to the Internet.

Source: Benson, T., "Brazil: Free Software's Biggest and Best Friend," *New York Times* (www.nytimes.com), March 29, 2005.

While many versions of Linux can be downloaded free of charge from the Web, most firms prefer to purchase a packaged version. Companies such as Novell, Red Hat, and VA Software sell the software and promise technical support. Usually, contracts also include updates. Companies such as IBM and HP have made millions of dollars by bundling Linux with other system software and business applications, such as database management systems.

SOFTWARE LICENSING

The next time you "purchase" software read carefully the "purchase" contract. You might be surprised to see that you do not own the software you have just obtained. Most of the software that organizations and individuals obtain is not purchased; it is licensed. The client receives a limited permission to use the software, either indefinitely or for a set time. When the use is time-limited, the client pays annual license fees. The only exceptions to this rule occur when an adopter uses its own employees to develop the software, when it hires the work of a software development firm, or when the adopter uses software developed by people who explicitly allow the user to change the software and sell the product.

POINT OF INTEREST

Frustrated with Software Licensing

A survey of 257 IT executives by the research firm IDC found that they were frustrated with software licensing agreements. Their feeling was that even when software vendors offer great discounts, the clients end up paying much more than the initial price. Usually, the extra payments are for software maintenance or subscription fees. Subscription fees are often charged for support and upgrades. Interestingly, the executives believed that their companies used only 16 percent of the software they buy.

Source: Koch, C., "Do You Really Want Software as a Service?" *CIO* (www.cio.com), March 17, 2005.

Software Piracy

Software piracy, the illegal copying of software, is probably one of the most pervasive crimes. Software piracy has several forms: making copies from a single paid copy of the software; using the Internet to download software from a Web site without paying for it, or copying software through use of peer-to-peer applications; using one licensed copy to install an application on multiple computers; taking advantage of upgrade offers without having paid for a legal copy of the updated version; using for commercial purposes copies that were acquired with discounts for home or educational use; and using at home a copy that was purchased by an employer under a license to use only on the employer's premises. The software industry established two organizations to protect software developers from piracy: Business Software Alliance (BSA) and the Software & Information Industry Association (SIIA). The two organizations were established by major software companies and are supported by the majority of the world's software development firms. Both organizations have Web sites that encourage everyone to report pirated software. Occasionally, the organizations sponsor studies that estimate the proportion and financial damage that piracy causes in various world regions.

As the amount of software sold on the market grows, so grow the estimated losses that the software industry suffers from piracy. In the 1980s and 1990s, the global financial damage was estimated at $10–$12 billion annually. However, a survey conducted jointly by BSA and the IT research company IDC (International Data Corporation) reported that the loss to the software industry reached $29 billion in 2003. The study found that of the $80 billion of software that was installed on computers worldwide, only $51 billion worth of software was legally purchased. Thus, about 36 percent of the world's installed software was pirated. A spokesperson for BSA explained: piracy deprives local governments of tax revenue, costs jobs in the technology supply chain (developers, distributors, retailers), and cripples local software companies. Eighty-six countries produce software. All are victims of the phenomenon.

Critics say that even if the estimates of pirated software are correct, the conclusions are exaggerated, because not all who pirated software would necessarily acquire it if they had to pay for it. Thus, if everybody was forced to pay for the software, the software companies would not collect the entire $80 billion, but much less. Still, it is reasonable to assume that many pirates actually needed the software, and would pay for it had piracy not existed.

The software piracy "map" varies in intensity and monetary damages: in the Asia-Pacific region 53 percent of the software used was pirated, causing $7.5 billion in losses; in Eastern Europe, 71 percent and $2.1 billion; in Western Europe, 36 percent and $9.6 billion; in Latin America, 63 percent and $1.3 billion; and in the African and Middle-East region, 56 percent and $1 billion. The rate in North America was the lowest, "only" 23 percent, but due to large absolute number of copies, the estimated loss was $7.2 billion.

A previous joint study by BSA and IDC estimated that a 10 percent drop in the rate of business software piracy by 2006 could boost Australia's GDP by $6.8 billion. It also estimated that a similar reduction globally would create an estimated 1.5 million jobs and generate $400 billion of economic growth. Reducing the piracy rate to 15 percent could add $142 billion to the U.S. gross domestic product (GDP), create more than 130,000 high-tech jobs, and generate an additional $23 billion in tax revenues by 2006.

Laws in most countries treat software the same way as they do books, videotapes, and other types of intellectual property: copies (except for one copy for archival purposes) may not be made without permission of the copyright or patent holder. Yet, the crime is pervasive because it is easy to commit and rarely is punished.

Licensing of software comes in several models. The *permissive* model allows anyone to use, modify, and make the software into a product that can be sold or licensed for profit. The Berkeley Software Distribution (BSD) operating system is an example of software under this model. Another is the *General Public License* (GPL), which permits anyone to use, modify, and make applications with the code, but not to use it in proprietary products for sale or licensing. This is the approach taken by the Free Software Foundation. Much of the software we use is *proprietary*, which means the code is owned by someone who has the right to sell or license it to us.

Microsoft, SAP, Oracle, and all other for-profit organizations that develop software own their software and license it. Such licensing takes several forms, such as a fee per user per year, or a one-time fee for a limited or unlimited use regardless of how many users use the software. The latter type of agreement is sometimes signed between a software vendor and a higher-education institution.

POINT OF INTEREST

Supply Chain of Revenues

Companies that sell enterprise software, such as supply chain modules, charge millions of dollars for licensing. How much of the licensing revenue is spent on improving the software? A mere quarter. Three-quarters of the money is spent on marketing. Namely, the money is spent on efforts to convince the same customers that they still need the same software. This is one reason why some experts expect to see a growing number of open source enterprise applications. Licensing is free, and therefore is not the main incentive for developers.

Source: Schonfeld, E., "Moving up the Stack," *Business 2.0*, April 7, 2005.

CONSIDERATIONS FOR PACKAGED SOFTWARE

When an application is developed specifically for an organization, specific program goals and custom requirements are considered during the development process. Such requirements include business needs, organizational culture needs, the need to interface with other systems, and performance issues, such as response time. However, organizations find ways to satisfy many needs with off-the-shelf software as well. Figure 5.9 summarizes important factors and details what you should look for when purchasing software.

FIGURE 5.9
Sample software evaluation form

Factor	What to Look For	Score
Fitness for purpose	◆ Try to maximize the number of needs satisfied.	_____
Ease of learning to use	◆ The shorter the learning time, the better.	_____
Ease of use	◆ The easier a program is to use, the better. ◆ Try to minimize the number of commands that need to be memorized. ◆ The more intuitive the icons, the better.	_____
Compatibility with other software	◆ Try to maximize compatibility with related software and with other operating systems. ◆ Try to maximize portability of data and output to other programs.	_____
Reputation of vendor	◆ Use professional contacts and references to gather background information on the vendor. ◆ Be sure the vendor can deliver what it promises. ◆ Be sure the vendor stands by its pricing.	_____
Availability and quality of telephone and online support	◆ Ask references about their experience. ◆ Look for knowledgeable staff on Web and phone support.	_____
Networking	◆ Try to maximize ability of many computers to share the software.	_____
Cost	◆ Seek detailed pricing information. ◆ Seek the best price, while maintaining quality and performance. ◆ Consider the total cost of ownership: annual license fees, support cost, and other costs associated with use of the software.	_____

While Figure 5.9 provides a general framework for evaluating off-the-shelf software, each item might be augmented with further inquiry, depending on the program's main purpose. For example, potential buyers often test a word-processing program for features such as availability of different fonts, dictionary size, response time to search operations, ability to create tables of contents and indexes, and other features. Electronic spreadsheet programs are tested for speed of recalculation of formulas, charting, and other features typical of this type of software. Web page development applications are tested for ease of creating various layouts and graphical designs. Many trade journals, such as *PC World* and *PC Magazine*, maintain labs in which they test competing applications. Experts test different applications on the same computer and report the results.

The factors to be considered when purchasing large software packages such as ERP software are significantly more complex. The purchasing organization must consider not only the cost of the software, which is usually millions of dollars, but also the amount of time it will take to implement the software, the cost of interrupting ongoing operations, the difficulty and cost of modifying the software for the organization's specific needs, and many other issues.

■ "Software" is the collective term for computer programs, which are sets of instructions to computer hardware.

■ Software is classified into two general categories. System software manages computer resources, such as CPU time and memory allocation, and carries out routine operations, such as translation and data communication. Application software is a program developed specifically to satisfy some business need, such as payroll or market analysis. Application software can include programs that carry out narrowly focused tasks, or general-purpose applications, such as spreadsheets and word processors.

■ To develop software, programmers use programming languages and software development tools. Third-generation languages (3GLs) are more English-like than machine language and assembly languages, and allow more productive programming, meaning that they use less time to develop the same code. Fourth-generation languages (4GLs) are even more English-like and provide many preprogrammed functions. Object-oriented programming (OOP) languages facilitate creation of reusable objects, which are data encapsulated along with the procedures that manipulate them. Visual programming languages help programmers develop code by using icons and other graphics while code is developed automatically by manipulating the graphics.

■ As an increasing amount of software is linked to the Internet, many software tools have been created especially for development of Web pages and the software that links Web pages with organizational information resources, such as databases. They include programming languages such as Java, JavaScript, and PHP, and Web page development packages such as FrontPage, Dreamweaver, and GoLive. Java and other languages for the Web produce code that runs on various computers and therefore is very useful for the Web.

■ All code written in a programming language other than machine language must be translated into machine language code by special programs, either compilers or interpreters. The translation creates object code from the source code. Software offered for sale is usually object code.

■ Some application programs are custom designed, but many are packaged. The majority of packaged applications are purchased off the shelf, although "off the shelf" might actually mean downloading the application through the Internet.

■ Office productivity tools helps workers accomplish more in less time. The most pervasive of these tools include word processors, spreadsheet, presentation tools, file and database management software, graphics programs, desktop publishing tools, and project management tools. Some of them are offered as suites.

■ Hypermedia and multimedia technologies are useful tools for training, education, research, and business.

■ Groupware combines hypermedia and multimedia with Web technologies to help people in separate locations collaborate in their work.

■ Virtual reality tools help build software models of products and structures. Virtual reality applications help in training and help build models that are less costly than physical ones.

■ Three-dimensional geographic software helps model city blocks and campuses. Combined with other information, it is useful in city service planning and real estate management.

■ The most important type of system software is operating systems, also referred to as "platforms." The newer operating systems carry out an ever-growing number of functions, and now include networking and security features. Other system software includes communications software and utilities.

■ Open source software is being adopted by a growing number of businesses and governments. The source code and its documentation are open to all to review and improve. Open source applications and system software can be downloaded from the Web. Programmers continually improve the code, not for monetary remuneration, but to prove their programming prowess and gain the appreciation of the users. This practice yielded the powerful operating system Linux, as well as hundreds of useful applications.

- While some software is purchased, much of it is licensed. The user purchases the right to use the software for a limited time or indefinitely, but does not own the software.

- Businesses can follow a systematic evaluation to determine the suitability of off-the-shelf software to their needs. Applications should be tested with real transactions to find out whether they satisfy minimum requirements, such as response time.

- Consideration of software includes many factors, among which are fitness for purpose, ease of learning to use, ease of use, reputation of the vendor, and expected quality of support from the vendor.

- While software prices have decreased over the years, software piracy is still a problem. About a third of the software used around the world has been illegally copied.

QUICKBIZ MESSENGERS REVISITED

QuickBiz has purchased quite a bit of software through the years. As QuickBiz has grown, it has used software to perform routine business functions, develop new routes, and generate employee schedules. It has also begun to use its financial software to analyze route profitability and to motivate healthy competition among its messengers.

What Would You Do?

1. When Andrew Langston decided he needed a new information system, he started by listing the basic functions that he needed software to perform. Why would he start with software needs first? Would you do the same?

2. Some QuickBiz employees have taken the wrong routes to make their deliveries. In addition to purchasing the routing software, Andrew is considering implementing a training program to familiarize staff with the streets of Seattle and the communities surrounding Puget Sound. He's asked you to help him come up with some different training ideas. Develop a report on general types of software he might use to train his employees.

3. Explain the importance to QuickBiz of keeping up to date on software developments. Where did Andrew get his information on current software? What business systems did this improve? Where else could QuickBiz look for software news? List some sources for Andrew.

New Perspectives

1. A couple of QuickBiz's messengers were skeptical of the new routing software's capabilities. They were discussing its usefulness at lunch. Debate the following statement from their discussion: "No software can do what a human can do. I can figure out my routes much better than it can."

2. Andrew's cousin works for a seafood company. His company uses a Linux-based system, and he is recommending that Andrew switch from his Windows-based system to Linux. List the pros and cons of this step for QuickBiz.

3. If you were Andrew, how would you use software to determine whether eliminating downtown Saturday deliveries could also have an effect on revenue from regular services?

applet, 152
application, 147
application software, 147
application-specific
   software, 154
assembly language, 148
compiler, 153
debugging, 149
driver, 161
general-purpose application
   software, 154
groupware, 157

hypermedia, 156
interpreter, 153
machine language, 148
multimedia software, 156
object code, 153
object-oriented programming
   (OOP) language, 150
open source software, 163
operating system (OS), 159
packaged software, 154
plug-and-play (PnP), 161
programming, 147

programming language, 148
proprietary software, 163
software, 147
source code, 153
suite, 155
system software, 147
utilities, 160
virtual memory, 161
virtual reality (VR), 157
visual programming
   language, 149
Web page authoring tools, 156

1. Why would any programmer today use an assembly language rather than a higher-level language?

2. What are the advantages of third-generation languages over lower-level languages?

3. The use of 4GLs is said to contribute to programmer productivity. How so?

4. 4GLs help nonprogrammers develop useful applications. How are they more suitable for this purpose than 3GLs?

5. What is multimedia? Give five examples of how this technology can be used in training, customer service, and education.

6. There are so many ready-made software packages; why do some companies commission software development projects?

7. Office applications are often called productivity tools. Why?

8. Electronic spreadsheets are great tools for modeling. Give an example of a model and describe how you would implement it in a spreadsheet.

9. Why can hypermedia not be implemented on paper? Give an example of what you can communicate with hypermedia that you would not be able to communicate on paper.

10. What are the different media in multimedia?

11. Immersion is an important element of virtual reality. What does it mean?

12. What is the importance of 3-D geographic software? For which types of organizations is it useful?

13. What is the difference between system software and application software?

14. System software is often written using low-level programming languages. Why?

15. Linux is a free and stable operating system, which is a great advantage. What are the disadvantages of adopting it?

16. What is the difference between an interpreter and a compiler?

17. Why can't compilers and interpreters detect logic errors in a program?

18. What are the main elements to consider when purchasing software for an organization?

19. What is open source software? To what does the word "source" refer?

20. Give three reasons why Linux has become a popular server operating system.

1. Why has the trend been to purchase (often, license) software rather than have it tailor-made for organizations?

2. Think of a standard application such as a payroll system. What might drive an organization to develop its own payroll application rather than purchase one off the shelf?

3. Give examples of a GUI in operating systems. What else can developers of operating systems do to simplify software use?

4. A decision to adopt Linux or another open source operating system is not an easy one for IS managers. What are their concerns? (*Hint*: Think of the relationships between OSs and applications.)

5. Some companies sell open source software, such as Linux. Thousands of people buy the software rather than download it free of charge. Why? Would you buy such software or simply download it from the Web?

6. Widespread application software, such as OpenOffice.org, that runs on a variety of OSs threatens the software giant Microsoft. Why?

7. The more an application takes advantage of a GUI, the more international it is. How so?

8. Increasingly accurate voice-recognition software and sophisticated software that can interpret commands in natural language are bringing us closer to the days of operating a computer by speaking to it. Would you rather speak to a computer than use a keyboard, mouse, or some other input device? Why or why not?

9. Why is software piracy so pervasive? What are your innovative ideas to reduce this problem?

10. Why does most pressure to legislate and enforce copyright laws for software come from North America and Western Europe and not from other parts of the world?

11. Do you think open source software will proliferate or disappear?

12. If you were so proficient in programming languages that you could improve open source code (such as the Linux operating system, the Firefox browser, or any of hundreds of applications), would you do it for no monetary compensation? Why or why not?

13. In what ways can young people who seek IT careers benefit by participating in improving open source software?

14. Some observers compare open source software to water. Both the software and water are free, but some companies manage to generate revenue from selling them. How?

1. HeadHunter, Inc., is a new personnel recruiting and placement company. The well-established and cash-rich management consulting company that founded HeadHunter is intent on providing adequate financial resources for the new firm to acquire information systems. HeadHunter has opened offices in eight major U.S. cities and two European cities.

Recruiting specialists exchange written correspondence with prospective clients, both managers looking for new positions and companies that might hire them. Records of both recruits and client companies must be kept and updated. All 10 branches should be able to exchange information in real time to maximize the potential markets on both continents. HeadHunter professionals will often travel to make presentations before human resource managers and other executives.

The majority of HeadHunter's own personnel are college graduates who lack programming skills. HeadHunter management would like to adopt software that is easy to learn and use.

a. List the types of software the firm needs, both system software and applications.

b. Research trade journals. Suggest specific software packages for the firm.

2. You are to code the following simple program: prompt the user to enter two numbers, find the larger number, and display it on the monitor. Use any third-generation programming language and write the code. Now, use a spreadsheet to write "code" to do the same thing. How many statements did you have to use for each assignment? How much time did it take you to write the code with either language?

HANDS-ON ACTIVITIES

Honest Abe and Cars R Us are two fiercely competitive car dealerships. Recently, both started to sell Sniper, a new model from Eternal Motors. Dealers' cost of the car is $19,600. Eternal pays a dealership $200 for each car sold, and the dealership also keeps whatever markup it adds to the cost. Both dealers start selling the car at the price of $20,600.

Immediately after the two dealerships started to offer the car, each decided to lower the price until the other dealership stopped selling the car. However, their price reduction policies differed. Honest Abe's policy is as follows: at the end of each day, the company sets the price for the next day at the competitor's price minus $50. Cars R Us's policy is the following: at the end of each day, the company sets the price for the next day at the competitor's price minus 1 percent.

Each dealership decided to stop selling the car as soon as it sells a car with a loss instead of profit.

1. Using a spreadsheet application such as Microsoft Excel, enter the initial numbers and build a model that will help you answer the following questions:
   a. Which dealer will stop selling the car first?
   b. How many days after it starts to sell the car will this dealer stop selling it?
   c. How much money will this dealer lose per car on the first day it loses money on this car?

2. E-mail the spreadsheet to your professor with your text answers to these questions inside the spreadsheet.

TEAM ACTIVITIES

1. Team up with two students from your class. As a team, choose two operating systems that run on PCs. Research their features. If both operating systems are available at your school, try them. Write a comparison of their features. Conclude with recommendations: which system would you prefer to adopt for a small business, and why? Focus only on features, not cost.

2. Team up with another student. Log on to www.openoffice.org and prepare a report that covers the following points: (1) Who established this site, and for what purpose? (2) What type of application is the subject of this site? (3) Who contributed the original source code for this project? (4) Who is invited to participate in this project? (5) Would you recommend to a small business with little cash to download and use the applications? (6) Would you recommend to a larger and richer organization to do so? Why or why not? In your assessment, address the issues of compatibility with other software, support, ease of training, and ease of use.

1. Do some research and list at least two visual programming languages. Why is visual programming better than the programming methods that came before?

2. Microsoft Office is perhaps the best known office productivity suite. Do some research and list at least two other programs. Compare them to MS Office. Which would you buy? Why?

VIDEO QUESTIONS

1. Would you buy software from one of the kiosks? Why or why not?

2. Other than the two issues mentioned on the clip, can you think of other downsides to this method of delivery?

FROM IDEAS TO APPLICATION: REAL CASES

Mr. Rounder at Your Service

The statistics are staggering. The Institution of Medicine in Washington, D.C., cited two studies showing that medical errors kill 44,000 to 98,000 Americans annually. According to the National Academy of Sciences Institute of Medicine, poor information kills some 7,000 Americans each year by missing drug-interaction problems. The *Chicago Tribune* newspaper found that 1,700 patients died over a period of 5 years because of errors made by overworked and undertrained nurses. According to the Institute of Safe Medication Practices, medication errors kill more people than workplace accidents. Economy. com, an organization that monitors economic developments, reported that the efficiency of health care in the United States decreased in the 1990s. That means that the same services, such as patient bedside visits, production and examination of x-rays, and the like, took more and more hours of the medical staff's time.

To some extent, proper software might alleviate this sad state of affairs. An increasing number of hospitals have implemented information technologies to make medicine safer and more efficient. According to the research organization Dorenfest Group, in 2004, U.S. hospitals spent $25.8 billion on IT. They were predicted to spend $30.5 billion in 2005. Case in point is Hackensack University Medical Center (HUMED) in Hackensack, New Jersey, a community hospital located nine miles from New York City.

The center spent $72 million on IT in general and innovative software in particular between 1998 and 2004. It implemented a drug-order system, the type of which can reduce erroneous prescriptions by up to 80 percent. Physicians can access an intranet, the hospital's internal Web site, from any personal computer, anywhere, and patients can use large flat monitors in their rooms to surf the Internet and look up information about their health condition and treatment. Doctors can also control a robot called Mr. Rounder from personal computers either at the hospital or at the doctors' homes. The robot's head is a computer monitor. It is dressed with a white robe and a stethoscope to mimic a doctor. The doctors remotely direct the robot to patient rooms and communicate with the patients via a two-way video and sound system.

Information resources of the various units are networked. Nurses use wheeled laptops that are equipped with wireless circuitry to log on to the patients' record database. They can see symptoms and receive information on where to move the patients through their stay for each treatment or recovery.

Doctors log on to order prescriptions and lab tests. There is minimal need for the staff to use telephones and fax machines, because they can receive through this network all the information they need, order what they need, and update records. The automated pharmacy, x-ray room, and all the labs are part of the network.

Mr. Rounder, too, is linked to the network. When doctors are away from the hospital or cannot come to work because of weather conditions, they use the robot to "visit" their patients. They can link to pharmacy, labs, or any other linked resources from wherever they are through a secure Internet link.

Since hospitals must interact with doctors who do not work directly for them, use of the new system is far from fully utilized. To convince those physicians to use the new systems, the hospital must demonstrate to them that the new "gadgets" and software can save time and are easy to learn and use while not interfering with their relationships with patients. Hospital officials say the task is not easy, but doctors are gradually signing on.

Despite the difficulty of persuading doctors to use the new technology, IT seems to be paying off and saving lives. One night a 40-year veteran HUMED physician examined a homeless man with HIV who had just been admitted. He decided which drug to administer, but first entered it into the system. The system warned not to give that drug to a patient who has taken the antidepressant the man was already taking. The experienced doctor admitted he would not have made the connection himself. He contacted the patient's psychiatrist to administer a lower dose of the antidepressant so that the patient could take the HIV drug.

The staff still does not take full advantage of the technology. For example, only 10 percent of tests and orders are entered electronically. However, IT has certainly proven itself. Economy.com estimated that since 2001, hospital efficiency has grown at an annual rate of 2 percent. At HUMED, patient mortality has decreased 16 percent in the period 2000–2004. The quality of care has increased. Management is confident that the investments in IT are to be credited for the changes. As the hospital's CEO put it, his institution could not become a top hospital had it not implemented top technology. The financial results are not bad, either. HUMED's operating margins (income before interest and taxes) rose from 1.2 percent in 2000 to 3.1 percent in 2004.

Source: Mullaney, T. J., Weintraub, A., "The Digital Hospital," *BusinessWeek* (www.businessweek.com), March 28, 2005; Hackensack University Medical Center (www.humed.com), 2005; Institute for Safe Medication Practices (www.ismp.org), 2005.

Thinking About the Case

1. Which of the two seems more sophisticated and harder to use in the hospital, hardware or software? Why?

2. Identify all the software that is discussed or implied in the case.

3. What other software would you implement at the hospital to increase productivity and care quality?

Stop! Wait! I Am Pulling Down a Menu!

San Jose, California, is considered one of the safest large cities in the United States. The city's 1,000 police officers serve 925,000 residents, making it the smallest officer-to-resident ratio in the country. From 1990 to 2004, the city's police department used a text-based mobile dispatch system. That system had been customized by its designer to meet the needs and preferences of the city's officers. Although there was some initial hesitation by officers to use the system, they eventually embraced it.

After more than a decade of reliable service, police and city officials decided to replace the system with new Windows-based touch-screen software. A new touch-screen computer was to be installed in every patrol car. It was designed to receive orders, send messages, write reports, receive maps of the city, and use GPS to let officers know where they are located and where other patrol cars are. San Jose government paid Intergraph, the company that developed the software, $4.7 million for the software, which was supposed to serve both the police and fire departments. However, the effort was plagued with problems from the start.

Even before the new system was installed, there were already grumblings at the department. Officers claimed nobody had ever sought their input about the design of the user interface. When they started using the new system, they were disappointed.

Tension had built up, but this was not the main concern of the San Jose Police Officers Association (SJPOA). The organization's leaders were not so much offended because they had not been asked about the system before it was developed. They were more concerned about the results of that failure to ask for their members' feedback. They were frustrated with the lack of training and error-infested software. There are always complaints when people have to adapt to new technology, but when their lives and those of the public depend directly on the software's performance, the stakes are much higher.

Since its June 2004 operational debut, the system has had numerous major problems. Of greatest worry is the increased difficulty in issuing the Code 99 command, the emergency contact when an officer is in danger and needs immediate help. Initially, officers had to strike one key to issue Code 99, but that resulted in too many false alarms. As a result, code entry for emergencies now requires a two-keystroke combination. Officers complain about having to find the right combination of touch-pad keys on a 12-inch screen while they are under fire or in hot pursuit of a suspect. One officer even crashed his squad car into a parked vehicle because he was so distracted by the information he had to enter using the touch-screen. Another problem was that with the new software it took patrol officers longer to find out whether a person they have stopped has a violent criminal record, which is vital information in a job that requires split-second decisions of life or death.

The police officers complained that they were not given sufficient training. However, the problems with the system had nothing to do with how the police officers used it; the software simply did not work. Two days after the system went live, it crashed. For the next few days, it was almost completely inaccessible. Its designers acknowledge that this was not a good way to build confidence with the officers. Yet, even after the system was modified to fix these problems, several more errors were discovered by the president of a user-interface design consulting firm that was hired by the SJPOA to review the software.

The mapping and GPS location tracking were supposed to be a great helper. Yet, the system's map information had some significant inaccuracies. Additionally, unneeded information took up screen space and display fonts were hard to read. Even a simple task such as checking a driver's license plate was difficult to perform after the system had already been treated for bugs.

Every new technology has a learning curve that can last weeks or months until users feel sufficiently comfortable with it, but with this software the difficulties were not only a matter of a learning curve. Even tolerant and receptive officers have faced obstacles in trying to adapt. Intergraph's specialists spent weeks in San Jose to fix bugs and streamline procedures for the most basic patrol tasks, like the license plate verification.

Officers complain about receiving only 3 hours of training on software that is supposed to ensure their safety. In response, the department has offered more training sessions. The software runs on the Windows operating system, a fact that complicated matters for many of the police officers. Older officers are not comfortable with pull-down menus and other features of the interface. As a result, they have been more resistant to the new software than their younger, more computer-literate colleagues.

Observing police work, the consultants brought in by the SJPOA noted that choosing a Windows GUI with complex menu hierarchies does not make sense for anyone who has to use the system while driving a car. In addition, officers were trained on desktop computers with track pads on keyboards instead of touch-screens they actually have to use in the squad cars.

Dispatchers, too, have expressed dissatisfaction with the Intergraph system, especially because of risky delays in task execution. With the new software, officers have to wait longer to access information about any previous arrests for a detained suspect. Dispatchers also note the same concern expressed by their comrades on patrol: the new software cannot perform multiple tasks simultaneously. Like the officers, the dispatchers feel they should have been consulted about the software during the interface design stage. San Jose's police chief admits that in hindsight, incorporating more end user input during the planning phase would have eased the introduction and implementation of the new system.

The Chicago Police Department had a similarly painful experience with a major dispatch system overhaul in 1999. Just as in San Jose's case, patrolling police officers were not asked for input before the software was developed, and the results left bad feelings across the department. Chicago eventually replaced that software with a newer system. This time, patrol officers were consulted, and their suggestions were considered before the programmers developed the applications. Unfortunately, San Jose's police department did not learn the lesson from the windy city's experience.

Police departments in two Canadian cities, Calgary and Winnipeg, had similar disappointing experiences with the Intergraph system. Officials in other cities also have been frustrated, and some planned to scrap the system.

Perhaps San Jose might not have to replace the Intergraph software after all. The San Diego Sheriff's Department has used Intergraph's touch-screen software for 6 years with eventual success. Initially, there were bugs similar to those experienced in San Jose, but Intergraph eventually fixed them. Also, San Diego officials conducted basic Windows training sessions for their sheriff's deputies, because some of these people had no previous computer experience whatsoever. There was some resistance to the new software in that department, too. But fixing the bugs and providing good training did the trick, and the deputies adapted. San Jose city officials hope for a similar happy end. However, unlike San Jose, San Diego squad cars do not have touch-screen devices.

Source: Hafner, K., "Wanted by the Police: A Good Interface," *New York Times*, Technology Section (www.nytimes.com), November 11, 2004; Zapler, M., "New S.J. Dispatch System Flawed," *Mercury News* (www.mercurynews.com), September 22, 2004.

Thinking About the Case

1. Are the problems encountered by the police officers due to hardware or software?

2. Whom do you think is at fault for the unsuccessful implementation of the new software? Why?

3. People, especially the "technologically challenged," are often not receptive of new technologies. Was this a major issue in this case?

4. If you were the CEO of Intergraph before it assumed the project for San Jose, what would you do differently?

6

SIX

Business Networks and Telecommunications

LEARNING OBJECTIVES

Modern telecommunications technology allows businesses to send and receive information in seconds. Except when a physical transfer of goods is involved, geographical distances are becoming meaningless in business transactions. When using computers and other digital devices, people can now work together as if they were sitting next to each other, even when they are thousands of miles apart. Financial transactions and information retrieval take seconds, and wireless technology enables us to perform these activities from almost anywhere and while moving. Understanding the technology underlying telecommunications—its strengths, weaknesses, and available options—is essential to making informed business decisions. When you finish this chapter, you will be able to:

■ Describe business and home applications of digital telecommunications.

■ Identify the major media and devices used in telecommunications.

■ Explain the concept of protocols.

■ Compare and contrast various networking and Internet services.

■ List networking technologies and trends that are likely to have an impact on businesses and information management in the near future.

■ Discuss the pros and cons of telecommuting.

QUICKBIZ MESSENGERS:
Communication Is Key

Mark Johnson, one of QuickBiz's longtime car messengers, was hopelessly stuck in traffic. A serious accident involving two semitrailer trucks had snarled traffic on Interstate 5; it was at a dead stop. He desperately needed to contact his customer—a medical supply firm—to alert it that his delivery would be delayed. So he used his hands-free cellular phone to call the customer. His contact at the supply firm acknowledged his delay and told him that the supplies were a routine delivery to a hospital pharmacy and not to worry—as long as the hospital received the delivery sometime that day, they'd be fine. Mark apologized for the glitch and promised to get off at the next exit as soon as he could move again. Then he used his group e-mail program to warn other messengers to stay off I-5 for the time being. Maybe he could save somebody else a headache.

From Beepers to Cellular Phones

When cellular phone technology hit the Seattle area, QuickBiz Messengers replaced its collection of beepers. Andrew Langston had seen their competitive advantage almost immediately. The company could contact its messengers instantly; they didn't need to find a pay phone. Also, text message alerts could be sent to the entire delivery fleet. Now messengers could be rerouted around trouble spots. Of course, there was always the occasional delay of one or two messengers, such as Mark Johnson was experiencing, but the problems now could be isolated.

As soon as the media began reporting a link between cell phone use and automobile accidents, Andrew decided to purchase hands-free car kits so that messengers could communicate safely with customers and the office. These devices also meant that his messengers didn't miss calls while they were fumbling for their phones.

Increasing Efficiency and Customer Satisfaction

Leslie Chen updated delivery information from the messengers' handheld computers into the database. As the business grew, however, Leslie spent more and more of her time uploading data from the handheld computers. A representative from the company's cell phone service provider told her about a wireless card that messengers could use to upload delivery information to the company's database. The messengers plug the card into a slot on their handheld computers and access the Internet through the cell phone providers' connection. Not only did this innovation save Leslie time, it also meant that messengers could update delivery information immediately upon delivery so that the company could provide this information to their customers right away. Delivery confirmations now could be sent via e-mail directly to the senders as soon as deliveries were made. Leslie Chen in the central office no longer had to confirm special deliveries. Messengers did that immediately and copied her on their transmittals, saving her time and the company money, all while increasing customer service.

Competitors Up the Ante

QuickBiz's competitors hadn't stood still either. One of its major competitors had improved its service by offering a standard one-hour delivery time in nearby communities—half of QuickBiz's standard delivery time. So, Andrew responded by opening two satellite offices to get messengers to remote destinations more quickly. That allowed Andrew to match his competitor's new time frame and still make a profit on deliveries.

An additional benefit of the three-office configuration was enhanced data security. In 2004, when pipes burst and flooded the main office, QuickBiz did not have a recovery plan. Now, every time any data is recorded at one of the offices, it is automatically duplicated on disks at the other two offices via the Internet. Andrew felt much more secure knowing that the duplication in computing services was ready, if needed.

Choosing the Right Network Service Providers

To link its three offices, QuickBiz used an Internet service provider (ISP) offering digital subscriber line (DSL) service, and a company that specialized in installation of virtual private networks (VPNs). Andrew found the DSL service to be fast enough for his company's needs and very affordable, but the connection was not reliable enough for QuickBiz. So Andrew and Sarah Truesdale, the office manager, found themselves looking for an alternative. They considered cable and even a T1 line hookup, but the companies that offered those services would have to string their lines to the office sites, and they couldn't get to QuickBiz for six to eight weeks.

Some time earlier, Andrew noticed strange antennas popping up in the neighborhood. He remembered someone mentioning that a telecom company was establishing fixed wireless service in the area.

Perhaps he could use that service. Indeed, the service was available at a fee comparable to the DSL service, and Andrew subscribed QuickBiz. The company that provided the VPN software made all the necessary arrangements to ensure that communication among the three offices remained private. Now, QuickBiz's three offices would have high-speed wireless Internet access as well as secure interoffice communications at a reasonable rate.

Intranets and Extranets

As the staff became more comfortable with Internet technology, they began to see its usefulness for other business functions. For example, the human resources manager set up an intranet to inform staff of the benefits program options and general company news. That information could be accessed from all three offices and through the cellular phones that messengers carried. He also set up a short orientation video to introduce new employees to the company.

Sarah and Leslie began to consider an extranet to expedite transactions with the firms that maintained their truck and bicycle fleets. They also explored the option to use the extranet of a national office supply superstore.

TELECOMMUNICATIONS IN BUSINESS

Telecommunications, which is essential to today's smooth business operations, is the transmittal of data and information from one point to another. The Greek word *tele*, which means "distance," is part of such words as "telegraph," "telephone," and other words referring to technologies that allow communications over large distances. Thus, telecommunications is communications over a distance. Telephone, fax, e-mail, the World Wide Web—none of these essential business services would be available without fast, reliable telecommunications. Networking technologies have brought several improvements to business processes:

- *Better business communication.* When no physical objects need to be transferred from one place to another, telecommunications technology can make geographical distance irrelevant. E-mail, voice mail, instant messaging, faxing, file transfer, cellular telephony, and teleconferencing enable detailed and instant communication, within and between organizations. Telecommunications can also be used by one person to monitor another person's performance in real time. The use of e-mail has brought some secondary benefits to business communications by establishing a permanent written record of, and accountability for, ideas. The result is more accurate business communications and less need for manual recording. Web-based instant messaging is used to support online shoppers in real time.

- *Greater efficiency.* Telecommunications has made business processes more efficient. Any information that is recorded electronically can become immediately available to anyone involved in a business process, even when the business units are located far apart. For example, as soon as an order is placed, anyone in the organization who will ever be involved with it can view it: from the marketing people, to purchasing officers, to manufacturing managers, to shipping workers, to billing and collection clerks.

- *Better distribution of data.* Organizations that can transmit vital data quickly from one computer to another no longer need centralized databases. Business units that need certain data frequently might store it locally, while others can access it remotely. Only fast, reliable transfer of data makes this efficient arrangement possible.

- *Instant transactions.* The availability of the Internet to millions of businesses and consumers has shifted a significant volume of business transactions to the Web. Both businesses and consumers can shop, purchase, and pay instantly online. Wireless technology has also made possible instant payment and data collection using small radio devices, such as electronic toll collection tags. In addition to commercial activities, people can use telecommunications for online education and entertainment.

- *Flexible and mobile workforce.* Employees do not have to come to the office to carry out their work as long as their jobs only involve the use and creation of information. They can telecommute using Internet connections. Salespeople, support personnel, and field workers are more mobile with wireless communication.

- *Alternative channels.* Services that used to be conducted through specialized dedicated channels can be conducted through alternative channels. For example, voice communication used to be conducted only through proprietary telephone networks but is now also conducted through the Internet, which decreased its cost. Radio and television broadcasts were conducted through radio frequencies and company-owned cables. Newer technologies enable organizations to broadcast over the Internet and provide telephone services over the Internet as well. Furthermore, Internet technologies allow individuals to broadcast text and sound to subscribers' computers or to Web-capable mobile devices. (We discuss these technologies in Chapter 8, "The Web-Enabled Enterprise.")

 At the same time you enjoy the great opportunities created by telecommunications technology, you must recognize that it poses great risks. Once an organization connects its ISs to a public network, security becomes a challenge. Unauthorized access and data destruction are constant threats. Thus, organizations must establish proper security controls as preventive measures. We discuss the risks and solutions in Chapter 14, "Risks, Security, and Disaster Recovery."

TELECOMMUNICATIONS IN DAILY USE

We have grown so used to networks that we no longer think much about them in daily life; however, they are pervasive. Here is an overview of the most widespread telecommunications uses.

Cellular Phones

Cellular phones derive their name from the territories of service providers, which are divided into areas known as cells. Each cell has at its center a computerized transceiver (transmitter-receiver), which both transmits signals to another receiver and receives signals from another transmitter. When a call is placed on a cellular phone, the signal is first transmitted to the closest transceiver, which sends a signal through landlines that dial the desired phone number. If the receiving phone is also mobile, the call is communicated to the transceiver closest to the destination phone. As the user moves from one area, or cell, to another, other transceivers pick up the transmission and receiving tasks.

Using cellular phone networks, people can transmit and receive calls almost anywhere, freeing them from a fixed office location. Cellular phones (often called mobile phones) can also be used for e-mail and faxing, and many are Web-enabled. Many mobile phones have been merged with digital cameras, PDAs, and GPS (global positioning system) circuitry. "My car is my office" is a reality for many professionals who spend much of their time traveling. As technology advances and more capabilities are squeezed into smaller casings, some professionals can say, "My pocket is my office."

The major advantage of cell phones is that they are attached to people, not offices. This is why, despite the higher cost of mobile phones over landline phones, some companies have decided to discard the latter and adopt the former for some or all of their employees. For example, in 2005, Ford Motor Company disconnected the landline phones of 8,000 employees and equipped them with mobile phones. The purpose is to make engineers more available to each other.

Some companies make the switch to mobile phones when they move their offices. Moving electronic switchboards and telephone lines to its new offices in Hawaii would have cost NovaSol, a scientific research firm, $30,000. The company decided to equip its 80 employees with cell phones. Other companies make the switch because so many employees already have both landline phones in the office and a cell phone for their time with customers or on manufacturing lines. For this reason, Dana Corp., a manufacturer of auto parts, removed most of the phones from its offices in Auburn Hills, Michigan. The lines left are used mainly for teleconferencing.

Videoconferencing saves time and travel expenses and reduces air pollution.

Courtesy of Polycom, Inc.

Videoconferencing

People sitting in conference rooms thousands of miles apart are brought together by their transmitted images and speech in what is called **videoconferencing**. Businesses use videoconferencing to save on travel costs and lodging, car fleets, and the time of highly salaried employees, whether they work in different organizations or at different sites of the same organization. From national and global perspectives, videoconferencing also reduces traffic congestion and air pollution. The increasing speed of Internet connections makes it easy for anyone with a high-speed link to establish videoconferences by either using a peer-to-peer link or by using the services of a third party, a company that specializes in maintaining videoconferencing hardware and software. In the latter case, businesses either pay a monthly fee for unlimited conferences, or every time they use the service.

Fax

Facsimile, or **fax**, is the transmission and reception of images over telephone lines. A fax machine digitizes an image and transmits the representative bits to a receiving fax machine. The receiving machine converts the digitized codes back into an image. Fax machines provide an easy means of communicating text and graphical images. Because it is based on digital images, faxing does not have to be executed through traditional telephone lines but can go through the Internet, using special software. Fax functions can also be combined with scanning, printing, and copying functions in "multifunction" machines.

Wireless Payments and Warehousing

Radio frequency identification (RFID) technology, mentioned in Chapter 3 and covered in more detail later in this chapter, enables us to conclude transactions and to make payments quickly. An increasing number of drivers never approach a cash register or swipe credit cards when paying for fuel at gasoline stations. If you use a speed payment device such as ExxonMobil's Speedpass, an RFID tag communicates with a device on the pump to record the details of the transaction. An antenna dish on the rooftop of the gas station communicates these details and checks your credit through a link to a large database located hundreds or even thousands of miles away and operated by the bank authorizing the charge. In this transaction, you use telecommunications twice: once between the device and the pump, and once between the gas station's antenna and the database. Wireless toll payment systems use a similar technology. A special transceiver

advantages of circuit switching are that data and voice can use the same line and that no special training or protocols are needed to handle data traffic. One disadvantage is the requirement that the communications devices be compatible at both ends.

Packet Switching

In **packet switching**, a message is broken up into packets. A **packet** is a group of bits transmitted together. In addition to the data bits, each packet includes sender and destination information, as well as error detection bits (see Figure 6.3). Each of the message's packets is passed from the source computer to the destination computer, often through intermediate nodes. At each node, the entire packet is received, stored, and then passed on to the next node, until all packets, either kept together or reassembled, reach the destination.

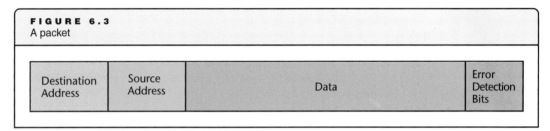

FIGURE 6.3
A packet

Destination Address	Source Address	Data	Error Detection Bits

On their way to their final destination, the packets are transmitted independently to intermediate nodes. Different packets of the same message might be routed through different paths to minimize delay and are then reassembled at their destination. This type of switching offers some advantages. Sending and receiving devices do not have to be speed-compatible because buffers in the network might receive data at one rate and retransmit it at another. The lines are used on demand rather than being dedicated to a particular call. With packet switching, a host computer can have simultaneous exchanges with several nodes over a single line. The main disadvantage of packet switching is that it requires complex routing and control software. When the load is high, there are delays. When the network is used for voice communication, a conversation with long delays might sound unnatural. Therefore, voice communication in traditional telephone systems uses circuit switching.

Frame relay is a high-speed packet-switching protocol used in WANs. The frames are variable-sized packets. The service provider's software determines the route for each frame so it can arrive at the destination the fastest. The variable size of packets allows more flexibility than with fixed-sized units; communication lines can be used more efficiently. One reason is the higher ratio of data bits to nondata bits (such as destination and source addresses) in each packet is greater. Larger packets also enable lines to stay idle for less time.

Circuit switching is ideal for real-time communications, when the destination must receive the message without delay. Packet switching is more efficient, but it is suitable only if some delay in reception is acceptable, or if the transmission is so fast that these delays do not adversely affect the communication. The switching rules in a network are part of the communication protocol. These protocols, along with increasingly faster Internet connections, enable the growing use of the Internet for packet-switching telephoning, known as VoIP, which we discuss later.

Multi-Protocol Label Switching (MPLS) is a relatively recent packet-switching technology that enhances services such as VoIP. Messages are broken up into packets, and packets are still transmitted independently, but all are routed through the same path on the network. This minimizes the time gaps between receptions of the packets. Therefore, content that must be communicated in real time—such as voice and video—is received at higher quality than if the packets are routed through different paths.

PROTOCOLS

A communications **protocol** is a set of rules that govern communication between computers or between computers and other computer-related devices that exchange data. When these rules govern a network of devices, the rule set is often referred to as a *network protocol*. If a device does not know what the network's agreed-upon protocol is, or cannot comply with it, that device cannot communicate on that network.

In a way, a protocol is like human language and basic understanding. Human beings make certain gestures when they start a conversation, and certain words signal its end. Each element of the language, be it English, Chinese, or Hindi, means the same thing to all parties who speak that language. Computers, too, need an agreed-upon set of rules to communicate. Some protocols are designed for WANs, others are designed for LANs, and some are designed specifically for wireless communications. This discussion addresses only some of these protocols. Protocols, often called "standards," do not necessarily compete with each other. They often work together or serve different purposes. The most important and pervasive set of protocols for telecommunications and networks today is called TCP/IP.

TCP/IP

Communication on the Internet follows mainly **TCP/IP (Transmission Control Protocol/ Internet Protocol)**, which is actually a set of related protocols. TCP ensures that the packets arrive accurately and in the proper order, while IP ensures delivery of packets from node to node in the most efficient manner.

A computer connected directly to the Internet **backbone**—the highest speed communication channels—is called a **host**. IP controls the delivery from one host to another until the message is received by the host to which it was sent or one that is connected to a device to which it was sent. The host forwards messages to devices connected to it. Often, we call hosts servers. For example, your school has at least one e-mail server. That e-mail server forwards to your computer e-mail messages addressed to you.

Every device on the Internet backbone is uniquely identified with a numerical label known as an Internet Protocol number, or **IP number**, a 32-bit numeric address, presented in four parts separated by periods, such as 146.186.87.220. Each of these parts can be a number between 1 and 254. If you know the IP number (also called the IP address) of a Web site, you can enter those numbers in the address box of a Web browser. However, it is easier to remember names and words, and therefore most organizations associate their IP numbers with names. The process of associating a character-based name such as *course.com* with an IP number is called domain name resolution, and the domain name resolution service is **DNS (Domain Name System)**. DNS servers are maintained by Internet service providers (ISPs) and other organizations. In large organizations, a server can be dedicated as a DNS server.

If a LAN is linked to the Internet through a router and a modem, the entire network has an IP number unique on the Internet. That number is stored in the router. To uniquely identify devices on the LAN, the router assigns local IP numbers to individual computers and devices. These IP numbers identify the computers only within the LAN. It is the router that is identified uniquely on the Internet.

Servers and many other computers and devices are assigned permanent IP numbers, called a **static IP number**. A computer connected to the Internet intermittently might be assigned a temporary IP number for the duration of its connection only. Such a number is called a **dynamic IP number**. It is assigned by the host through which that computer is connecting to the Internet. Dynamic IP numbers give an organization flexibility with its limited number of assigned IP numbers: only modems seeking a connection to the Internet are assigned IP numbers. And the number is disassociated from a device that logs off. The server can then reassign the IP number to another modem that has just logged on. Some broadband providers assign static IP numbers; others assign only dynamic IP numbers.

Ethernet

The Institute of Electrical and Electronics Engineers (IEEE) sets standards for communication protocols. IEEE 802.3, known as **Ethernet**, is a highly popular LAN protocol. Ethernet uses either coaxial cable or Cat 5 or 6 twisted pair cable. Different generations of Ethernet support speeds from 10 Mbps (10Base-T) to 100 Mbps (100Base-T or Fast Ethernet) to over 1 Gbps

(**Gigabit Ethernet** and 10 Gigabit Ethernet). Ethernet is known as a contention-based protocol, because devices on the network "contend" with other devices on the network for transmission time. Each device constantly monitors the network to see if other devices are transmitting. A protocol called CSMA/CD (Carrier Sense Multiple Access with Collision Detection) ensures that there are no collisions in transmission and that each device transmits without interfering with another.

Wireless Protocols

All wireless devices use radio transceivers (transmitter-receivers). The radio waves carry the digital signal, the bits. Depending on the protocol followed, the devices use different radio frequencies for their work.

IEEE 802.11 Wi-Fi

IEEE 802.11 is a family of wireless protocols, collectively known as **Wi-Fi** (for Wireless Fidelity). The term originally applied to the IEEE 802.11b standard that supports communication within about 100 meters (300 feet) of a wireless router at a maximum speed of 11 Mbps. The more advanced 802.11g standard supports speeds of up to 54 Mbps for the same range. The g standard is backward-compatible with the b standard, meaning that you can add b or g devices to a g network. However, in a mixed b and g network, throughput for the b devices will likely be at the lower 802.11b speed. Both standards use a radio frequency in the 2.4–2.5 GHz range. This is the same frequency used by microwave ovens and some cordless phones. However, the Wi-Fi transmitting and receiving circuitry constantly looks for the best frequency (such as 2.401 GHz or 2.402 GHz) on which to communicate within that range, so "collisions" with other devices are minimized. If interference with other devices or nearby wireless networks is a problem, the 802.11a standard is an option. The 802.11a standard operates in the 5 GHz range, and supports speeds of up to 54 Mbps at distances of about 20 meters (60 feet). However, the a standard is incompatible with the other Wi-Fi standards, and therefore is much less popular. Both the 2.4 GHz and 5 GHz radio frequency ranges do not require government licenses (referred to as "unlicensed"), and therefore are used for wireless communication. At this writing, the 802.11n standard, which supports speeds of 100 Mbps or faster and over greater distances than 802.11 b, g, or a, is not yet endorsed by IEEE.

POINT OF INTEREST

From Your Weight Scale to the Clinic

Tens of thousands of U.S. patients use remote monitoring devices, such as blood cuffs and weight scales, that can transmit readings of physical conditions from a patient's home to a health-care facility. The wireless devices transmit data to a device connected to the telephone line. These devices are prescribed primarily for patients with chronic illnesses to ensure that their situation does not become worse. For example, a heart patient's sudden weight gain is often an indication that the heart is failing, because when the heart stops pumping blood normally, fluids accumulate in the lungs, abdomen, and lower limbs. When the cuff or scale detects a suspicious indication, it transmits the data via the telephone line to a computer monitor attended by a nurse.

Source: Baker, M. L., "Bathroom Scales Aim to Save Lives (and Money)," *CIO Insight*, May 12, 2005.

A single Wi-Fi router can be connected to an **access point (AP)**, which in turn is connected to a wired network and usually to the Internet, allowing tens to hundreds of Wi-Fi-equipped devices to share the Internet link. A direct link to a wireless router or AP creates a **hotspot**. Hotspots allow Internet access to anyone within range who uses a wireless-equipped device, provided logging in is not limited by controlled access codes. Figure 6.4 illustrates a home wireless LAN (WLAN).

As mentioned earlier, security has been a concern for Wi-Fi networks. The earliest 802.11 standards had serious security flaws; 802.11g and 802.11a have improved security by offering the Wired Equivalent Privacy (WEP) protocol and the Wi-Fi Protected Access (WPA) and WPA2 security protocols. These protocols offer **encryption**, the ability to scramble and code messages through encryption keys that are shared only between the sender and receiver. Of course, to receive the protection of these protocols, they must be enabled on your wireless computer or device.

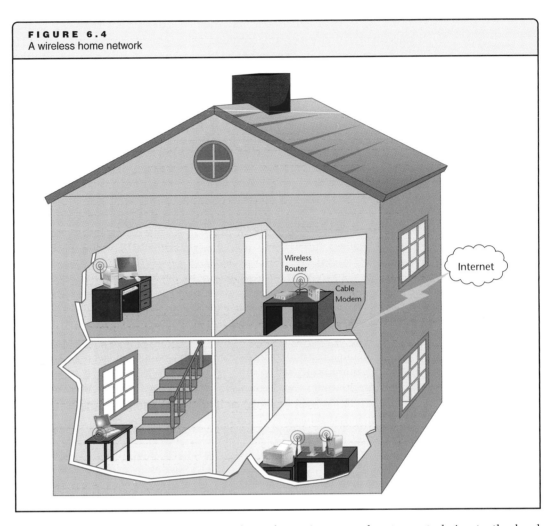

FIGURE 6.4
A wireless home network

Wi-Fi hotspots are appearing everywhere, from airports and restaurant chains to the local library and barbershop. However, businesses also use wireless LANs for many types of operations. You will find a WLAN in almost every warehouse. Workers holding PDAs or specialized electronic units communicate with each other and receive information about the location of items by section, shelf, and bin. For example, General Motors equipped the forklifts in all its warehouses with Wi-Fi transceivers to help their operators locate parts. On sunny days retailers place merchandise and cash registers on sidewalks. The cash registers are linked to a central system through a WLAN. Conference centers and schools use WLANs to help guests, students, and staff to communicate as well as link to the Internet through a hotspot.

All new airplanes for long flights are equipped with WLANs. Boeing started equipping its large airplanes with Wi-Fi in 2003. Lufthansa, British Airways, Japan Airlines, Scandinavian Airlines System, and other airlines have equipped their long-range jetliners with the technology to allow paying passengers to use a hotspot 12 miles above ground.

Utility companies are converting manually read electric, gas, and water meters to wireless meters. Older versions still require a person to read the meter and record the reading, but new meters use networks that relay the signal to the utility company's office and automatically update each customer's account in the company's computers. Wireless meters save millions of labor hours and overcome common problems, such as meters enclosed in locked places, inaccurate reading, and, occasionally, an aggressive dog.

A growing number of electronic devices, such as cell phones, PDAs, digital cameras, and video game consoles, are equipped with wireless circuitry. This rids their owners of the need to physically connect a device to a computer or a router for communication. For example, with a wireless-enabled digital camera you can send digital pictures from your camera to your PC, or directly to a friend via a hotspot over the Internet.

Bluetooth supports a personal area network. A wireless music player like this will not need wires between the player and headphones.

© Yoshikazu Tsuno/AFP/Getty Images

IEEE 802.15 Bluetooth

Named after a Scandinavian king who unified many tribes, the **Bluetooth** standard was developed for devices that communicate with each other within a short range of up to 10 meters (33 feet) in the office, at home, and in motor vehicles. It transmits voice and data. Bluetooth was later adopted by IEEE as its 802.15 standard, which is compatible with the early versions of Bluetooth. Typical Bluetooth devices include wireless keyboards and mice, wireless microphones for cellular phones (especially for use in cars while driving), and increasingly, digital entertainment devices. For example, you can purchase a wrist-worn MP3 player that uses Bluetooth to transmit the music to earbuds or headphones, avoiding the wires that typically connect a portable player to headphones. Bluetooth is considered a personal area network (PAN) technology, because it typically supports a network used by only one person. Bluetooth use the 2.4–2.5 GHz radio frequency to transmit bits at a rate of 1 Mbps.

IEEE 802.16 WiMAX

IEEE 802.16, Worldwide Interoperability for Microwave Access **(WiMAX)**, increases the range and speed of wireless communication. It might potentially reach up to 110 kilometers (about 70 miles) with a speed of 100 Mbps; however, it typically reaches 13–16 kilometers (8–10 miles). Experts say that with an investment of no more than $3 billion, WiMAX can cover 98 percent of American homes. This is a much lower investment than required for laying fiber optic cables. WiMAX uses licensed radio frequencies of 2–11 GHz. This standard can cover whole metropolitan areas and provide Internet access to hundreds of thousands of households that either cannot afford an Internet service or for some reason cannot obtain access. This has created a threat to the business of ISPs, who count on subscriber fees for revenue, because an entire metropolitan area can become one huge hotspot. Several states in the United States legislated against the creation of WiMAX networks. However, some cities are using the technology, which enables households that cannot afford Internet connectivity to have access to this important resource. Philadelphia is the first American metropolis to do so.

WiMAX is a metropolitan area network (MAN) technology. Figure 6.5 shows how WiMAX works. A household, office, or public hotspot can use a router to link multiple devices either by linking directly to a WiMAX base antenna that is linked to the Internet, or by using a relay antenna that receives the signal and retransmits it to the Internet-linked antenna. If a mobile user's equipment included the proper WiMAX communication device, the user could communicate with the Internet moving at speeds of up to 150 Km/H (about 94 MPH), which enables convenient use of the Internet while sitting in a moving vehicle (though the driver should not be going that fast!). An extension of this standard, 802.16e, supports mobile Internet communication. However, a newer, special standard dedicated to mobile communications is 802.20.

IEEE 802.20 MBWA

Mobile Broadband Wireless Access (MBWA) functions similarly to cell phone communications, because it controls communication from stationary towers. The purpose of MBWA is to provide mobile communication that is compatible with IP services. This should enable worldwide deployment of affordable, always-on wireless access. The principle is simple: place wireless routers on towers, so that mobile phones can use VoIP and access other Internet resources over wide areas, and, eventually, globally. MBWA is expected to work at speeds over 1 Mbps, using licensed radio frequencies below 3.5 GHz. If the standard is successfully implemented globally, it will reduce subscriber fees significantly and pose severe competition to providers of cell phone services.

The 802.20 standard is designed to be compatible with 802.11 (Wi-Fi) and 802.15 (Bluetooth). It can support Internet communication at a moving speed of up to 250 Km/H (156 MPH). MBWA promises to support practically everything that we now do with telephones and through the Internet: Web browsing, file transfer, e-mail, VoIP, video telephony and videoconferencing, audio streaming (such as listening to transmitted music), Web-based gaming, and file sharing. The technology includes security measures that meet the standards of the U.S. Department of Defense for protection of sensitive but unclassified information. To a large extent, this standard is still under development.

Figure 6.6 summarizes relevant features of the 802.xx wireless protocols discussed here.

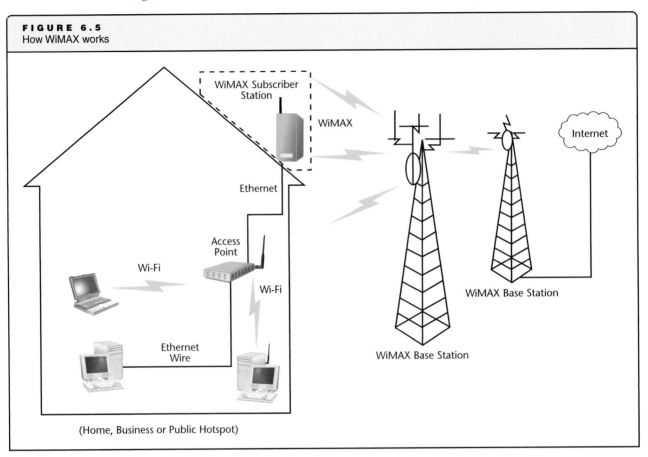

FIGURE 6.5
How WiMAX works

FIGURE 6.6
Wireless networking protocols

Protocol	Max. Range	Max. Speed	Main Use
802.11a	19 meters (60 feet)	54 Mbps	LAN
802.11b	100 meters (300 feet)	11 Mbps	LAN
802.11g	100 meters (300 feet)	54 Mbps	LAN
802.15 Bluetooth	10 meters (33 feet)	1 Mbps	PAN
802.16 WiMax	50 km (31 miles)	100 Mbps	MAN
802.20 MBWA	Global	4 Mbps	Mobile voice, data, and Internet communications

Generations in Mobile Communications

Networking professionals often refer to generations of mobile communication technologies. Each generation refers to a communication protocol or a combination of protocols. The differences among generations are mainly in capabilities (e.g., enabling a mobile phone to access additional resources) and transmission speed. The first generation, 1G, was analog and used circuit switching. Then 2G protocols became the first to provide digital voice encoding, and they worked at faster transmission rates. They include the GSM (Global System for Mobile) and CDMA (Code Division Multiple Access) protocols, the details of which are outside the scope of this discussion. They lack security measures. 2.5G, between 2G and 3G, stepped up the speed of digital mobile communication to 144 Kbps and enabled limited Internet access by cell phones through packet switching. The 2.5G protocol combines digital mobile telephoning with some IP capabilities. This is the set of protocols used by most mobile phones in the early 2000s.

POINT OF INTEREST

Complementary Technologies

In a way, 3G cellular technologies compete with Wi-Fi, but it seems that eventually the technologies will complement each other: we will use 3G outdoors and Wi-Fi indoors. Wi-Fi is significantly less expensive to use than 3G.

The 3G protocols support transmission rates of 1 Mbps. The protocols support video, videoconferencing, and full Internet access. Residents of San Diego enjoy 3G cellular phone services. For $79 per month they can use their phones to watch videos, download music, or browse the Web at 320 Kbps. 4G protocol devices operate only digitally and with packet switching, transmit at bandwidths of up to 100 Mbps, and include tighter security measures. Some of the protocols that comprise 4G are still under development. The high speed of the technology will enable the holder of a mobile phone handset to watch a DVD-quality video, listen to CD-quality music files, browse the Web, and make a telephone call at the same time.

INTERNET NETWORKING SERVICES

Both organizations and individuals can choose from a variety of options when subscribing to networking services. Figure 6.7 summarizes the major services offered by telecommunications companies. Note that the bit rates shown are for **downstream**, which is the speed of receiving from the network; **upstream** speeds, the speeds of transmitting into the network, are usually much lower. Also be aware that these are typical speeds in the United States. They might be different in other countries. Monthly costs, too, are typical and vary from region to region. For some services, such as T1 and T3, companies also offer fractions of the speeds for lower fees.

The proliferation of high-speed connection services, also called broadband services, is mainly the result of businesses' and individuals' rush to the Internet. Some of the services, such as cable, DSL, and satellite links, are offered both to businesses and residences. Others, such as T1 and T3 lines and the OC class, are offered only to businesses, largely because of their high cost. Note that some of the services are actually groups of services that differ in speeds. For example, some DSL services designed for businesses provide the same speed downstream and upstream, while options for households (see later discussion of ADSL) always provide a greater downstream speed than upstream speed.

Cable

Cable Internet links are provided by television cable firms. The medium is the same as for television reception, but the firms connect the cable to an Internet server. At the subscriber's residence, the cable is split—one part is connected to the television set, and the other is connected to the computer via a bridge that is often called a cable modem. Both television transmission and data are transmitted through the same line. The cable link is always on, so the computer is constantly connected to the Internet. The subscriber does not have to dial up any telephone number. More than 90 percent of cable operators in the United States offer Internet access.

The major downside of cable is that cable nodes are shared by all the subscribers connected to the node. Therefore, at peak times, such as television prime time (7–11 p.m.), communication speed slows down. The speed also slows down as more subscribers join the service in a given territory.

Digital Subscriber Line (DSL)

With normal telephone service, the telephone company filters information that arrives in digital form and then transforms it to analog form; thus, it requires a modem to transform the signal back to digital form. This conversion constrains the capacity of the link between your telephone (or computer) and the telephone company's switching center to a low speed of 56 Kbps.

FIGURE 6.7
Typical features of Internet services

Service	Downstream Speed	Availability	Monthly Fee
Dial-up	56 Kbps	Universal	$9–11
Cable	0.5–3 Mbps	Widespread; Available nearly everywhere TV cable service is offered	$30–50
DSL	0.5–8 Mbps	More limited than cable, but spreading faster; speed also depends on distance from telco office	$30–50
T1, T3	1.544 Mbps, 44.736 Mbps	Widespread	$300–1,000, $3,000–10,000
Satellite	1 Mbps	Widespread; practical only with view to the southern sky	$40–50
Fixed wireless	100 Mbps	Limited, but spreading	$2,000
OC-3	155.52 Mbps	Limited availability	$60,000
OC-12	622.08 Mbps	Limited availability	Several hundred thousand dollars
OC-48	2.488 Gbps	Limited availability	Several hundred thousand dollars
BPL	3 Mbps	Limited Availability	$30–40

POINT OF INTEREST

Broadband on the Rise

In 2005, there were 150 million subscribers to broadband links (cable and DSL) in the world, most of them in the Asia-Pacific region. The number is expected to grow to 400 million by 2009. The gap between the number of DSL subscribers and cable subscribers is growing. The reason is simple: while there are more than 1 billion telephone subscriber lines in the world, there are only 530 million homes with cable service.

Source: IMS Research, 2005.

With **digital subscriber line (DSL)**, data remains digital throughout the entire transmission; it is never transformed into analog signals. So, the telephone company can transmit to subscribers' computers at significantly higher speeds of up to 8 Mbps (although speed rarely exceeds 1.5 Mbps). To provide DSL service, the telecommunications company connects your telephone line to a DSL bridge (often called a DSL modem). At the telephone company's regional central office, DSL traffic is aggregated and forwarded to the ISP or data network provider with which the subscriber has a contract. Often, the telephone company is also the ISP.

There are several types of DSL, whose details are beyond the scope of this book, but they can be generally placed in one of two categories: symmetric and asymmetric. Asymmetric DSL (ADSL) allows reception at a much faster rate than transmission, that is, it is faster downstream than upstream. (Often, the respective terms "download" and "upload" are used.) The reason for the faster download is that home users and small businesses usually receive significantly more information (from the Web, for example) than they transmit. Symmetric DSL (SDSL) is designed for short-distance connections that require high speed in both directions. Many ADSL technologies are actually RADSL (Rate Adaptive DSL) technologies; the speed is adjusted based on signal quality. Some ADSL technologies let subscribers use the same telephone lines for both Internet connection and analog voice telephone service. Symmetric DSL lines cannot share lines with telephones.

The bit rates of DSL lines are closely related to the distance of the subscriber's computer from the regional central office of the telephone company. Telecommunications companies might offer the service to subscribers as far as 6,100 meters (20,000 feet) from the central office, but the speed then is usually no faster than 144 Kbps, unless the company has installed a DSL repeater on the line. Some companies do not offer the service if the subscriber's address is not within 4,500 meters (15,000 feet) of the central office. Most subscribers have ADSL, so the upstream speed is significantly lower than the downstream speed.

T1 and T3 Lines

T1 and T3 lines are point-to-point dedicated digital circuits provided by telephone companies. A T1 line is made of 24 channels (groups of wires) of 64 Kbps each. T3 lines are made up of 672 channels of 64 Kbps. T1 and T3 lines are expensive. Therefore, only businesses that must rely on high speeds are willing to accept the high cost of subscribing to the service. Most universities, as well as large companies, use T1 or T3 lines for their backbone and Internet connections.

Satellite

Businesses and households in rural areas and other regions that do not have access to cable or DSL might be able to obtain satellite services, which use microwave radio transmission. In fact, satellite service providers target these households. The service provider installs a dish antenna that is tuned to a communications satellite. Satellite connections might reach a speed of 45 Mbps. The antenna for satellite communication can be fixed, as the ones you can see installed in the yards of private houses, or mobile, such as those installed on the roofs of large trucks. Most of the subscribers of fixed satellite dishes are households. Most of the users of mobile dishes are shipping and trucking businesses. Subscribers to fixed satellite service must purchase the dish antenna, with a typical cost of $400, and pay a monthly fee of about $50. Trucking companies must have an antenna installed on each truck.

Many people use a free satellite service, the global positioning system (GPS). While a proper device is required to enable reception from the satellites (which were launched into orbit by the U.S. government), anyone can communicate free of charge. The satellite transmits back to any GPS device its location on earth by longitude and latitude.

Fixed Wireless

Another alternative for households and small businesses that cannot obtain cable or DSL connections to the Internet is fixed wireless. Fixed wireless is point-to-point transmission between two stationary devices, usually between two buildings, as opposed to mobile wireless, in which people carry a mobile device. Companies such as Sprint, AT&T, and many ISPs offer the service. ISPs that specialize in fixed wireless services are often referred to as WISPs, wireless ISPs. They install microwave transceivers on rooftops instead of laying physical wires and cables. Subscribers

Telecommuting: Pros and Cons

Often, when you are introduced to people, you mention your occupation, and then you might be asked, "Where do you work?" Many employed people now answer, "At home." They do not commute; they *telecommute*, or, as some prefer to call it, they *telework*. They have the shortest commute to work: from the bedroom to another room in the home that is equipped with a PC and a broadband Internet link. For an increasing number of workers, IT provides all that's needed to create the goods their employers sell: software, analysis reports, literature, tax returns, and many other types of output. If they need data from the office, they can connect to their office intranet using VPN software and retrieve the required information. If they need to talk to supervisors or coworkers, they use their computers to conduct videoconferencing. And when they complete their product, they can simply e-mail it or place it on a remote server.

- **Telecommuting on the Rise.** Nearly a third of the U.S. workforce, more than 44 million individuals, work at home at least part time, and almost 14 million of whom are expected to work from home full time by 2008. Autodesk, Inc., a supplier of PC design software and digital content creation, established a pilot program in 1996 that allowed 20 workers to telecommute. Today, half the company's 3,000 workers telecommute, and every manager has the option to allow subordinates to telework. The program helps the company retain skilled workers and serves as an inducement when recruiting new employees. Telecommuting has increased productivity and reduced employee stress. Pitney Bowes, a business communications company with 32,000 employees, noticed increased productivity in employees on their telecommuting days. Managers there believe that telecommuting increases productivity because it accommodates both the "morning person" and "night owl" who can work at the time of day that best fits their preferences. The International Telework Association & Council estimates that in 2003 there were 27 million workers in the United States who telecommuted at least one day per week, and that this number will grow to 42 million workers by 2010. From a national economic perspective, telecommuting saves travel cost and time. It also decreases pollution. And it might reduce unemployment by allowing people who would otherwise not work because they are not within commuting distance the opportunity to join the workforce.

- **Employment Opportunities.** Telecommuting enables people who could otherwise not work to join or rejoin the workforce. This includes not only people who live far away from the offices of companies that would like to hire them but also whole groups in the population that otherwise might not be able to join certain businesses. Disabled people and parents of small children can work from home. Older people who would rather retire than commute might stay in the workforce if allowed to work at home. Organizations hungry for labor can tap a larger supply of workers if they offer telecommuting.

- **Saving Time and Money.** Organizations like telecommuting because it saves the cost of office space. Studies have shown that for each teleworker the annual saving on office space is $5,000–10,000. When Nortel Networks allowed 4,000 of its 13,000 employees to telecommute, it saved $20 million per year on real estate. Studies also have shown that teleworkers are more productive by 15–50 percent than their office counterparts. Telecommuters like their arrangement because they save the time and money they would spend on commuting. Telecommuting reduces millions of tons of pollutants, saves billions of gallons of gasoline, and frees billions of personal hours for leisure time. AT&T, the telecommunications giant, reported in 2000 that its telecommuting program increased productivity by 45 percent and saved 50 percent on office space costs. Another report, by British Telecom and Gartner Group, said that telecommuting reduced office space and other costs equivalent to 17 percent of annual salary costs.

  State governments in the United States realize all this and therefore offer tax incentives to companies that institute telecommuting. For example, Oregon allows tax deduction on expenditures for equipment and software required by companies that allow their employees to telecommute.

- **The Downside.** However, not everyone is so enthusiastic about telecommuting. Sociologists have mixed opinions about the phenomenon. On one hand, telecommuting allows people to work who would otherwise remain outside the workforce, such as older professionals and many disabled people. On the other hand, it has been found that employers tend to pressure telecommuters to work harder than office workers. In the office an employee works a set number of hours, but the home worker has no defined workday; his or her workday is, the employer often assumes, 24 hours per day. In addition, telecommuters are more estranged from their fellow workers. For telecommuters, there is no office in which to foster new social ties and camaraderie.

The AT&T report said that teleworkers typically worked an hour more per day than their office-bound colleagues, which amounted to 250 hours per year. The British Telecom and Gartner Group report said that the average telecommuter works 11 percent more hours than his or her office-bound brethren. Perhaps this extra time is what companies observe as added productivity. Although this extra work time is good for corporations, it is not so good for workers: when you telecommute, you work more for no additional compensation.

Telecommuting might foster isolation. Teleworkers share fewer experiences with other people. In addition, leaving the workplace behind means leaving behind one more community that gives many people a sense of belonging, even if this belonging amounts only to having a sandwich together at lunchtime and complaining about the boss. At the same time, some managers might prefer to see their employees in the office and keep them in their "line of sight."

On a national level, telecommuting could severely affect some segments of the economy. Imagine the huge drop in revenue of New York restaurants during lunchtime if only half of the 3 million or so commuters did not rush to grab lunch between 12 and 2 p.m. Some cities' dining industries could crumble if the telecommuting trend continues at the current pace. Many people live in cities mainly because of proximity to their offices, thus further movement to suburbs and remote residential areas would gut many other industries in central cities.

Many workers, given the option to work at home, have decided to return to the office. Interestingly, this happens also in the very industries that are so amenable to telecommuting, such as software development. These returning workers claim they missed social interaction with their peers, hallway chats, lunches with friends, and direct communication with fellow workers and supervisors. But telecommuting has grown, and will probably continue to grow, especially thanks to greater availability of broadband services and their declining monthly fees. Only a third of all Americans have broadband service at home. Among telecommuters the proportion is 87 percent. If the trend continues, offices occupied by organizations will be significantly smaller than they are now and will serve as the symbolic rather than physical centers of the organizations' activities.

connect their computers to the rooftop transceiver. They can communicate at speeds up to 2 Mbps. Repeaters are installed close to each other to enhance the signal, which can deteriorate in the presence of buildings, trees, and foul weather. Transmission rates depend on the distance between the receiver and the base station. Up to 14 kilometers (9 miles) from the base station, the speed is 100 Mbps; speeds drop to about 2 Mbps at about 56 kilometers (35 miles) from the base.

Fixed wireless is highly modular—the telecommunications company can add as many transceivers as it needs to serve a growing number of subscribers. Unlike cable service, the company does not need franchise licenses. The technology is suitable for both urban and rural areas. For example, Daytona Beach, Florida, is served by a fixed wireless network that provides a broadband connection to anyone who is interested in the service. The local government of rural Owensboro, Kentucky, wanted to keep the town's businesses competitive. Since other options were not available, it built a fixed wireless network that provides broadband links to the Internet for $25 per month.

Optical Carrier

Companies willing to pay high fees can enjoy very high connection speeds. The services are denoted with **OC**, the acronym for **optical carrier**, because all of these services are provided through optical fiber lines. The number next to OC refers to data speed in multiples of 51.84 Mbps, considered the base rate bandwidth. Thus, when available, the services are denoted as C-1, C-3, C-9, C12, C-18, C-48, and so on through C-3072. For illustration, OC-768 (40 Gbps) enables you to transmit the content of seven CDs in 1 second. Typical businesses that purchase the services are ISPs, providers of search engines, and businesses that wish to support content-rich Web sites and high-volume traffic. However, media companies have also purchased such services because the high speeds support streaming video. Among companies that use OC-768, for instance, are Deutsche Telecom, NBC, Disney, the U.S. Department of Defense Advanced Research Projects Agency (the agency that developed the Internet), NASA, and Nippon TV.

Broadband over Power Lines (BPL)

As mentioned in the discussion of communications media, electric power lines are capable of carrying digital signals. Subscribers simply plug their BPL modem into standard electrical wall outlets. Usually, utility companies partner with telecommunications companies to provide Broadband over Power Lines (BPL). For example, Cinergy, a Cincinnati-based utility company that serves 2 million customers in Ohio, Kentucky, and Indiana, partnered with Current Communications to provide broadband service. The service is offered to 50,000 households for a monthly fee of $30–40, based on transmission speed desired by the subscriber. Some experts estimate that the BPL market in the United States will reach $2.5 billion by 2010, while others expect only households that currently use dial-up to link to the Internet to adopt this type of service.

Interestingly, even if BPL service availability is to lag far behind cable and optical fiber in terms of subscribers and revenue, utility companies are likely to invest in the technology for their own use. They can use BPL to monitor power consumption down to the household, detect power failure in real time, track power outages by region, automate some customer services, and remotely control substations. Collecting and analyzing such business information might make the utility companies more efficient.

The speed and monthly service for BPL are similar to those of DSL, but the highest current speeds are lower than the highest speeds offered by DSL providers. The hope was that households in rural areas, where neither cable nor DSL service is available, could enjoy BPL. However, the density of households in rural areas is lower than the density of households where the other services are already offered. Utility companies have found that investing in the equipment required to provide BPL to a small number of households does not make business sense, and therefore it is unlikely that many rural areas will be offered BPL.

THE FUTURE OF NETWORKING TECHNOLOGIES

 This section takes a look at networking technologies and trends that are likely to have a great impact on businesses and the management of information in the near future: broadband telephoning, radio frequency identification, and the convergence of digital technologies.

Broadband Telephoning

While regular long-distance telephone companies charge according to the number of minutes a call lasts, Internet service providers (ISPs) charge customers a flat monthly fee for connection to the Internet. With the proper software and microphones attached to their computers, Internet users can conduct long-distance and international conversations via their Internet connection for a fraction of regular calling costs. The technology is called Internet telephoning, IP telephoning, or VoIP (Voice over Internet Protocol). Organizations can purchase the proper software or use the services of companies that specialize in providing IP telephoning. Companies such as Vonage, Cablevision, and Comcast offer inexpensive use of their VoIP hardware and software for PC-to-PC, PC-to-telephone, and telephone-to-telephone voice communication.

PC-to-PC calls can be conducted free of charge by using the service of a company such as Skype. Phone-to-phone service requires an additional modem, but it does not require a new phone or phone number, and it does not require routing calls through a home computer.

VoIP is a standard for software that digitizes and compresses voice signals and transmits the bits via the Internet link. Some companies learned that they can save money using VoIP. Hamon Corp., a company that manufactures devices for control of air pollutants, noticed a significant increase in telephone costs as its staff grew from 130 to 500. The firm's CFO decided to subscribe the company to Internet telephoning. The company's

PC-to-PC conversations over the Internet can be conducted free of charge with services such as Skype.

Skype Technologies S.A.

For a low monthly fee subscribers can use VoIP telephoning, which uses the Internet.

Courtesy of Vonage

telephone cost decreased by at least $12,000 per month. The accounting firm Ernst & Young uses an Internet phone system it purchased from Cisco Systems to connect its 84,000 employees worldwide. Many households, especially in countries where telephone rates are high, use VoIP. Close to 40 percent of all international calls from India use VoIP. VoIP service is charged monthly, not by destination or duration of calls.

In 2005, there were about 3 million subscribers to VoIP services in the United States. The number is expected to grow to 27 million by 2009. The number is small compared with the current 180 million landline phones and 173 million cell phones, and the reason is that only 30 percent of U.S. homes have broadband connections. However, as the number of broadband links grows, so will the number of VoIP subscribers.

In addition to sound quality, there are other differences between traditional and VoIP telephone services. Most VoIP services do not include the ability to call an emergency number such as 911. Also, when your link to the Internet is down, so is your VoIP service. Since the phone uses a modem that requires electric power, if power is out the phone cannot be used. However, VoIP providers offer some advantages over traditional telephoning. A subscriber receives a special converter into which the telephone number is programmed. The subscriber can take the converter anywhere there is a broadband link to the Internet and use it. This makes the VoIP telephone portable.

Some experts see the future of telephony in a convergence of the cell phone and VoIP phone: you will use only one mobile phone. When outside the home or office, you will use the cell phone network; when back home or in the office, the phone will communicate through a VoIP service. This will reduce the higher cost of cell phone minutes.

Radio Frequency Identification

In Chapter 3 you learned about the great efficiency and business intelligence that companies, especially in manufacturing and retail, can gain from one particular type of communications technology: radio frequency identification (RFID). This section explains in more detail how RFID works. RFID tags can be very tiny, about the size of a rice grain, or several square inches, depending on the amount of information they need to contain and the environment in which they are used. They are not always flat; they can be cylindrical. The tags need very little power. Passive tags use power from the reader that queries them; active tags have their own tiny batteries, which increase the range of the reading range. These tiny batteries last a long time.

An RFID system works as follows: objects are equipped, often embedded, with a tag. The tag contains a transponder. A transponder is a radio transceiver (transmitter-receiver) that is activated for transmission by a signal that is transmitted to it. The tag is equipped with digital memory that is given a unique electronic product code (EPC). The interrogator, a combination of an antenna, a transceiver, and a decoder, emits a signal activating the RFID tag so the interrogator can read data from it and write data to it. (Although the interrogator also writes to the tag, it is often called a reader.) When an RFID tag enters the reader's electromagnetic zone, it detects the reader's activation signal. The reader decodes the data stored in the tag's memory, and the data is passed to a host computer for processing.

Wal-Mart, Gillette, Procter & Gamble, and 84 other companies embarked on a project that might radically change supply chains. The companies use microchips that are embedded in products to replace the ubiquitous bar codes for tracking and checkout at store registers. Each microchip holds a product identification number. The microchips communicate with wireless computers, including handheld and laptop computers, as they are moved in the production line, packed, picked, shipped, unloaded, shelved, and paid for by customers. As the product moves, the information about its location is communicated to a network of computers to which all businesses involved in the production and sale have access. This is often a Wi-Fi network. The big benefits are a just-in-time (JIT) system that minimizes inventory throughout the supply chain to almost zero and shelves that are always stocked. JIT, or a situation that is close to JIT, can be accomplished thanks to up-to-the-minute information about available inventory and when the next shipment from a supplier is needed. "Smart shelves," equipped with tiny wireless transceivers, alert staff whenever the shelf is running out of units, so the staff can put more units on the shelf immediately.

RFID is used for many other purposes as well, as Figure 6.8 shows. For many businesses, the main impediment is the price of an RFID tag. The average price in 2005 was 30 cents. It is expected that the price will decrease to 5 cents within just a few years. When the price is so low, you might begin to see many other uses of the technology, as listed in Figure 6.9.

Converging Technologies

Recall the discussion of converging hardware technologies in the previous chapter. Convergence occurs also in networking technologies. Cell phones used to be able to transmit and receive only through a dedicated network of analog or digital transceivers. Now many are constructed with dual technologies, so that they can serve both as a "traditional" cell phone and a wireless Web phone. When the circuitry detects that it is within the range of a hotspot, calling switches to VoIP to save cost. As mentioned earlier, a landline phone is no longer just a line phone but can be also a VoIP phone. And eventually, we will be able to use the same phone as a landline phone, a VoIP phone, and a cell phone, depending on availability of service and the cost and quality we are willing to accept.

At home, new television sets are designed to connect to cable, satellites, and the Internet, not only alternately, but concurrently. Thus, we will be able to watch a sports game and chat online about it at the same time through the same device, using two different networking technologies. PDAs can already function as television sets and phones. Soon they will be able to do so simultaneously. For individuals, this means they can carry a single device that will connect them to any type of network, erasing the lines between radio, television, telephone, and Internet surfing. To businesses this gives an opportunity to provide new information services and manage a more effective and efficient salesforce.

Wireless technologies can be combined in the same device to enhance functionality. For example, a portable digital music and video player can use Wi-Fi to communicate with your PC or another Wi-Fi device (possibly another music/video player) to download files. It can then use Bluetooth to transmit the music to your wireless earphones. When WiMAX is implemented, some local radio stations are likely to use MANs as additional broadcast channels. With proper software you can then select from the songs to which you have just listened and have them downloaded to your portable player or home computer.

FIGURE 6.8
RFID applications

Use		Example
Access Control		Cards used to replace door keys.
People Tracking	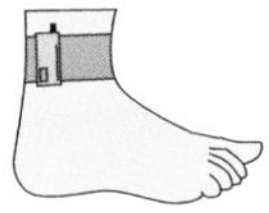	Keep children within school. Track prisoners on probation and prevent fleeing.
Animal Tracking		Track pets.
Livestock Management		Track life cycle of farm animals (e.g., feeding and immunization). Equip each cow with a unique ID to track diseases.
Antitheft Measures		Transponders integrated into car keys. Only a legal key can start the engine.
Transportation		At airport, safety inspection of tagged luggage.
Retail		Tracking products in pallets and on shelves. Contactless payment.
Pharmaceuticals		Prevent drug counterfeiting.
Health Care		Tag people who enter and leave an epidemic zone.

1. Wi-Fi is all around us. Is there any downside to its pervasiveness?

2. People express themselves differently when they speak (either face to face or via the telephone) versus when they send and receive e-mail. What are the differences? Which do you prefer when communicating with someone you don't know personally? Which do you prefer when you know the person?

3. Every home with access to the Internet can now inexpensively become a hotspot. How so? Are there any risks in turning a home into a hotspot?

4. What are the implications of telecommunications for group work?

5. As broadband services cover larger and larger regions and become less expensive, the number of small businesses and home businesses grows. What is the relationship?

6. Some organizations stopped allocating offices to their sales representatives. Why, and is this a wise move?

7. List and explain the benefits of videoconferencing to an organization. List and explain the benefits to society.

8. Anything that does not take space can be traded solely via telecommunications networks. Do you agree? Explain your answer.

9. Do you see any undesirable effects of humans communicating more and more via computer networks rather than in person or over the telephone? What don't you like and why? What do you like about it?

10. List several industries in which telecommuting would be infeasible. Explain why.

11. Wi-Fi circuitry is now embedded in consumer electronic devices such as digital cameras and cell phones. Give an example of what you could do with the Wi-Fi capability of a digital camera.

12. If you were given the opportunity to telecommute, would you? Why or why not?

13. Suppose that you are a middle manager. Would you allow the people who report to you to telecommute? Why or why not?

1. Ima Jeenyes completed her book, *How to Become a Millionaire upon Graduation*. She used a word processor to type the manuscript. She saved the book as a file of 5.7 MB. Ima lives in Philadelphia. The publisher asked that Ima transmit the book via the Internet to the publisher's office in Boston. Ima can transmit the file at a guaranteed speed of 400 Kbps. Because each packet of data transmitted must also contain some nondata bits, assume the total number of bits to transmit is equivalent to 6 MB.

   How long (in minutes) does it take to transmit the book? Ignore the distance between the cities. Remember how many bytes make up 1 MB. Show your calculations clearly using a spreadsheet. Use measurement units throughout your calculation. E-mail the spreadsheet file to your professor.

2. Justin Tyme uses a DSL modem to transmit a report from his office to headquarters. The DSL affords an average bit rate transmission (upload) of 250 Kbps. Since the transmission protocol adds additional bits to data bytes, assume that, on average, there is 1 additional bit for each transmitted byte. On average, a page contains 3,000 characters, including spaces. Justin is allotted only 3 minutes for the transmission. How many pages can he transmit?

3. Of the residential telecommunications services listed in Figure 6.7 find out which are available where you live and how much they cost. You might find several DSL and cable services, and perhaps also satellite and BPL services. Calculate the ratio of maximum bit rate per dollar (downstream) to monthly fee for each service. Which service provides the "biggest bang for the buck," that is, the greatest speed per dollar of monthly fee?

1. Broadband services provided in Japan, South Korea, and Canada are usually faster and less expensive than in the United States. Use the Web to research why this is so. Write a one-page report discussing the reasons.

2. Search the Web for a site that enables you to check your high-speed (broadband) link: DSL, cable, or (if you connect from school) T1 or T3 line. Follow the instructions. Usually, you simply have to click one button. Do so and wait for the response. Print out the response. Wait a minute, and repeat the process. The speeds are likely to be different. Why? Type up the answer, write your name on both copies, then staple and submit them to your professor.

3. You are a telecommunications guru and love to help individuals and businesses. Assume that dial-up, cable, DSL, T3 line, and satellite links to the Internet are available everywhere unless the particular scenario indicates otherwise. Consider the following scenarios and suggest the best overall type of link (consider communication speed, cost, and any other factor you believe is relevant). Each scenario is independent of the others. For each scenario, explain why you selected the option.

   a. An author works at home writing articles for a magazine. Once per week she must transmit an article to her editor. She rarely uses the link for any other purpose.

   b. A large company maintains its own Web site for online catalogs and purchase transactions by its customers. Hundreds of customers visit the sites daily and make purchases.

   c. A small business uses the Internet for daily research. Owners have heard that some links are shared by other subscribers in the same area, which might slow down the connection or even pose security threats. Thus, they would like to avoid such a service. They do need a speed of at least 200 Kbps.

   d. A farm in New Mexico needs a link of at least 200 Kbps. People on the farm can receive television signals only through antennas. The closest telephone central office is 12 miles away.

   e. An Internet service provider specializes in hosting Web sites of small businesses.

   f. A cruise ship wants to provide Internet service to vacationers on the third deck. The ship cruises in the Caribbean. The link's speed must be at least 250 Kbps.

1. Team up with another student from your class. Select a bank branch close to your school. Interview the branch personnel about the telecommunications equipment used between the branch and (a) other branches, (b) headquarters, and (c) other institutions, such as credit information companies, if any. Use the discussion in this chapter to identify the various communications devices that the branch uses. List the devices and state their roles at the bank.

2. Team up with two other students from your class. Each of you should send an e-mail message to one other team member. One of you may use the school's facilities, but the other two should use a subscriber's address, such as an AOL or Comcast address. When you receive the messages, try to get the routing information: which servers did the messages pass through on their way to you? How long did it take the messages to get to the server from which your own computer retrieves the messages? Print out the route your computer generated. Report your findings to your professor.

1. This chapter discusses RFID as an application of wireless networking. Some people have raised privacy concerns about the use of RFID. Do some research and summarize these concerns. Do you agree with them? Why or why not?

2. Do you have a network at home? If so, which type of network is it? What made you decide on this type of network? If not, if you were to set one up, what kind would you choose and why?

VIDEO QUESTIONS

1. The video segment does not define Wiki. What is a Wiki?

2. Could QuickBiz use a Wiki? In which ways?

FROM IDEAS TO APPLICATION: REAL CASES

Networking the Customers

ABF Freight System is a trucking company that specializes in less-than-truckload (LTL) freight shipping. In LTL shipping a trucking company does not wait until a truck is fully loaded before dispatching it. Often, the shipper devotes the entire vehicle to a customer, rather than trying to consolidate shipments. LTL freight shipping can be less complex and offer faster service than truckload (TL) shipping, whereby shipments of disparate clients are consolidated to fill up the truck. Because clients pay more for LTL, they expect high-quality service and full attention to their needs.

ABF utilizes the latest networking technologies to improve service. Customers can use its Web site to schedule shipments. As soon as a truck starts moving, customers can use the Web site to see exactly where a shipment is at any time.

ABF customers want to ensure that their own customers receive shipments on time. They want to know the status of each shipment so there are no surprises. ABF's customers do not need to wait until drivers return to the terminal to know that a delivery was made to their clients. The company equipped its drivers and terminal workers with Nextel cell phones capable of connecting to the Internet. They use the phones to transmit information into ABF's database. This enables ABF customers to receive delivery and pick-up information in real time.

Michael Newcity, director of e-systems and emerging technologies at ABF, says customers love being able to get their own updates, rather than having to call and ask a company rep where their shipments are. Some customers clearly prefer never to talk to anybody at ABF as long as they can serve themselves via the Web site.

ABF periodically conducts short surveys of three to six questions on its Web site to receive feedback from customers. The company also conducts usability interviews to learn how it can improve the site. Its purpose it to provide customers with the online tools and information they need, and to this end managers often interview sales reps. Chris Baltz, vice president of marketing and pricing at ABF, observed that when companies design networking and their Web sites "around the customer," it results in cost savings.

Indeed, management listened. Responding to customer demands, the company decided to allow customers to use the Web site to reroute their shipments in transit. Other companies usually require such rerouting requests in writing, so the client must fax the request, but faxes are sometimes misread or misinterpreted. If an ABF customer notices an error in shipment details, the customer can resolve the problem within 5 minutes. With other shippers it typically takes much longer.

If customers wish, they have the option of linking their information systems to ABF's via the Internet. This enables them to access shipment data directly. Doing so allows them to display shipping data at their own Web site for their own clients. It also lets their accounting and other "back-end" systems receive data directly from the source, for accounting, billing, and other operations.

Not all customers are fully comfortable completing entire transactions via the Web site, but improvements have helped a growing number to do so. When this service was first offered, 73 percent of customers who started a transaction completed it at the site. Now, 80 percent of customers who use the Web site successfully conclude their transactions.

In addition to seeing the status of their shipments, customers can use the site to review invoices and to create weekly custom reports. They can either view the reports online or have them sent to an e-mail address, where they can retrieve them. Baltz observed that the key to success in this industry is not to be a commodity. Giving the customers visibility and control of their transactions and status of their shipped items differentiates ABF from other shippers. The extra services attract customers and increases customer loyalty. When customers get used to the technology ABF puts at their disposal, they are less likely to switch to a competitor.

Source: Dragoon, A., "Nice Doing Business with You," *CIO*, February 15, 2005; www.abfs.com, 2005.

Thinking About the Case

1. In terms of types of networks (WANs, LANs, etc.), what type of network does ABF use? Which parties use this network?

2. In addition to serving customers well, networking helps ABF save costs. How?

3. Networking helps not only customers but also the customers' customers. How?

Mickey Can Relax

What would happen if terrorists attacked the "happiest place on earth" in Anaheim, California? More than 200 local, state, and federal first responders tackled such an event in an evening drill at Disneyland, the commercial heart of Anaheim. The 3-hour simulation left almost 30 "casualties" and more than 50 people "wounded" by stray bullets or shrapnel.

Anaheim police officers and firefighters, California National Guard personnel, FBI agents, and Disney security staff involved in the exercise frantically tried to evacuate employees and guests while treating the "wounded" and eliminating the "terrorists." Two out of three attackers were "killed" by police and the third "committed suicide."

After the drill ended, authorities determined that their most important goal was to significantly reduce the casualties if such an event were ever to take place. In order to save lives and the financial viability of Orange County's largest employer, security agencies had to employ better communication methods in their first response execution. Failure to do so risked not only the $3.6 billion pumped into the local economy each year by Disneyland's guests but also the jobs of more than 65,000 local residents.

On a typical weekend in the summer, more than 70,000 tourists crowd 54 hotels and motels spread over slightly more than 2 square miles of what is known as The Resort District. In most years, Disneyland's guests contribute $325 million to the county just in taxes. The Walt Disney Co. has maintained its policy of not discussing its security arrangements in public in order to maintain its happy, carefree, youthful image. Orange County's public sector cannot afford that luxury.

In a quickly changing environment with unexpected elements affecting a huge area of land, communication based on real-time information available to the greatest number of responders is a key to success. To help Anaheim in its emergency preparation, Electronic Data Systems Corp. (EDS) has developed a new product called Enterprise Virtual Operations Center (EVOC). The Plano, Texas, company's Homeland Security Solutions division began work on the EVOC system in response to the attacks in New York and Washington, D.C., on September 11, 2001.

The first U.S. city to install the software, Anaheim has legitimate concerns, as officials from both the Department of Homeland Security and the FBI have labeled Disneyland a potential target for terrorists. EVOC has been operating in Anaheim since June 2004. In case of an attack, the system collects data from as many relevant agencies as possible and simultaneously provides this information to all first responders involved.

In addition to viewing developments on monitors ranging in size from desktops to laptops and even 4-inch displays in handheld equipment, EVOC enables its users to immediately access contact information for specialists such as hazardous material units and explosives experts. Critical figures such as the number of police cars within a specific radius of the attack and real-time reports of traffic jams, which would delay the arrival of first responders, are quickly available through EVOC.

The system's processing of information from so many sources allows the police chief, the fire chief, the mayor, and local hospitals to coordinate a plan for elimination of the terrorists and the fastest possible medical attention to the wounded. Success toward those endeavors relies on a reduction in redundant efforts, alerting first responders to possible dangers as they head toward a location, and designating specific responsibilities to emergency response personnel.

Firefighters and police officers benefit from the software's connection to more than 200 digital cameras positioned at central venues like the Anaheim Convention Center, major intersections, and essential utility spots such as electrical substations and sewage sites. Local authorities patrolling Anaheim's streets have never had such detailed information accessible so quickly. Digital cameras are equipped in most Anaheim police cars, so officers can instantly share real-time situational changes with everyone connected to EVOC.

Emergency phone calls to 911 dispatchers can be sent to particular responders closest to the scene, and geographical references to nearby businesses, along with electronic street maps, can mean the difference between life and death. Building entrances and exits, gas and water lines, and similar information are all visually accessible via EVOC.

Whereas past primitive communication systems could only be accessed at the main police station, the EVOC software is installed on two different servers across Anaheim. This reduces the risk of the system's destruction if one server were destroyed in an attack. Authorities can watch what is happening in response to a specific incident from any laptop in the world. The freedom to cooperate on the same rescue even if all commanders are in separate locations or are not even connected to a telephone is a huge asset and saves critical time.

If a police officer approaches a ride in Disneyland to investigate a related death and two more cops are headed his way, EVOC can trace the connection of all three and indicate every available resource. This includes the names of detectives who can work the case and the station from which emergency medical technicians have been dispatched. Effectively, each responder connected and participating in this situation can know who is going, where they are going, and when they will get there.

The software's contributions are not limited to massive emergencies and terrorist attacks. Because of the enormous amount of information processed so quickly by EVOC and the system's ability to track individual participants, police officers with specialized skills can be sent to particular crime scenes when there are many simultaneous incidents. Subsequently, the most able personnel with the best training and equipment can be used where they are most needed. This maximization of limited resources enables successful performance on previously unreachable levels.

Private-sector organizations in Anaheim can also benefit from EVOC through their security partnerships with local police and firefighters. Retail operations throughout Orange County, like Macy's West division, have introduced full-scale evacuation drills several times a year and now support their internal emergency response leaders with software that can connect to EVOC. Macy's E-Team software system enables its store managers to report significant developments at each location, and this information is easily accessible within Macy's corporation and instantly available for sharing with first responders throughout Orange County.

Easily navigable contact information is available to local Macy's management, so whether there is a flood outside the store or the electrical power suddenly goes out, each incident is reported and the right emergency personnel are contacted. Other major companies throughout Orange County have also implemented similar systems to maintain business operation and contact with authorities during any sort of large disaster. These include Toyota Motor Sales, Yamaha Corp. of America, and The Capital Group Cos. Huge

events arenas, including Angel Stadium and Arrowhead Pond, have also joined this group of businesses working more closely and productively with local authorities.

Certainly, the safety of customers and employees is an essential factor in the increased collaboration between the private and public security sectors. Still, there is a huge economic motivation that cannot be ignored. Orange County annually outputs more than $142 billion through entertainment, professional services, merchandise retailing, and manufactured goods. Businesses understand that local, state, and federal emergency workers can offer their expertise and enable consumer traffic to continue with as little interruption as possible if information is consistently shared in the fastest, clearest ways possible.

Source: Barret, L., "Keeping Disneyland Safe," *Baseline* (www.baselinemag.com), May 4, 2005.

Thinking About the Case

1. The EVOC communication system has some redundancy. What is redundant, and for what purpose?

2. Is this system wired or wireless? Why is this so important?

3. The network used for EVOC is scalable to include private businesses. Explain this scalability and give an example of it from the case.

SEVEN

Databases and Data Warehouses

LEARNING OBJECTIVES

Data is usually collected in a way that does not make it immediately useful to businesspeople. Imagine building a model palace from a pile of building blocks. You have a good idea of what you want to build, but first you have to organize the blocks so it is easy for you to find and select only the blocks you need. Then you can combine them into substructures that eventually are integrated into your model. Similarly, data collected by organizations must be organized and stored so that useful information can be extracted from it in a flexible manner.

When you finish this chapter, you will be able to:

■ Explain the difference between traditional file organization and the database approach to managing digital data.

■ Explain how relational and object-oriented database management systems are used to construct databases, populate them with data, and manipulate the data to produce information.

■ Enumerate the most important features and operations of a relational database, the most popular database model.

■ Understand how data modeling and design creates a conceptual blueprint of a database.

■ Discuss how databases are used on the Web.

■ List the operations involved in transferring data from transactional databases to data warehouses.

QUICKBIZ MESSENGERS:
The Value and Uses of Databases

As QuickBiz grew, so did its reliance on databases. By the time the company had grown to a size of 90 employees, Andrew was using databases to create weekly schedules for part-time and full-time employees, track customer orders, store and access employee and customer information, organize and report financial data, and provide crucial information for marketing strategies. As his database needs expanded, he transitioned from one database management system to another.

Moving Up: From Microsoft Access to Oracle

In the early days, Andrew had relied on Microsoft Access and Excel for his company's database needs. When he hired his first part-time messengers, he used an Excel spreadsheet to set up weekly schedules. He stored customer and order information in an Access database. As business grew, so did the size of the database. Kayla Brown, an IT consultant who worked in an office on the second floor of his building, told him that he should consider using a more powerful database management system (DBMS). When Leslie Chen suggested that QuickBiz create an intranet so that messengers could upload delivery information through their wireless connections, the need to switch to a more powerful DBMS became urgent. Microsoft Access wouldn't be able to handle the number of concurrent users that QuickBiz anticipated. Andrew decided to hire Kayla to help the office shift to Oracle. An Oracle database would be able to accommodate both the increased size of the database and the need for concurrent access.

Tapping the Power of Databases

Then Andrew turned his thoughts to using his data to better his service—to maintain his existing customers and strengthen his relationships with them.

He also wanted to find out who would be good potential customers. He hired Kayla to run SQL queries and create reports. Surely he could find valuable information by exploring customer information and buying patterns.

First Andrew wanted to find out who his preferred customers were—those who used his service most often and provided the most revenue. The consultant used data-mining software to delve into the data and identified a profile. To his surprise, Andrew found that the legal and medical-supply firms were most profitable. He'd always thought the art gallery owners were his best clients because of the special handling their objects required. But lawyers and pharmacists needed faster delivery and special services, such as delivery confirmation, which commanded premium rates and generated additional revenue at no further cost per delivery to QuickBiz. Andrew designated those customers as VIPs and tagged their database files. VIPs would receive priority delivery on the routes from now on.

Also, Andrew was interested in the purchasing patterns of customers. He planned to target those opportunities with a promotion to gain new clients. Again, the consultant came back with interesting news: larger law firms with branches throughout the Puget Sound area used QuickBiz's service most often on weekdays between the hours of 10 a.m. and 1 p.m. So Andrew decided to locate other similar firms and develop a direct-mail promotion to them—discounted deliveries for setting up an account and scheduling 30 orders in a month's time. Andrew also added additional messengers during that time frame to be sure to handle deliveries smoothly.

Businesses collect and dissect data for a multitude of purposes. Digital data can be stored in a variety of ways on different types of media, as discussed in Chapter 4. They can be stored in what can be called the traditional file format, in which the different pieces of information are not labeled and categorized, but are stored as continuous strings of bytes. The chief advantage of this format is the efficient use of space, but the data is nonetheless difficult to locate and manipulate. By contrast, the database format, in which each piece of data is labeled or categorized, provides a much more powerful information management tool. Data in this format can be easily accessed and manipulated in almost any way desired to create useful information and optimize productivity.

The impact of database technology on business cannot be overstated. Not only has it changed the way almost every industry conducts business, but it has also created an information industry with far-reaching effects on both our business and personal lives. Databases are behind the successful use of automatic teller machines, increased efficiency in retail stores, almost every marketing effort, and the numerous online search engines and electronic storefronts on the Web. Combined with interactive Web pages on the Internet, databases have made an immense contribution to commerce. Without them, there would be no online banking, no online consumer catalogs, no online searches for information, no online stock brokerages, and no online chat rooms. Their impact on business has allowed fewer people to complete larger tasks, and their power has allowed organizations to learn more about us, as consumers, than we might realize. Imagine: every time you enter the address of a Web site, a special program performs a search in a huge database and matches your request with one of millions of addresses. Every time you fill out an online form with details such as your address, phone number, Social Security number (SSN), or credit-card number, a program feeds the data into a database, where each item is recorded for further use.

In virtually every type of business today, you must understand the power of databases. This chapter reviews approaches to organizing and manipulating data.

The Traditional File Approach

There are two overall approaches to maintaining data: the **traditional file approach**—which has no mechanism for tagging, retrieving, and manipulating data—and the **database approach**, which does have that mechanism. To appreciate the benefits of the database approach, you must keep in mind the inconvenience involved in accessing and manipulating data in the traditional file approach: program-data dependency, high data redundancy, and low data integrity.

Consider Figure 7.1, which is an example of a human resource file in traditional file format. Suppose a programmer wants to retrieve and print out only the last name and department number of each employee from this file. The programmer must clearly instruct the computer to first retrieve the data between position 10 and position 20. Then he must instruct the computer to skip the positions up to position 35 and retrieve the data between positions 36 and 39. He cannot instruct the computer to retrieve a piece of data by its column name, because column names do not exist in this format. To create the reports, the programmer must know which position ranges maintain which type of data and insert the appropriate headings, "Last Name" and "Department," so that the reader can understand the information. If the programmer miscounts the positions, the printout might include output like "677Rapap" as a last name instead of "Rapaport." This illustrates the *interdependency of programs and data* of the traditional file approach. The programmer must know *how* data is stored to use it. Perhaps most importantly, the very fact that manipulation of the data requires a programmer is probably the greatest disadvantage of the file approach. Much business data is still processed this way. New data resources rarely are built this way, but the existing ones must be maintained with this challenge in mind.

Other challenges with traditional file storage are high data redundancy and low data integrity, because in older file systems files were built, and are still maintained, for the use of specific organizational units. If your last and first name, as well as address and other details appear in the files of the department where you work as well as in the payroll file of the Human Resource department, there is duplication of data, or **data redundancy**, which wastes storage

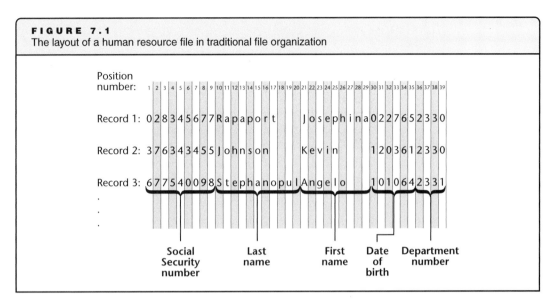

space (and consequently money) and is inefficient. When corrections or modifications need to be made, every change has to be made as many times as the number of locations where the data appears, which takes time and might introduce errors. If the same data was entered correctly in one place but incorrectly in another, your record is not only inaccurate, but might appear to represent a different person in each place. Inaccuracies hurt **data integrity**. Often, the traditional file approach to storing data leads to low data integrity.

The Database Approach

In the database approach, data pieces are organized about entities. An **entity** is any object about which an organization chooses to collect data. Entities can be types of people, such as employees, students, or members of fan clubs; events, such as sales transactions, sports events, or theatre shows; or inanimate objects, such as inventoried or for-sale products, buildings, or minerals. In the context of data management, "entity" refers to all the occurrences sharing the same types of data. Therefore, it does not matter if you maintain a record of one student or many students; the entity is "student." To understand how data is organized in a database, you must first understand the data hierarchy, described in Figure 7.2, which shows a compilation of information about students: their first names, last names, years of birth, SSNs, majors (department), and campus phone numbers. The smallest piece of data is a **character** (such as a letter in a first or last name, or a digit in a street address). Multiple characters make up a field. A **field** is one piece of information about an entity, such as the last name or first name of a student, or the student's street address. The fields related to the same entity make up a **record**. A collection of related records, such as all the records of a college's students, is called a **file**. Often, several related files must be kept together. A collection of such files is referred to as a database. However, the features of a database can be present even when a database consists of a single file.

Once the fields are assigned names, including Last Name, First Name, SSN, and the like, the data in each field carries a tag—a field name—and can be easily accessed by that field name, no matter where the data is physically stored. One of the greatest strengths of databases is their promotion of application-data independence. In other words, if an application is written to process data in a database, the application designer only needs to know the names of the fields, not their physical organization or their length.

Database fields are not limited to holding text and numbers. They can hold pictures, sounds, and video clips. Fields can hold any content that can be digitized. For example, when you shop online, you can search for a product by its product name or code, and then retrieve its picture or a video clip about the product.

While a database itself is a collection of several related files, the program used to build databases, populate them with data, and manipulate the data is called a **database**

FIGURE 7.2
Data hierarchy

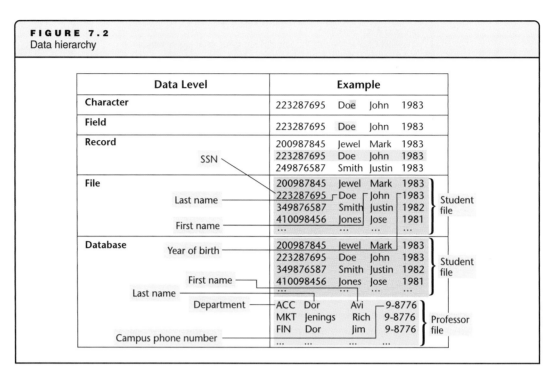

Data Level		Example
Character		223287695 Doe John 1983
Field		223287695 Doe John 1983
Record	SSN	200987845 Jewel Mark 1983 223287695 Doe John 1983 249876587 Smith Justin 1983
File	Last name First name	200987845 Jewel Mark 1983 223287695 ┌Doe ┌John ┌1983 } Student file 349876587 Smith Justin 1982 410098456 Jones Jose 1981 ... ...
Database	Year of birth First name Last name Department Campus phone number	200987845 Jewel Mark 1983 223287695 Doe John 1983 } Student file 349876587 Smith Justin 1982 410098456 Jones Jose 1981 ... ... ACC Dor Avi 9-8776 MKT Jenings Rich 9-8776 } Professor file FIN Dor Jim 9-8776 ... ...

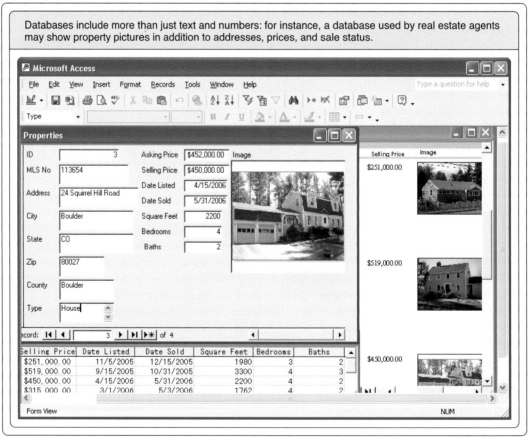

Databases include more than just text and numbers: for instance, a database used by real estate agents may show property pictures in addition to addresses, prices, and sale status.

management system (DBMS). The files themselves *are* the database, but DBMSs do all the work—structuring files, storing data, and linking records. As you saw previously, if you wanted to access data from files that were stored in a traditional file approach, you would have to know exactly how many characters were designated for each type of data. A DBMS, however, does much of this work (and a lot of other work) for you.

If you are using a database, you want to be able to move rapidly from one record to another, sort by different criteria, create different types of reports, and analyze the data in different ways. Because of these demands, databases are stored on and processed from direct access storage devices, such as magnetic disks or CDs. They can be backed up to sequential storage devices such as magnetic or optical tapes, but cannot be efficiently processed off such media because it would take too long to access the records.

Queries Data is accessed in a database by sending messages called "queries," which request data from specific records and/or fields and direct the computer to display the results. Queries are also entered to manipulate data. Usually, the same software that is used to construct and populate the database, that is, the DBMS, is also used to present queries. Modern DBMSs provide fairly user-friendly means of querying a database.

Security The use of databases raises security and privacy issues. The fact that data is stored only once in a database for several different purposes does not mean that everyone with access to that database should have access to *all* the data in it. Restricting access is easily dealt with by customizing menus for different users and requiring users to enter codes that limit access to certain fields or records. As a result, users have different *views* of the database, as abstractly illustrated in Figure 7.3. The ability to limit users' views to only specific columns or records gives the **database administrator (DBA)** another advantage: the ability to implement security measures. The measures are implemented once for the database, rather than multiple times for different files. For instance, in the database in Figure 7.4, while a human resource manager has access to all fields of the employee file (represented by the top, middle, and lower parts of the figure), the payroll personnel have access only to four fields of the employee file (middle part of the figure), and a project manager has access only to the Name and Hours Worked fields. Views can be limited to certain fields in a database, or certain records, or a combination of both.

DBMSs are usually bundled with a 4GL (fourth-generation programming language) module. Programmers can use this module to develop applications that facilitate queries and produce predesigned reports.

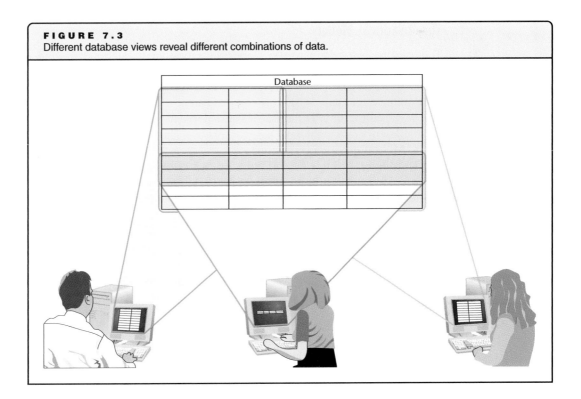

FIGURE 7.3
Different database views reveal different combinations of data.

FIGURE 7.4
Different views from the same database

View of Human Resource Manager				
SSN	Name	D.O.B.	Hire Date	Marital Status

View of Payroll Personnel			
SSN	Hourly Rate	Benefits Code	Hours Worked

View of Project Manager	
Name	Hours Worked

DATABASE MODELS

A *database model* is the general logical structure in which records are stored within a database and the method used to establish relationships among the records. There are several database models. They differ in the manner in which records are linked to each other. These differences, in turn, dictate the manner in which a user can navigate the database, retrieve desired records, and create reports. The oldest models, the hierarchical and network models, are still used in some databases that were built in the 1970s and 1980s, but are no longer used in newly constructed databases. Virtually all new databases are designed following the relational and object-oriented models.

The Relational Model

The **relational model** consists of **tables**. Its roots are in relational algebra, although you do not have to know relational algebra to build and use relational databases. However, database experts still use relational algebra terminology: in a relational database, a record is called a *tuple*, a field—often referred to as column—is called an *attribute*, and a table of records is called a *relation*. This text uses the simpler terms, as do the popular software packages: fields, records, and tables.

To design a relational database, you need a clear idea of the different entities and how they relate. For example, in a DVD store database, the entities might be Customer, DVD Rental, DVD, and Distributor. A single table is built for each entity (though each table can contain from only a few to potentially millions of records). DVD Rental is an associative entity, and you can see in Figure 7.5 that the DVD Rental table associates data from the Customer and DVD tables.

Maintenance of a relational database is relatively easy because each table is independent of the others, although some tables are related to others. To add a customer record, the user accesses the Customer table. To delete a record of a DVD, the user accesses the DVD table. The advantages of this model makes relational database management systems the most popular in the software market. Virtually all DBMSs that are offered on the market accommodate the relational model. This model is used in supply chain management (SCM) systems and many other enterprise applications and local, individual ISs.

To retrieve records from a relational database, or to sort them, you must use a *key*. A key is a field whose values identify records either for display or for processing. You can use any field as a key. For example, you could ask the database for the record of John Smith from the Customer

table by using the CustName field as a key. That is, you enter a query, a condition that instructs

FIGURE 7.5
A relational database

Customer Table

CustID	CustName	CustPhone	CustAddr
33091	Jill Bronson	322-4907	203 Oak Dr
35999	John Smith	322-5577	519 Devon St
36002	John Sosik	342-0071	554 Spring Dr
36024	Jane Fedorow	322-7299	101 Jefferson Ave

↑
Primary key

Composite primary key

DVD Rental Table

CustID	CopyNum	Date Rented	Date Returned
35999	4452-1	5-1-06	5-3-06
36002	4780-3	5-3-06	
36024	5312-2	5-2-06	5-5-06

Copy Table

CopyNum	TitleNum
4452-1	4452
4452-2	4452
5312-1	5312
5312-2	5312
5312-3	5312
7662-1	7662
7662-2	7662
5583-1	5583

Primary key in *Title* and part of a
composite primary key in *Copy-Title*

Title Table

TitleNum	Title	Category	DistribNum	RentPrice
4452	Enter the Dragon	Martial Arts	277	$4.00
5312	The Ring II	Thriller	305	$4.00
7662	Star Wars III	Sci-Fi	372	$5.00
5583	White Noise	Thriller	589	$2.50

Primary key in *Distributor* and foreign key in *Title*

Distributor Table

DistribNum	DistribName	Phone
277	HK Corp	1-877-555-0550
305	Columbia	1-888-222-3654
372	Lucas Films	1-247-233-6996
589	Booh Inc	1-866-222-9999

the DBMS to retrieve a record with the value of CustName as "John Smith." A key is *unique* if the value (content) in that field appears only in one record. Sometimes a key is composed of several fields so that their combination provides a unique key.

As you can see, database design requires careful forethought. The designer must include fields for foreign keys from other tables so that join tables can be created in the future. A table might include foreign keys from several tables, so that there is much flexibility in creating reports with related data from several tables. The inclusion of foreign keys might cause considerable data redundancy. This complexity has not diminished the popularity of relational databases, however.

Know About Data Management

A national car rental company knows the precise number of automobiles to hold for late-booking, high-paying travelers. A restaurant chain detects consumer buying patterns that the company then uses to boost its sales of special meals. How do businesses find this information?

Transactions are recorded at the boundaries of a company in its contacts with external entities, such as customers and suppliers. Data captured this way makes up the greater part of most organizational databases. It provides the raw material for essential information that helps answer questions such as: What is the total amount of money we owe debtors? What is the backlog of a certain product that we manufacture? What was the average sales volume per employee last quarter? However, to be able to extract useful information, the data must first be organized in well-designed databases. And to know what information you can draw from a database, you must understand how databases are structured and what combinations of data can be created for you on demand.

Imagine a salesclerk who cannot immediately respond to a customer about the availability of an item or an online shopper who cannot display the details of an item that is actually available for sale at the site. Customers experiencing this are not likely to patronize the business again. Imagine a treasurer who cannot figure out in real time how much cash the company has in the bank. The company might miss an important deal. Available and reliable information is the most important resource of any business, in any industry. Thus, professionals must understand at least the fundamentals of data organization and manipulation. You will be a more productive professional if you know how databases and data warehouses are built and queried, and what types of information can be extracted from them.

If there is more than one record with "John Smith" (because several customers happen to have that same name) in the CustName field, you might not retrieve the single record you desired. Depending on the application you use for the query, you might receive the first one that meets the condition, that is, a list of all the records with that value in the field. The only way to be sure you are retrieving the desired record is to use a unique key, such as a Social Security number, an employee ID, or, in our example, a customer ID (CustID). A unique key can serve as a **primary key**. A primary key is the field by which records in a table are uniquely identified. If your query specified that you wanted the record whose CustID value is 36002, the system would retrieve the record of John Sosik. It will be the John Sosik you wanted, even if there are more records of people with exactly the same name. Because the purpose of a primary key is to uniquely identify a record, there must be a unique value in that field for each record.

Usually, a table in a relational database must have a primary key, and most relational DBMSs enforce this rule; if the designer does not designate a field as a key, the DBMS creates its own serial number field as the primary key field for the table. Once the designer of the table determines the primary key when constructing the records' format, the DBMS does not allow a user to enter two records with the same value in that column. Note that there might be situations in which more than one field can be used as a primary key. Such is the case with motor vehicles, because three different fields can uniquely identify the record of a particular vehicle: the vehicle identification number (VIN), its title, and its state license plate number. Thus, a database designer might establish one of these fields as a primary key to retrieve records. In Figure 7.5 in the DVD Rental table both CustID and CopyNum can be used as a primary key.

For some business needs you must use a **composite key**, a combination of two or more fields that together serve as a primary key, because it is impractical to use a single field as a primary key. For example, consider flight records of a commercial airline. Flights of a certain route are the same every week or every day they are offered, so the daily Oz Airlines' flight from Houston to Geneva—OZ1602—for instance, cannot serve us well to retrieve a list of all the passengers who took this flight on May 3, 2006. However, we can use the combination of the flight number *and* date as a composite primary key. To check who sat in a particular seat, a composite key consisting of three fields is needed: flight number, date, and seat number.

To link records from one table with records of another table, the tables must have at least one field in common (i.e., one column in each table must contain the same type of data), and that field must be a primary key field for one of the tables. This repeated field is a primary key in one table, and a **foreign key** field in the other table. In the DVD store example, if you will ever want to create a report showing the name of every distributor and all the DVD titles from that distributor, the primary key of the Distributor table, DistribNum, must also be included as a foreign key in the Title table. The resultant table (Figure 7.6) is called a **join table**. Note that although DistribNum was used to create the join table, it does not have to be displayed in the join table, although it could be.

FIGURE 7.6
A join table

Distributor	Telephone	Title
HK Corp	1-877-555-0550	Enter the Dragon
Columbia	1-888-222-3654	The Ring II
Lucas Films	1-247-233-6996	Star Wars III
Booh Inc	1-866-222-9999	White Noise

Since the relationships between tables are created as part of manipulating the table, the relational model supports both one-to-many and many-to-many relationships between records of different tables. For example, a **one-to-many relationship** is created when a group of employees belongs to only one department. All would have the same department number as a foreign key in their records, and none will have more than one department key. There is *one* department, linked to *many* employees. A **many-to-many relationship** can be maintained, for instance, for professors and students in a college database. A professor might have many students, and a student might have many professors. This can be accomplished by creating a composite key of professor ID and student ID. In our example of the DVD store, there is a many-to-many relationship between customers and the DVDs they have rented. The DVD Rental table enables the store manager to create a history report of customers and their rentals. It is clear that more than one customer has rented a certain DVD, and the same customer has rented many different DVDs.

The major vendors of relational DBMSs are IBM, Oracle, and Microsoft, at a worldwide market share in licensing revenues of about 34 percent, 34 percent, and 20 percent, respectively. IBM licenses DB2, Oracle licenses DBMSs by the company name, and Microsoft licenses SQL Server and Access. These DBMSs are an essential part of enterprise applications such as SCM and CRM systems.

The Object-Oriented Model

The **object-oriented database model** uses the object-oriented approach, described in Chapter 5, to maintaining records. In object-oriented technology, an object consists of both data and the procedures that manipulate the data. So, in addition to the attributes of an entity, an object also contains relationships with other entities and procedures to manipulate the data. The combined storage of both data and the procedures that manipulate them is referred to as **encapsulation**. Through encapsulation, an object can be "planted" in different data sets. The ability in object-oriented structures to create a new object automatically by replicating all or some of the characteristics of a previously developed object (called the parent object) is called **inheritance**. Figure 7.7 demonstrates how the same data maintained in a relational database at the DVD rental store would be stored and used in an object-oriented database. The relationships between data about entities are not kept by way of foreign keys, but through the relationships of one object with another. One advantage of this is the reduction of data redundancy.

Some data and information cannot be organized as fields, but they can be handled as objects, such as drawings, maps, and Web pages. All these capabilities make object-oriented DBMSs (OODBMSs) handy in computer-aided design (CAD), geographic information systems, and applications used to update quickly thousands of Web pages daily, because they can handle a wide range of data—such as graphics, voice, and text—more easily than the relational model.

Similar to relational DBMSs, OODBMSs provide a graphical user interface (GUI) to manage the DBMS. The user can choose objects from "classes," which are groups of objects that share similar characteristics. Elements of OODBMSs are often incorporated into relational databases, and such databases are sometimes known as *object-relational databases*.

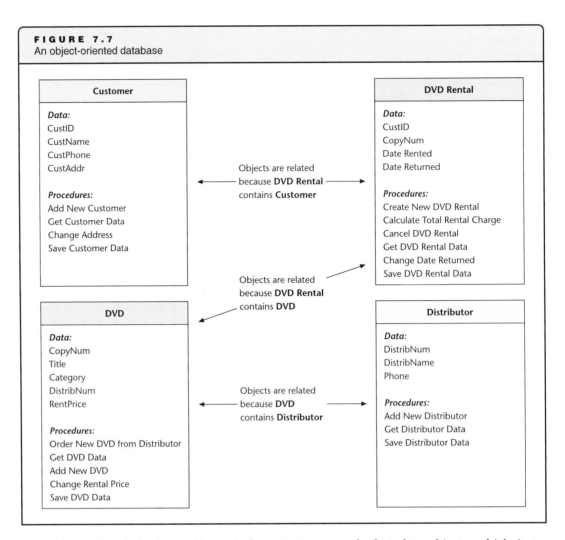

FIGURE 7.7
An object-oriented database

Customer

Data:
CustID
CustName
CustPhone
CustAddr

Procedures:
Add New Customer
Get Customer Data
Change Address
Save Customer Data

Objects are related because **DVD Rental** contains **Customer**

DVD Rental

Data:
CustID
CopyNum
Date Rented
Date Returned

Procedures:
Create New DVD Rental
Calculate Total Rental Charge
Cancel DVD Rental
Get DVD Rental Data
Change Date Returned
Save DVD Rental Data

Objects are related because **DVD Rental** contains **DVD**

DVD

Data:
CopyNum
Title
Category
DistribNum
RentPrice

Procedures:
Order New DVD from Distributor
Get DVD Data
Add New DVD
Change Rental Price
Save DVD Data

Objects are related because **DVD** contains **Distributor**

Distributor

Data:
DistribNum
DistribName
Phone

Procedures:
Add New Distributor
Get Distributor Data
Save Distributor Data

Object-oriented databases (OODBs) do not store records, but data objects, which is an advantage for quick updates of data sets and the relationships among them. For instance, in the example of the DVD store, in the OODB the relationship between a DVD and its distributor is not established through a foreign key; it exists because the DVD class contains the Distributor class. However, object-oriented databases also have some disadvantages, compared with relational databases. For example, there is dependence between applications and data; they are simply "wrapped" together. Changing the structures of tables in a relational database does not require changes in applications that use the data in those tables, while it would require changes in applications in an object-oriented database. This dependence also limits the ability to enter *ad hoc* queries in an OODB, that is, to enter queries at will. While not as popular and as well understood as relational databases, OODBs are gaining adopters.

Several software companies have developed popular object-oriented DBMSs. Among them are Objectivity/DB (Objectivity Inc.), ObjectStore (Progress Software Inc.), and Versant (Versant Corporation).

RELATIONAL OPERATIONS

As mentioned before, the most popular DBMSs are those that support the relational model. Therefore, it would be beneficial for you to familiarize yourself with a widely used relational database, such as Access, Oracle, or SQL Server. To use the database, you should know how relational operations work. A **relational operation** creates a temporary table that is a subset of the original table or tables. It allows you to create a report containing records that satisfy a condition, create a list with only some fields about an entity, or produce a report from a join table, which combines relevant data from two or more tables. If so desired, the user can save the newly created table. Often, the temporary table is needed only for *ad hoc* reporting and is immediately discarded.

The three most important relational operations are *select*, *project*, and *join*. *Select* is the selection of records that meet certain conditions. For example, a human resources manager might need a report showing the entire record of every employee whose salary exceeds $60,000. *Project* is the selection of certain columns from a table, such as the salaries of all the employees. A query might specify a combination of selection and projection. In the preceding example, the manager might require only the ID number, last name (project), and salary of employees whose salaries are greater than $60,000 (select).

One of the most useful manipulations of a relational database is the creation of a new table from two or more other tables. As you might recall from our discussion of the relational model, the joining of data from multiple tables is called a *join*. We have already used a simple example from the DVD store database (Figure 7.6). However, join queries can be much more complex. For example, a relational business database might have four tables: SalesRep, Catalog, Order, and Customer. A sales manager might wish to create a report showing, for each sales rep, a list of all of the customers who purchased anything last month, the items each customer purchased, and the total amount spent by each customer. The new table is created from a relational operation that draws data from all four tables.

The join operation is a powerful manipulation that can create very useful reports for decision making. A join table is created "on the fly" as a result of a query and only for the duration the user wishes to view it or to create a paper report from it. Design features allow the user to change the field headings (although the field names are kept the same in the internal table), place the output in different layouts on the screen or paper, and add graphics and text to the report. The new table might be saved as an additional table in the database.

Structured Query Language

Structured Query Language (SQL) has become the query language of choice for many developers of relational DBMSs. SQL is an international standard and is provided with most relational database management programs. Its strength is in its easy-to-remember intuitive commands. For instance, assuming the name of the entire database is DVD_Store, to create a list of all titles of thriller DVDs whose rental price is less than $5.00, the query would be:

> SELECT TITLE, CATEGORY FROM DVD_STORE
>   WHERE CATEGORY = 'Thriller' and RENTPRICE < 5

Statements like this can be used for *ad hoc* queries or integrated in a program that is saved for repeated use. Commands for updating the database are also easy to remember: INSERT, DELETE, and UPDATE.

There are several advantages to integrating SQL in a DBMS:

- With a standard language, users do not have to learn different sets of commands to create and manipulate databases in different DBMSs.

- SQL statements can be embedded in widely used third-generation languages such as COBOL or C and object-oriented languages such as C++ or Java, in which case these languages are called the "host language." The combination of highly tailored and efficient 3GL or object-oriented statements with SQL statements increases the efficiency and effectiveness of applications accessing relational databases.

- Because SQL statements are portable from one operating system to another, the programmer is not forced to rewrite statements.

Some relational DBMSs, such as Microsoft Access, provide GUIs to create SQL queries: SQL queries can be placed by clicking icons and selecting menu items, which are internally converted into SQL queries and executed. This capability allows relatively inexperienced database designers to use SQL.

The Schema and Metadata

When building a new database, users must first build a schema (from the Greek word for "plan"). The **schema** describes the structure of the database being designed: the names and types of fields in each record type and the general relationships among different sets of records or files. It includes a description of the database's structure, the names and sizes of fields, and details such as which field is a primary key. The number of records is never specified because it might change, and the maximum number of records is determined by the capacity of the storage medium.

Fields can hold different types of data: numeric, alphanumeric, graphic, or time-related. Numeric fields hold numbers that can be manipulated by addition, multiplication, averaging, and the like. Alphanumeric fields hold textual values: words, numerals, and special symbols, which make up names, addresses, and identification numbers. Numerals entered in alphanumeric fields, such as Social Security numbers or zip codes, cannot be manipulated mathematically. The builder of a new database must also indicate which fields are to be used as primary keys. Many DBMSs also allow a builder to positively indicate when a field is not unique, meaning that the value in that field might be the same for more than one record.

Figure 7.8 presents the schema of a database table created with the Microsoft Access DBMS. The user is prompted to enter the names and types of fields. Access lets the user name the fields and determine the data types. The Description section allows the designer to describe the nature and function of the fields for people who maintain the database. In the lower part of the window the user is offered many options for each field, such as field size, format, and so on. In Access the primary key field is indicated by a little key icon to its left.

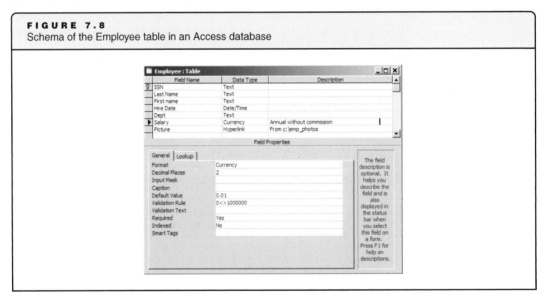

FIGURE 7.8
Schema of the Employee table in an Access database

The description of each table structure and types of fields become part of a **data dictionary**, which is a repository of information about the data and their organization. Designers usually add more information about each field, such as where the data comes from (such as another system, or entered manually); who owns the original data; who is allowed to add, delete, or update data in the field; and other details that help DBAs maintain the database and understand the meaning of the fields and their relationships. (Some people prefer to call this **metadata**, meaning "data about the data.") Metadata includes:

- The source of the data, including contact information.
- Tables that are related to the data.
- Field and index information, such as the size and type of the field (whether it is text or numeric), and the ways the data is sorted.
- Programs and processes that use the data.
- Population rules: what is inserted, or updated, and how often.

DATA MODELING

Databases must be carefully planned and designed to meet business goals. How they are designed enables or limits flexibility in use. Analyzing an organization's data and identifying the relationships among the data is called **data modeling**. Data modeling should first be done to decide which data should be collected and how it should be organized. Thus, data modeling should be proactive. It is a good practice to create data models periodically, so that decision makers have a clear picture of what data is available for reports, and what data the organization might need to start collecting for improved decision making. Managers can then ask experts to change the relationships and design new reports or applications that generate desired reports with a few keystrokes.

Many business databases consist of multiple tables with relationships among them. For example, a hospital might use a database that has a table holding the records of all its physicians, another one with all its nurses, another one with all the current patients, and so on. The administrative staff must be able to create reports that link data from multiple tables. For example, one report might be about a doctor and all her patients during a certain period. Another might revolve around a patient: details of the patient and a list of all the caregivers who were involved in his rehabilitation, as well as a list of medications. Thus, the database must be carefully planned to allow useful data manipulation and report generation.

Effective data modeling and design of each database involves the creation of a conceptual blueprint of the database. Such a blueprint is called an **entity relationship diagram (ERD)**. An ERD is a graphical representation of all entity relationships, an example of which is shown in Figure 7.9, and they are often consulted to determine a problem with a query or to implement changes. Boxes are used to identify entities. Lines are used to indicate a relationship between entities. When lines shaped like crow's-feet are pointing to an object, there might be many instances of that object. When a link with a crow's-foot also includes a crossbar, then all instances of the object on the side of the crow's-foot are linked with a single instance of the object on the side of the crossbar. A second crossbar would denote "mandatory," which means that the relationship must occur, such as between a book title and author: a book title must have an author with which it is associated. A circle close to the box denotes "optional."

- In the figure, the crow's-foot on the Department end of the Department/College relationship indicates that there are several departments in one college, indicating a one-to-many relationship between College and Department. In addition, the crossbar at the College end of the College/Department link indicates that a department belongs to only one college.

- A department has many professors, but a professor might belong to more than one department; thus, the relationship between Professor and Department is many-to-many, represented by the crow's-feet at both ends of the link.

- A course is offered by a single department, indicated by the crossbar at the Department end of the Department/Course link.

- A professor might teach more than one student, and a student might have more than one professor, thus the crow's-feet at both the Professor and Student ends of the many-to-many relationship between Professor and Student.

- However, the ring at the Student end indicates that a professor does not have to have students at all. The ring means "optional," and is there for cases in which professors do not teach.

Figure 7.9 provides an initial ERD. The designers must also detail the fields of each object, which determines the fields for each record of that object. The attributes are listed in each object box, and the primary key attribute is underlined. Usually, the primary key field appears at the top of the field list in the box. Figure 7.10 is an example of possible attributes of a Professor entity. You should be aware that database designers might use different notations. Therefore, before you review an ER diagram, be sure you understand what each symbol means.

The examples given here are quite simple. In reality, the reports that managers need to generate can be quite complex in terms of relationships among different data elements and the number of different tables from which they are assembled. Imagine the relationships among data maintained in libraries: a patron might borrow several titles; the library maintains several copies

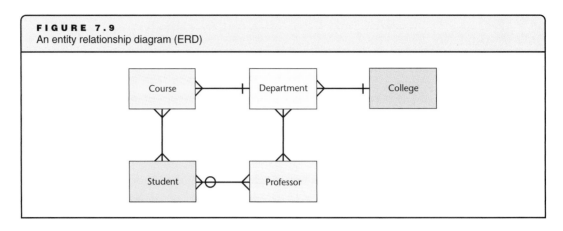

FIGURE 7.9
An entity relationship diagram (ERD)

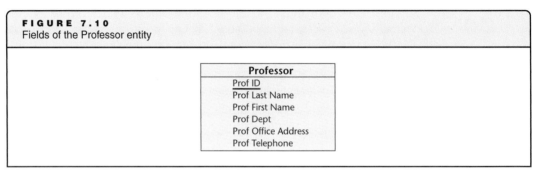

FIGURE 7.10
Fields of the Professor entity

Professor
Prof ID
Prof Last Name
Prof First Name
Prof Dept
Prof Office Address
Prof Telephone

of each title; a title might be a book, a videotape, or a CD; several authors might have published different books with the same title; librarians must be able to see availability and borrowed items by title, by author, and by patron; they should also be able to produce a history report of all the borrowing of each patron for a certain period of time; and so on. All of these relationships and the various needs for reports must be taken into account when designing the database.

DATABASES ON THE WEB

The Internet and its user-friendly Web would be practically useless if people could not access databases online. The premise of the Web is that people can not only browse appealing Web pages but also search for and find information. Most often, that information is stored in databases. When a shopper accesses an online store, he or she can look for information about any of thousands, or hundreds of thousands, of items offered for sale. For example, when you access the site of Buy.com, you can receive online information (such as an image of an electronics item, price, shipping time, and consumer evaluations) for thousands of items offered for sale. Wholesalers make their catalogs available online. Applications at auction sites receive inquiries by category, price range, country or origin, color, date, and other attributes and identify records of matching items, which often include pictures and detailed descriptions. Behind each of these sites is a database. The only way for organizations to conduct these Web-based businesses is to give people outside the organizations access to their databases. In other words, the organizations must link their databases to the Internet.

From a technical point of view, online databases that are used with Web browsers are no different from other databases. However, an interface must be designed to work with the Web. The user must see a form in which to enter queries or keywords to obtain information from the site's database. The interface designers must provide a mechanism to figure out data that users insert in the online forms so that they can be placed in the proper fields in the database. The system also needs a mechanism to pass queries and keywords from the user to the database. There are several such interface programs, including CGI (Common Gateway Interface), Java servlets, and active server pages (ASPs), as well as API (application program interface). The technical aspects of these applications are beyond the scope of this book. The process is diagrammed in Figure 7.11.

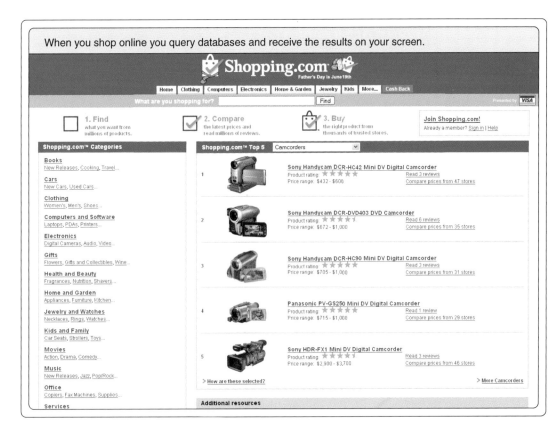

When you shop online you query databases and receive the results on your screen.

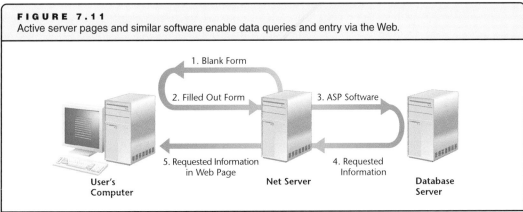

FIGURE 7.11
Active server pages and similar software enable data queries and entry via the Web.

1. Blank Form
2. Filled Out Form
3. ASP Software
5. Requested Information in Web Page
4. Requested Information

User's Computer

Net Server

Database Server

To ensure that their production databases are not vulnerable to attack via the Internet, organizations avoid linking their transaction databases to the Internet unless these are databases dedicated to online transactions, in which case the organization must apply proper security software. They must also be careful when linking a data warehouse (discussed next) to the Internet.

DATA WAREHOUSING

The great majority of data collections in business are used for daily transactions and operations: records of customers and their purchases and information on employees, patients, and other parties for monitoring, collection, payment, and other business or legal purposes. The transactions do not stay in these databases long; usually only a few days or weeks. However, many organizations have found that if they accumulate transaction data, they can use it for important management decisions, such as researching market trends or tracking down fraud. Organizing and storing data for such purposes is called data warehousing.

A **data warehouse** is a large, typically relational, database that supports management decision making. The database is large because it contains data, or summaries of data, from millions of transactions over many years and/or from national or global transactions rather than from a short period or a single region. It might maintain records of individual transactions or summaries of transactions for predetermined periods, such as hourly, daily, or weekly. The purpose of data warehouses is to let managers produce reports or analyze large amounts of archival data and make decisions. Data-warehousing experts must be familiar with the types of business analyses that will be done with the data. They also have to design the data warehouse tables to be flexible enough for modifications in years to come, when business activities change or when different information must be extracted.

Data warehouses do not replace transactional databases, which are updated with daily transactions such as sales, billing, cash receipts, and returns. Instead, transactional data is copied into the data warehouse, which is a separate database. This large archive contains valuable information for the organization that might not be evident in the smaller amounts of data typically stored in transactional databases. For example, an insurance company might keep monthly tables of policy sales; it can then see trends in the types of policies customers prefer in general or by age group. Such trends are meaningful only if they are gleaned from data collected over several years. Data from transactional databases are added to the data warehouse at the end of each business day, week, or month, or it might be added automatically as soon as a transaction is recorded in a transactional database. While a transactional database contains current data, which is disposed of after some time, the data in data warehouses is accumulated and might reflect many years of business activities.

Organizations often organize their data warehouse as a collection of **data marts**, smaller collections of data that focus on a particular subject or department. If data marts need to be used as one large data warehouse, special software tools can unify data marts and make them appear as one large data warehouse.

Every Move You Make

The widespread use of database management systems coupled with Web technologies allows organizations to collect, maintain, and sell vast amounts of private personal data fast and cheaply. Millions of credit-card transactions take place in the world, each carrying private information. Millions of personal data items are routed daily to corporate databases through sales calls and credit checks. Millions of consumer records are collected and updated daily on the Web. For businesses, such data is an important resource; for individuals, such large data pools and the ways they are used threaten a fundamental human right: privacy.

- **Out of Hand—Out of Control.** You have just received a letter from the John Doe Investment Co. In the letter, the president tells you that at your age, with a nice income like yours, the company could provide you with innovative investment services. How did the company know about your existence? About your annual income? Could it be that some time ago you applied for a credit card? The company receiving the information sold part of it, or all of it, to the John Doe Investment Co. You now enjoy your credit card but you paid a hidden cost for it.

- **The Web: A Source of Data Collection.** In the preceding example, you were at least aware that you gave somebody information. But many consumers provide information routinely without being aware of it. A huge amount of personal data is now collected through the Web. You might wonder why the home pages of so many Web sites ask you to register with them. When registering, you often provide your name, address, and other details. The site asks you to create a user ID and password. If the pages you are accessing contain private data such as your investment portfolio, a user ID and password protect you, but if you are accessing news or other nonpersonal pages, a user ID and password actually serve the site operator. From the moment you log on to the site, the server can collect data about every move you make: which pages you are watching and for how long, which icons you click and in which order, and which advertising banners you click. In many cases, the organization that collects the data doesn't even own the site. The site owner hires a business such as DoubleClick to collect data. When you click an advertisement, that information is channeled into DoubleClick's huge database. What does the firm do with the database? It sells parts of it to other companies, or it slices and dices the information to help other companies target potential buyers belonging to certain demographic groups. And, no, it does not bother to tell you.

While the software of such companies as Double-Click can only identify the computer or IP number from which you logged on to a site and not you, personally, the information can be matched with you, personally, if you also use your personal ID and password.

In addition to Web cookies, companies also use clear GIFs to track our Web movements. A "clear GIF," better known as a "Web beacon" or "Web bug," is a graphic image on a Web site used to monitor a surfer's activity. The image is usually undetectable because it usually consists of a single pixel. The bug links the Web page to the Web server of a third party, such as DoubleClick. The third party's server obtains the URL (Web address) of the user as well as the URL of the site from which the user views the page. As long as the bug is "displayed" by the user's computer, the third-party server can request session information from the user's Web browser. Session information includes click stream and other activities performed by the user while visiting the site. In DoubleClick's own words: "Companies use clear GIFs on their Web sites to learn more about their visitors' use of their Web sites and may be used to target ads to those visitors on other Web sites" (*www.doubleclick.com/us/about_doubleclick/ privacy/clear-gifs.asp*).

- **Our Finances Exposed.** Everyone is very sensitive when it comes to finances. In the United States, the Gramm-Leach-Bliley law, which went into effect on July 1, 2001, was supposed to protect consumer privacy. The law entitles consumers to opt out of having their private information shared with "nonaffiliated" third parties. It requires companies to tell consumers what information they collect and how they might use it and to establish safeguards against fraudulent access to confidential information.

Yet, critics claim that the law does not provide the most important protection it was supposed to provide: not allowing companies to share private financial information with other organizations. Whether you opt out or not, the law allows companies that reside under the same corporate umbrella to share your information. "Companies under the same umbrella" include a bank and its subsidiaries or sister companies such as an insurance company and a bank owned by the same parent company. Also, companies are allowed to share information with unaffiliated companies if they have service or marketing agreements with those unaffiliated companies.

Consider this sentence from the privacy policy of one bank: "We recognize that an important benefit for our customers is the opportunity to receive offers for products and services from other companies that may work with us." Consumer advocates read the sentence this way: "Whether you like it or not, we will share your information with other companies, and they can do with it whatever they wish, including bombarding you with unsolicited mail and e-mail."

- **Our Health Online.** Allowing medical staff and pharmacists to share patient medical information might help them help us. Imagine yourself being injured on a trip thousands of miles from your home. If the doctor treating you can immediately receive information about your sensitivities to certain medications, it might save your life. However, any electronic record residing on a database that is connected to a public network is potentially exposed to unauthorized access by people who do not have a legitimate need to know.

The Health Insurance Portability and Accountability Act of 1996 (HIPAA) is the U.S. federal law that was enacted to—among other purposes—mandate how health-care providers and insurance firms are to maintain records and disclose information so that patient privacy is not violated. The law restricts who accesses your medical records. Yet, even this law recognizes the inability of organizations to ensure patient privacy. For example, you can ask your doctor not to share your medical record with other doctors or nurses in the clinic, but they do not have to agree to do what you ask.

- **The Upside.** In spite of the downside of collection of personal data, there is also a positive side. Database technology enables companies to provide us with better and faster services. It also makes the market more competitive. Small firms often cannot afford the great expense of data collection. For much less money, they can purchase sorted data—the same data that are available to the big, strong industry leader. So, the wide availability of data contributes to a more egalitarian and democratic business environment. The winners are not only vendors but also consumers, who can purchase new and cheaper products.

And while many of us complain that these huge databases add to the glut of junk mail and spam, better information in the hands of marketers might actually save consumers from such annoyances. After all, those annoying communications are for products and services you don't need. With more specific information, marketers can target only those individuals that might be interested in their offerings. While you shop, special tracking software can tell the online business, at least indirectly, what you do not like about the site. This enables businesses to improve their services. For example, many online retailers discovered that a hefty proportion of shoppers abandoned their virtual shopping carts just before the final purchase. Analysis of collected information discovered that some people wanted to know the handling and shipping charges before they charged their credit cards. Now, most online retailers provide clear shipping information and charges earlier.

From Database to Data Warehouse

Unlike data warehouses, transactional databases are usually not suitable for business analysis because they contain only current, not historical, data. Often, data in transactional databases are also scattered in different systems throughout an organization. The same data can be stored differently and under other names. For example, customer names might be recorded in a column called Name in one table and in two columns—First Name and Last Name—in another table. These discrepancies commonly occur when an organization uses both its own data and data it purchases from other organizations, or if it has developed more than one database that contains the same data under a different label. When management decides to build a data warehouse, the IT staff must carefully consider the hardware, software, and data involved in the effort.

The larger the data warehouse, the larger the storage capacity, the greater the memory, and the greater the processing power of the computers that are needed. Because of capacity needs, organizations often choose mainframe computers with multiple CPUs to store and manage data warehouses. The computer memory must be large enough to allow processing of huge amounts of data at once. The amount of storage space and the access speed of disks are also important. Processing millions of records might take a long time, and variations in disk speed might mean the difference between hours or minutes in processing time. And since a data warehouse is considered a highly valuable asset, all data must be automatically backed up. Keep in mind that data warehouses grow continually, because their very purpose is to accumulate historical records. Retail chains such as Wal-Mart and Costco record millions of sales transactions daily, all of which are channeled into data warehouses. Some have data warehouses that hold tens or hundreds of terabytes of data. However, not only retailers have augmented their hardware for large data warehouses. So have banks, credit-card issuers, and health-care organizations, among other industries. Many organizations accumulate not only sales transactions but also purchasing records so they can produce information from which to make better purchasing decisions, such as which suppliers tend to offer lower prices for certain items at certain times of the year.

POINT OF INTEREST

The Data Behemoth
Wal-Mart, the world's largest company, is well-known for its appetite for retail data. With 6,000 stores worldwide and 100 million people passing through its doors every week, the company is a voracious collector of data. In 2005, the company had 260 terabytes of data in its data warehouses on mainframe computers in Bentonville, Arkansas, where it is headquartered. Experts estimated that this amount of data was twice as large as all the data posted on the world's Web sites.

The data from which data warehouses are built usually comes from within an organization, mainly from transactions, but it can also come from outside an organization. The latter might include national or regional demographic data, data from financial markets, and weather data. Similar to metadata in any database, data-warehouse designers create metadata for their large data pools. To uncover the valuable information contained in their data, organizations must use software that can effectively "mine" data warehouses. Data mining is covered in Chapter 11, "Business Intelligence and Knowledge Management."

The designers must keep in mind scalability: the ability of the data warehouse to grow as the amount of the data and the processing needs grow. Future growth needs involve good planning in terms of both hardware and software.

Phases in Building a Data Warehouse

Once an organization has ensured that it has adequate hardware and software, it can begin building the data warehouse. Three phases are involved in building a data warehouse from transactional data: extraction, transforming, and loading (ETL). Figure 7.12 describes the process.

FIGURE 7.12
Phases in preparing and using a data warehouse

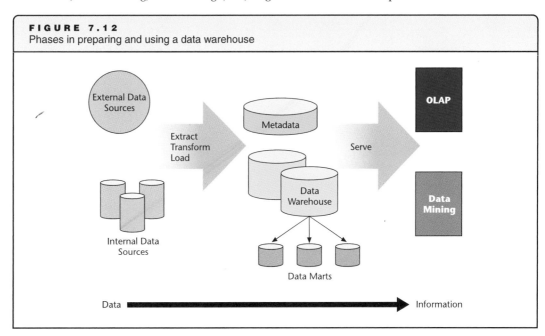

In the *extraction* phase the builders create the files from transactional databases and save them on the server that will hold the data warehouse. In the *transformation* phase the builders "cleanse" the data and modify it into a form that allows insertion into the data warehouse. For example, they ascertain whether the data contains any spelling errors, and if there are any, they fix them. They make sure that all data is consistent. For instance, Pennsylvania might be denoted as Pa., PA, Penna, or Pennsylvania. Only one form would be used in a data warehouse. The builders ensure that all addresses follow the same form, using uppercase or lowercase letters consistently and defining fields uniformly (such as one field for the entire street address and a separate field for zip codes). All the data that expresses the same type of quantities is "cleansed" to use the same measurement units.

In the *loading* phase the builders transfer the transformed files to the data warehouse. They then compare the data in the data warehouses with the original data to ascertain completeness. They document the data for users, so the users know what they can find and analyze in the data warehouse.

The new warehouse is then ready for use. It is a single source for all the data required for analysis, it is accessible to more users than the transactional databases (whose access is limited only to those who record transactions), and provides a "one-stop shopping" place for data. In fact, it is not unusual for a data warehouse to have large tables with fifty or more fields (attributes).

Once the data warehouse is in operation, much of the ETL activity can be automated. Depending on the needs of its users, the structure and content of the data warehouse might be changed occasionally. Once the data warehouse is ready, techniques such as data mining and online analytical processing (OLAP) can be used to exploit it. Managers can then extract business intelligence for better decision making. Data mining, OLAP, and business intelligence are discussed in Chapter 11.

- In their daily operations, organizations can collect vast amounts of data. This data is raw material for highly valuable information, but data is useless without tools to organize it, store it in an easily accessible manner, and manipulate it to produce that information. These functions are the great strength of databases: collections of interrelated data that, within an organization and sometimes between organizations, are shared by many units and contribute to productivity and efficiency.

- The database approach has several advantages over the more traditional file approach: less data redundancy, application-data independence, and greater probability of data integrity.

- The smallest piece of data collected about an entity is a character. Multiple characters make up a field. Several fields make up a record. A collection of related records is a file, or in the relational model, a table. Databases usually contain several files, but the database approach can be applied to a single file.

- A database management system (DBMS) is a software tool that enables us to construct databases, populate them with data, and manipulate the data. Most DBMSs come with 4GLs that can be used to develop applications that facilitate queries and produce reports.

- There are several database models, which are general logical structures of records in a database: hierarchical, network, relational, and object-oriented. By far, the most popular model is the relational model, which is used to build most new databases, although object-oriented databases are gaining popularity. Some vendors offer DBMSs that accommodate a combination of relational and object-oriented models, called object-relational.

- The links among entities in a relational database are maintained by the use of keys. Primary keys are unique identifiers. Composite keys are combinations of two or more fields that are used as a primary key. Foreign keys link one table to another within the database.

- In an object-oriented database, data sets along with the procedures that process them are objects. The relationship between one set of data and another is by way of one object containing the other, rather than by foreign keys.

- SQL has been adopted as an international standard language for querying relational databases. SQL statements can also be embedded in code that is produced using many programming languages.

- To construct a database, a designer first constructs a schema and prepares metadata, which is information about the data to be kept in the database.

- To plan databases, designers conduct data modeling. Before they design a database they create entity relationship diagrams, which show the tables required for each data entity and the attributes (fields) it should hold, as well as the relationships between tables. Then they can move on to constructing a schema, which is the structure of all record structures of the entities, and the relationships among them.

- Many databases are linked to the Web for remote use. This arrangement requires Web server software, such as active server pages and Java servlets, which allow users to enter queries or update databases over the Internet.

- Data warehouses are huge collections of historical transactions copied from transactional databases, often along with other data from outside sources. Managers use software tools to glean useful information from data warehouses to support their decision making. Some data warehouses are made up of several data marts, each focusing on an organizational unit or a subject.

- In each addition of data from a transactional database to a data warehouse, the data is extracted, transformed, and loaded, a process known by its acronym, ETL.

- The low price of efficient and effective database software exacerbates a societal problem of the Information Age: invasion of privacy. Because every transaction of an individual can be easily recorded and later combined with other personal data, it is inexpensive to produce whole dossiers on individual consumers. This poses a threat to privacy. However, commercial organizations insist that they need personal information to improve their products and services and to target their marketing only to interested consumers.

QUICKBIZ MESSENGERS REVISITED

QuickBiz gathers and maintains many types of data in its database. It has tried to ensure its security and safe backup while still being accessible to customers and employees. Let's explore some of the issues it faces in managing its database.

need a database management system, he decided to take her advice and purchase Oracle. What sort of research should Andrew have done to make sure that Oracle was the best solution? What advantages and disadvantages should he have considered when purchasing a new DBMS?

What Would You Do?

1. QuickBiz's database is vital to its operations. The case at the beginning of the chapter didn't mention its supplier data. QuickBiz has suppliers for its fleet of cars and trucks and for its office supplies. What sorts of data would QuickBiz likely keep about its suppliers? What controls and limits should it put on its supplier data? Make a recommendation to Andrew Langston on who should be able to review and change that data and where the data should be maintained.

2. Andrew had run into IT consultant Kayla Brown many times and began talking to her about his IT concerns. When he realized that he was going to

New Perspectives

1. QuickBiz has used SQL queries and reports to identify VIP customers and discover its most profitable clients and services. QuickBiz also has a Web site. How could it use Web site tracking data to enhance its services? What departments would be interested in this information? Discuss and list as many as you can.

2. Andrew has heard that databases can also store digital images. Are there any parts of QuickBiz's data operations that might use digital images? If so, which?

KEY TERMS

character, 219
composite key, 224
data dictionary, 228
data integrity, 219
data mart, 232
data modeling, 229
data redundancy, 218
data warehouse, 232
database administrator
    (DBA), 221
database approach, 218
database management system
    (DBMS), 219

encapsulation, 225
entity, 219
entity relationship diagram
    (ERD), 229
field, 219
file, 219
foreign key, 225
inheritance, 225
join table, 225
metadata, 228
many-to-many
    relationship, 225

object-oriented database
    model, 225
one-to-many relationship, 225
primary key, 224
record, 219
relational model, 222
relational operation, 226
schema, 228
Structured Query Language
    (SQL), 227
table, 222
traditional file approach, 218

1. It is easier to organize data and retrieve it when there is little or no dependence between programs and data. Why is there more such dependence in a file approach and less in the database approach?

2. Spreadsheets have become quite powerful for data management. What can be done with database management systems that cannot be done with spreadsheet applications? Give several examples.

3. What is the difference between a database and a database management system?

4. DBMSs are usually bundled with powerful 4GL modules. Why?

5. What are the advantages and disadvantages of object-oriented databases?

6. What is the relationship between a Web site's local search engines and online databases?

7. When constructing a database, the designer must know what types of relationships exist between records in different data sets, such as one-to-many or many-to-many. Give three examples for each of these relationships.

8. Can you think of a one-to-one relationship in a relational database? Give an example.

9. What is SQL? In which database model does it operate? Why is it so popular?

10. What is a data warehouse? How is it different from a transactional database?

11. Why is it not advisable to query data from transactional databases for executive decision making the same way you do data warehouses?

12. What are the phases of adding data to a data warehouse?

13. What does it mean to cleanse data before it is stored in a data warehouse?

14. What are data marts? How different are they from data warehouses?

1. Retail chains want to ensure that every time a customer returns to purchase something, the record of that purchase can be matched with previous data of that individual. What objects that consumers often use help the retailers in that regard?

2. Increasingly, corporate databases are updated by their consumers rather than corporate employees. How so?

3. Can you think of an industry that would not benefit from the promise of a data warehouse? Explain.

4. Shouldn't those who build data warehouses trim the data before they load it to data warehouses? Why do they usually not cut any data from transactions?

5. The combination of RFID and database technology will soon enable retailers to record data about consumers even when they have not purchased anything at the store. Can you think of an example and how the data could be used?

6. A retailer of household products maintains a data warehouse. In addition to data from sales transactions, the retailer also purchases and maintains in it daily weather data. What might be the reason?

7. Many organizations have posted privacy policies at their Web sites. Why do you think this is so?

8. Consider the following opinion shared by some people: database management systems and data-warehousing techniques are the greatest threat to individual privacy in modern times. What is your opinion?

9. The proliferation of organizational databases poses a threat to privacy. After reading the following passage, what would you say to someone in response to these statements: "I'm a law-abiding citizen and pay my taxes promptly. I don't care if anyone reviews my college grades or my income statements, because I have nothing to hide. I have no reason to worry about violation of my privacy. All these complaints about violation of privacy are not valid. Only individuals who have something to hide need to worry."

10. Civil rights advocates demand that organizations ask individuals for permission to sell personal information about them. Some also demand that the subjects of the information be paid for their consent. Organizations have argued that they cannot practically comply with these demands and that the demands interfere with the free flow of information. What is your opinion?

11. Organizations whose Web sites offer visitors some control of how their personal information is collected and used offer one of two options: "opt out" or "opt in." Explain each term.

12. Some people say that as long as the concept of "informed consent" is applied, individuals should not complain about invasion of their privacy. What is "informed consent"? Do you agree with the argument?

13. The affordability of sophisticated DBMSs and data warehouses makes the business world more "democratic" and puts all businesses almost on an equal footing. How so? Explain.

14. Businesses rarely allow customers to scrutinize and correct records that the organizations keep about them. Technologically, does the Web make it less expensive for organizations to allow that?

APPLYING CONCEPTS

1. Acxiom is a data services firm. Browse this company's site and research its activities at its own site and at other Web sites. Write a two-page summary of the company's activity: What does the company sell? How does it obtain what it sells? Who are its customers, and what do they do with what they purchase from Acxiom?

2. Research the business of DoubleClick Inc. What type of data does the company collect and sell? How does it collect the data? Who are the company's customers, and how do they use the services or data they buy from DoubleClick?

3. Research Web resources to write a two- to four-page research paper titled "Object-Oriented Databases," in which you explain the differences and similarities between relational databases and object-oriented databases, and their comparative advantages and disadvantages.

HANDS-ON ACTIVITIES

1. Mid-County Hospital holds data on doctors and patients in two tables in its database (see the following tables): DOCTOR and PATIENT.

Use your DBMS to build the appropriate schema, enter the records, and create the reports described.

DOCTOR					
ID#	LIC#	Last Name	First Name	Ward	Salary
102	8234	Hogg	Yura	INT	187,000
104	4666	Tyme	Justin	INT	91,300
221	2908	Jones	Jane	OBG	189,650
243	7876	Anderson	Ralph	ONC	101,800
256	5676	Jones	Ernest	ORT	123,400
376	1909	Washington	Jaleel	INT	87,000
410	4531	Carrera	Carlos	ORT	97,000

PATIENT					
SSN	Last N	First N	Admission Date	Insurance	Doc ID
055675432	Hopkins	Jonathan	4/1/06	BlueCross	221
101234566	Bernstein	Miriam	4/28/07	HAP	243
111654456	McCole	John	3/31/06	Kemper	221
200987898	Meanny	Marc	2/27/07	HAP	221
367887654	Mornay	Rebecca	4/3/06	HAP	410
378626254	Blanchard	George	3/30/07	BlueCross	243
366511122	Rubin	David	4/1/06	Brook	243

a. A report showing the following details for each doctor in this order: Last Name, First Name, and Ward. Arrange the report by ascending alphabetical order of the last names.

b. A report showing the entire record with the original order of columns of all the doctors whose salary is greater than $100,000 who work for either one of the following wards: Internal (INT), Obstetric-Gynecological (OBG), Oncology (ONC).

c. A report showing the following details for all of Dr. Anderson's patients. Dr. Anderson's first and last name should appear once at the top of the report. In each record, the join report should show Doctor's ID, Last Name, and Ward (from the DOCTOR table), and Patient's Last Name, First Name, and Date of Admission (from the PATIENT table).

2. Mr. Lawrence Husick is an inventor who, with other inventors, obtained several U.S. patents. Find the site of the U.S. Patent and Trademark Office. Conduct a patent search at the site's online patent database. Find all the patents that mention Lawrence Husick as an inventor. Type up the patent numbers along with their corresponding patent titles (what the invention is). E-mail the list to your professor. Find and print out the image of patent No. 6469. Who was the inventor and what was the invention?

TEAM ACTIVITIES

1. Your team is to design a relational database for an online pizza service. Customers log on to the site and provide their first and last names, address, telephone number, and e-mail address. They order pizza from a menu. Assume that each item on the menu has a unique number, a description, and a price. Assume there is one person per shift who receives orders and takes care of them from giving the order to the kitchen to dispatching a delivery person. The system automatically records the time at which the server picked up the order. The business wants to maintain the details of customers, including their orders of the past six months. The following are reports that management might require: (1) a list of all the orders handled by a server over a period of time; (2) summaries of total sales, by item, for a period; and (3) a report showing all of the past week's deliveries by server, showing each individual order— customer last name and address, items ordered, time of order pickup, and last name of delivery person. (You can assume the last names of delivery people are unique, because if there is more than one with the same last name, a number is added to the name.)

   a. Chart the table for each entity, including all its fields and the primary key.

   b. Draw the entity relationship diagram.

2. Your team should contact a large organization, such as a bank, an insurance company, or a hospital. Interview the database administrator about the database he or she maintains on customers (or patients). What are the measures that the DBA has taken to protect the privacy of the subjects whose records are kept in the databases? Consider accuracy, timeliness, and appropriate access to personal records. Write a report on your findings. If you found loopholes in the procedures, list them and explain why they are loopholes and how they can be remedied. Alternatively, log on to the site of a company that posted a detailed privacy policy and answer the same questions.

COMPANION CD QUESTIONS

1. You and a friend would like to catalog your CD collections. Create a simple database that will hold all of your titles in one table and your friend's titles in another table.

2. Write a query to show you which titles you and your friend both own.

FROM IDEAS TO APPLICATION: REAL CASES

When Customers Attack...

Overstock.com, self-proclaimed and trademarked as "Earth's greatest discounter," faced a situation that might have seemed like a good problem to have. Too many shoppers wanted to buy too many items too fast. One day, when traffic peaked, the company's servers could not support both Web traffic and running internal applications. To avoid slowing down customer activity online, the leading online retailer of excess inventory had to shut down internal applications. Executives were happy with customer enthusiasm but bemoaned the fact that they couldn't monitor sales in real-time fashion, to which they had become accustomed.

Operating on limited budgets and passing virtually all savings on to customers had built the retailer a huge consumer base but also pushed the IT department to the edge trying to serve customers. The company's founders had envisioned doubling business each year, and they have consistently met this target by guaranteeing shoppers low prices on slow-selling merchandise they purchased from other retailers.

The Salt Lake City company's 2004 revenues were five times its total from just two years earlier, and gross profit before interest had increased more than 300 percent since 2002, from $18.3 million to $65.8 million. Although Overstock.com has yet to earn an annual profit, it had a quarterly profit of $2.5 million for the fourth quarter of 2004. Overstock.com keeps improving performance thanks to focusing on information gleaned from its experience with customers. This simply comes down to storing sales transactions in large databases and trying to detect what customers like and dislike.

Overstock.com had to continually increase the storage space and speed of its database processing. Managers used an application that allowed them to view real-time sales. This enabled them to quickly receive information about what items sold fast and search for similar items for replenishing inventory. When customer activity grew, there was so much strain on the system that they had to shut down the application. The transaction databases were the only source of data for executives.

IT managers at the company realized that if growth in customer activity were sustained, the company would reach sales of a quarter billion dollars by the end of 2004. However, that growth rate required an IT infrastructure that could function like those of billion dollar companies. The task was challenging because management made it clear that due to the slim profit

generation the IT department could count only on a frugal construction of the new infrastructure.

One of the first things the IT managers wanted to build was a mirror of the transaction and database systems, so that if one site failed, a duplicate system elsewhere could still process and record transactions. Although the company already had a backup of the transaction data, the backup files were located at the same place as the originals. In 2004, for security reasons, the IT people wanted the backed-up data located elsewhere. The choice: co-location. In a co-location arrangement an organization uses a Web server at a facility owned by another organization. The host organization maintains the server and ensures power backup and technical support. Co-location is attractive to companies with limited Internet connections or IT personnel to manage the server.

Overstock.com purchased a pair of networked storage systems from EMC Corp. and spent several weeks testing the new hardware and software at a co-location facility. When testing was successful, Overstock.com relocated the transaction database to the new facility in 2004. To head off further strain due to growth, the IT managers selected the Oracle 9i DBMS for the online storefront and added another DBMS, an Oracle 10g to facilitate a new auction venture that would compete with the world's online auction leader, eBay. The auction business was launched in September 2004. The company distributed its database across seven networked computers running the Linux operating system.

To take advantage of the huge amount of data collected in sales transactions, the IT team decided to build a data warehouse to capture and analyze customer information. Overstock.com contracted with Teradata, a division of NCR and a leader in data-warehousing technology. The data warehouse will enable Overstock.com to better understand customer motivations and the impact of pricing policies. Overstock.com is especially interested in using data analysis to avoid losing its best customers. Customer retention will derive partially from better customer service, which itself could be influenced by analyzing the warehoused data.

The changes Overstock.com has made to its data-storage capabilities have proved their worth, as the company recorded its best holiday season sales ever, $221 million, in 2004. As sales have grown over the last five years, so has Overstock.com's staff. Since 2002, the company has more than doubled its employee roster, to 427. Of those, 49 work in IT, almost four times the 13 IT personnel who handled

Overstock.com needs in 2002. IT managers for Overstock.com have noted that two of the major reasons for their successful redesign have been the coupling of new employees with veterans and the hiring of employees who are motivated not just by material gains but also by intellectual challenges.

Apparently, professional challenges are a great motivator for some team members. Case in point is the design-your-own-jewelry option on the company's site that was initially proposed in November 2004. A programmer who did most of the work on a new site was determined the project would be completed in time for Valentine's Day. With barely three months left, the programmer slept several nights in the office so he could devote all his waking hours to the project. The project was completed in time. The employee received a special two-week vacation in spring 2005.

Source: McDonald, D. "Overstock.com Overcomes Overloads," *CIO Insight* (www.cioinsight.com), May 5, 2005; www.overstock.com, 2005; Westervelt, R., "Overstock Is Newest Grid Convert," SearchOracle.com, August 31, 2004.

Thinking About the Case

1. Pure-play companies—companies that sell only via the Web, such as Overstock.com—have a certain advantage over other retailers in terms of data collection. How so?

2. Overstock.com used a transactional database for their monitoring and analysis. What were the results? Why is this unadvisable?

3. What can executives do now that they could not do in 2004 in terms of data analysis?

4. What information can proper analysis of the warehoused data teach executives?

Rescued by Data

Not knowing enough about yourself might be dangerous. One company learned this lesson in time to come out of bankruptcy with the help of IT. Leiner Health Products Inc., the world's largest manufacturer of private label vitamins, minerals, and nutritional supplements, is also the second largest manufacturer of private label over-the-counter (OTC) pharmaceuticals in the United States. Private label products are the same products sold by leading brand-name manufacturers, but under another name and for a lower price. The company markets more than 480 vitamins and stocks more than 6,000 items. It holds a 50 percent share of the private label vitamin market (more than

twice the market share of its next largest competitor), and a 25 percent share of all mass-market vitamin product sales in the United States. However, despite its market position, inefficiencies and lack of access to critical information almost brought the company to its knees, and it recovered only thanks to implementation of new information technologies.

In January 2001, management knew the situation was bad. Leiner finished the previous year with revenues of $662 million, 60 percent of which came from large retailers such as Wal-Mart, Sam's Club, and Costco. Maintaining a profit on vitamins and food supplements is not easy, because the profit margins are low. Thus, constantly pursuing efficiency is critical. Yet, Leiner's operations were far from efficient.

Ostensibly, Leiner had every reason to be in good shape. It had 150 customers to whom it sold 4,000 different products manufactured in five plants. However, customer service was unsatisfactory. Thirty percent of deliveries were either not on time or incomplete. Its inventory of finished goods turned over only 2.5 times per year, which is half the industry's typical turnover in profitable years.

Managers did not have the information they needed. They could not figure out who their best and worst customers were. They did not have the information needed to schedule deliveries based on customers' needs. The financial situation was not good. In 1999, an international cartel of 27 vitamin companies was found guilty of price fixing, an event that depressed prices just when Leiner was holding $150 million of inventory. It had to cut the prices on that inventory to well below cost, and ended the year 2000 with a loss of $2 million before interest and taxes. The firm was left with only $8 million in cash and was about to default on its bank loans of $280 million and its own bonds of $85 million. To top off its woes, Wal-Mart threatened to stop purchasing from Leiner, because the company was often late in restocking Wal-Mart's shelves.

The executive team called in a consulting firm that generated the proper reports from Leiner's databases. The main report was a list of customer accounts and the profit margin derived from each of them. Executives discovered that many customers were costing Leiner more than its revenue from them. The firm asked those customers to choose between paying more and being dropped from its clientele. It was left with only half of the customers, all now profitable. Similarly, it produced reports on profit by product, and decided to drop 40 percent of the products it made. Now that Leiner produced much less, it shut down three of its five plants, saving $40 million annually.

Although Leiner had a MRP II (manufacturing resource planning) system, its MRP (materials requirement planning) component was not in sync with the production process. A new order triggered lists of materials to be purchased, but without regard to manufacturing capacity and future orders. To save money, purchasing officers decided which of the system's recommended materials to purchase and which to hold off. Consequently, the plants could not produce some of the ordered lots, and some customers could not receive completed shipments. It was clear that data on manufacturing capacity was missing from the decision-making process.

Another consulting firm was hired, which put in place a new database. Over a period of six months the database collected data from point-of-sale systems of Leiner's most important customers, as well as from its own manufacturing facilities. More than 17,000 pieces of data were collected, which the consultants fed into the MRP system. The MRP system was modified to receive up-to-the-minute data on customer orders and delivery timetables. Now, the amounts of raw materials ordered were not too high or too low. The combined costs of overstocking raw materials and warehousing finished products decreased by $50 million.

From the data collected, executives discovered that they had based pricing on the fastest machines Leiner had in its two plants. Slower machines meant greater cost, and therefore offering products for higher prices so that profit is not eroded. The new data helped produce models for pricing of the various products at different quantities and timetables. Managers could use the models to price profitable contracts when existing ones expired.

Timely collection of money from customers is extremely important. Leiner had too much money tied up in disputes with customers who often required details on billing. Because Leiner accountants and salespeople did not have easy access to such data, collection often took up to 3 months. To solve the problem, management hired a third consulting firm. The consultants established a database and applications that replaced the manual process. Instead of handing a typed or written contract to the accounting people, salespeople now had to enter contract data into the database.

The database and applications enabled both sales and billing people to keep track of payments from invoicing to collection. There were no more paper orders. Every change in pricing or quantities ordered could be made only after the change was made to the cash management system. Whenever a customer asked to verify a bill, the software could immediately determine who originated the order and where, and then e-mail the salesperson the details, which the salesperson could forward to the customer. The customer then had all the necessary information to pay immediately. Within 6 weeks of installation, the software reduced the number of backlogged payments by 75 percent. The improved inventory and accounts receivable systems increased cash in the firm's coffers from $8 million to $20 million.

The IT makeover helped the company escape from bankruptcy. By mid-2002, output per employee increased 63 percent. Ninety-five percent of shipments were accurate and on time. Shipping cost decreased 15 percent. Accounts receivable were collected in fewer days than the industry's average. Inventory turnover is up from 2.5 to 4 times per year. After losses in 2000 and 2001, Leiner had a profit of $40 million in 2002 and expected profit to increase to $70 million in 2003.

How did the experience impact executives' own behavior? Well, Leiner's CEO now has a monitor on his desk that shows continuously updated key financial information: working capital, accounts receivable, accounts payable, cash flow, and inventory. As one observer said, Leiner might see difficult times again, but at least management will know what is going wrong and what should be fixed.

Source: Rothfether, J., "How Leiner Health Cured Its IT Woes," *CIO Insight* (www.cioinsight.com), March 1, 2003; www.leiner.com, May 2003; "Leiner Sustains Healthy Market Share with High-Volume Warehouse Management Solutions from Apriso," www.apriso.com, May 2003.

Thinking About the Case

1. One of Leiner's executives likened the firm's situation in 2001 to an injured person, saying it was bleeding but didn't know from where. Explain this observation in business terms.

2. Was all the data required for better operations and decision making available within the company? Which data was not?

3. What information is required for fast collection of accounts receivable, and what data can it be derived from?

4. The title of this case is "Rescued by Data." Was the collection and organization of proper data alone enough to save the company? Explain.

5. How could the company use a data warehouse to improve operations?

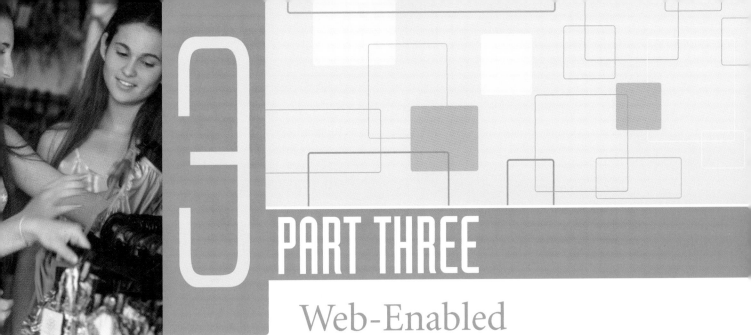

3 PART THREE

Web-Enabled Commerce

CASE III: IT FITS OUTFITS

"OK, are we all here? I'm going to start off by introducing you all to Adina Silverman, our new Director of Web Operations. Adina, this is Martin from information systems, Jean from finance, Tony from marketing, Devon from buying, Jun from manufacturing operations, Suzanne from retail operations, and James from design. That's everyone. Let's get this meeting under way."

Shari Steiner, the chief executive of It Fits Outfits was calling to order the quarterly strategic planning meeting of her top managers. Today was a big day for her company. She had been waiting for this day for four years. Today they would begin phase two of her original mission plan: their move to the Internet.

A New Concept in Teen Clothing

Shari was a young executive who'd studied fashion design and merchandising at the Fashion Institute of Technology in New York City. She started in the business by designing her own clothing line and selling it on commission to other chains. But she wasn't satisfied with that small niche and needed to

accomplish more. No stores in which her fashions were sold had the image that she wanted her clothes to convey—they were part of a culture that she thought "preached or beseeched." Some stores used their brand names to establish fashions that were emerging from Paris, New York, and Milan. Other stores tried to court teens by playing loud music and catering to the latest fads.

Shari wanted to side-step conformity and connect directly to teens, involving them in the design process. So, she took the next step and opened her own store. She actively recruited teens from nearby high schools to work for her. She chose a location that was next door to a coffee shop that was popular with teens. She set up stations around the store. In the front, she put up a bulletin board where people could post messages. A touch screen monitor was set up so that teens could vote on different issues each week. At first, weekly votes focused on the coolest band or the lamest movie, but soon Shari and her staff came up with more creative ideas. They would ask weekly questions like "If you could rename Everest High School, what name would you give it?" Then they would post the top 10 answers.

Every two months, she and her staff would organize an after-hours fashion show. Using a suggestion box, teens would scribble down any words or phrases that came to mind and Shari would design outfits that reflected their thoughts. The staff and other volunteers would organize the show. When someone dropped the expression "totally tubular," which had became popular at one of the local high schools, into the suggestion jar, Shari and her staff had a hoot coming up with ideas. Other suggestions like "casual lace" and "understated" helped Shari create lines that sold well nationally. She called this line of designs "Teen Voices."

The Next Step

Her store quickly became popular and received local and regional media attention. Within four years, she'd built a small chain of 24 stores concentrated in major urban centers in the East. Now it was time to launch phase two.

Shari looked up at Martin Tate. It would not be easy for him to step aside and let Adina Silverman take over some of his IT responsibilities. Martin had set up the computer system the chain currently used for its marketing, sales, and financial needs. He had contracted with a local graphic designer to set up the company's first Web site. He had trained local store managers. But Martin didn't have the expertise Shari needed for this second phase of her plan. Adina had helped manage the Web site of the most technologically innovative clothing chain in the country for the past three years. Adina would hire the staff, set up the standards, and oversee the creation of a Web site that would allow Shari to reach beyond local groups of teens to college campuses. Most of her original customers were now in college. She could reach out to them by establishing an online storefront based on the same principles of It Fits Outfits.

"As you all know, Adina is going to help us move into the college market by establishing an It Fits Outfits storefront that is entirely Internet-based. Let me start this meeting off by telling you what we are NOT going to do. We are not simply going to take our merchandise, policies, supply and manufacturing structure and dump it on to a Web site. What we are going to do is take our original idea, customer participation in design, and create a new operation that will meet the needs of our loyal clientele as they leave home and head off to school. These customers aren't going to have as much time to shop and most of them won't have as much expendable income. Many of them are going from big cities into small college towns. Their needs are changing. How can we meet them? We're going to all have to work together to figure this out. We'll start by setting up work groups."

Warehousing, Supply and IT

"Martin, you're going to have to work with Jun and Adina to figure out how to avoid a warehousing nightmare. You're also going to need to focus on how we can use IT to tighten up our supply chain for our current operations."

Most of It Fits Outfits' manufacturers were located in China. Shari had met Jun Kaui at her favorite coffee shop when she was still in college. Before their first conversation, she had thought that he was shy and studious. One day when the coffee shop was crowded, he asked if she would share her table. From there, she found out that his father had owned and managed a number of textile mills in Asia before retiring. She also discovered that while Jun was smart, he was actually extremely assertive. They remained close friends even after he had completed his business degree. When she shared her dream of opening her own store with him, Jun had made it possible by taking charge of manufacturing. He visited textile mills, set up contracts, and dealt with shipping and customs information.

Using the Web to Build Networks for the Future

"Suzanne, James, and Tony, you need to work with Adina to figure out the needs of our college-aged customers. I have a list of our former employees who've gone off to school. I want you to contact them and involve them in this process. Use the Internet—maybe start with an online survey—some mechanism to gather their feedback."

Shari had planned to expand into college campuses from the start. Rather than losing touch with former employees as they left for college, she had deliberately kept in touch. It Fits Outfits' Web site hosted a bulletin board where former employees could contact each other and an area where they could request references from their former bosses. About twice a year, the company organized an It Fits Outfits online reunion that Shari herself attended. While only store managers might know staff from other offices, the reunion offered college students a chance to visit with old friends and make connections that might help them in the future. Now, it was time to utilize this network she had built up.

Shari had set a deadline of six months to get the online storefront up and operational. It was now February. She wanted it up and running smoothly by the first semester of the following school year.

"We're going to meet monthly until the launch, so make sure your schedules are updated on the intranet. During lunch, you can break up into your work groups and start talking details. And now Jun is going to discuss the next item on our agenda."

BUSINESS CHALLENGES

It Fits Outfits is facing some potential opportunities and problems. Most of its design and retail functions are directly tied to its information systems. So, the success of its ISs are central to its continued survival. Some of those issues are explored in the following chapters:

- In Chapter 8, *"The Web-Enabled Enterprise,"* you learn how businesses use the Internet to achieve strategic advantage and how It Fits Outfits can use the Internet to extend its reach and develop a college-aged clientele.

- In Chapter 9, *"Challenges of Global Information Systems,"* you learn how sharing electronic information and operations among companies and across international boundaries can bring tremendous efficiencies—and challenges—to operations such as It Fits Outfits.

© Bob Torrez/Getty Images

8

EIGHT

The Web-Enabled Enterprise

LEARNING OBJECTIVES

The Web has been the most exciting development in the field of information systems and telecommunications in recent years. The combination of advanced telecommunications technology and innovative software is revolutionizing the way people communicate, shop, make contracts and payments, educate, learn, and conduct business. Numerous companies throughout the world have been established thanks to the enabling power of the Web, and existing ones have used the Web to extend their operations. Firms conduct business electronically with each other and directly with consumers, using a variety of business models. This chapter focuses on Web technologies and businesses on the Web.

When you finish this chapter, you will be able to:

- Describe how the Web and high-speed Internet connections are changing business operations.

- Explain the functionality of various Web technologies.

- Compare and contrast options for Web servers.

- Explain basic business-to-business and business-to-consumer practices on the Web.

- Explain the relationship between Web technologies and supply chain management.

- Give examples of features and services that successful business Web sites offer.

- Learn about online annoyances such as spam and adware, and how to protect against online identity theft.

IT FITS OUTFITS:
Setting up Operations on the Internet

It Fits Outfits was holding their second quarterly strategic planning meeting of the year. It was one of the company's most important meetings to date. Martin Tate, the CIO of It Fits Outfits, had hired an outside contractor to create the original Web site for It Fits Outfits. The Web site was little more than an advertisement. All that was changing. Now that It Fits Outfits was reaching out to the college market, the company needed to establish a site that was a fully functional online storefront.

Connecting to College Students

From the beginning, Shari Steiner, CEO of It Fits Outfits, had planned to launch an online storefront for college students. First, she had established a teen market through her concept of involving teens in the design process. Then she had carefully established a network of former employees who had gone off to college. Finally, she hired Adina Silverman away from the most innovative online clothing retailer. Shari knew that college students rarely had the time or opportunity to shop for clothes even though their clothing needs were changing. With Adina on board, Shari felt confident that she could meet the needs of her former clientele as they went off to school.

Adina took charge of Web Operations for the new It Fits Outfits online storefront. Adina had spent the past two months working hard with the directors of sales, marketing, and design to discover the needs of their college-bound clientele and figure out ways to meet those needs. They had e-mailed a link to an online survey to all former employees in college asking them for their ideas, advice, and experiences. They had conducted online weekly chats with former employees, former customers, and college students who were interested sharing their ideas. Now, Adina was certain she had a plan for online store that would be as successful as the retail chain—or even more successful.

The Virtual Fitting Room

Adina looked around at the other managers. She was the newbie, but she knew that by the time the meeting was over and she had explained the basic functionality of the online store, she would have won the confidence of every member of the senior team.

"First, the survey told us what we already knew —that college students don't have time to shop, and often—if they are in a small college town, they don't have the opportunity. Second, we confirmed our suspicion that freshmen often need to make adjustments to their wardrobe. They often gain weight within the first month or two and go up a size. College dress is different from high school dress and as we know, each crowd dresses differently. And our customers often mix with a different crowd when they reach college.

"To meet this need we've established a prototype called the Virtual Fitting Room. Customers enter their height, weight, coloring, shape, and other measurements and the program saves this information. Then the customer can go shopping, trying on different combinations of items and view the model from the front, sides, and back. They select the items that they want to purchase and enter them into a shopping cart. When they are ready, they check out. The Virtual Fitting Room comes complete with a virtual salesperson, who makes suggestions. For example, if a customer is trying out a skirt, the salesperson might suggest a series of shirts or shoes that would go nicely with the skirt. She might say, 'Need accessories? I've got something that will look fabulous on you!' We're trying to take this concept further than other online clothing retailers by actually repeating the buying experience—without the hassles of actually going to the store in person.

"We also have a number of former employees on campus who are willing to rejoin us and serve as customer sales representatives who customers can chat with in real time. So if customers run into any serious snags, they can talk to a real live person."

Travel Blog and Fashion Chats

The Virtual Fitting Room would not be enough to provide It Fits with the advantage it needed over well-established clothing e-tailers. The operation would have to take the ethos of the retail business that targeted teens and somehow re-create it within the college environment. The idea behind It Fits Outfits was to channel teen voices and spirit into the store and the product. Adina's workgroup had asked former employees how they could do this. What was the best way college students could participate in the design process?

Adina explained the answers her group had come up with. "The first thing that we discovered that kind of surprised us was that the college students were very interested in Shari's professional life. They wanted to know what shows and conferences she'd been to, how she got her start, and what were her future plans. A lot of our former employees spend part of their downtime looking over adult fashion magazines and they're beginning to wonder about things like how the world works—including the fashion world. They're considering how they should adjust to professional attire and lifestyle as they move toward the careers of their choice. They want to know how they can take the part of them that is unique—the part that Teen Scene gave a voice to—and integrate it into the adult world."

"That's *our* role," Shari interrupted. "That's what we have to help them do!"

"Exactly," Adina continued. "So, we've established an area for you, Shari, to record a travel diary. Next week, you're going to Paris. You'll describe Paris, discuss the shows, and post photos. You'll talk about what people are wearing on the streets, in the shops, and in the offices. You'll describe the personalities and the nuts and bolts of the industry."

Shari looked flabbergasted. "And since," Adina went on, "we all know that you have NO time to do this and that you can't write to save your life, Hector from marketing will do the actual writing." The group laughed. "Hopefully, though, you'll agree to participate in pre-arranged chat sessions to discuss major events in the industry."

Campus Clothing E-Zine

"We'll also have an e-zine on the site. We're going to have students report on dressing fashions at their universities. We'll do a story a week and archive them. At first, we'll have our former employees write the stories, but we'll open it up right away to volunteers. Students can then respond—telling Shari what they liked about the styles at the university. At the end of the semester, we'll list the top 10 or 20 designs—and of course, allow students to purchase them.

"Since college is the time of life when people stay up all night talking philosophy, we'll also directly address issues related to conformity, modesty, and symbolism in dress. We'll ask students to submit personal stories and then set up discussion groups to talk about the personal story and the philosophical issue behind it. We're hoping to design products connected to the stories or ideas that are shared in this forum.

"We've been brainstorming other ideas. Each week, we might hold a competition where students vote for the best dressed physicist or the best dressed park ranger. Not everything is squared away yet and we're open to all ideas and feedback. So why don't you all jump in with questions and comments."

Adina looked around the table. She could feel the excitement of the senior team. They knew the company was on the verge of another great enterprise.

WEB BUSINESS: GROWING AND CHANGING

With approximately 8,900 company-operated and franchised stores, Blockbuster Inc. is the world's largest video rental company. It uses a Web site to promote its services, but the company's online presence did not amount to more than advertising until 2003, when management decided to allow customers to rent movies through the Internet. What happened to make management change its tune? It was competition. Netflix and Walmart.com, the online arm of Wal-Mart, began offering an online movie order method: pay a monthly fee, select your movies online, get them in the mail (free shipping!), mail the movies back, and they'll send you more. No need to drive to any store. This business model was popular with renters, and Wal-Mart and Netflix started nibbling into Blockbuster's revenues. Blockbuster management could not allow the company to be left behind. It decided to offer a similar service with the added convenience of being able to return your tapes and DVDs to any Blockbuster store. Blockbuster, like an increasing number of brick-and-mortar businesses, had jumped on the e-commerce bandwagon.

Is this the most efficient way to satisfy the movie-at-home audience? Experts say that shipping a physical object such as a tape or DVD to customers will soon be a thing of the past. Movies are information, and any information can be digitized and whisked to a customer over the Web. As the number of customers with high-speed Internet links grows, enjoying a movie at home will take one of two forms: either a requested movie will be streamed to the customer while the customer is watching, or a copy of the movie will be transferred to the customer. This business model is already a reality in South Korea: more than half of Korean households can download video to watch on their high definition television (HDTV) sets. In the United States, Movielink will let you download a movie to your PC for a few dollars and watch it within 24 hours, or extend the watching period for a small fee. As broadband increases in speed and availability, you will be able to watch movies not only on your computer's monitor but also on a regular HDTV set. Just as the movie rental industry has changed dramatically within a few years from in-store rental to over-the-Web order to over-the-Web download, other industries have changed and will continue to change thanks to faster Internet links and new Web technologies. Business on the Web is growing and changing form all the time.

WEB TECHNOLOGIES: A REVIEW

Several standards and technologies enable the Web to deliver rich information. The following is a review of some nonproprietary standards and technologies.

HTTP

In Chapter 6, you learned about protocols. The protocol used to transfer and download Web information is **Hypertext Transfer Protocol**, or **HTTP**. A secure version of the protocol for confidential transactions is **HTTPS (HTTP Secure)**. Under this protocol, each Web server is designated a **Uniform Resource Locator (URL)**, which is a unique address for a Web site. The address is the IP number (also called IP address) assigned to the site, but in most cases the site also has a **domain name** made up from letters. The term "URL" also refers to the domain name. Each Web page has its own URL, which contains the IP number or domain name of the site. Because the domain name must be unique, when an owner of a Web site reserves a domain name to be associated with an IP number, no other site can be associated with that domain name. Note that domain names often start with—but do not have to include—*www*.

The last part of a URL, such as the ".com" in www.pinzale.com, is the top-level domain (TLD). In addition to .com, .org, and .edu, many other TLDs can be requested for a domain name, some of which are reserved for certain types of organizations and professions, and some that are not. The only organization that is authorized to approve new TLDs is the Internet Corporation for Assigned Names and Numbers (ICANN), a not-for-profit organization established specifically for this purpose.

While domain names consisting of catchy and meaningful words were considered prized assets, companies such as Amazon.com and Google have demonstrated that the name itself is worthless unless the service provided is excellent. Few people know what these names mean (abundant like the Amazon rainforest; and googol, an impossibly large number), but everybody knows of these sites and the purpose of their business. Therefore, new Internet companies do not spend as much energy seeking an attractive domain name as they did in the past.

POINT OF INTEREST

The Most

The Web has become the world's largest library, and the major catalog and search engine for this library is Google. Every day, Google serves 200 million searches in 8 billion Web pages. "Google" comes from googol, which is the number 10^{100} (1 followed by 100 zeroes). There is nothing in the universe whose quantity is so large. "Google" is so popular that it has become a verb. Let's Google it...

Source: McDonald, D., "The 2005 Wired 40," *Wired*, May 2005, p. 111.

HTML and XML

Hypertext Markup Language (HTML) is the most common programming language for creating Web pages and other information viewable in a Web browser. It determines the look and location of text, pictures, animations, and other elements on a Web page. Extensible Markup Language **(XML)** enables the creation of various types of data. It is most often used not for determining the *appearance* of visual elements on a Web page but to convey the *meaning* or content of the data. The World Wide Web Consortium (W3C), the organization responsible for Web standards, has combined the two markup languages HTML and XML into a standard called Extensible Hypertext Markup Language **(XHTML)**.

Every file displayed on the Web is coded with a markup language such as HTML or XML. Simply put, markup languages provide a system of standardized "tags" that format elements of a document, including text, graphics, and sound. Formatting includes opening and closing tags preceding and following a part of the document, such as <b> at the start of bold text, and </b> at the end of bold text. Other tags are marked to link to another page either at the same site or another site, and others create links to e-mail addresses. Browsers interpret HTML and XML tags and display the text in the fashion defined by the tags, or allow other software to pick up data from the page and process it or copy it into the proper place in a database.

As in HTML, tags are used in XML to mark data elements. However, XML tags define "what it is," as opposed to "how it looks." The following illustrates the difference between HTML tags and XML tags:

HTML
<font size ="2">Oz Enterprises, Ltd.</font>
<b>610-555-1234</b>

XML
<company name>Oz Enterprises, Ltd.</company name>
<telephone>610-555-1234</telephone>

XML tags can be used in the same page with HTML tags to indicate both what the data means (which is not visible to the user) and how each element should be displayed.

File Transfer

File Transfer Protocol (FTP) is a common way of transmitting whole files from one computer to another. Every time you download a file from a Web site or attach files to e-mail, you are using an FTP application. The file transmitted can be of any type: text, graphics, animation, or sound. FTP is embedded in browsers and therefore is "transparent" to the users. You can also use a separate FTP utility, many available as shareware, to manage transmitting files.

Businesses use FTP to place files on a server for sharing among professionals. FTP is also useful for placing files on a server that hosts a Web site. And it's convenient for retrieving large files that might exceed an e-mail box's size limits. For example, authors can place large chapter and figure files in a folder on a server maintained by their publisher. Manufacturers often place whole assembly and maintenance manuals or videos at their Web site so customers can download them any time.

FTP has already changed the way in which many software firms sell their products. Instead of spending millions of dollars copying new software on storage media, packaging it, and shipping it, developers simply post their software products on their Web sites and let buyers download them for a fee. Music lovers can use FTP to download music files.

RSS

Really Simple Syndication (or in a newer version, Rich Site Summary) (**RSS**) is a family of XML file formats. An RSS file is installed at Web sites to help users check updates to the site. When users subscribe to the RSS service of a site, the software communicates to their computers short descriptions of Web content along with the link to the site. Users can instruct the software to automatically transmit new or updated information to their own computers. This software is useful for news Web sites and sites that host blogs and podcasts (see the next sections). Subscribers to mass media sites such as newspapers and news services such as Reuters can receive the latest news without actively going to the site or receiving e-mail messages. At some Web sites you might see a button with the letters RSS or XML. If you click them, the site will automatically send your computer updates of designated information, by topic.

Blogs

A **blog** (a contraction of "Web log") is a Web page that invites surfers to post opinions and artistic work, as well as links to sites of interest. Blog sites focus on a topic or a set of related topics, and provide an easy way to post Web pages or update existing ones. Most blogs contain commentaries and humorous content. Users can simply click a button to open a window in which they type text, and click another button to post it. The text is added to the Web page either automatically or after a review by the blog's operators. Some blog sites simply let "bloggers" add comments on a topic, with the most recent comment appearing at the top, similar to the way online newsgroups work. Many companies have established blogs, and invite employees to use them for self-expression. The policy might encourage new ideas from which the company can benefit. Some, however, shun the idea, because management believes blogs are too informal and uncontrolled.

One interesting feature of some blogs is *trackback*. Trackback software notifies bloggers when their posts have been mentioned elsewhere on the Web, so they and their readers can extend the discussion beyond the original blog. Below each post there is a BackTrack button or similar option. When it is clicked, a new window pops up listing the sites mentioning the post.

The commercial potential of blogs has not escaped businesspeople. As traffic grows at some popular blogs, entrepreneurs have started selling advertising space at the sites. The old rule on the Web is still much in force: the greater the number of eyeballs, the greater the commercial potential of the site.

Web technologies continue to progress and enable a growing number of business activities. A growing proportion of revenues of traditional brick-and-mortar businesses come from online sales. "Pure-play" online businesses add new features to their sites almost daily. By linking corporate systems to the Web, information resources, searching software, and transaction applications are increasingly tied in a way that allows employees and customers to receive the information they need in a timely manner and rich fashion. New technologies that seem to be just "fun" all of a sudden are utilized for serious business activities. Streaming audio and video, and chat applications are just two examples. Understanding Web technologies and the potential of the technologies for increased efficiency and richer experience for business customers might help you be a better-educated and more innovative professional.

The importance of blogs to commercial organizations is primarily to find out what blog participants think and say about the organizations. Many organizations use special software that combs blogs for postings that mention the organizations' names. PR people then read the content and relay feedback to others in the organization as needed. For example, an anonymous blogger boasted that he could break Kryptonite bicycle locks with a pen. Within a week the posted item was mentioned in *The New York Times*, and Kryptonite recalled the locks. Companies such as IBM and PubSub offer software that combs blogs, identifies company names, and automatically tracks discussions. Such tools can turn blog data into useful market research information.

Podcasting

While blogging is publishing text and other visual material, podcasting is publishing sound. To **podcast** is to make a digital audio recording, usually of voice, and post the file on the Web so that people can download it and listen to it. RSS software called an *aggregator* or *feed reader* automatically checks for new content and downloads files from a designated site in the same way as is done for text files from online newspapers. Similarly to subscribing to such newspapers, users can subscribe to a podcast site to receive the latest audio files. The files are usually in MP3 format, which can be played on any portable player, including Apple Computer's iPod, from which the word "podcast" was born. However, one does not need this specific MP3 player to enjoy podcasts.

Podcasting has several potential uses. It already serves as "time-shifted" broadcast of radio stations that post their programs for later listening. It is used by some museums for audio tours. Some schools have experimented with the concept to deliver lessons to remote students. Whatever the use, people can listen to their favorite content wherever they can obtain a link to the Internet, without paying radio license fees.

Podcasting opens business opportunities. For example, garageband.com is a Web site that invites aspiring musicians to post their music tracks free of charge so they can be podcast. This exposes to the world talented people who could not otherwise afford to broadcast their work. Podcasting does more than post MP3 files for downloading. By allowing computers to automatically check for new music tracks, the method helps create a following for an artist, which might result in a future fan base willing to pay for a CD or downloaded music files.

Instant Messaging

Instant messaging (IM) offers users real-time online interactivity. It might be thought of as "real-time e-mail," because, unlike e-mail, it is synchronous. IM allows a user to detect whether another person who uses the service is currently online, and the user can then exchange information with an entire group (referred to as a "chat room"), or with only one other "chatter" in privacy. Some IM applications include two-way video, which turns the chat into a video-conference, and most also include FTP to allow sending and receiving files.

Free IM applications are operated through a server, or a group of connected servers, which provides a directory and functions as the hub for all callers. Some IM setups, such as AOL Instant Messenger (AIM), Yahoo! Messenger, MSN Messenger, and ICQ, have become the electronic meeting places for millions of people, making them an attractive target for online advertisers. To overcome the need to use multiple IM applications, some software developers produced universal IM applications that allow, for example, an AIM user to chat with an MSN Messenger user. Trillian and Gaim are two of these applications.

While IM sounds as if it is just for fun, it also can serve an important business purpose. Many online retailers post a special button on their Web pages that lets shoppers establish real-time communication with a sales representative. This instant access fosters more personal service and saves telephone costs. For example, Venus Swimwear, a company that specializes in direct mail junior bathing suits, uses InstantService, a chat application that enables employees to answer customer questions online. The Director of e-Commerce Marketing added this option to the three sites operated by the company because customers often abandoned the site when they could not get answers while shopping. Using the telephone was a bad option for those who used their telephone line for a dial-up Internet connection, and e-mail was inefficient and time-consuming. IM enables sales agents to handle up to five inquiring customers at a time. The application also enables the company to "push" answers from a library of answers such as a sizing chart, instead of typing them. The live chat reduced the amount of e-mail employees have to handle and decreased the customer abandonment rate by 15 percent despite the increasing traffic at the sites.

Cookies

If you have ever surfed the Web, your computer probably contains cookies. A **cookie** is a small file that a Web site places on a visitor's hard disk so that the Web site can remember something about the surfer later. Typically, a cookie records the surfer's ID or some other unique identifier. Combined with data collected from previous visits, the site can figure out the visitor's preferences. The user can opt to allow cookies, and the option is exercised by checking a box in the browser's configuration window. On the user's hard disk, the cookie subdirectory (folder) contains a cookie file for each cookie-using Web site that the surfer has visited. Cookies might hold server URLs. When you instruct the browser to reach a URL from which you have a cookie, the browser transmits the information from the cookie to the server.

Cookies have an important function in Web-based commerce, especially between businesses and consumers. They provide convenience to consumers. If the cookie contains your username and password for accessing a certain resource at the site (e.g., your bank account), you do not have to reenter the information. Cookies often help ensure that a user does not receive the same unsolicited information multiple times. For example, cookies are commonly used to rotate banner ads that a site sends so that a surfer receives different advertisements in a series of requested pages. They also help sites to customize other elements for customers. For example, when a retailer's site identifies a returning customer, it can build a page showing a list of items and information in which the customer might be interested based on previous purchases.

Some cookies are temporary; they are installed only for one session, and are removed when the user leaves the site. Others are persistent and stay on the hard disk unless the user deletes them. Many cookies are installed to serve only first parties, which are the businesses with which the user interacts directly. Others serve third parties, which are organizations that collect information about the user whenever the user visits a site that subscribes to the service of these organizations. These organizations include DoubleClick, FastClick, and Avenue A.

While cookies can make online shopping, investing, and reading more convenient, they also open the door for intrusion into a person's privacy. Remember that every piece of information you provide while your browser is configured to permit cookies can be recorded and kept for further use—use over which you have no control. Choices you make when selecting menu items, clicking buttons, and moving from one page to another are also recorded. Such activities are often called **clickstream tracking**. Although some organizations post privacy policies at their Web sites and tell you what they will or will not do with the information they gather, you cannot

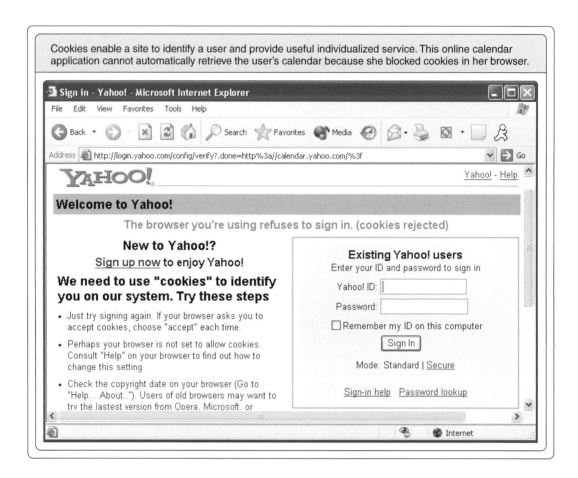

Cookies enable a site to identify a user and provide useful individualized service. This online calendar application cannot automatically retrieve the user's calendar because she blocked cookies in her browser.

see what information they have compiled by using cookies and how they use it. Especially worrisome are third-party cookies, which collect your browsing and shopping habits across many Web sites. This is akin to a spy who follows you from one store to another. Software designed to trace and report your online behavior without your knowledge is called **spyware**. It includes cookies and other, more sophisticated applications that are installed on your computer unbeknownst to you and transmit information about you while you are online.

Proprietary Technologies

In addition to these and other widely used and usually free Web technologies, many companies offer proprietary technologies. A proprietary technology is the intellectual property of its developer and is not free for all to use. These software packages include local search engines for finding information about specific items; shopping cart applications for purchase, including selection of items to place in a virtual cart and credit-card charging; wish lists, which allow shoppers to create lists of items they would like others to purchase for them; and a host of software packages that are invisible to visitors but help the site owner to analyze and predict visitor behavior, especially shopper behavior. The latter technologies might not be considered Web technologies per se, but they analyze data that is collected from visitors accessing Web sites. For example, Amazon.com uses software that follows the estimated age for those whom a shopper purchases items, and offers new items that fit the progressing age of the shopper's family and friends.

A Web site is, practically speaking, the Web pages that make up the information and links to Web technologies that the site provides. To establish a Web business, an organization must have access to an Internet server and the ability to control its content. Recall that an Internet server is a computer that is connected to the Internet backbone. Businesses have two options when establishing a Web site: installing and maintaining their own servers, or contracting with a Web hosting service.

Owning and Maintaining a Server

Installing and maintaining a server at the business's own facility is a costly option, but it gives the business the greatest degree of control. Setting up a server requires expertise, which may or may not be available within the business. The business must obtain a high-speed physical link to the Internet backbone. It must also employ specialists to maintain the server or many servers on which the Web site resides. In large organizations these specialists might be employees of the company; in smaller ones, they might be contract personnel whose services the company hires. The specialists purchase a server (or several servers) for the company, connect it to the Internet through a high-speed dedicated line, register a domain name for the site, and install the proper software for managing the server and creating Web pages. The specialists "scale up" the server system when the business grows and handle issues such as load balancing to ensure quick response and to minimize the probability of site crashing. A site crashes when too many people try to log on and the software stops responding to anyone. **Load balancing** transfers visitor inquiries from a busy server to a less busy server for identical information and services. Thus, the specialist often must connect **mirrors**, servers on which the same content and applications are duplicated.

A large company whose entire business is done online, often called a **pure-play** Web company, or a **brick-and-mortar** company that owns stores but also offers the same or many of the same items for sale online, usually has its own servers and manages them fully. These companies employ crews that manage Internet networking, the hardware and software of the site, and the people responsible for updating the Web pages.

Using a Hosting Service

A majority of organizations that have a commercial presence online either do not own servers or own servers but let someone else manage at least some aspect of the site. These organizations use **Web hosting** services. Web hosting companies specialize in one or several types of Web hosting: shared hosting, virtual private server hosting, dedicated hosting, or co-location. Some also offer free service, but this service rarely involves features beyond posting Web pages. Therefore, this option is not viable for most businesses.

In **shared hosting** the client's Web site is stored on the host's same physical server along with the sites of other clients. The hosting company owns the server and the server management software. It offers space on the servers for hosting Web sites. This is a relatively inexpensive option. The client can use templates provided by the hosts for building pages, or, for an extra fee, have the host's designer design the Web site. However, many clients prefer to design and upload their own Web pages. The service includes transaction and payment software for use by the subscribing businesses' clients. If the server is shared, the host might not be able to allow a client to maintain its own domain name, such as www.myownco.com, but only a subdomain that contains the host's domain name, such as myownco.myhost.com. However, special software employed by many hosts allows clients to use their own domain names, and although the server has only one IP address, the software directs traffic to the proper site on the server. If an independent domain name is important, this is a factor that a business must consider before selecting a hosting service.

economists call perfect markets. In a perfect market no single buyer or seller can affect the price of a product. On the Internet, all buyers and sellers have access to the same information at the same time. Thus, no single buyer or seller has an information advantage over competitors.

Online Business Alliances

Companies in the same industry—competitors—often collaborate in establishing a Web site for one or several purposes. One major purpose might be to create buying power by consolidating purchases. Another might be to create a single place for customers, assuming that a greater choice will benefit the group. The concept is not new: Realtors have collaborated in the multiple listing system (MLS), whereby multiple agencies have access to real estate that is registered for sale with one of them. This system, which was in place many years before the Web, is now managed on the Web.

In some cases, the purpose of an alliance site is the same as an auction site operated by a single company, but the operator is a business that works for the allied companies. The purpose of such a site is to set the prices of purchased products and services. Big players in an industry, such as airlines or automakers, establish a shared company that operates the site. Suppliers are invited to sell through the site and compete among themselves. The competition drives prices down. The allies enjoy lower costs and greater profit margins. A grand attempt by the auto industry to use this method through an alliance called Covisint failed because suppliers refused to compete against each other online. The Covisint software was sold to Compuware, a software development company in Detroit. However, Star Alliance, an alliance of 16 airlines, has done well with its online joint purchasing.

Star Alliance is one of several airline alliances, such as OneWorld, SkyTeam, and Orbitz. Star Alliance established an extranet for two purposes: to concentrate purchases from parts and service providers, and to represent the group to its clients, airline passengers. The alliance includes Air Canada, Air New Zealand, Austrian Airlines, Lufthansa, Scandinavian Airlines, United, Varig, and other companies. On the consumer side, the airlines collaborate in frequent flier programs: you can fly with any of them and accrue miles with the entire alliance rather than with a single airline. The Star Alliance site provides several useful services for travelers of all member airlines. On the B2B side, the alliance solicits bids from suppliers of aircraft parts and maintenance services, food, ground equipment, office supplies, and other products and services. The allies use the extranet to share information about inventory levels, facilitate joint planning and forecasting for material requirements, and facilitate communication and business transactions between the airlines and suppliers. The hub for joint purchasing has saved the allies millions of dollars annually.

Orbitz was established by United Airlines, Delta Air Lines, Continental Airlines, Northwest Airlines, and American Airlines to serve customers through a single Web site. The allies wanted to establish a site that "would provide comprehensive and unbiased travel information" as well as one that would make planning and buying travel on the Internet easy and hassle-free instead of the usual "scavenger hunt." The site provides a comprehensive search engine, list of flights by lowest price and number of stops without favoring any airline, and special Internet-only fares with over 455 airlines. By using their own Web site, airlines can stop paying the $5 to $10 commission they usually pay to online brokers such as Expedia, Travelocity, and Priceline.com. They can also eliminate fees to online database companies that link travel agencies, airlines, and other travel companies. In addition to the airlines, the site serves 22 rental car companies, and tens of thousands of lodging establishments.

Similar alliance sites have been established by firms in the general retail industry, the food industry, and the hospitality industry (hotels).

B2C Trading

Although business-to-business trading on the Internet is much larger in volume, online business-to-consumer (B2C) trading has caught the headlines in recent years, and that has prompted the establishment of a multitude of Internet companies. According to Forrester Research, in the United States B2C revenues more than doubled between 2002 and 2005, from $75.7 billion, to $172.4 billion (Figure 8.4).

Some e-tailers have hundreds or even thousands of affiliates. Amazon.com and other large e-tailers probably have tens of thousands of affiliates. These programs provide huge, effective advertising for online businesses.

Some companies make money by being affiliate aggregators. LinkShare (www.linkshare.com) and Commission Junction (www.cj.com) let you choose from hundreds of affiliate advertisers, some offering commissions of up to 40 percent. You can pick the ones you want to mention at your Web site.

Competition Amazon.com has taken a step beyond affiliate programs to cooperate with competitors. It includes its competitors on its own site. When you use the search engine at the company's site for a certain item, it brings up the product description and price from Amazon. com's database and also the same type of information from other companies' databases. Although these companies are direct competitors, Amazon benefits from this cooperation in two ways: it attracts more shoppers to visit its site first, because they know there is a high probability that they will find the item they want at the site, even if they end up buying from another company; and it receives a fee from these affiliated companies whenever they sell through Amazon's site. In 2005, one-third of the dollars spent at Amazon.com purchased items from other companies.

Conversion One measure of online retail success is **conversion rate**, the proportion of site visitors who make a purchase to the total number of visitors in a period of time, usually one year. This proportion has steadily increased over the years from a mere fraction of a percent in the late 1990s to several percentage points in 2005. In a survey of 250 online retailers by E-tailing Group Inc., 35 percent of the responding online retailers said their conversion rates were 4 percent or higher. The same survey discovered that cart abandonment rates—the proportion of "almost buyers" who did not complete the purchase—was from 11 percent for some retailers to more than 70 percent for almost a tenth of the retailers.

In general, pure-play e-tailers, companies that sell solely over the Web, enjoy higher conversion rates than brick-and-mortar retailers who also sell online. A 2005 survey of the largest retailers in the United States that was conducted by Nielsen//NetRatings found that the top ten "converters" did not include a single brick-and-mortar. All but one were online-only e-tailers, and the best performer was QVC, which sells through its television channel and online (see Figure 8.6). The survey included eBay and Yahoo! Shopping, although they do not sell products but a service for sellers.

FIGURE 8.6
The top ten U.S. online retailers based on conversion rates in February 2005

Online Retailer	Conversion Rate (%)
QVC	16.3
Lands' End	14.8
sportsmansguide.com	13.5
FTD.com	13.4
llbean.com	13.4
Amazon.com	12.8
Coldwater Creek	12.7
eBay	12.3
Yahoo! Shopping	12.1
proflowers.com	11.8

Source: Nielsen//NetRatings MagaView Online Retail

Auctions and Reverse Auctions

Similar to auctions among companies, some Web sites serve as auction hubs for individuals. The most prominent of the sites is eBay, but there are others, such as uBid and AAANDS. The business model is simple: sellers list information about the items or services they offer for sale, and if a sale is executed, the site owner collects a fee. Because the sites provide only a platform for a transaction that eventually takes place between two consumers, some people like to call online auctions consumer-to-consumer e-business. To participate in auctions one needs to register as a member. To help bidders know better to what extent they can count on the integrity of the seller, eBay publishes the number of feedback comments it received on a member, and the number and percentage of positive feedbacks.

POINT OF INTEREST

Don't Get Stuck Without Transporation

Suppose it is only three days before you have to fly a few family members and friends to the Bahamas. You can't find any commercial flight with so many first-class seats. No need to panic. You can use Charterauction.com. Enter your departure and arrival information. Private jet owners will bid for your business. Note, however, that you will have to place a sum of $100,000 in an escrow account before they will bid. A typical flight between New York and San Francisco costs $30,000.

Source: Tynan, D., "30 Things You Didn't Know You Could Do on the Internet," *PC World*, July 2005, p. 79.

The ability of Web sites to serve as prompt exchanges of information has supported another popular business model, the **reverse auction** or **name-your-own-price auction**. Priceline.com invites consumers to post requests for services and prices they are willing to pay. Although they also deal in home mortgages, the services are mostly for travel, such as flights, cruises, lodging, and car rentals. Customers can post the destination, day, and time of a flight, as well as the maximum price they are willing to pay. Then, airlines are invited to consider the requests. The first airline to accept the terms wins the offer. Shoppers are required to transmit a credit-card account number. The account is charged as soon as an airline accepts the deal. Priceline.com's revenue comes from the fees that airlines and other businesses pay to use the service.

Content Providers

On the Web, content means information, such as news, research results, statistics, and other useful information, as well as artistic works such as music, pictures, and video clips. Some put in this category classified ads, including job postings and online dating services. Over the years, individuals and organizations have spent increasing amounts of money on content. Although most news can be obtained free of charge, many articles cannot. Some audiences welcome for-fee content, especially if it is highly specialized. Given a choice, many people prefer to read the same information online rather than on paper because they can use search operations to quickly find specific articles. This might be one reason why many prefer to subscribe to the electronic version of a newspaper. Content revenues also have grown since companies such as Apple and Wal-Mart started selling individual song files online.

Bill Presentment and Payment

Because it is so easy to transfer funds online from one bank account to another, and it is so easy to send information, including bills, by e-mail, many utility companies try to convince customers to accept electronic bills and pay them online. Some customers accept the option of electronic bill presentment but refuse to sign an agreement that would enable the company to automatically charge their bank account. Obviously, banks are always a participant in electronic payment if the charge is to a bank account (which is how most utility and mortgage companies want to be paid), but some banks, for their own reasons, refuse to join such trilateral initiatives.

Electronic bill presentment and payment (EBPP) saves utility companies and financial institutions that bill customers regularly—mainly for loan payments—millions of dollars. The bills are presented automatically, directly from the companies' information systems to payers' e-mail addresses, and therefore save labor, paper, and postage. Direct charge to a bank account saves the labor involved in receiving and depositing checks. Yet, EBPP is spreading slowly. Most people still prefer to pay their bills by check and through the mail, partly because fraud on the Internet has increased in recent years, especially through a practice called **phishing**, discussed in the Ethical & Societal Issues feature. Figure 8.7 illustrates the practice. Note that the fictitious site is not secure. The legitimate one is secure; note the "s" in https://. Also note the bank warnings to customers. This particular e-mail was sent to a person who does not even have an account with the bank.

Dispersed Workforce

The Web enables companies to purchase labor from many more people than their own employees. For example, companies can augment their intellectual pool by using the Web to employ talent beyond their own employees'. They can enjoy more labor for less money by offering cash for research and development (R&D) solutions provided by researchers outside their organizations.

InnoCentive Inc. is a subsidiary of the pharmaceutical company Eli Lilly and Company. It operates InnoCentive.com, a Web site connecting scientists with companies. Companies whose R&D staffs cannot find a solution to a biological or chemical problem can post the challenge at the site and offer a cash reward for a practical solution. Scientists and researchers from around the world can register with the site and work on solutions. The site is operated in seven languages to accommodate scientists and organizations from all over the world. So far, Eli Lilly and 30 other companies, including Dow Chemical Co. and the giant consumer product company Procter & Gamble, have awarded sums of $4,000 to $100,000. The site has more than 150,000 registered scientists located in 150 countries.

When a company employs a staff of researchers it must pay them regardless of how fruitful their efforts are. When offering cash for solutions, many more scientists might work for the company, but the company pays only the scientist who solves the problem. The cost savings can be huge.

M-Commerce

In Chapter 6 you learned about the many wireless technologies that enable people to access the Web while away from the office or home. Wireless technologies enable what some people call mobile commerce, or **m-commerce**. Mobile devices already let users log on to the Internet, but they can also provide an additional benefit to businesses: a device can be located with an accuracy of several feet, much like locating a cellular phone. As soon as you come within a few blocks of a store, your handheld computer or phone could beep and display a promotional message on its monitor.

M-commerce allows people to use their mobile devices to experience an event and react immediately. For example, they might view a horserace and place bets from their seat. Or, they can see a demonstration of a product at a public place and order it online. Impulse shopping will no longer be limited to shopping malls. Recall our discussion in Chapter 6 of future uses of RFID. Mobile devices might be equipped with RFID readers so their owners can use a product's electronic product code (EPC) to download information about it from the Web.

Smart mobile devices might be helpful in salesforce automation. Traveling salespeople are able to access data through the mobile device almost anywhere. They are able to access corporate databases through their company's intranet. Both traveling salespeople and consumers already practice m-commerce whenever they transact while using a hotspot or a Web-capable cell phone.

Experts believe that the most attractive mobile application might not be online buying, but the delivery of highly relevant information, custom-tailored to the user's current location and activity. Location services include downloading coupons at the store in which the consumer has just entered, finding out about nearby restaurants, or reading product reviews while shopping at an appliance store.

In the United States, cell phones manufactured as of 2006 must, by law, include global positioning system (GPS) capability, so that people can be located in case of emergency. As telephoning and other technologies are merged into a single device that can also link to the Web, the potential for marketing and pushing information might be too tempting for businesses.

So far, however, predictions about the growth of m-commerce in North America and Europe have not materialized. The only countries where m-commerce has become popular are Japan and South Korea. In Japan, subscribers to the DoCoMo's i-mode service use their smart cell phones to purchase soda cans from vending machines, buy food at fast-food restaurants, and shop at Web sites of online retailers. Purchases are charged to the cell phone service provider, NTT. It is expected that the United States will catch up to Japan and South Korea. In Coral Gables, Florida, drivers can already pay for parking by keying into their cell phones the number of the parking meter. When time is up, the meter calls the cell phone, and the driver can add funds without rushing to the meter.

FIGURE 8.7
Phishing plagues Web commerce. An e-mail arrives (below) that prompts the recipient to update personal information at a fictitious but legitimate-looking Web site (left image on the next page). Note how similar the features in the fictitious (left) and legitimate Web site (right) are.

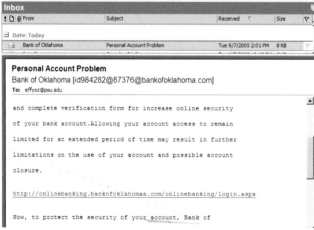

Privacy proponents have already voiced concerns about m-commerce. Apparently, not many people are happy to find out that commercial organizations can track them down anytime when their mobile device is on. These devices not only allow consumer profiling, as already practiced by many online retailers, but can also tell retailers and other organizations your exact location at any given time. The result might be "we know who you are, what you have done on the Web, and where you are now."

SUPPLY CHAINS ON THE WEB

Supply chains extend from commercial organizations to both suppliers and buyers. Organizations connect their supply chain management (SCM) systems to their suppliers at one end, and to their buyers at the other end. Thus, an organization might be a participant among other buyers in an extranet managed by one of its suppliers, and a participant among several sellers in an extranet of a buyer. Large retailers manage extranets through which their suppliers' SCM systems can provide useful information to their own, so they can track orders and shipments, as well as collect useful information for decision making on which supplier to select for which order. In this regard, a large retailer's extranet becomes a marketplace for many sellers and a single buyer.

In the years before the opening of the Internet to commercial activities many companies invested in Electronic Data Interchange (EDI) systems to exchange documents electronically with business partners. EDI consists of certain standards for formatting documents such as orders and invoices, software that translates the data properly, and the networks through which the information flows between subscribing organizations. The networks are owned and managed by

Notice the extra "a" in "Oklahomaa" in the faked Web site on the left.

value-added network (VAN) companies, telecommunications companies that manage the traffic of EDI between the business partners. Subscribers pay for this service. Although EDI provides some advantages, such as a high degree of data security and nonrepudiation (inability to deny sent messages), companies that want to connect to establish similar data exchange with business partners can use the Web technologies on the Internet. XML, in particular, enables business partners to set standards for data formats in Web pages. Dynamic page technologies, the software that links Web pages with databases, automate much of the business activity with business partners. Orders can automatically trigger notices to warehouse personnel on their stationary or handheld computers to pick and pack items for shipping. The information automatically flows into the accounting ISs as well as SCM systems of both the buyer and seller. Figure 8.8 illustrates how information flows between organizations.

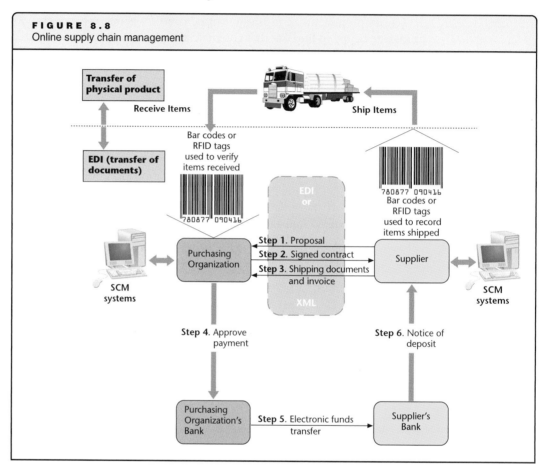

FIGURE 8.8
Online supply chain management

Companies encourage their suppliers to join their extranets. For example, the bookstore chain Barnes & Noble uses an extranet to do business with thousands of its 30,000 suppliers. So does the office supplies retailer Office Depot. It uses an extranet to order 7–8 billion items annually. The extranet saves the company much paper and administrative labor. Wal-Mart, the world's largest retailer, uses an extranet with Procter & Gamble and hundreds of other manufacturers. In addition to labor and paper saving, the results are smaller inventory and greater in-stock availability of products.

XML is used extensively in Web technologies so that the SCM systems of two organizations can "speak to one another." This ensures that the meaning of data exchanged between the organizations can not only be displayed for employee eyes through Web browsers but that the received data can be interpreted correctly by systems that automatically capture and store it in a database for further processing.

Large retailers invite suppliers to join their extranets.

RULES FOR SUCCESSFUL WEB-BASED BUSINESS

Most organizations that operate a Web site do so to sell either products or services. Web software and the ability to connect Web servers to organizational information systems open great opportunities. Often, whether online business succeeds depends not only on availability of the proper software but how it is used. There are several elements to consider, especially if the site is to support B2C commerce.

Target the Right Customers

Targeting the people or organizations that are most likely to need the products and services you offer has always been the most important effort in marketing, with or without the Web. On the Web, targeting includes identifying the sites your audience frequently visits. For instance, a business that sells sporting goods should create clickable links at sites that cover sporting events and provide sports statistics. Banks that offer mortgage loans should create links at realtors' sites. And any business that targets its products to young people should do so at popular music sites. This principle should also apply to blogs and popular podcasts. Podcasting can include visual advertisements displayed by the player software.

Online Annoyances and Worse

The Web provides excellent opportunities but its wide availability combined with ingenuity have created some practices that range from mildly annoying to criminally dangerous.

- **Spam.** Spam is the term for unsolicited commercial e-mail. Spam does not have to be camouflaged to be so. The mere fact that it is not invited makes it spam. The reason for spam is simple: it is the most cost-effective marketing method. Even if a fraction of a percent of the recipients end up purchasing the product or service touted, the spammer profits. Both individuals and organizations dislike spam. Individuals have to wade through a long list of unsolicited e-mail to get to useful e-mail. Organizations face an increasingly costly burden. Consider: if spam makes up half of the e-mail the organization receives, the organization must employ twice the bandwidth it really needs for communications and twice the space on e-mail servers. Obviously, it pays twice as much as it could for operating an e-mail system. Screening software, known as antispam software, has helped to some extent, but spam is still on the rise and still causes waste of resources. By some estimates, spam constitutes about three-quarters of all e-mail flowing on the Internet.

  The Direct Marketing Association (DMA) defends the right of businesses to send unsolicited commercial e-mail as a legitimate and cost-effective way of doing business. Indeed, the method gives small, entrepreneurial businesses a chance to compete. The DMA sees no difference between junk "snail" mail, which most of us reluctantly tolerate, and the spam.

  On the other hand, the Coalition Against Unsolicited Commercial E-mail (CAUCE) calculated the amount of spam we might soon receive unless new laws stop the phenomenon. There are 24 million small businesses in the United States. If just 1 percent of those businesses sent you just one e-mail message per year, you would receive 657 messages in your inbox each day. And this number does not include e-mail from large and non-U.S. companies. Opting out is not a realistic option: who has the time to respond to 657 organizations with a request to stop? CAUCE does not believe that opting in—avoiding sending e-mail unless you specifically ask for it—would solve the problem either. Antispam legislation in many countries has not reduced spam. In the United States, the CAN-SPAM law has not reduced the practice. According to this law, spam is a crime only if the sending party hides its true identity.

Is unsolicited commercial e-mail a legitimate marketing tool, or is it a nuisance that should be eradicated by strictly enforced laws? Would it be fair to outlaw an efficient way for businesses, especially entrepreneurial businesses, to approach potential customers?

- **Pop-Up Windows.** You browse the Web, stop to read an interesting article, and a few seconds later a window pops up, partially covering the text you were reading. The pop-up contains an advertisement. You look for the little X to close the window. It is not in the normal top-right corner. You finally manage to close the window, but as soon as you do, another one pops up. And so on, and so forth, more and more windows. When you finally close the main site's window, you discover that several other windows popped up *behind* the window. The site owner is paid by advertisers to run these pesky windows, which is legitimate. However, many people are quite annoyed by the practice. Some employ special applications or turn on a browser option that prevents pop-up windows. Is this a good solution? Not always. Many sites have links that open a little window, such as a window with help or explanation of a term. If you block all pop-up windows such windows do not open. If you use a selective pop-up "killer," you have to program it to allow pop-up windows for individual sites. Thus, even with a solution, pop-up windows waste surfers' time. Web surfers might not like pop-up windows, but advertisers love them, because they are an effective marketing tool.

- **Adware.** A growing number of organizations use adware, software that delivers ad banners or pop-up advertising windows on the Web. Often, the banners hide large parts of the information on the page. Adware is often tailored to users, based on their profiles, such as previous interests. Some companies use adware that pops up deliberately to cover banners of competing companies that paid to advertise at the site a user visits. The visitor might not even know that the ad is not originating from the Web site, but from another one.

- **Spyware.** A more disturbing "ware" is spyware. As discussed in this chapter, spyware is software that uses the Internet connection of a computer to transmit information about the user without the user's knowledge or permission. Usually, the software transmits information about users' activities with their computers, including their every move on the Internet. It sits on the computer's hard disk, secretly collects information, and transmits it to the computer of a company, usually for marketing purposes, but also for industrial espionage. Some surreptitious software is also designed to pop up windows. Some countries have criminalized adware and spyware, but in much of the world the software does not violate any law. A bill against spyware and adware has been introduced in the U.S. Senate.

- **Phishing.** A growing number of Web users receive a special kind of spam that intends not to sway them to buy something but to defraud them. The practice is called phishing, a play on "fishing." Criminals send thousands of messages that look as if they were sent from a bank, a credit-card company, or any other financial institution or an organization where the recipient has authority to withdraw funds. The e-mail provides a Web link where the recipient is urged to go and supply personal information, including codes that are used to withdraw or transfer funds. One of many "reasons" is "explained" in the message: your account must be renewed, the bank lost your details, you verify your personal information or the account

will be revoked, and many others. Thousands of people have fallen prey to the con artists, who used the information to withdraw funds. The most obvious sign that an e-mail message tries to phish is a message from an institution with which you have never transacted, such as a bank where you do not have an account. A more subtle sign is the URL that appears in the browser once you click the link: the domain name is not the one of the legitimate organization. Suspect every e-mail message that asks you to update your personal information online. Call the organization using the legitimate number you have on file and ask if the message is genuine. Banks and other institutions rarely use e-mail to ask for "account information update." Phishing continues to grow. The Anti-Phishing Working Group—an industry association that works to eliminate phishing and identity theft—reported that in one month alone, April 2005, there were 14,411 phishing attempts involving millions of potential victims and numerous financial institutions. This number was almost five times greater than a year earlier.

 ## Capture the Customer's Total Experience

By using cookies and recording shoppers' movements, CRM software can create electronic consumer profiles for each shopper and buyer. The shopper's experience with the site then becomes an asset of the business. Such marketing research fine-tunes the portfolio of products that the business offers and tailors Web pages for individual customers. It also can be used to "market to one" by e-mailing the shopper about special deals on items in which he or she has shown an interest.

Personalize the Service

CRM software and Web page customization software can be combined to enable customers to personalize the pages and the service they receive when they log on to the site. Letting shoppers and readers select the type of e-mail content they want is welcome, but sites should respect privacy by letting customers opt in rather than opt out. Opting in means that the customer can actively check options to receive e-mail and other promotions, while opting out requires the customer to select *not* to receive such information—an annoyance to many customers.

The Web also enables companies to let consumers tailor products. Land's End's Web site invites men to dress a virtual model with a build like theirs and order pants online. Although a pair costs significantly more than one a customer would purchase in a store, Land's End has been very successful with the concept. It has acquired many loyal customers because there is little reason to return a pair of pants that is made to order, although the company's policy allows returns.

Shorten the Business Cycle

One reason people like to do business on the Web is that it saves them time. Businesses should keep looking for opportunities to shorten the business cycle for their customers, from shopping to paying to receiving the items they ordered. Fulfillment, the activities taking place after customers place orders online, is one of the greatest challenges for online businesses.

Those who can ship the ordered products fastest are likely to sustain or increase their market shares. Some have decided to outsource the entire fulfillment task to organizations that specialize in fulfillment, such as UPS's e-Logistics and FedEx's Supply Chain Services. E-Logistics, for example, offers to receive and store the business's merchandise in its warehouses, receive orders online, and then pick, pack, and ship them to the online business's customers. It also offers a product return service. A shorter business cycle is not only important for customer satisfaction but also enables the company to collect faster because credit cards are usually charged upon shipping.

Let Customers Help Themselves

Customers often need information from a Web-enabled organization. Such information includes the status of an order, the status of a shipped item, and after-sale information such as installation of add-on components and troubleshooting. Placing useful information and downloadable software at the site not only encourages customer loyalty but also saves labor.

Practically every online business now sends e-mail messages with the status of the order, a tracking number, and a link to the shipping company for checking the shipping status. Hardware companies can post online assembly instructions for their "assembly required" products. In addition to including Frequently Asked Questions (FAQs) information, some companies have used knowledge management software (discussed in Chapter 11) that can answer open-ended questions.

Be Proactive and De-Commoditize

Expecting customers to visit your Web site every time they need your service might not be enough in today's competitive marketplace. Customers now demand not only prompt e-mail replies to their queries but also proactive alerts. For example, the travel Web sites Orbitz and Travelocity e-mail airline customers gate and time information if a customer's flight is delayed or if gates change. Some manufacturers e-mail customers about product recalls or to schedule periodic service appointments. Online drugstores invite customers who regularly take a certain medication to register for automatic replenishment of their drugs. The company's software calculates when the next lot is to be shipped and ensures that it arrives in time.

All these initiatives, as well as many others, are efforts to *de-commoditize* what companies sell. A commodity is any product that is sold for about the same price by a multitude of vendors in a highly competitive market, usually with a thin margin of profit. By adding a special service or additional information, the company keeps the products it sells from becoming a commodity. Adding an original service or information to the product differentiates the "package" that online shoppers purchase from the "package" sold by competitors.

E-Commerce Is Every Commerce

You might have noticed that the title of this chapter does not contain the term "e-commerce." You might have also noticed that this is not the only chapter in which Web-enabled business activities are discussed. In fact, every chapter in this book gives examples of what is popularly referred to as e-commerce. Web technologies have been integrated into the business world to a degree that makes it difficult at times to realize which activities take place inside the organization and which involve information flowing from other places through the Internet. We have become so used to the integration of the Web into our daily activities, especially the commercial ones, that the lines between commerce and e-commerce have been blurred. We will eventually stop using the term "e-commerce" and simply consider the Web another means of supporting business, much the way we consider technologies like the telephone and fax.

- Some industries have changed dramatically and continue to change thanks to Web technologies. Any product whose sole purpose is to deliver information or any other product that can be digitized will eventually be delivered over the Web.

- HTTP is an Internet standard that enables addressing of Web servers with domain names. HTTPS is a secure version of the protocol for confidential transactions. HTML is a markup language for presentation of Web pages. XML is a markup language for delivery of information about data communicated through Web pages. XHTML combines features of HTML and XML. FTP is a protocol for uploading and downloading files. RSS is software that uses XML to automatically update text and audio from the Web site that posts it to subscriber online devices. It is the main enabler of podcasting. Blogs enable people to conveniently create discussion Web pages by posting comments and responding to them. Instant messaging online chat services enable people to correspond in real time and help businesses serve online customers. Cookies help Web sites to personalize the experience of visitors. Along with other software that spies on unwitting Web surfers, they might provide detailed information about Web users.

- In addition to a large number of nonproprietary Web technologies, many more are developed and licensed to organizations by software vendors.

- An organization has two options when deciding to do commerce online: own and maintain its own Web servers at its own facilities, or contract with a Web hosting company. When contracting with a Web host, there are several degrees of service: shared hosting, virtual private servers, dedicated hosting, and co-location.

- When selecting a Web hosting company, organizations should consider several factors: type and quality of application provided, storage space, quality of technical support, traffic limits, availability of e-mail accounts and services, scalability, support of page design, security, uptime ratio, setup fee, and monthly fee.

- Web-enabled commerce can generally be classified as business-to-business (B2B) or business-to-consumer (B2C). In the former, businesses use networks to trade with other businesses, possibly through an extranet. In the latter, businesses advertise and sell goods and services to consumers via the Web. The greater volume of e-commerce is conducted between businesses.

- Business-to-business trading often relies on electronic data interchange (EDI), which is conducted over value-added networks. XML facilitates interorganizational online trading similar to EDI. When linked to internal ISs, Web technologies enhance supply chain management. Online interorganizational commerce often takes place through an extranet.

- With the proliferation of wireless handheld computers and smart mobile phones, the next wave in B2C might be mobile commerce, popularly called m-commerce. It is already popular in Japan, but to a much smaller degree in the United States and Europe.

- To be successful, an online business must target the right customers, capture the customer's total experience, personalize the service, shorten the business cycle, let customers help themselves, and be proactive.

- Spam, and to a lesser degree spyware, adware, and pop-up windows, have become online annoyances. Society is trying to strike a balance between allowing these phenomena to continue as a form of commercial promotion and free speech, and curbing them to reduce the public's waste of resources. Phishing has become a pervasive crime, defrauding people and stealing their identities.

IT FITS OUTFITS REVISITED

It Fits Outfits is expanding onto college campuses by establishing an online storefront. Let's explore some of the issues it faces in managing its Web site.

What Would You Do?

1. The online store has arranged for customer service representatives to answer questions in real-time chat rooms. What can the company do to make sure that these representatives are not wasting time answering the same questions over and over again?

2. Consumer profiling would help the online store target its customers individually and offer products that they would be most interested in. Some people consider consumer profiling to be a violation of individual rights. Should It Fits Outfits profile its customers?

New Perspectives

1. Shari Steiner opened the very first It Fits Outfits store next door to a coffee shop that was popular with local high school students. She also hired students from local high schools to run the store. What steps should It Fits Outfits take to attract college students? How can It Fits Outfits encourage students to drop by their storefront on their way to and from their favorite online hangouts?

KEY TERMS

B2B, 262
B2C, 262
banner, 263
blog, 253
brick-and-mortar, 257
clickstream tracking, 255
co-location, 259
consumer profiling, 268
conversion rate, 269
cookie, 255
dedicated hosting, 258
domain name, 251
dynamic Web page, 259
extranet, 264
File Transfer Protocol (FTP), 252

fulfillment, 267
Hypertext Markup Language (HTML), 252
Hypertext Transfer Protocol (HTTP), 251
Hypertext Transfer Protocol Secure (HTTPS), 251
impression, 263
instant messaging (IM), 254
intranet, 264
load balancing, 257
m-commerce, 272
mirror, 257
phishing, 271
podcast, 254

pure-play, 257
reach percentage, 263
reverse auction (name-your-own-price auction), 270
RSS, 253
search advertising, 263
shared hosting, 257
spyware, 256
Uniform Resource Locator (URL), 251
virtual private server, 258
Web hosting, 257
XHTML, 252
XML, 252

1. What is streaming video and on what does the success of companies that stream video rather than rent DVDs depend?

2. What is HTML, and why is it needed to use the Web?

3. What is XML? How is it different from HTML, and what purpose does it fulfill in Web commerce?

4. What is the relationship between a domain name and an IP number?

5. When you visit a Web site and click a Download button, you activate software that adheres to a certain protocol. What protocol is that?

6. What is instant messaging (IM), and how can it support business operations? How does IM reduce telephone costs?

7. What is RSS, and for which industry is it especially useful?

8. What is blogging, and what potential does it have for businesses?

9. What is podcasting, and how is it different from radio broadcasting?

10. In the context of the Web, what is a cookie? What is the benefit of cookies for online shoppers? What is the risk?

11. What is the difference between first-party cookies and third-party cookies? Which is usually disliked more by consumers, and why?

12. What is an intranet, and what purposes does it serve?

13. What is an extranet, and what purpose does it serve?

14. When contracting with a Web hosting company, what is the difference between a shared server and a dedicated server?

15. What is co-location? What are its benefits?

16. When selecting a Web hosting company, one of the important factors to consider is uptime ratio. What is it, and why is it important?

17. What does "unique monthly visitors" mean in online lingo? Who uses this metric and for what purpose?

18. What is a reverse auction? Would it be practical without the Web? Why or why not?

19. What is phishing? How do people get "phished"?

1. Streaming movies to subscribers' homes over the Web has already replaced video stores in some parts of the world. What other services do you think will change business models when large parts of the population have high-speed broadband connections?

2. Sun Microsystems Corp. coined the slogan "The network *is* the computer." What does that mean?

3. Some top-level domains (TLDs) are reserved for certain organizations. Why is this important? Would you prefer that anyone could register a TLD of his or her choice?

4. Podcasting is said to allow subscribers to "time-shift." What does that mean, and does this give listeners a benefit they do not have with radio programs?

5. E-tailers can use their software to charge different shoppers different prices. This is called price discrimination, and it is legal. Some observers say that shoppers discriminate based on price when they decide from whom to buy, and therefore it is ethical for e-tailers to price-discriminate. Do you agree?

6. Do you see blogging and podcasting as a threat to the written and broadcast media? Explain.

7. One of the most frustrating types of events to an e-tailer is shopping cart abandonment. From your own online shopping experience, what are the things that would cause you to abandon an online shopping cart?

8. M-commerce will give organizations the opportunity to send location-related advertising, that is, they will send to our handheld devices advertising based on where we are. What is your feeling about this?

9. Some states (e.g., Washington) have legislated voting through the Internet. There are thoughts of a wider "teledemocracy." In addition to electing their representatives and other officials, citizens will be able to vote via the Internet on other issues, such as international alliances, tax cuts or new taxes, federal and state budgets, and other issues that are now dealt with only by their representatives. Do you favor this teledemocracy? Why or why not?

10. Gambling on the Web is growing fast. Do you see a danger in this phenomenon more than in gambling in traditional ways? Does Web gambling have more or less social impact than casino gambling?

11. You have a new home business. You sell a consumer product for which you have a patent. You believe there will be much demand for it. To promote it, you decide to purchase a list of 2,000,000 e-mail addresses of people who fall in the demographic groups that are likely to purchase the product. The seller told you that these were only addresses of people who did not opt out from receiving messages from businesses. After you e-mailed the promotional message, you received hundreds of angry e-mail messages, including one from the Coalition Against Unsolicited Commercial E-mail (CAUCE). Was there anything wrong in what you did? Why or why not?

12. The owners of a small business tell you that they would not be able to reach enough customers to survive if they couldn't use mass, unsolicited e-mail. You strongly object to spamming. How do you respond to them?

13. Scott McNealy, CEO of Sun Microsystems, said: "You already have zero privacy. Get over it!" Some observers say that expecting privacy when using the Internet is ridiculous; the Internet is a public network, and no one should expect privacy in a public network. Do you agree? Why or why not?

14. A student established a Web site that serves as an exchange of term papers. Students are invited to contribute their graded work and to search for term papers that other students contributed. When criticized, the student claims that this, too, is a way to do research. He argues that the moral responsibility rests with those who access his site, not with him. Do you agree? Why or why not?

15. There have been international efforts to harmonize laws addressing free speech on the Web. Do you think such efforts can succeed? Why or why not?

APPLYING CONCEPTS

1. Find three commercial sites that operate in three different markets and offer affiliate programs. Write up a summary: What do they sell? What do their affiliate programs promise, and in return for what? Classify each program as pay per sale, pay per click, pay per lead, or another type, and explain why you classified the way you did.

2. Choose a topic in which you are interested. Select three different search engines (e.g., Google, Yahoo!, and MSN) and use them to look for information about the subject. Rank the performance of each site. A long list of sites that provide too broad a range of information is bad; a shorter list of sites that provide more narrowly defined information is good. Explain your ranking.

3. You have been hired by a pizza delivery service to design a Web site. The site should be attractive to families and young professionals and should allow them to order home delivery. Use a Web page development application to build the home page of the business. Submit your page to your instructor.

4. The following table contains some of the elements offered by a Web hosting firm. Assume that all other elements are satisfactory. Explain in writing to a person who has never learned about the subject what each of the shown elements means, including restrictions. Your "student" is a small-business owner who sells 500 unique dolls and is interested in also selling online. Will this be a good option for her in the short run? Explain. If you need to make some reasonable assumptions that are not mentioned here, do so.

Feature	Description
Storage	5 GB
Your own domain name	Yes
Monthly data transfer	110 GB
MySQL database	Available
Shopping cart	Available
E-mail accounts	30
Web site templates	Available
Setup fee	None
Monthly fee	$29.95

HANDS-ON ACTIVITIES

1. Prepare your résumé as an HTML document. If you wish, include your scanned photograph. Submit your work by e-mail, or post it to your Web site and e-mail the Web site link to your professor.

2. Consider the following options for a business that wishes to use a Web site: maintaining their own server at their facility, using a host for a shared server, using a host for a virtual private server, using a host for a dedicated server. You are a consultant. Consider each of the following scenarios independently of the others, and recommend the best hosting option to the business. Consider all the relevant factors, such as purpose and cost.

   a. A family store at a shopping mall. The owners want to make the public aware of what the store offers. They want to pay as little as possible for this Web presence.

   b. A large retail company. Management wants to be able to execute purchases from suppliers through the new Web site, and to allow their own customers to shop and buy through the site. It is willing to employ its own team and facility for the servers.

   c. A small business. The owners insist on having their own domain name. They wish visitors to have every sense that the site is run and controlled by the owners.

   d. A small business. Management does not want to register and pay for its own domain name.

   e. A large pure-play (Internet-only) e-tailer. It needs to change the list of products daily. Its Web design team might want to change the DBMS, shopping cart application, and other applications when the need arises. It already owns the servers but no longer wants to manage networking, backup, redundancy, and security.

   f. A brick-and-mortar retailer that wants to extend its sales operations to the Web. It has a Web design crew that is capable of changing content and is expert at using and modifying Web applications such as dynamic pages and shopping cart applications. However, management does not want to purchase servers or manage their networking and security.

1. Team up with another student to analyze the privacy policies of three companies that specialize in collecting consumer information on the Web. All must be companies that install third-party cookies. There are at least 10 such companies. List the common factors of the three companies. Then list the factors in which they differ. For each of the differing elements, which company treats consumers better, in terms of less invasion of privacy and more disclosure of its activities? Among other factors, see if the companies offer opt-in or opt-out options.

2. With two other team members, prepare a rationale for an original business idea that could generate revenue on the Web. Prepare the rationale in a way that would convince a venture capitalist to invest money in this new business.

COMPANION CD QUESTIONS

1. Have you paid for a product or service using e-cash? If so, describe your experience. Would you do it again? If not, would you consider using e-cash? Why or why not?

2. Visit three sites that use e-commerce. Compare the look and feel of each site. Is it easy to make a transaction on the site? Does the site have any features that make doing business extremely easy or difficult? What are they?

VIDEO QUESTIONS

1. Have you downloaded music from an online site? If so, describe your experience. Would you do it again? If not, would you consider doing it? Why or why not?

2. Do you think pay-as-you-go music services are a good alternative to illegal music file sharing? Why or why not?

FROM IDEAS TO APPLICATION: REAL CASES

Banking on Web Technologies

Sovereign Bank is based in Reading, Pennsylvania. It employs more than 10,000 people, operates more than 650 branches throughout the northeastern region of the United States, and maintains 1,000 ATMs. With financial assets of $59 billion, it is the 19th largest bank in the United States. Sovereign has experienced a dramatic increase in the number of customers doing business through its Web site. Management believes that a key to increasing its customer base is to offer a large financial institution's services in a personal manner typical of small community banks. To that end, the bank is relying on consumer-centric multichannel marketing. In marketing, a channel is a manner in which the marketing effort is carried out: mail, e-mail, Web advertising, newspaper advertising, and so forth.

Executives know that most customer interactions occur online, so the bank has decided to restructure its contact procedure with a focus on its Web site. The bank's Director of Online and Affinity, Marianne Doran-Collins, believes that online banking will improve customers' interaction and increase their business relationship with Sovereign. Results from a recent study by comScore, an online rating and research firm, confirm Doran-Collins' view. Surveying more than 1,500 people who regularly bank online, the researchers found that online banking customers tend to be more satisfied with their bank and in turn refer their friends to their bank's Web site. The study also found that users of online banking demonstrate greater bank loyalty and higher cross-sell rates than offline customers. Cross-selling is the selling of a service not related to the service a customer already pays for.

In January 2004, the bank launched its redesigned Web site, developed jointly for Sovereign by Agency. com, Ltd., and Tallán, Inc. Bringing together a decade-old interactive marketing and technology company and an application and systems development firm with 20 years of experience to create a new, easier-to-use site earned Sovereign high marks from industry reviewers. But Sovereign sought to reap deeper rewards from its site in the long-term, as well. So the bank turned to highly specific customer analysis and personas.

A persona is a model archetypical customer representing groups whose members have common needs and goals. Thus, a persona includes particular values and attributes that guide individuals' behavior in the marketplace. Identifying these values and attributes through a combination of behavior and demographic analyses enables vendors not just to better frame their products and services but to determine which ones to offer. By deciphering what drives its customers' behaviors, Sovereign can influence those behaviors.

The bank hired the services of Claritas, a firm that specializes in gleaning knowledge from customer data for marketing purposes. Claritas used the bank's customer database to analyze geographic, demographic, and psychographic information and help the bank build personas. In 2003, shortly before its revamped Web site went live, Sovereign completed its development of four personas. Each persona is built on the occupational, residential, and purchasing attributes of its members.

The personas enable Sovereign to predict its customers' motivations, financial needs, and ways in which the bank can further increase their banking experience. With this new information, the bank can appropriately mold its online presence. Doran-Collins acknowledges that personas, rather than products, dictate the bank's online appearance and conduct. Words and images specifically cater to personas. When a young mother logs on she might see a picture of a young couple with two children on the front lawn of a new house, because young people are likely to want to finance a new home. A couple that plans to retire early might receive a Web page that features a couple in their 50's golfing or relaxing by the pool.

Building on personas to interact with customers, creating customer profiles can reap benefits across and between Sovereign's marketing channels. As soon as a customer logs on to the Web site, the site "knows" which services customers already have and what might interest them. This helps to avoid redundancy in delivering information and improve efforts to cross-sell. The customers enjoy a better Web site experience, and the bank sells more services.

To implement personas, management had to overcome tradition. Traditionally, the marketing people for each product used similar promotions for all customers, and they rarely shared information with the marketers of other products. Marketing with personas in mind forces marketers to share information.

Managers of the various product lines meet regularly with the Web program manager to ensure that all communication and data collection strategies work together rather than as internal competitors. Since adopting the use of personas, Sovereign customers have launched more online applications for additional services and referred more people to Sovereign than before. To enhance its service, the bank provides a chat option on the Web site, so customers can receive help immediately whenever they bank online.

As the personas have proved their worth online, Sovereign plans to use them increasingly to improve mail and e-mail campaigns. The bank sends close to six million pieces of direct mail each year, an effort that costs much money. Reducing mail by better knowing customer needs would save costs. Although e-mailing is not as expensive as mail, it, too, could benefit the bank if optimized along personas' lines. Eventually, management hopes to personalize each letter and e-mail sent to customers.

The bank contracted with Click Tactics, a firm that specializes in using information collected through Web sites for multichannel marketing. The Web site helps collect rich information about customers and their preferences. Combining this information with the four personas, Click Tactics develops marketing campaigns for Sovereign.

Although the information is gleaned mostly from customer interaction with the Web site, the marketing campaigns are not limited to the Web. They are also conducted through other channels, based on customer preferences as expressed at their visits. For example, customers are asked to indicate how they prefer to receive information about short-term investments. If the answer is "by e-mail," this is how information about short-term investment products will be communicated to the customer.

Click Tactics' automated integration of customer information streaming through the Web site also helps Sovereign create different campaign versions to fit each of the four personas. The bank can communicate 50,000 versions of a marketing effort for the same cost of producing 5,000 different versions in its pre-persona days. Instead of focusing so much on production, Sovereign can concentrate more on content, timing, and ideal channel selection. With the use of personas and improved multichannel marketing, response rates to direct mail campaigns have significantly increased. More customers feel that the bank seeks to serve them better rather than simply trying to get as much business from them as possible.

Collecting so much data from the Web site has helped the bank in other ways, too. Because the bank has gained more information about its customers, it has become better prepared to answer their questions and propose solutions to needs previously unacknowledged.

In light of its demonstrable success, Sovereign has plans to add more technologies to the Web site. One is a search engine that supports free-form inquiries. The purpose of such search engines is to help customers find information with their own words rather than go to a FAQ page or engage bank employees with their

inquiries. However, software will capture the questions and analyze them to give the bank better business intelligence about customer interests. Another effort is to use analysis software to localize content presentation at the Web site for customers in different regions.

What happens when the bank has little or no information about visitors to its Web site? Prospective customers, about whom data is limited, and existing customers who do not fit into any of the four personas, receive less personalized Web site information. In other words, if this is your first visit to the site, you might receive a "plain vanilla" Web presentation.

Sources: Mummert, H., "Channeling the Customer," *Catalog Success*, 2005; www.sovereignbank.com, 2005; www.claritas.com, 2005.

Thinking About the Case

1. What is a marketing channel? How does the bank use the Web as a marketing channel?

2. Most of the information that the bank collects about customers is collected at the Web site. Why?

3. How does the Web site help marketing in other channels?

4. Explain what personalized Web presentation is and how the bank uses it for its purposes.

5. The bank intends to install a free-form search engine at the Web site. Apart from helping customers with their searches, how can this help the bank's marketing effort?

6. A growing number of people have added their telephone numbers to "do not call" lists. Do you think this has anything to do with the bank's increased Web efforts?

Your Money Pal

PayPal, based in San Jose, California, was founded in 1998 by Peter Thiel and Max Levchin. PayPal enables parties that trade online to transfer funds for purchases, eliminating the need for paper transactions such as checks or money orders. Yes, many make purchases using credit cards, but many others either do not have a credit card or prefer not to use it online. For these people, PayPal is a convenient solution. PayPal functions as a money transfer service for all, not necessarily for online purchases, but its growing success has been most evident with person-to-person Web commerce, especially in the online auction industry.

PayPal can be likened to an online Western Union Financial Services. Account holders do not have to give

PayPal their money. They designate from which real account they would like money drawn for purchases they make: a checking account, credit card, debit card, or a PayPal account. Web sites that accept PayPal payment present the company's button. When clicked, buyers are taken to their PayPal account, where they instruct how much to pay and to whom. PayPal uses the subscriber's designated financial source to withdraw the money and place it in the seller's PayPal account.

PayPal built its reputation by helping eBay vendors to avoid the risk and time involved with doing business through paper checks. The business was established 3 years after eBay debuted, and its founders recognized that many of the frequent sellers at eBay were too small to qualify for the typical credit-card merchant account. PayPal experienced tremendous growth in the early 2000s and was the single largest competitor to eBay's similar subsidiary service, BillPoint. When eBay acquired PayPal in October 2002 for $1.5 billion, more than 50 percent of the online auctioneer's registered members were PayPal subscribers who preferred to use PayPal for payments. eBay phased out BillPoint and started to promote PayPal's service. PayPal is at present almost "the only game in town." Competitors include BidPay, eCount, and ProPay, but all trail far behind PayPal.

In spite of the strong relationship with eBay, management recognizes that more than 90 percent of global online commerce does not involve the parent company. PayPal has contracted to process payments for Overstock.com and Apple Computer's iTunes Music Store. Additionally, the company has signed exclusive contracts with smaller operations such as Detroit Coffee Co. and Saylor's Pizza. The company is also focusing on international expansion. Since 2004, it has opened local sites in eight countries. The company's goal is to become the sole online payment service.

PayPal has multiple appeals to merchants, beginning with lower fees than those charged by credit-card companies. Almost 50 percent of PayPal members select their bank account as their funding source, so the payees do not have to pay credit-card processing fees. For example, iTunes Music Store has to pay approximately 16 cents in processing fees to its credit-card affiliates on a 99 cent song download, but PayPal charges only 9 cents for the same service.

PayPal promotes its fraud protection to attract customers, claiming that it and eBay have a combined force of over 1,000 employees dedicated specifically to fight fraud. In addition, PayPal has developed its own models for detecting fraud and verifying buyer bank accounts. PayPal estimates that when payments are made through PayPal merchants lose just 0.17 percent of their receipts. This rate is much smaller than the 1.8 percent loss online merchants experience when customers use credit cards.

PayPal's effective branding as an early and trustworthy Internet success has built strong consumer loyalty. The company has already passed American Express in number of accounts. PayPal has more than 71 million accounts around the world. American Express has 65 million. Still, PayPal significantly lags behind Visa International and MasterCard International, Inc., which have 1 billion and 680 million accounts, respectively. Although Visa's 2004 transaction volume of $3 trillion dwarfed PayPal's total of $19 billion, the latter's growth rate of 44 percent per year is faster than Visa's 14 percent.

PayPal uses its lower fees and fraud rates to promote its service as better than that of banks and credit cards. It can offer lower fees because, although members can deposit money in their PayPal accounts, the company is not considered a bank (because it does not offer loans) and therefore is not subject to banking laws. However, while PayPal prides itself as not being a bank, its customers are also not protected with the same standards to which banks are subjected.

Some practices have angered merchant subscribers. For example, when a buyer has a dispute with a seller, the company often withholds funds due to the merchant, without explanation, until the investigation is concluded. The company stops service to the merchant for the duration of the investigation. The company uses this policy to protect customers against fraud.

Sources: Hof, R. D., "PayPal Spreads Its Wings," *BusinessWeek*, May 23, 2005; www.x.com, 2005; http://www.absoluteastronomy.com/encyclopedia/P/Pa/PayPal1.htm, 2005.

Thinking About the Case

1. People who buy or sell at auction Web sites mainly use PayPal. Why?

2. Explain the symbiotic relationship between eBay and PayPal. Why are they so dependent on each other?

3. E-tailers have said that once they contract with PayPal they experience growth in business. What might be the reason for that?

4. Some observers predict that in the future PayPal will issue credit cards of its own. If it does, what will it rely on to promote its credit cards?

9

NINE

Challenges of Global Information Systems

LEARNING OBJECTIVES

A growing number of organizations operate globally or, at least, in more than one geographic market. These organizations face some challenges that have a considerable impact on their information systems. The organizations have to meet the challenge of operating globally by providing international information systems to accommodate the free flow of information both within a single company's divisions and between multinational corporations. These issues are important especially because so many companies operate a Web site, and Web sites are accessible globally.

When you finish this chapter, you will be able to:

- Explain why multinational corporations must use global information systems.

- Provide elementary advice for designing Web sites for an international audience.

- Cite the cultural, legal, and other challenges to implementing international information systems.

IT FITS OUTFITS:
Expanding Globally

Jun Kaui, Director of Manufacturing for It Fits Outfits, turned away from his computer and put his head in his hands. A moment later, his cell phone rang. It was Shari Steiner, his old friend and CEO. "I've got news," Jun said. An hour later, they were sitting at a table in Cuppa Joe, the coffee shop where they had first met.

Global Connections

Shari Steiner had studied design at the Fashion Institute of Technology in New York City and later designed clothing for many different companies. When she decided to open her own retail chain, she turned to Jun Kaui. As a designer, she had interfaced very little with the manufacturing end of the textile business. Jun had been a business major and his father had managed textile mills in Asia. He had the experience necessary to contact, evaluate, and contract with textile factories. Jun also spoke fluent Mandarin and this made it possible for It Fits Outfits to use Chinese textile factories to manufacture outfits based on Shari's design. Manufacturing clothing was cheaper in China, but a far more complicated process. With Jun's language skills, business experience, and personal contacts, they were able to establish relationships with reliable manufacturers and jump through the bureaucratic hoops involved in exporting the goods from China to the United States.

The News

"Remember in January," Jun said, "when the World Trade Organization's export quotas were lifted and the textile factories were free to increase exports? Well, the textile industries in the European Union and the U.S. became very unhappy about that. They didn't want to lose business to China – understandably. However, in response to U.S. pressure, the Chinese government just increased export taxes by 400 percent."

Shari leaned forward. "So, what can we expect?"

"If their profit margins plummet, some of our manufacturers will close – and maybe quite suddenly. Others might try to pass the cost on to us."

"Depending on how much it is, passing the cost onto us might be doable. Unexpected closings would be a disaster." Shari leaned back. "What do we do?"

"Order lunch," Jun smiled.

Analyzing the Impact of the Chinese Tariff Hike

Over the next two days, Jun and his staff read and analyzed the reports coming out of China. Seventy-four products were to be affected by the hike. They needed to find out which of their manufacturers would be subject to the rate increase. For each manufacturer, would the hike squeeze out enough of their profit so that they would be forced to close shop? If the manufacturers passed this expense onto foreign retailers, would It Fits Outfits be able to afford to remain with the manufacturer?

After a careful analysis, Jun determined that the hardest hit would be the cotton shirt manufacturers. The tariff was to go into effect June 1. By August and September, many manufacturers would be forced to close. It Fits Outfits would have to consider looking for cotton shirt manufacturers outside of China.

Considering Alternatives

"We need to brace ourselves," Jun told his team. Fortunately, Jun was in a much better position to look elsewhere than he would have been four years earlier when Shari had first persuaded him to come aboard. At that point, he had contacts only in China and Asia. Today, he knew people in the textile industry from all over the world. The global textile market had turned to the Internet to facilitate trade. Business-to-business Web portals reported the latest textile news on the national and international scene. A company in the states or the EU could bid on a shipment of jeans produced in Bahrain or Indonesia. Retailers could review textile manufacturer directories from all over the world. They could then make contact and visit the facilities. National consulting businesses could help retailers deal with the legal issues of exporting the goods.

Still, a number of obstacles would need to be overcome if It Fits Outfits moved out of China. Jun and his team would have to bridge language and cultural differences, study tariff laws and export legislation, and keep an eye on political and economic factors that could influence the industry.

Back at Cuppa Joe a week after the tariff hike had been announced, Jun explained to Shari, "In the short term, I'm going to check out a couple of manufacturers in the states. It would be expensive, but it'll cover us if our cotton shirt manufacturers close down at the end of the summer. In the long term, we're looking into Bangladesh. They've decided not to continue cash incentives to the industry, so the market should be stable – at least for a while."

Shari smiled. "Until the next crisis…." Then she looked at Jun seriously. "You realize your proactive approach to tackling potential manufacturing problems keeps our company stable in the short term and the long term."

"You're welcome." Jun smiled, "Do you think you're grateful enough to split that chocolate éclair?"

MULTINATIONAL ORGANIZATIONS

An increasing number of the world's corporations have branched into countries all over the globe, becoming true multinationals. While they might have headquarters in a single country, they operate divisions and subsidiaries in different countries to take advantage of local benefits. For instance, a company might establish engineering facilities in countries that offer large pools of qualified engineers, build production lines in countries that can supply inexpensive labor, and open sales offices in countries that are strategically situated for effective marketing.

Because of this spread of operations, a company's nationality is not always obvious. For example, consider IBM and Philips. While IBM is known as an "American" corporation because its headquarters and most of its research activities are in the United States, the company has numerous subsidiaries in other countries. These subsidiaries are registered and operate under the laws of the respective countries, and they employ local workers. Likewise, not many Americans realize that Philips' headquarters is in the Netherlands and that it owns one of the largest U.S. sellers of electric razors, Norelco. Similarly, Intel, an American company, has major research and development facilities in Israel, where some of its latest microprocessors have been developed.

One hundred of the 500 largest Canadian companies have majority U.S. ownership, and 90 percent of U.S. multinational companies have Canadian offices. Japanese companies own whole U.S. subsidiaries in every imaginable industry. British companies have the largest foreign investment in the United States. Thanks to the North American Free Trade Agreement (NAFTA) and agreements between the United States and the European Union, we might witness the internationalization of many more American, Canadian, Mexican, and European corporations.

Multinational corporations must use **global information systems**, which are systems that serve organizations and individuals in multiple countries. These companies might have unified policies throughout their organizations, but they still have to abide by the laws of the countries in which each unit operates, and be sensitive to other local aspects of their interaction with other businesses as well as consumers. Therefore, unlike organizations that operate in a single country, multinational companies have the burden of ensuring that their information systems and the information flowing through the systems conform to laws, cultures, standards, and other elements that are specific to countries or regions.

THE WEB AND INTERNATIONAL COMMERCE

 The emergence of the Web as a global medium for information exchange has made it an important vehicle for both business-to-business (B2B) and business-to-consumer (B2C) commerce. In 2004, more than 888 million people regularly logged on to the Internet across the globe. About two-thirds of them come from non-English-speaking countries, as Figure 9.1 shows, and more than half of all e-commerce revenues come from these countries. The ratio of non-English speakers to English speakers has steadily grown over the years.

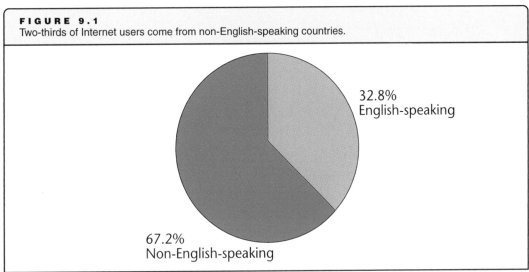

FIGURE 9.1
Two-thirds of Internet users come from non-English-speaking countries.

32.8%
English-speaking

67.2%
Non-English-speaking

Source: Internet World Stats (www.internetworldstats.com)

The spread of Internet use opens enormous opportunities for businesses the world over. Some of the countries with current low participation rates have the greatest potential, such as China. About 87 million Chinese logged on in 2005, but more than a billion Chinese might do so in the future, and the Chinese market is expected one day to be the world's largest in terms of consumer spending.

POINT OF INTEREST

Low Penetration

In 2005, the world population was estimated at 6.4 billion people. About 13.9 percent of the population used the Internet on a regular basis. Africa is second only to Asia in population size, with 900.5 million people. Yet, only 13.5 million of Africa's inhabitants (1.5 percent) used the Internet regularly. In contrast, 67.4 percent of the inhabitants of North America used the Internet regularly.

Source: www.internetworldstats.com.

The Web offers opportunities not only to increase revenue but also to save on costs. Consider, for example, how much money is saved when instead of printing product and service manuals on paper and shipping them to customers, companies publish them on the Web, ready to be downloaded at a user's convenience. Furthermore, imagine the convenience if the manuals were prepared not only using hypertext and graphics but also animation for easier and more informative use. Some companies place video clips to instruct buyers how to assemble the products they purchased. Many companies have stopped enclosing manuals with their retail products. They invite you to log on to their Web site and peruse the product's manual in your own language. This saves not only paper and printing but also much of the labor involved in customer service. By placing maintenance manuals in multiple languages on their Web sites, some companies cut as much as 50 percent of their customer service costs.

Organizations that wish to do business globally through their Web sites must be sensitive to local audiences. Thus Web sites should be tailored to the audiences they are meant to reach. A majority of Web users prefer to access the Web using a language other than English, so organizations must provide their online information and services in other languages, as well as English. As Figure 9.2 shows, organizations must plan and carefully design their global sites so that they also cater to local needs and preferences, a process sometimes called **glocalization**.

FIGURE 9.2
Imperatives to heed when designing Web sites for an international audience

Plan	Plan the site before you develop it. A site for an international audience requires more planning than a national one.
Learn the Preferences	Learn the cultural preferences, convention differences, and legal issues, or use experts who know these preferences. Tailor each local site (or the local section of your site) to the way in which the local people prefer to shop, buy, and pay.
Translate Properly	Use local interpreters to translate content for local audiences. Do not use software or other automated methods, unless humans review the translated material. Experienced translators are attentive to contemporary nuances and connotations.
Be Egalitarian	Do not let any audience feel as if it is less important than other audiences. Keep all local sections of your site updated and with the same level of information and services.
Avoid Cultural Imperialism	If the local language or cultural has a word or picture for communicating an idea, use it; do not use those of your own country. Give the local audience a homey experience.

Glocalization is a combination of universal business models and management philosophy with some adaptations for local audiences. One example of an organization that glocalizes is McDonald's. While the restaurant chain's logo and many other features are the same throughout the world, it makes some menu changes to appeal to local palates. Sometimes, other elements are changed. For example, in France, the restaurant chain replaced its familiar Ronald McDonald mascot with Asterix the Gaul, a popular French comic book character. Much like the presence of a global restaurant chain, Web sites are present everywhere someone can link to the Web. Therefore, Web site designers must keep glocalization in mind.

Think Globally, Act Locally

Marketing experts often advise companies that operate internationally to "think globally, act locally." Acting locally means being sensitive to regional customs and language nuances. When interest in the company's business increases, especially from consumers, it is advisable to open a local office and let a local team handle both the Web site and fulfillment operations. Recall that fulfillment in online business includes picking, packing, and shipping. When most of the business comes from one country or region, the business, its Web site, and its information systems are managed centrally, but when a growing proportion of transactions take place in other regions, businesses find that they must decentralize control.

Thinking globally and acting locally might sound like contradictory ideas, but they are not. Recall our discussion of strategies in Chapter 2. Thinking globally has to do with the company's strategic planning. It involves decisions such as product lines and business alliances. However, the same strategy can be followed with a local flavor. For example, the same product, in whose design and production the company holds a competitive advantage, can be packaged and advertised with local motifs. The local branch of the company might still recruit the engineers with the same excellent qualifications as those of their peers in other countries but apply different interview tactics and social benefits, which fit the customs and holidays of that country.

Why You Should...

Learn About Challenges of Global ISs

By default, every business that establishes a Web site in some way uses a global information system. Multinational corporations have used global information systems many years before the advent of the Web. They used private international banking systems and other EDI systems. All businesses can benefit from the use of global ISs, but they also face challenges. Neglecting to pay attention to such issues as different cultures, language nuances, conflicting national laws, and different standards can hurt the business's reputation and cause loss of revenue. Professionals who work for companies that conduct international business or for organizations that might do so in the future must be aware of the challenges involved in designing Web sites and using ISs for international trade.

CHALLENGES OF GLOBAL INFORMATION SYSTEMS

While the Web offers great opportunities for establishing international ISs, global ISs are not without their challenges, both for B2B and B2C commerce. Some of the challenges that businesses must address are technological barriers, regulations and tariffs, electronic payment mechanisms, different languages and cultures of the audiences, economic and political considerations, different measurement and notation standards, legal barriers, and different time zones. These challenges are discussed in the following sections.

Technological Challenges

Not all countries have adequate information technology infrastructures to allow resident companies to build international ISs. International ISs, especially those using the Web, often incorporate graphics to convey technical or business information, and those applications, as well as interactive software, require increasingly fast (broadband) communication lines. The bandwidth available in some countries, such as China, is too narrow for high-volume transmission of graphically and animation-rich Web pages. Thus, companies might have to offer two versions of their sites, one for wide bandwidth and another for narrow bandwidth. Often, companies use one site, but provide the same content in both graphically rich and text-only pages, or the same video for download at different speeds.

> ### POINT OF INTEREST
>
> #### Let's Get Along Better
> The Global Business Dialogue on Electronic Commerce (GBDe) is a worldwide organization of chief executive officers. Its purpose is to help develop global policies regarding international online commerce. Established in 1999, the organization has provided recommendations in areas such as broadband service, consumer confidence, Internet security, intellectual property rights, spam, and electronic payments. Many of the recommendations have been incorporated into the laws of some countries. You can read more about the organization and its efforts at *www.gbde.org*.

Businesses that cater to international audiences must "glocalize" their Web sites.

Another technological challenge has to do with language. You might recall the earlier discussion of how characters are represented by bytes in computers. This setup is fine for languages with up to 256 (2^8) characters, such as English and other languages whose alphabetic root is Latin. But eight-bit bytes are not sufficient for languages with larger numbers of characters, such as Chinese. The solution for this obstacle is to ensure that computers can use Unicode, with double-byte characters—allowing for up to 65,536 (2^{16}) characters. However, if only the servers are programmed to accommodate Unicode, while the other systems (such as databases and applications on computers interacting with the servers) work with single-byte characters, then these back-end systems will record and display gibberish. Thus, entire systems must be reprogrammed or use special conversion software. As computers convert to operating systems that support Unicode, displaying different character sets should be less of a problem.

Other points that might sound trivial can also wreak havoc in international ISs or prevent individuals and companies in some world regions from transacting with companies that did not make their Web sites and applications flexible. For example, fields such as telephone numbers should be set for variable length, because the number of digits in telephone numbers varies by country. Many sites still offer forms that limit telephone numbers to 10 digits and do not accept shorter or longer numbers even when they are meant for audiences outside the United States and Canada. Similarly, postal codes are organized differently in different countries and are not called zip codes, and yet some U.S. sites are still designed with only a 5-digit (or extended 9-digit) postal code field.

Regulations and Tariffs

Countries have different regulations on what may or may not be imported and which tariff applies to which imported product. While many executives know they might be missing out on great deals with overseas businesses, they are afraid that exploring international opportunities would entail too many hassles. They are also afraid that even with the proper research, employees might not know how to comply with the laws of destination countries, let alone calculate how much the organization would have to pay in taxes, tariffs, custom duties, and other levies on exported or imported goods.

Companies such as NextLinx help exporters and importers who use the Web for commerce. The NextLinx software is integrated with a company's ERP systems and Web site. When a business from another country places an order, the information—such as type of item and destination country—is captured by the software, and an export manager can see how much the company will have to pay in tariffs, receive an estimate of how long the goods will stay in the seaport or airport before they are released from customs, and, if the manager wishes, also receive information on regulations, license required, shipping companies in the destination country, and other useful information. Since the software is linked to the Web, it is continuously updated and provides useful information immediately. The software also calculates, on the fly, the total cost of delivering the goods to the buyer's door. It also provides more than 100 forms that exporters can fill out and save electronically. The logistics component of the application offers

shipping options with land, sea, and air carriers; books shipping space; and tracks shipping status. Several studies have shown that U.S. companies have turned away about 80 percent of online orders that come from other countries because they are not familiar with export regulations. This service can expedite the process.

Differences in Payment Mechanisms

One of the greatest expectations of e-commerce is easy payment for what we buy online. Credit cards are very common in North America and are the way businesses prefer to be paid online. However, this practice is not widespread in other regions of the world. The high rate of stolen credit cards, especially in Eastern Europe, attaches risk to such payments and deters potential online customers. Also, most Europeans prefer to use debit cards rather than credit cards. (The holder of a debit card must maintain a bank account from which the purchase is immediately deducted; the holder of a credit card receives a grace period of up to a month and pays the credit-card issuer in any way he or she prefers.) Americans are more willing to give credit-card details via the Web than people from other nations. Until citizens of other countries become willing to do so, payment through the Web, and therefore B2C trade, will not reach its full potential.

Americans pay with credit cards in 20 percent of all transactions and in almost all of online transactions. In Japan, on the other hand, only 8 percent of transactions involve credit cards, and most Japanese are reluctant to use credit cards for online purchases. This calls for a different mechanism of payment. In Japan, many people who order merchandise online prefer to pick it up at convenience stores called "konbini," and pay there for what they purchased. Since shipping companies are reluctant to leave parcels unattended when the recipient is not home, the alliance of e-tailers and konbini affords not only payment confidence but also convenience. E-tailers from other countries who want to operate in Japan must be aware of these preferences.

Language Differences

To communicate internationally, parties must agree on a common language, and that can create problems. For instance, data might not be transmittable internationally in real time because the information must first be translated (usually by human beings). Although some computer applications can translate "on the fly," they are far from perfect. Another hurdle is that national laws usually forbid businesses to run accounting and other systems in a foreign language, leading to an awkward and expensive solution: running these systems in two languages, the local one and English, which is the *de facto* international language.

Companies that are in the forefront of Web-based e-commerce have translated their original Web sites into local languages. They localize their sites by creating a dedicated site for each national audience. But translation can be tricky. For instance, the Taiwanese use the traditional set of Chinese characters, but people in the People's Republic of China prefer the simplified character set. Spanish terms in Spain might be different from those in Latin America. In addition, mere linguistic translation might not capture cultural sensitivities. Therefore, some companies prefer to leave Web design and translation to their local overseas offices.

Several companies, such as TRADOS Inc., offer translation software and services to companies involved in global commerce. TRADOS' software package by the same name translates Web pages into many languages, including those requiring special characters such as Hindi, Chinese, Greek, and Hebrew, but also ensures consistency of terms and sentence structure in different languages. When Web pages are translated, the software ensures that the XML tags and statements are retained from the original languages, so that the company maintaining the Web site can continue to use the same XML code for online transactions with companies and shoppers in its new markets. Other tools translate MS-Word documents to multiple languages. One such tool is Wordfast.

Cultural Differences

Cultural differences refer in general to the many ways in which people from different countries vary in their tastes, gestures, preferred colors, treatment of people of certain gender or age, attitudes about work, opinions about different ethical issues, and the like. ISs might challenge cultural traditions by imposing the culture of one nation upon another (cultural imperialism). Conservative groups in some countries have complained about the "Americanization" of their young generations. Governments might be inclined to forbid the reception of some information for reasons of undesirable cultural influence. An example of such fear is the French directive against use of foreign words in government-supported mass media and official communications. A similar example is the ban by the Canadian province of Quebec on the use of non-French words in business signs. These fears have intensified with the growth of the Internet and use of the Web. Because the Internet was invented and first developed in the United States and is still used by a greater percentage of Americans compared with any other single nation, its predominant culture is American.

As mentioned previously, companies that use the Web for business must learn cultural differences and design their sites accordingly. Web designers need to be sensitive to cultural differences. People might be offended by the use of certain images, colors, and words. For example, black has sinister connotations in Europe, Asia, and Latin America; the index-finger-to-thumb sign of approval is a rude gesture meaning "jackass" in Brazil; the thumbs-up sign is a rude gesture in Latin America, as is the waving hand in Arab countries; and pictures of women with exposed arms or legs are offensive in many Muslim countries.

Conflicting Economic, Scientific, and Security Interests

The goal of corporate management is to seize a large market share and maximize its organization's profits. The goal of a national government is to protect the economic, scientific, and security interests of its people. Scientific information is both an important national resource and a great source of income for foreign corporations, so occasionally those interests conflict.

For instance, companies that design and manufacture weapons have technical drawings and specifications that are financially valuable to the company but also valuable to the security of their country. Hence, many governments, including the U.S. federal government, do not allow the exchange of weapon designs. Transfer of military information to another country, even if the receiving party is part of an American business, is prohibited. Often, products whose purpose has nothing to do with the military are included in the list of prohibited trade items, because of the fear that they could be converted for use against the country of origin. In recent years, the list has included some software packages. The result is that, although American divisions of a company can use such software, their sister divisions in other countries cannot.

Consider some of the encryption applications offered by software developers. When Phil Zimmermann, developer of PGP (Pretty Good Privacy), offered this encryption application for free downloading, he was faced with federal criminal charges and severe penalties. His purpose was to allow individuals and companies to scramble their communications via computer networks. Companies use such software to protect corporate information. However, strong encryption methods are on the U.S. federal government's list of restricted exports because, like weapons, they could compromise America's national security. Under public pressure, the government dropped the charges. In 2001, when it was found that the 9/11 terrorists used the software to encrypt their communication, Zimmermann expressed regret.

Some nations are afraid that cross-border information flow promotes cultural imperialism.

© Getty Images

Another problem that arises with international information interchange is that countries treat trade secrets, patents, and copyrights differently. Sometimes business partners are reluctant to transfer documents when one partner is in a country that restricts intellectual property rights, while another is in a country that has laws to protect intellectual property. On the other hand, the employees of a division of a multinational corporation might be able to divulge information locally with impunity. Intellectual property is tightly protected in the United States and Western Europe, and American trade negotiators and diplomats have pressured some countries to pass and enforce similar laws. Reportedly, the legislatures of several Asian nations have passed such laws or have revised existing laws in response to U.S. pressure.

Political Challenges

Information is power. Some countries fear that a policy of free access to information could threaten their sovereignty. For instance, a nation's government might believe that access to certain data, such as the location and quantity of natural resources, might give other nations an opportunity to control an indigenous resource, thereby gaining a business advantage that would adversely affect the resource-rich country's political interests.

Governments are also increasingly recognizing software as an important economic resource, leading some countries to dictate that companies operating within their borders must purchase software from within their borders. For example, until 1997, Brazil's authorities allowed local businesses to purchase software from other countries only after demonstrating that the software was not available domestically. The rule was enforced even if the business was owned by a foreign company. These policies can hinder standardization and compatibility of international ISs by preventing use of the same software throughout a multinational corporation.

As mentioned in Chapter 5, however, the recent trend in less rich countries is to adopt free open source software to avoid high costs. National governments in South America as well as local governments in Asia and Europe have adopted policies of using only open source software whenever it is available. Global corporations must ensure compatibility with the software adopted by governments and corporations in such locales.

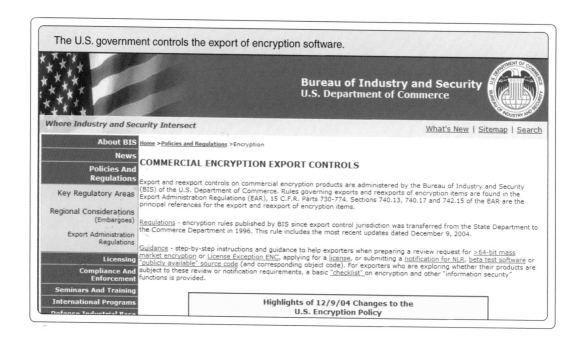

The U.S. government controls the export of encryption software.

Bureau of Industry and Security
U.S. Department of Commerce

Where Industry and Security Intersect

What's New | Sitemap | Search

About BIS
News
Policies And Regulations
Key Regulatory Areas
Regional Considerations (Embargoes)
Export Administration Regulations
Licensing
Compliance And Enforcement
Seminars And Training
International Programs
Defense Industrial Base

Home >Policies and Regulations >Encryption

COMMERCIAL ENCRYPTION EXPORT CONTROLS

Export and reexport controls on commercial encryption products are administered by the Bureau of Industry and Security (BIS) of the U.S. Department of Commerce. Rules governing exports and reexports of encryption items are found in the Export Administration Regulations (EAR), 15 C.F.R. Parts 730-774. Sections 740.13, 740.17 and 742.15 of the EAR are the principal references for the export and reexport of encryption items.

Regulations - encryption rules published by BIS since export control jurisdiction was transferred from the State Department to the Commerce Department in 1996. This rule includes the most recent updates dated December 9, 2004.

Guidance - step-by-step instructions and guidance to help exporters when preparing a review request for >64-bit mass market encryption or License Exception ENC, applying for a license, or submitting a notification for NLR, beta test software or "publicly available" source code (and corresponding object code). For exporters who are exploring whether their products are subject to these review or notification requirements, a basic "checklist" on encryption and other "information security" functions is provided.

Highlights of 12/9/04 Changes to the
U.S. Encryption Policy

POINT OF INTEREST

Collaborating with the Censors

Companies that wish to do business in a large market where political interests limit freedom of speech often yield to government pressure. Microsoft Corp. cooperates with China's government in censoring the company's Chinese-language Web portal. The company's policy of cooperation affects blogs. It works with the authorities to omit certain forbidden language. Bloggers are not allowed to post words such as "democracy," "human rights," and "Taiwan independence." Attempts to enter such words generate a message notifying the blogger that such language is forbidden. Several groups have tried to pressure executives at Microsoft, Yahoo!, Google, Cisco Systems, and other companies to urge the Chinese government for reforms on free expression, but free speech is no match for the economic interest of these companies. China's estimated online population is 87 million, second only to the United States.

Source: Woodward, C., "Microsoft Censors Blogs at Chinese Portal," *The Associated Press*, June 13, 2005.

Companies must also be aware of limits that some governments impose on Internet use. China, Singapore, and many Arab countries impose restrictions on what their citizens can download, view, and read. Free speech is not a universal principle. In practical terms, this means that executives might want to rephrase or cut out some content from their Web sites or risk their sites being blocked by some governments. This is an especially sensitive issue if a company enables employees or customers to use blogs at its Web site, in which they express their personal opinions.

Different Standards

Differences in standards must be considered when integrating ISs internationally, even within the same company. Because nations use different standards and rules in their daily business operations, sometimes records within one company are incompatible. For instance, the book-keeping records of one division of a multinational company might be incompatible with the records of other divisions and headquarters. As another example, the United States still uses the English system of weights and measures (inches, feet, miles, quarts, pounds, and so on), while the

Legal Jurisdictions in Cyberspace

Imagine: you surf the Web and come across a virulent site that preaches hatred and violence. You file a complaint in court, but the court cannot do anything because the site is maintained in another country that does not uphold your country's law. Or, you shop on the Web and purchase an item from a site that is physically maintained on a server in another country. When you receive the item, you discover that it is of a lower quality than promised. When you contact the site, the owners are rude and unresponsive. You decide to sue, but under which country's laws? These problems are two examples of the legal challenges in today's electronic global markets.

- **Global Free Speech.** In the spring of 2000, the International League against Racism and Anti-Semitism (LICRA), the Movement against Racism (MRAP), and the Union of French Jewish Students (UEFJ) filed a lawsuit against the American Internet company Yahoo! in a French court. The organizations complained that Yahoo!'s auctioning of more than 1,200 Nazi-related items amounted to "banalization of Nazism," which violates French law. The Nazi items offered for sale on the site included everything from Nazi flags and uniforms to belt buckles and medals. In November 2000, Judge Gomez ruled that a French court had jurisdiction over Yahoo! for violations that occur within France. He ordered Yahoo! to block French citizens' access to auctions of Nazi items within 3 months or face a fine of 15,000 Euros ($13,000 at the time) per day.

  Like many global e-commerce sites, Yahoo! did not require its Webmasters to maintain a dedicated site for each language. French users merely saw a customized overlay using the main Yahoo! pages that are viewed by all visitors. This technique has enabled Yahoo! to offer country-specific and language-specific versions of its site at relatively low cost. Yahoo! screened out the items from its French site, but this did not satisfy the court because French citizens could still view the items via the general site.

  To countries that have been subjected to a ruthless occupation, free speech is less important than preventing offenses such as "banalization of Nazism." In the United States, however, free speech is legally protected even when we dislike someone's opinion or trade of objects that we find offensive. Yahoo! decided to remove such items from all its servers but also received a California court decision that nullifies the decisions of non-U.S. courts regarding U.S. firms.

Consider this situation: a ruling against a company registered in India by a court in Germany, and an appeal in a court in India of a court decision made under the laws of Germany. This legal tangle is the result of doing business globally. More than one law might govern a business practice or communication of ideas. The legal environment used to be confined to national boundaries, and jurisdiction used to refer to a territory. No longer so. Now the "territory" is cyberspace. It is difficult to define jurisdictions in cyberspace. The lingering question is, "Whose law applies?"

- **Consumer Protection by Whom?** Where can consumers sue for e-commerce transactions gone wrong? Suppose you purchased an item from a site located in another country, and the item has a defect or arrived after the time promised. Because your request for compensation or another remedy has not been answered satisfactorily, you decide to sue the e-tailer. Where do you file the lawsuit? Your own country? The e-tailer's country? The venue of e-commerce lawsuits is still undecided in many parts of the world.

  In November 2000, the European Union (EU) passed a law that lets consumers file lawsuits against an online business in any of the member countries composing the EU. Before the amendment to the 1968 Brussels Convention (which regulates commercial-legal issues in the Union), consumers could sue an online business only in courts in the country of the online business. Now, if a Web site has directed its business at consumers in a certain country, the consumers can sue the Web site's owner in their own national courts. Businesses vehemently opposed the move, but consumer advocates said people would be more confident about online shopping if they knew they could get redress in their local courts.

- **Two Approaches to Jurisdiction.** As you have seen, the issue of e-commerce jurisdiction is broad. The U.S. Federal Trade Commission and European government organizations have examined the issue in an attempt to reach an international agreement such as the one reached within the EU.

  There are two approaches to such agreement. One approach is the *country-of-origin* principle, whereby all legal matters are confined to the country from which the site operates. Under this principle, the laws of that country apply to the operations and conduct of the site and whoever interacts with the site, regardless of their own location. Therefore, a lawsuit could be brought only in the country of the Web site and would be adjudicated according to that country's laws. Under this principle it is likely many firms would opt to establish Web sites in countries with lax consumer protection laws.

The other approach is the *country-of-destination* principle, whereby the laws of the country to which the site caters apply regarding dealings with the site, regardless of the site's country. The EU adopted this approach within its territory. It might take several years until there is international agreement on e-commerce jurisdiction.

rest of the world (including England) officially uses the metric system (centimeters, meters, liters, kilograms, and the like). There are also different standards for communicating dates, times, temperatures, and addresses. The United States uses the format of month, day, year, while the rest of the world records dates in the format of day, month, year. A date recorded as 10/12/08 might be misinterpreted. The United States uses a 12-hour time notation with the addition of a.m. or p.m., while other parts of the world use a 24-hour notation (called "military time" in the United States because the U.S. military uses this notation). The United States uses Fahrenheit temperatures, while other countries use Celsius temperatures. Americans communicate addresses in the format of street number, street name, and city name. Citizens of some other countries communicate addresses in the format of street name, street number, and city name.

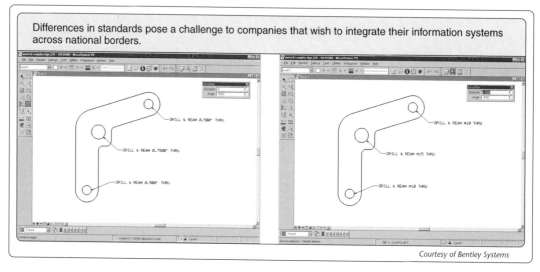

Differences in standards pose a challenge to companies that wish to integrate their information systems across national borders.

Courtesy of Bentley Systems

Using different standards can be extremely costly. In 1999, NASA lost track of a spacecraft that it sent to Mars. Reportedly, an investigation found that an error in a transfer of information between the Mars Climate Orbiter team in Colorado and the mission navigation team in California led to the spacecraft's loss. Apparently, one team used English units, and the other used metric units for a key spacecraft operation. The information was critical to the maneuvers required to place the spacecraft in the proper Mars orbit. The cost to U.S. taxpayers was $125 million.

Companies that want to operate globally must adapt their ISs to changing formal or *de facto* standards. In recent years the growing number of countries joining the European Union (EU) imparted significant power to this bloc. Corporations in non-EU countries have grown accustomed to adapting their systems to those of the EU. For example, in 1976, Europeans adopted the 13-digit **European Article Number (EAN)**, while American companies used the 12-digit **Universal Product Code (UPC)**. The additional bar in the EAN bar code identifies the product's country of origin. For seven years the American **Uniform Code Council (UCC)** promoted the use of the European standard. In 2004, the organization officially adopted it.

Retailers embarked on a hectic effort to modify information systems to recognize, record, and process UPCs of 13 bars instead of 12 bars so they could meet the January 2005 deadline. Most bar-code readers could already read the extra bar, but the software in back-office systems—such as sales, shipping, receiving, and accounting systems—had to be modified. Best Buy, the large electronics and appliance retailer, spent 25,000 hours of staff and hired consultant time to ensure that cash registers, several software applications, and databases could process and store the extra digit.

The UCC is trying to expand product codes to 14-digit **Global Trade Item Numbers (GTINs)**. This code is large enough to identify more than 100 times the number of products and manufacturers that the 12-digit UPCs could. GTINs are designed to support global supply chains. Eventually, manufacturers and retailers might have to use either GTINs or another standard of larger codes embedded in RFID tags. The major push for using RFID tags is taking place in the United States, and American standards could expand to Europe and the rest of the world.

Legal Barriers

The fact that countries have different laws has a great impact on global business in general, and on e-commerce in particular. The differing laws can pose serious challenges to international transfer of data, free speech, and the location of legal proceedings when disputes arise between buyer and seller.

Privacy Laws

Although many of the challenges involved in cross-border data transfer have been resolved through international agreements, one remains unresolved: respect for individual privacy in the conduct of international business. Interestingly, despite the importance attached to privacy, that value is not even mentioned in the constitutions of the United States and many other countries. Nonetheless, a majority of the democratic nations try to protect individual privacy.

POINT OF INTEREST

International Hall of Shame

Privacy International (PI) is an international organization that monitors governments and commercial organizations around the world for violations of privacy. Each year, the members and affiliated organizations of PI present the "Big Brother" awards to the government and private sector organizations in their countries that have done the most to threaten personal privacy in their countries. By 2005, more than 40 ceremonies had been held in 16 countries and hundreds of awards had been given out to some of the most powerful government agencies, individuals, and corporations in those countries. A "lifetime menace" award is also presented. To counterbalance the shameful awards, PI also gives awards to individuals and organizations that have made an outstanding contribution to the protection of privacy. You can read more about it at www.privacyinternational.org/bba.

Countries differ in their approaches to the issue of privacy, as reflected in their laws. Some are willing to forgo some privacy for the sake of a freer flow of information and better marketing. Others restrict any collection of personal data without the consent of the individual.

Data protection laws from various countries can be generally described by three different criteria:

- Whether the law applies to the collection and treatment of data by the private sector (companies), the public sector (governments), or by both.
- Whether the laws apply to manual data, to automated data, or to both.
- Whether data protected under the law are only those concerning human beings or those concerning both human and "legal" entities (that is, organizations).

Except for the U.S. and Canadian privacy acts, privacy laws apply to both the public and private sectors; that is, government and private organizations are subject to the same regulation of collection, maintenance, and disclosure of personal data. More than half the laws (including U.S. federal statutes) encompass manual and computerized record-keeping systems. Denmark, Austria, and Luxembourg are among the countries that protect the privacy of some types of corporations.

Countries that support protection of corporate data argue that it is difficult to separate data about individuals from data on business activities involving or performed by individuals, especially with small businesses. For example, the financial information of a small business also reveals financial information about the people involved with and/or running the business. Furthermore, a large corporation might unfairly compete against a smaller firm if it has access to the smaller firm's data.

The European Union (EU) enforces a privacy law called the Directive on Data Privacy. The EU defines personal data as "any information relating to an identified or identifiable natural person; an identifiable person is one who can be identified, directly or indirectly, in particular by reference to an identification number or to one or more factors specific to his physical, physiological, mental, economic, cultural, or social identity." Some of the principles of the directive are in stark contrast to the practices of U.S. businesses and therefore limit the free flow of personal data between the United States and the EU. For example, consider the following provisions and how they conflict with U.S. practices:

- Personal data can be collected only for specified, explicit, and legitimate purposes and not further processed in a way incompatible with those purposes. However, in the United States, businesses often collect data from people without having to tell them how the data will be used. Many U.S. corporations use personal data for purposes other than the original one, and many organizations purchase personal data from other organizations, so subjects do not even know that the data is used, let alone for what purpose. Obviously, these activities would not be allowed under the EU directive.

- Personal data can be processed only if the subject has given unambiguous consent or under other specific circumstances that the directive provides. Such circumstances are not required by American laws. In the United States, private organizations are allowed to process personal data without the subject's consent, and for practically any purpose.

- Individuals or organizations that receive personal data (the directive calls them "controllers") not directly from the subject must identify themselves to the subject. In the United States, many organizations purchase personal data from third parties and never notify the subject.

- People have the right to obtain from controllers "without constraint at reasonable intervals and without excessive delay or expense" confirmation that data about them are processed, to whom the data is disclosed, and the source that provided the data. They are also entitled to receive information on the "logic involved in any automatic processing of data concerning" them at least in the case of automated decision making. Decision making, practically speaking, means using decision-support systems and expert systems to make decisions on hiring, credit extension, admittance to educational institutions, and so forth. None of these rights is mandated by any U.S. law.

- People have the right to object, "on request and free of charge," to the processing of personal data for the purpose of direct marketing, or to be informed before personal data is disclosed for the first time to third parties or used for direct marketing. Furthermore, controllers must expressly offer the right to object free of charge to disclosure of personal data to others. American companies use personal data *especially* for direct marketing, never tell subjects that they obtain data about them from third parties, and rarely offer subjects the right to object to disclosure of such data to other parties.

American companies are very busy collecting, buying, and selling personal data for decision-making and marketing purposes. The American view is that such practices are essential to efficient business operations, especially in marketing and extension of credit. Thus, this huge discrepancy between the European and American approaches does not allow unrestricted flow of information.

The EU directive is only a framework within which member states may maintain their own, more restrictive, laws. Consider, for example, the French law, which states, "An individual shall not be subject to an administrative or private decision involving an assessment of conduct which has, as its sole basis, the automatic processing of personal data defining his profile or personality." This provision limits the use of a computer as a decision aid in certain circumstances. For instance, this law forbids automatic decisions for credit applications or admittance to a college. While the latter decision is often accompanied by human intervention, the former is often automated in the United States and other countries.

The EU directive recognizes that countries outside the EU use personal data that are transferred from the EU. It therefore provides that when a "third country does not ensure an adequate level of protection within the meaning of [the directive], member states shall take the measures necessary to prevent any transfer of data of the same type to the third country." This provision has created an interesting situation: agents of the European Data Protection Authorities (DPAs) arrive at least monthly in the United States to monitor American companies that process personal data of European citizens to ensure that the EU Directive on Data Protection is obeyed regarding these citizens. These representatives monitor the ISs of companies such as Visa, MasterCard, American Express, and other credit-card issuers. Companies that want to do business in EU member states must accept the restrictions of the directive on their practices. Business leaders on both continents hope that a way can be found to bridge the gap between the two approaches to data privacy, but it seems that a legal solution will not come before a change in culture.

In the meantime, a practical solution has been sponsored by the U.S. federal government. The EU agreed that the U.S. Department of Commerce could establish a **Safe Harbor**, an arrangement for U.S. companies that have agreed to comply with the EU directive regarding EU citizens so that European companies can trade with these U.S. companies without fear of violating the directive. By June 2005, 739 U.S. companies had joined the list. You can view information about the Safe Harbor arrangement and the list of companies that have joined at www.export.gov/safeharbor.

Since privacy laws regarding employees—not just consumers—are also different in the United States and European Union, American companies employing European citizens must comply with EU laws regarding transfer of employment information. They must comply with the DPAs. Under the Safe Harbor arrangement, claims of European citizens against U.S. companies regarding privacy are heard (with some exceptions) in the United States. To be sure they are not breaking the law, European companies that wish to transfer personal data to U.S. companies can simply check at the abovementioned Web site to see if those U.S. companies are listed.

Applicable Law

As discussed in the Ethical & Societal Issues box in this chapter, countries have differing laws regarding free speech, which can have a grave impact on what a company may or may not display from its servers. Other laws that can affect online business address gambling, auctioning, sales of alcoholic beverages and drugs, and other areas. After establishing online business in some countries, some companies discovered that their practice was not in compliance with a local law. For example, eBay discovered that Dutch and Italian laws required that a certified auctioneer be present at any auction. This made its online auctions illegal in these countries. Some countries have changed their laws to accommodate online business, but others have not. Such legal discrepancy among jurisdictions should not come as a surprise to executives; they must research the legal environment in every jurisdiction where they intend to do business. The lessons of Yahoo!, eBay, and other online pioneers prompted many companies to employ legal research experts before they start business in a new jurisdiction. Often, this effort is part of a larger effort to research the local culture and practices. Some companies have hired local experts to help them in assessing local considerations, and in some cases executives decided to avoid doing online business in certain countries altogether.

Different Time Zones

Companies that operate in many global regions, especially multinational corporations, must craft policies for the work of both their employees and information systems. Teleconferencing systems must be available much of the day, and in many cases, 24 hours per day, so that employees many time zones apart can communicate to discuss problems that need immediate resolution. Teams in support centers might have to work in shifts to accommodate clients worldwide. When scheduling teleconferencing sessions, managers in North America should remember, for instance, that scheduling a session for Friday afternoon to accommodate their Australian counterparts will force the Australians to come to the office on Saturday morning.

Different time zones must be considered by all organizations that do business in multiple countries.

© Steven Swintek/Getty Images

In their global supply chain management systems, managers must be aware of what might seem to be incorrect time stamping in shipments and payment records. For example, consider interaction between a corporation's Pennsylvania manufacturing plant and its South Korean assembly plant. Because South Korea is 14 hours ahead of Pennsylvania, shipping records could show that subassemblies were shipped from Pennsylvania a day before they were ordered in South Korea. To eliminate confusion, the systems at both locations can be designed to record the local times of both locations, or only that of a single location, such as the company headquarters' time.

- As more and more companies use the Web for business, both B2C and B2B, they realize that they must accommodate non-English-speaking audiences and tailor their sites to local preferences. They also must be carefully attuned to the cultural differences and payment preferences of different world regions, as well as be aware of legal and tariff issues.

- Organizations that engage in international trade, especially through the Web, must also be aware of the linguistic, cultural, economic, and political challenges involved in such trade.

- One important unresolved issue is the discrepancy between the laws governing the collection and manipulation of personal data in two economic powers, the United States and the European Union, which have incompatible data privacy laws. This difference restricts the flow of personal data between the United States and the EU. The Safe Harbor arrangement enables EU companies to do business with U.S. businesses that comply with EU policies on handling personal data of its citizens.

- Several cases have demonstrated that the old legal approach of territorial jurisdiction is inadequate when so much information is communicated and so much business is conducted on the Internet. Issues such as free speech and consumer litigation of e-tailers have brought to light the need for an international legal reform for cyberspace.

IT FITS OUTFITS REVISITED

It Fits Outfits is a global enterprise. The company's clothing is manufactured in China and exported to the United States. They would also like to extend their e-tail and retail operations to other countries. Let's explore some of the issues it faces in operating globally.

What Would You Do?

1. Contracting with manufacturers in another country involves communicating with the company, understanding the laws of the country, and uncovering political, economic and technological issues that might affect trade. Describe the obstacles you think It Fits Outfits might face as it expands to other countries such as Bangladesh.

2. It Fit Outfits recently created an online storefront for the college market. They would like to be able to sell these products to Europe and Asia as well. How should they deal with payment and currency issues?

New Perspectives

1. In the future, Shari Steiner hopes to open branches of It Fits Outfits in large cities around the world. How do you think the company's unique business principle, customer participation in design, will be received in different countries? What adjustments should the company make to accommodate other cultures?

European Article Number (EAN), 300

global information system, 290

Global Trade Item Number (GTIN), 301

glocalization, 292

Safe Harbor, 303

Uniform Code Council (UCC), 300

Universal Product Code (UPC), 300

REVIEW QUESTIONS

1. What is meant by the term "global information systems"?

2. Executives of multinational corporations are advised to think globally and act locally. What does this mean?

3. Manufacturers and retailers have used product bar codes for many years. What information does the 13-digit European Article Number (EAN) contain that the 12-digit Universal Product Code (UPC) did not, and why is this information important?

4. Is every Web site a form of global IS? Why or why not?

5. Using software for automatic translation of Web pages into other languages for local audiences saves much labor cost and time. If you were an executive for a company that maintains a multilingual Web site, would you settle for software-based translation only? Why or why not?

6. Many organizations, especially multinational corporations, must consolidate reports to ensure smooth operations. These reports include currency, measurements, and dates. How would you help them receive reports "on the fly" that are in the desired currency and format?

7. Many European countries have stricter privacy laws than the United States. What is the impact of this discrepancy on multinational corporations with offices on both continents? In terms of business functions, which activities, in particular, are affected?

8. Give three examples of cultural imperialism. Why do you think your examples reflect cultural imperialism?

9. Some countries have laws restricting collection and maintenance of data on small companies. Do such laws make sense to you? How can they protect the privacy of individuals? Give an example.

10. What are the implications of different time zones for global supply chain management systems?

11. Countries can adopt either a country-of-origin law or a country-of-destination law. What is the difference between the two approaches? Which is more helpful to consumers and which is more helpful to e-tailers? Explain.

DISCUSSION QUESTIONS

1. Test yourself: what are the "nationalities" of the following corporations? Consider nationality to be the country where the corporation is registered: Total (gasoline), Bull (computers), Olivetti (office appliances), BP (gasoline), CheckPoint (security software), LG (electronics), Corona (beer), Heineken (beer), Thomson (electronics), Goodyear (tires), JVC (electronics), Braun (small appliances), Siemens (electronics), Nokia (mobile telephones).

2. Some observers said that modifying applications and databases to move from 12- to 13-digit product bar codes was similar to the efforts to address the Y2K problem in the years leading to 2000. Search the Web to learn about the Y2K issue. In what way are the two issues similar?

3. Several technologies have been practically given away by the United States to the world. Name at least two such technologies. Do you think that this was "charity" or that the United States reaps some benefits from having given the technologies away? Explain.

4. The U.S. Department of Commerce has relaxed restrictions on the export of encryption (scrambling) software for communications, but it still bans the export of many such applications. Do you agree with this policy? Why or why not?

5. Thirteen of the European Union countries use the Euro as their common currency. Does this help or hinder international ISs? Explain.

6. Do you agree with the rule of the French court in the Yahoo! Nazi item auctions case? Why or why not?

7. Consider sensitivity to privacy in the United States. Are Americans more sensitive to *government* handling of private information or to *business* handling of private information? Now answer the question regarding Western European countries.

8. Apparently, the EU has stricter privacy laws than the United States, and not many U.S. companies are willing to comply with the EU Directive on Data Protection. The Safe Harbor arrangement is one way to resolve the issue, but only several hundred companies have subscribed. How would *you* resolve the conflict?

9. If a non-English-speaking country had established the Internet, do you think that country would impose its own "cultural imperialism" on the Web? Why or why not?

10. Which legal approach do you prefer for e-commerce: country of origin or country of destination? Answer the question as a businessperson, then answer it as a consumer.

11. If some countries clearly adopt the country-of-origin approach for legal issues of e-commerce, online retailers might move to operate from those countries. Why?

12. An American company employs engineers in California and in several Asian and European countries. The engineers exchange e-mail and communicate via VoIP, teleconferencing, and collaborative project management tools. The Americans often use phrases such as "Let's touch base in a week," "Right off the bat..." and "...all the way to the end zone." An executive instructs them to avoid such phrases in communication with colleagues from other countries, and perhaps even with any colleague. Why?

APPLYING CONCEPTS

1. You are an executive for Bidway.com, an auction site that has successfully competed with eBay and Yahoo! in the United States. Management decided to open use of the site to residents of all countries. You were given an important assignment: collect intelligence that will ensure the company's move from a national business to an international business is smooth. If you envision that there might be too many difficulties in certain countries, management will accept your recommendation to block bidding by residents of those countries, but you must be careful not to miss potentially profitable markets. Prepare an outline of all the aspects about which you will collect intelligence for each country, and explain why this item is important.

2. The United States is the only country that still uses English measurement units rather than metric ones. Even the English officially moved to the metric system many years ago. The U.S. Congress has unsuccessfully attempted to make the official move. Research on the Web and summarize your findings in two pages: Why does the United States still use the English system? When was the last attempt to officially move to the metric system? Does the use of English measurement units put U.S. companies at a disadvantage when competing on international contracts? How has software solved the challenge? Give examples of engineering software that resolves this challenge.

1. You are the international sales manager for Aladdin Rugs Inc., a multinational company headquartered in the United States. At the end of every month, you receive reports from the national sales managers of your company's operations in England, Germany, and Japan. The products are sold by area. The managers report the units sold and income from sales in their national currencies: pounds sterling (£), euros (€), yen (¥), and U.S. dollars (US$). Use your spreadsheet program to consolidate the sales reports you received, as follows.

   a. Under "Totals," enter formulas to convert square yards to square meters and enter another formula to total the area in square meters for all four countries.

   b. In a financial newspaper such as the *Wall Street Journal* or on the Web, find the rates of exchange for the three currencies against the US$ on the last business day of last month. Enter a formula that will convert all non-U.S. currencies to US$. (Extra challenge: program a macro to do the calculations.)

   c. Test all formulas with actual numbers.

2. Google and other sites offer Web-based translation services. Test the quality of such tools. Write a message of 50 words in English. Use the tool to translate it to German or another language with which you might be familiar. Copy the translated text, paste it to be translated, and translate it to English. Compare the original and translated English messages. Write a short report and e-mail it to your professor: how good is the translation tool? About how much of the text in the translated version came out identical to the original? Did you find anything funny in the back-translated text?

1. Team up with three other students. Decide on three keywords with which the team will conduct a Web search. All of you should use the same search engine. One team member should record the number of sites found in the United States, another in Germany, another in France, and another in the Netherlands. Also, record the sites the team found whose domain name is non-U.S. but that used English rather than, or in addition to, the local language.

   Prepare a brief report detailing what you recorded. Write your own conclusion: how dominant is English on the Web? Do you think the Web is "Americanized"? Do you consider what you found to be cultural imperialism?

2. "Electronic immigrants" are residents of one country who are employed by a company in another country. They are the result of what some people call "offshoring" of jobs. They deliver the results of their work through the Internet or private communications networks. Your team should conduct research with four companies in four different industries, one of which is in software development. The title of your research is "The Electronic Immigrant: Economic and Political Implications." Contact the human resource managers of the four companies, present the issue, and ask for the managers' opinion: can the company use "electronic immigrants"? Can it be hurt if competitors use them? Do the HR managers think the national economy can gain or lose from the phenomenon? Do they foresee any political ramifications? Your team should use a word processor to prepare a neat report starting with half a page of background on each company.

1. The version of MS Office you own probably has been manufactured for use only in the country in which you live. Why would software manufacturers limit sales of software versions to various countries?

2. Assume you have built a Web site for It Fits Outfits. The company now wants to sell its products overseas. Other than modifying the site to accept other currencies, what other changes have to be made to the site?

FROM IDEAS TO APPLICATION: REAL CASES

Export with Confidence

The products of Fairchild Semiconductor are installed in a large array of items, from satellites and motor vehicles to cell phones, medical devices, and home appliances. The company is a world leader in design and manufacturing of microprocessors that control power. It calls itself The Power Franchise. The company has manufacturing facilities in the United States, South Korea, China, Malaysia, Singapore, and the Philippines, and 36 offices in 17 countries. It sees the entire world as its market. Fairchild ships more than 17 billion units of products annually. Some products are shipped to as few as 6 countries, while others are shipped to as many as 45 countries.

The microchips are designed in the United States and South Korea. Manufacturing starts in the United States. Then, the chips are sent to plants in Asia for assembly and testing. The products are then shipped to customers around the globe. Customers can order products online at the company's Web site. Over the past decade Fairchild established additional design and manufacturing facilities in Korea and China. With facilities as well as customers in a growing number of countries, complying with both U.S. and other countries' export and import laws became complex. Work-in-progress is often shipped from one country to another, and then to another or back to the original country for further processing. Logistics managers decided to use the services of a company that specializes in software that helps manage such complex operations. Fairchild approached NextLinx, a company with expertise in software that supports online logistics.

Together, the companies configured and implemented NextLinx software called Trade Export Solution, which automates Fairchild's global logistics. The software provides information on laws and regulations of each country where Fairchild transacts, as well as customs duties. For each shipment it figures out the fastest and least costly carriers as well as the minimum duties to be paid. The application provides digital forms that enable employees to enter details on content, value, and destination of a shipment. The various costs are calculated automatically for the country and particular seaport or airport. The system ensures full compliance with the country's regulations. In recent years, many new regulations have had to do not with economics but with homeland security. They may forbid the export of certain types of microchips to some countries, or the export of certain items from some

countries. All this information is closely monitored by NextLinx and added to the documentation and automated forms.

The software has been implemented in every facility of the company in the world. It is integrated into Fairchild's enterprise resource planning (ERP) systems as well as into the shipment application of its major shipping carrier. Shipping clerks can check easily retrievable trade documentation and be sure that all shipping complies with the destination country's regulations. This saves the typical labor-intensive search for trade compliance documentation. This helps the company to clear 90 percent of its shipments with the proper authorities before the shipment reaches the destination country. The system also shortened shipping durations and reduced shipping delays. As a result, Fairchild could reduce the amount of raw materials inventory it carries.

The use of the new system reduced the number of employees involved in shipping processes, but it also had another positive effect. It standardized shipping procedures and records worldwide. The same shipping procedures and records are maintained at every facility of the company, anywhere in the world. This enables the company to easily implement the procedures and documentation in new facilities it might establish in the future.

Sources: www.nextlinx.com/news/casestudies/case_fairchildsemi.shtml, 2005; www.fairchildsemi.com, 2005.

Thinking About the Case

1. The software Fairchild integrated into its ERP system reduces risk. What risk?

2. The software saves costs. What costs?

3. Why is it important to integrate an application such as NextLinx's to the ERP system of the adopting global company?

4. Why is standardization of processes so important to a company such as Fairchild?

If You Want to Do Business Here...

Sometimes standards at a foreign market force a business to improve its products or leave that market. The higher standard could require better information systems, and the results could have long-lasting positive effects on the products worldwide. Such seems to be the case with Kia Motors, the Korean car manufacturer.

In 1995, when Kia Motors first started selling cars in North America, it found itself the butt of many jokes. The Korean company offered its cars for low prices. Prices were so low that Kia managed to increase sales from 12,000 cars in 1995 to 270,000 in 2004. Yet, the cars were notoriously of low quality, which translated into costs involved in fixing repeated defects. Until 2002, Kia was ranked at the bottom of J.D. Power and Associates' annual quality survey. J.D. Power's survey reports on car quality are considered the most trusted in the United States and many other countries. J.D. Power reports rely on responses of vehicle owners after 90 days of ownership of a new car. In 1997, a car manufactured in North America had 1.1 defects on average, whereas Kia had 2.75 defects. In 2002, the auto industry average was 1.33 defects per vehicle, whereas Kia cars had 2.12. An expert noted that such improvement over just 5 years is impressive in this industry, but Kia's ratio was still significantly worse than the average. In addition, the expert said, it takes a long time to change consumer perception of quality.

The company operates in America through its subsidiary, Kia Motors America. The subsidiary's CEO, Peter Butterfield, was determined to change the defect ratio and remove Kia's stigma as a manufacturer of low-quality vehicles. He set a goal: by 2007, Kia's defect average would reach the auto industry average, and by 2010, Kia's quality would be equal to that of the top Japanese manufacturers.

The CEO announcement came after a U.S. federal mandate was declared. In 2000, the U.S. Congress adopted the Transportation Recall Enhancement, Accountability, and Documentation (TREAD) Act. Under the new law, all manufacturers of motor vehicles sold in the United States were ordered by the National Highway Traffic Safety Administration (NHTSA) to operate systems that can report all defects, accidents, and injuries involving their vehicles. The deadline for implementing the system was December 1, 2003. Under the Act, if senior executives failed to include any of the required details in the quarterly reports, they could be prosecuted and sentenced to time in prison. The key to improving quality was monitoring defects, and monitoring defects required better information systems. Many of the elements of such a system were required by the new law anyway. But Kia decided to do more, for its own sake.

Management faced daunting challenges. The data from which the company could glean the information required by the new law resided in seven different databases on different computer systems, mainly because each system was owned and operated by a different department. The warranty department, the parts department, and the legal and consumer affairs department managed their data on different computers that were neither networked nor integrated. For example, if a consumer complained about failed brakes, the complaint was recorded by the legal and consumer relations department in its database, but the other departments did not have access to the data. Other customers might have had the same problem, but had it fixed without complaining to that department, so the department had no record of those occurrences.

To create the quarterly reports for NHTSA it was possible to retrieve the disparate information from the databases and combine the pieces manually. However, this would not only entail much labor but also cause Kia to miss a great opportunity. Management's purpose was not only to comply with the law but also to ensure that the CEO's commitment to quality was fulfilled. One expert noted that the problem of maintaining information in separate places is that managers can never receive a complete picture. A car owner might call the consumer relations department and file a complaint only after she had the air-conditioner in her car fixed three times. This is the first time that department knows about the problem. By that time the owner might have decided never to purchase a Kia again. Other owners might not file a complaint with the department at all but reach the same decision. However, if the customer relations department learns about the problem at first occurrence, managers can see an overall picture created by these puzzle pieces, and draw the engineers' attention much sooner.

In late 2002, Kia engaged Infogain, a software consulting firm. Infogain professionals implemented a central application that links to each of the databases. It can reach out to each database and break down and categorize all the data around individual car components, such as power train, steering assemblies, or headlights. The aggregated information is stored on a Microsoft SQL Server database. The application retrieves data from the disparate databases on a daily basis. It combines data from areas such as warranty claims, parts sales, vehicle identification number master storage files, and vehicle inventories. It is also connected to a customer relationship management (CRM) system that monitors consumer complaints. The system automatically creates reports of repeating problems. For example, if a dealership tried three times to fix a steering system and still cannot find out why the failure recurs, Kia would send out one of its engineers to the dealership to investigate. The engineer files the report in the CRM system.

Analyzing parts used in repairs is easy, because this is structured data. Customer relations are much more difficult to analyze, because they are not structured. Customers often telephone Kia or send e-mail messages to complain. Under the new Act such communication must be reviewed to see if it contains details that must be reported to NHTSA. Evaluating recorded communication manually could double the agents' amount of labor.

Infogain implemented an application that uses keywords to search recorded text reports. Keywords include "fire," "burn," "spark," "combustion," and "smolder." If a keyword is found, the application prompts the customer relations agent to conduct further investigation and see if the incident needs to be included in the NHTSA reports. If a pattern emerges, engineers might be called to investigate and propose changes to designs. However, the agent might find out that a customer was just angry and suggested they "fire the salesperson." This "fire" might trigger an investigation of the dealership but is not reported to NHTSA.

Kia employs 50 agents at its main customer call center in Irvine, California. With the help of the new system it did not have to add a single employee to comply with the new law. Managers now have a rich database in SQL Server. They use a business intelligence application called Crystal Analysis, which is sold by Business Objects SA, a company that specializes in OLAP and data mining software. (These techniques are discussed in detail in Chapter 11.) Managers can get information about a world region or drill down to focus on a recurring problem with a specific part across all dealerships. They can retrieve information across departments by daily, weekly, or quarterly reporting periods, and by car models, model years, and components.

Managers have found that part sales are the first indicator of a defect and that warranty claims are the second. For example, if Kia receives a monthly order that is 15 percent or larger than the historical average for a particular part, an investigation is triggered because this is a good indication that something must be wrong with that item. Managers might notice that brake pads are inordinately ordered only for the four-wheel drive version of a model but not for the two-wheel drive models, and therefore the problem might have to do with vibrations of the vehicle, not the pads. The decision will then be made to look into the structural design of the vehicle. With 60,000 different parts that go into assembling a car, decisions such as these can save the company much money and help improve the design of new cars.

The new law and pressure for higher quality in the United States might have helped this Korean company. J.D. Power reports show that Kia had 1.53 defects per vehicle for its 2004 model year, and that the ratio decreased to 1.40 for the 2005 model year. Kia did particularly well in the compact car category. The Kia Spectra was ranked second after the Toyota Prius and ahead of the Honda Civic and Toyota Corolla. As Kia's Web site says, the company now has so much confidence in the quality of its cars that it includes in the car sale a warranty for 10 years or 100,000 miles.

Sources: Duvall, M., "Kia Motors America: Lemon Aid," *Baseline* (www.baselinemag.com), June 10, 2005; *www.kia.com*, 2005; *www.businessobjects.com*, 2005.

Thinking About the Case

1. Do you think market forces would push Kia Motors to invest in IT the way it did if the U.S. government had not passed the TREAD Act? Why or why not?

2. What was the role of IT in raising the quality of Kia's cars? Is IT alone the reason for improvement?

© USDA Photo by: Tim McCabe

PART FOUR

Decision Support and Business Intelligence

CASE IV: DEBOER FARMS

The DeBoer family's roots run deep in their South Dakota farm. Carl DeBoer's great-grandfather Johann began farming in the Dakota Territory just before it became a state in 1889. Through the years, each generation worked hard, saved, built improvements, and added to the farm, until it grew from its original several hundred acres to its current size of 12,000 acres. His great-grandfather would hardly recognize the place these days, Carl thought. DeBoer Farms' acreage is planted in corn, soybeans, wheat, oats, and alfalfa. Carl inherited the farm last month when his father passed, although he had been managing the farm on his own for the past ten years. Big changes lay ahead for both Carl and DeBoer Farms.

when John Deere started manufacturing the first steel plows, it would have taken him about 300 hours to produce 100 bushels of wheat. Today, Carl could do it in just under 3 hours.

Like other businesses caught in the industrial revolution, farms had to adopt new innovations or they would become less productive than their competitors. His great-grandfather, Johann, had planted the first hybridized corn and spread the first mixed chemical fertilizers on the farm. His grandmother Elizabeth had bought the first tractor during the Second World War. His father had introduced new pesticides and no-till methods to curb erosion. Now, Carl had brought the farm into the computer age.

Relying on Scientific and Technological Advances

The farm industry had always relied on the benefits of scientific discoveries and inventions. Advances in machinery, fertilizers, insecticides, land use, and plant breeding had fostered a healthy agricultural industry since—well, even before Johann DeBoer's time. Carl scanned his wheat field. In the late 1830s,

The IT Revolution

The computer revolution came to farming 15 years or so ago. About 6 or 7 years ago, only a little more than half of all farms used personal computers. The DeBoer farm couldn't have afforded to wait that long if they were to keep up with other mid-sized and large farms. Back in the late 1980s, Carl had

313

converted the farm's manual financial and accounting systems to computer applications. They began to use spreadsheets and then databases to track information such as crop yield and test results from soil samples sent out for analysis. Then the DeBoer family discovered the Internet. Carl could get the latest weather information and investigate pricing issues, as well as order farm equipment, parts, and repairs online.

The real revolution came in the mid-1990s. Carl remembered taking his 15-year-old daughter Allie to an exposition that featured a global positioning system (GPS). The GPS was part of precision farming, a new approach to farming that handles a variation of factors, such as soil nutrients, within a field. Up until that point, farmers had practiced whole-field management. Now they could program their equipment to spread more fertilizer in one area and less in another. Allie thought the system was cool. Carl moaned about the headache of converting databases and installing new software. They both agreed that precision farming would decrease nitrogen runoff and be better for the environment.

After the expo, Carl had taken a "wait-and-see" approach for a few years, but when other farmers began to report increased profits with precision farming, Carl decided that it was time to try it out for himself. Since Allie was now helping him manage the farm, she could help him sort out technological issues.

Growing Information in the Farming Industry

In the past, Carl often drove over to the South Dakota Cooperative Extension Service to discuss soil and other crop-related issues with a staff member, usually Steve Janssen. The Cooperative Extension Service provided invaluable information to the farming community: what counties were being affected by the corn borer moth; whether heavy rains were depleting the soil of nitrogen; how to record restricted use of pesticides in accordance with federal law. The service provided worksheets to determine whether farming practices might have affected groundwater and drinking water. It also provided information on drinking water treatment systems. The service also helped farm owners with strategic planning, commodity marketing, and production and risk.

Today most of this information was available on the service's Web site. In a couple of clicks, Carl could download a PDF publication on weed control in soybean fields. He could read an announcement from the Environmental Protection Agency (EPA) that an exemption had been granted to South Dakota farmers, allowing them to use tebuconazole on wheat to combat Fusarium head blight. He could access maps of soil temperature. He could even research the history of soybean aphids. Nowadays, he and Steve exchanged e-mails regularly. If the extension service didn't also hold expositions, well, Carl would hardly ever see his old friend.

As a matter of fact, Carl was heading to the regional manure handling exposition this afternoon. He should probably start getting ready now. Carl looked at the watch his grandfather had given him as a high school graduation gift. It seemed like every time he looked up from this watch something was gone or replaced—farmhands were implementing some new technique, planting a new type of grain, or using a new piece of machinery. Carl sighed. It was all part of life.

10:45? Carl shook his wrist. The watch had stopped. He bent over and picked up his cell phone. It was 11:38—exactly.

BUSINESS CHALLENGES

If you were Carl DeBoer, how would you decide which technologies to use to improve your farm production? Technology is costly, but it also provides astounding benefits, as the DeBoers have seen on their farm. In the upcoming chapters, you learn how to recognize and evaluate decision support systems, expert systems, and knowledge management systems.

- In Chapter 10, "Decision Support and Expert Systems," you learn how to determine the characteristics of businesses and decisions that can benefit from decision support systems and what is involved in creating and using them.

- In Chapter 11, "Business Intelligence and Knowledge Management," you learn how knowledge management systems support the business process and how data mining can be used to establish strategic advantage.

© USDA Photo by: Tim McCabe

Soon the DeBoers would be harvesting their corn crop, and they were particularly interested in the fields given additional insecticide. Would the soil insecticide be effective this year in reducing corn rootworm? Did the resistant hybrid seed help reduce the pests? They hadn't experienced a drought this year, which could hamper the insecticide's effectiveness in the soil. From their casual inspections and collected data so far, the rootworm population did seem to be lower. After the harvest, they would feed the yield information into the system. It would factor in the weather and general soil condition readings and formulate additional recommendations for the next year. It had taken a long time to develop that system—it was refined based on multiple readings over the years, and the results were continually compared with the judgments of Dr. Wildes and other expert entomologists. But the system seemed to be working. As Carl entered the data, counting the number of beetles in the sticky traps he had collected and replaced, the system reported that he had trapped fewer beetles than last year at this time.

Carl immediately e-mailed Steve. "Nice chatting with you this afternoon. Entered the data from the beetle traps and PestPRO is working. You, my friend, are outdated." Carl chuckled to himself as he clicked Send.

DECISION SUPPORT

The success of an organization largely depends on the quality of the decisions that its employees make. When decision making involves large amounts of information and a lot of processing, computer-based systems can make the process efficient and effective. This chapter discusses two types of decision support aids: decision support systems (DSSs) and expert systems (ESs). In recent years applications have been developed to combine several features and methods of these aids. Also, decision support modules are often part of larger enterprise applications. For example, ERP (enterprise resource planning) systems support decision making in such areas as production capacity planning and inventory replenishment.

Furthermore, many vendors of computer-based decision support tools, such as Pilot Software and Cognos Inc., no longer call their applications decision support systems. They prefer to call them business analysis tools, business intelligence applications, or other names. In a way, almost any system that produces useful information is a decision aid. Decision support systems and expert systems are especially designed to streamline the decision-making process by providing either a single optimal solution to a question or problem, or a narrow set of solutions from which decision makers can select.

THE DECISION-MAKING PROCESS

When do you have to make a decision? When you drive your car to a certain destination and there is only one road, you do not have to make a decision. The road will take you there. But if you come to a fork, you have to decide which way to go. In fact, whenever more than one possible action is available, a decision must be made.

A decision is easy to make when one option will clearly bring about a better outcome than any other. Decisions become more difficult when more than one alternative seems reasonable and when the number of alternatives is great. In business, there can be dozens, hundreds, or even millions of different courses of action available to achieve a desired result. The problem is deciding on the best alternative. (You can see why problem solving and decision making are so closely related.)

Herbert Simon, a researcher of management and decision making, described decision making as a three-phase process (see Figure 10.1). First, in the *Intelligence* phase, decision makers collect facts, beliefs, and ideas. In business, the facts might be millions of pieces of data. Second, in the *Design* phase, the method for considering the data is designed. The methods are sequences of steps, formulas, models, and other tools that systematically reduce the alternatives to a manageable number. Third, in the *Choice* phase, when there is a reduced number of alternatives, decision makers make a choice; that is, they select the most promising alternative.

FIGURE 10.1 The three phases of decision making	
Intelligence	• Collect data from inside the organization. • Collect data from outside the organization. • Collect information on possible ways to solve the problem.
Design	• Organize the data; select a model to process the data. • Produce reasonable, potential courses of action.
Choice	• Select a course of action.

Businesses collect data internally (from within the organization) and externally (from outside sources). They use models to analyze data. Generally speaking, a **model** is a representation of reality. For instance, in architecture, a tabletop representation of a building or a city block is a model of the full-sized structure. A map is a small-scale representation—a model—of a particular geographic area that can include topographic information and political boundaries. And in business, mathematical equations that represent the relationships among variables can be models for how businesses respond to changes, such as: what happens to profits when sales and expenses go up or down? Managers either use universal models, such as certain statistical models, or design their own models to analyze data. Then they select what they perceive as the best course of action.

STRUCTURED AND UNSTRUCTURED PROBLEMS

A **structured problem** is one in which an optimal solution can be reached through a single set of steps. Since the one set of steps is known, and since the steps must be followed in a known sequence, solving a structured problem with the same data always yields the same solution. Mathematicians call a sequence of steps an **algorithm** and the categories of data that are considered when following those steps **parameters**. For instance, when in considering the problem of the shortest route for picking up and delivering shipments, the parameters are the time when shipments are ready for pickup, the time when shipments are needed at their destinations, the distance of existing vehicles from the various destinations, the work schedules of the drivers, the capacities of the trucks, and so on.

Most mathematical and physical problems are structured. Finding the roots of a quadratic equation is a structured problem: there is a formula (an algorithm) you can use to solve the problem. For the same equation the roots are always the same. Predicting how hot a liquid will get in a particular setting is a structured problem: if you know the properties of the liquid, the size of its container, the properties of the energy source heating the liquid, and the exact length of time the energy will be applied, you can figure out what temperature the liquid will reach. Unfortunately, the majority of problems in the business world cannot be solved so easily.

An **unstructured problem** is one for which there is no algorithm to follow to reach an optimal solution—either because there is not enough information about the factors that might affect the solution or because there are so many potential factors that no algorithm can be formulated to guarantee a unique optimal solution. Unstructuredness is closely related to uncertainty. You cannot be sure what the weather will be tomorrow, let alone two months from now; nobody can guarantee what an investment in a certain portfolio of stocks will yield by year's end; and two physicians might diagnose the same symptoms differently. These are all areas where unstructured problems predominate.

Some management scientists refer to semistructured problems. A **semistructured problem** is one that is neither fully structured nor totally unstructured. The problem "How much will I earn after 2 years if I invest $100,000 in municipal bonds that pay 3 percent per annum tax free?" is structured. To find the solution you have to follow a simple algorithm that takes as parameters your $100,000, the 2 years, and the 3 percent interest rate. Unless the city that issued the bonds goes bankrupt, your calculated income is guaranteed. However, the problem "If I invest $100,000 in the stock of XYZ, Inc. and sell the stock after 2 years, how much money will I make?" is semistructured. Too many factors must be taken into account for it to be considered structured: the demand for the company's products, entrance of competitors into its market, the market of its products in this country and overseas, and so on. So many factors affecting the price of the stocks might change over the next 2 years that the problem is semistructured at best and totally unstructured at worst.

Stock investment, weather forecasting, and medicine are domains of unstructured or semistructured decision making.

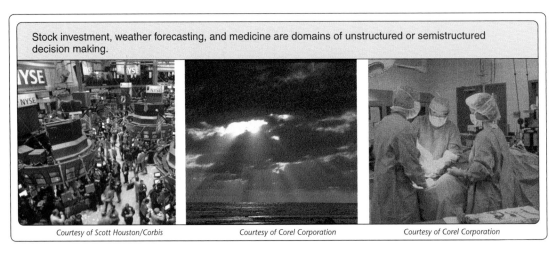

| *Courtesy of Scott Houston/Corbis* | *Courtesy of Corel Corporation* | *Courtesy of Corel Corporation* |

Managers encounter semistructured problems almost daily in many different industries and in many different business functions (see Figure 10.2).

FIGURE 10.2
Examples of structured and semistructured problems

Structured Problems	Semistructured Problems
How many workers are needed to fully	What are the benefits of merging with XYZ, Inc.? staff production line A?
What is our optimal order quantity for raw material Z, based on our production?	Where should we deploy the next five stores of our retail chain?
How many turbines are needed to supply power to Hickstown?	How will the consumer react if we lower the price of our product by 10 percent?
Which of our regions yields the highest revenue per salesperson?	What is the best advertisement campaign to launch our new financial service?
Which money market fund currently yields the highest return?	What are the benefits of opening an office in Paris, France?
How much would the implementation of pollution-preventing devices cost us?	Which stock will yield the highest return by the end of the year?

A manager solving a typical semistructured problem faces multiple courses of action. The task is to choose the one alternative that will bring about the best outcome. For example:

- In manufacturing, managers must provide solutions to semistructured problems such as: (1) Which supplier should we use to receive the best price for purchased raw materials while guaranteeing on-time delivery? (2) There is a stoppage in assembly line B; should we transfer workers to another assembly line or wait for B to be fixed? (3) Demand for product X has decreased; should we dismantle one of the production lines, or should we continue to manufacture at the current rate, stock the finished products, and wait for an upswing in demand?

- Managers of investment portfolios must face semistructured decision making when they decide which securities to sell and which to buy so they can maximize the overall return on investment. The purpose of research in stock investing is to minimize uncertainties by trying to find patterns of behavior of stocks, among other trends. Managers of mutual funds spend much of their time in semistructured decision making.

- Human resource managers are faced with semistructured problems when they have to decide whom to recommend for a new position, considering a person's qualifications and his or her ability to learn and assume new responsibilities.

- Marketing professionals face semistructured problems constantly: should they spend money on print, television, Web banners, e-mail, or direct-mail advertisements? Which sector of the population should they target?

Because of the complexities of the problems they face, managers in many functional areas often rely on decision support applications to select the best course of action.

Why You Should... Be Familiar with Decision Aids

The terms "decision support systems" and "expert systems" are mentioned less and less frequently in recent years. However, the concepts of modeling decision-making processes and automating them and the transformation of human expertise into software are alive and thriving. While there are many situations in which only an experienced professional can make good decisions, much of the decision-making process can be automated through use of computer-based decision aids. The raw materials for many decisions are already in corporate databases and data warehouses, and they can be accessed through ISs such as supply chain management systems. Your ideas of how to automate routine decisions can save much labor and time for your organization. Knowing how expert systems and geographic information systems work might stimulate fresh ideas in your mind for implementation of new ISs, which can not only save labor and time but also be a competitive tool for your organization.

DECISION SUPPORT SYSTEMS

To save time and effort in their decision making, managers use several types of decision support applications. One such type, a **decision support system (DSS)**, is a computer-based information system designed to help managers select one of many alternative solutions to a problem. DSSs can help corporations increase market share, reduce costs, increase profitability, and enhance product quality. By automating some of the decision-making process, the systems give managers access to previously unavailable analyses. Technically, certain analyses could be performed by managers, but it would be prohibitively time-consuming and would render late, and therefore bad, decisions. DSSs provide sophisticated and fast analysis of vast amounts of data and information. Although the use of DSSs typically increases with the level of management, the systems are used at all levels, and often by nonmanagerial staff.

The definition of a DSS has been changing over the years. The following sections discuss the components of stand-alone DSSs: either self-contained applications or applications that are designed to address a rather narrow decision-making domain. You should realize that some components of a computer-based decision aid, such as databases, might already be in place when a new DSS is developed. Therefore, consider the following discussion a general framework and not a rigid recipe for the development of all DSSs.

The majority of DSSs comprise three major components: a data management module, a model management module, and a dialog module (see Figure 10.3). Together, these modules (1) help the user enter a request in a convenient manner, (2) search vast amounts of data to focus on the relevant facts, (3) process the data through desired models, and (4) present the results in one or several formats so the output can be easily understood. These steps follow the decision-making sequence described by Herbert Simon.

The Data Management Module

A DSS's **data management module** is a database or data warehouse that provides the data for the intelligence phase of decision making. For example, an investment consultant always needs access to current stock prices and those from at least the preceding few years. A data management module accesses the data and provides a means for the DSS to select data according to certain criteria: type of stock, range of years, and so on.

 A DSS might use a database created specially for that system, but DSSs are usually linked to databases used for other purposes as well, such as purchasing, shipping, billing, and other daily transactions. When organizations use a supply chain management (SCM) or customer relationship management (CRM) system, the databases of such systems provide the data for the DSS. In fact, the DSS itself might be part of that system. Companies that have built data warehouses often prefer their DSSs to access the data warehouse rather than the transactional database, to provide substantially more historical data than transactional databases can provide. This enables the DSS to consider data that covers a longer time period and/or a larger geographic area.

Many DSSs are now closely intertwined with other organizational systems, including data warehouses, data marts, and ERP systems, from which they draw relevant data. For example, Rapt Inc. offers a decision support application that helps optimize purchasing decisions of high-tech and automotive components. The application, called Rapt Buy, captures business variables in data marts through an SAP or Oracle SCM system. The application's analytical software builds models that identify various elements of risk and then recommends purchasing strategies. It considers dozens of economic variables, including demand for the raw materials and yield (the percentage of the materials that are actually used in the final products). The system suggests how many units of each component the company should purchase to avoid carrying too much or too little inventory. In addition, the system provides multiperiod plans for optimizing procurement into the future. At Sun Microsystems Corp., forecasting demand for new products can be off by up to 70 percent. Before implementing this system, procurement officers at this large manufacturer of servers spent many hours of manual analytical work. Now, they use this system to calculate forecasts faster and more accurately.

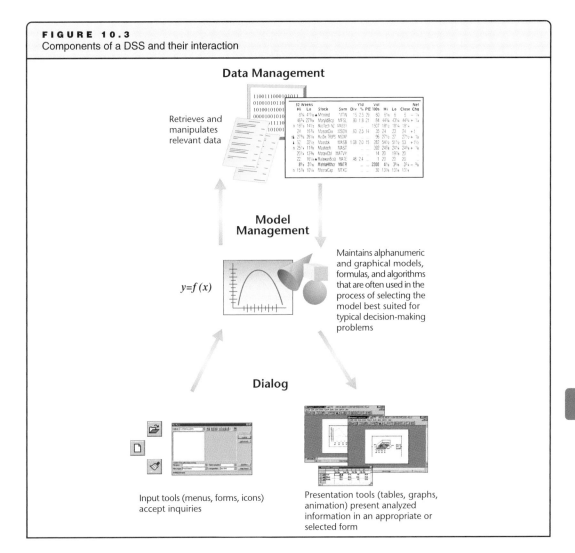

FIGURE 10.3
Components of a DSS and their interaction

Data Management

Retrieves and manipulates relevant data

Model Management

$y = f(x)$

Maintains alphanumeric and graphical models, formulas, and algorithms that are often used in the process of selecting the model best suited for typical decision-making problems

Dialog

Input tools (menus, forms, icons) accept inquiries

Presentation tools (tables, graphs, animation) present analyzed information in an appropriate or selected form

The Model Management Module

To turn data into useful information, the system utilizes its **model management module**, which offers a single fixed model, a dynamically modified model, or a collection of models from which either the DSS or the user selects the most appropriate one. A fixed variable model does not change. A dynamic model is one that is automatically adjusted based on changing relationships among variables.

A sequence of events or a pattern of behavior might become a useful model when the relationships among its inputs, outputs, and conditions can be established well enough that they can be used to analyze different parameters. Models are used to predict output on the basis of different input or different conditions or to estimate what combination of conditions and input might lead to a desired output. Models are often based on mathematical research or on experience. A model might be a widely used method to predict performance, such as best-fit linear analysis, or it might be built by the organization, using the experience that employees in the firm have accumulated over time. Many companies will not divulge details of the models they have programmed because they view them as important trade secrets and valuable assets that could give them competitive advantages. Patterns or models might be unique to a certain industry or even to an individual business. For example:

- In trying to serve bank customers better, operations research experts create a model that predicts the best positioning and scheduling of tellers.

- In the trucking business, models are developed to minimize the total mileage trucks must travel and maximize the trucks' loads, while maintaining satisfactory delivery times. Similar models are developed in the airline industry to maximize revenue.

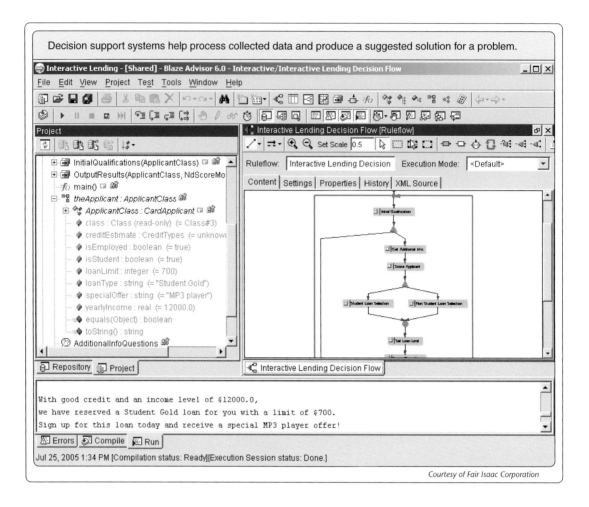

Decision support systems help process collected data and produce a suggested solution for a problem.

Courtesy of Fair Isaac Corporation

- Another model for revenue maximization in the airline industry will automatically price tickets according to the parameters the user enters: date of the flight, day of the week of the flight, departure and destination points, and the length of stay if the ticket is for a round-trip flight.

- Car rental companies use similar models to price their services by car class, rental period, and drop-off options in different countries.

Among the general statistical models, a linear regression model is the best-fit linear relationship between two variables, such as sales and the money spent on marketing. A private business might develop a linear regression model to estimate future sales based on past experience. For example, the marketing department of a shoe store chain might apply linear regression to the relationship between the dollar amount spent on television commercials and change in sales volume. This linear relationship can be translated into a program in a DSS. Then the user can enter the total amount to be spent on television commercials for the next year into the DSS, and the program will enter that figure into the model and find the estimated change in the sales volume. The relationship between the two variables can be plotted, as shown in Figure 10.4.

Note that the actual data points rarely lie on the regression line produced from the data. This illustrates the uncertainty involved in many models. For instance, in Figure 10.4, if the marketing managers tried to estimate the sales volume resulting from spending $1.4 million per month on advertising, their estimates for both months plotted on the graph would be more than the actual sales. In spite of these discrepancies, the regression line might be adequate in general for modeling, with the understanding that results are not necessarily precise. Also note that models often describe relationships among more than two variables and that some models can be expressed as a curve, rather than a straight line.

FIGURE 10.4
A linear regression model for predicting sales volume as a function of dollars spent on advertising

Advertising ($M/month)	Sales ($M/month)
1.1	20.3
1.3	21
1.2	20.1
1.5	22.7
1.4	21.9
1.4	22
2.5	32
2.8	36
2.8	35
2.8	34.8

Usually, models are not so simple. In this advertising and sales example, for instance, many more factors might play a role: the number of salespeople, the location of the stores, the types of shoes offered for sale, the television programs during which the commercials are presented, and many more parameters. Therefore, before models are programmed to become part of a DSS, the environment in which the decision will be executed must be carefully considered.

Not all DSS models are business-oriented. In some areas, especially engineering, DSS models might simulate physical rather than business environments. For example, aeronautical engineers build computer models of wind tunnels to view how an aircraft with a new wing design might behave. It is significantly less expensive to construct a software model than to build a physical model. The simulation provides valuable information on vibrations, drag, metal fatigue, and other factors in relation to various speeds and weather conditions. The output, in the form of both animated pictures and numerical tables, enables engineers to make important decisions before spending huge amounts of money to actually build aircraft—decisions such as the angle in which the aircraft wings are swept, the shape of the fuselage's cross section, the spreading of weight over different parts of the plane, and so forth. When using this type of model, engineers base part of their decision on visual examination of the behavior of the simulation model.

The Dialog Module

For the user to glean information from the DSS, the system must provide an easy way to interact with the program. The part of the DSS that allows the user to interact with it is called the **dialog module**. It prompts the user to select a model, allowing the user to access the database and select data for the decision process or to set criteria for selecting such data. It lets the user enter parameters and change them to see how the change affects the result of the analysis. The dialog might be in the form of commands, pull-down menus, icons, dialog boxes, or any other approach. In essence, the dialog module is not much different from the user interfaces of other types of applications. As an increasing number of DSSs are available for use through the Internet, some dialog modules are especially designed to be compatible with Web browsers.

The dialog module is also responsible for displaying the results of the analysis. DSSs use various textual, tabular, and graphical displays from which the decision maker can choose. Take the previous advertising effort scenario, for example, where the company's marketing manager is trying to decide how to spend promotional dollars. The dialog component of the DSS presents a menu allowing the marketing executive to select "TV advertising" from a variety of promotional choices and to choose the amount to be spent in that channel (see Figure 10.5). Now the dialog module calls up the part of the database that holds current data on advertising expenditures and sales volumes for the corresponding months. At this point, the system might either present a list of models for analyzing the data from which the user can choose or, if it is sophisticated enough, select a model automatically, based on the problem at hand. The model projects sales figures based on the data from the database, and the dialog component presents the results of the analysis. The output helps the executive make a decision by answering the question, "Will the proposed amount to be spent on television commercials yield a large enough boost in sales?"

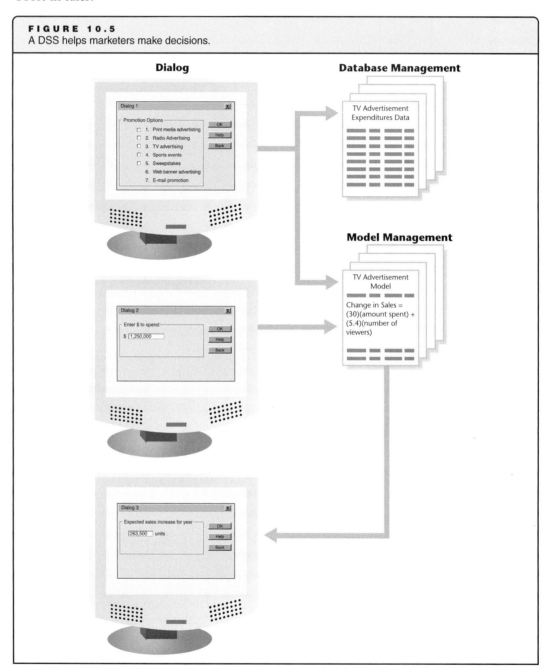

FIGURE 10.5
A DSS helps marketers make decisions.

Sensitivity Analysis

An outcome is almost always affected by more than one parameter; for instance, the sales volume of a product is affected by the number of salespeople, the number of regional sales representatives, the amount spent on national and local television advertising, price, competition, and so on. However, outcomes rarely respond in equal measure to changes in parameters. For instance, a small change in price per unit might result in a dramatic increase in sales, which means sales volume has a high sensitivity to product price. However, the same sales might increase only slightly in response to a huge investment in advertising dollars, which means that sales have a low sensitivity to advertising expenditure. It is important to pinpoint the parameters to which the outcome is highly sensitive, so that an organization can focus efforts where they are most effective. Sometimes the parameters to which an outcome is most sensitive also affect other parameters, so these interactions must be carefully tracked as well.

If a company wishes to maximize profit, managers must find the optimal combination of many factors. To equip a DSS to help achieve this goal, an approximate mathematical formula that expresses the relationship between each factor and the total profit is built into the DSS. Then a **sensitivity analysis** is conducted to test the degree to which the total profit grows or shrinks if one or more of the factors is increased or decreased. The results indicate the relative sensitivity of the profit to the changes. If the outcome is affected significantly even when the parameter is changed only a little, then the sensitivity of the outcome to the parameter is said to be high. The opposite is also true: if the outcome is affected only a little, even when the parameter is varied widely, the outcome is said to be insensitive to the parameter. For instance, a manager might ask, "What is the impact on total quarterly profits if television advertising is decreased by 10 percent and the number of commissioned sales representatives is increased by 5 percent?" Because questions typically are phrased in this format, sensitivity analysis is often referred to as *what if analysis*. Note that you can use a DSS to perform what if analyses on multiple parameters at the same time.

You might be familiar with sensitivity analysis from using electronic spreadsheets. Spreadsheets enable you to enter both data and formulas in cells. Thus, they are an excellent tool for building both the data and the models that decision support systems need, and therefore they make excellent tools for building decision support software. Changing data in one or several cells will result in a different solution to a problem. This allows you to see the effect that a change in one parameter has on the calculated outcome.

Decision Support Systems in Action

DSSs can be used on demand, when a manager needs help in making an occasional decision, or they might be integrated into a scheme that enforces corporate policy. In either case, DSSs help maintain standard criteria in decision making throughout the organization. A growing number of organizations implement software applications that produce decisions automatically and in real time. The only labor involved is the entry of relevant parameters, and when the DSS is linked to the organization's Web site, even this activity might not be performed by employees but by clients. Following are some examples of how DSSs are used for various purposes.

Food Production and Retailing

How much of each type of cookie should a cookie store produce today? Which ingredients should be taken out of the refrigerators, and how long before they are to be mixed and put in the oven? These are only some of the decisions that operators of a Mrs. Fields Cookies store would have to make. However, the decision making is done for them by a DSS. The system, installed in each store, decides for the managers which types of cookies to make, what quantities of each type, and which ingredients to use, on the basis of the store's historical sales volumes and corporate-dictated baking instructions. The company—which operates 390 stores in the United States and more than 80 stores in other countries—has structured the business environment for the store managers. Each store manager must follow the system's instructions regarding which baked products to make and their quantities. The system prescribes the ingredients for each product, when to pull dough from refrigerators, and how to bake, including oven temperatures and time. The prescriptions are the result of input such as region, average traffic in the shopping mall, and previous day sales volumes.

In the restaurant industry, managers have to forecast the number of patrons and the amount of ingredients to purchase, as well as where to purchase it to minimize cost. FoodPro, a DSS developed and sold by Aurora Information Systems, helps make such decisions. Based on the historical data restaurants accumulate, the system helps with these decisions. A recipe database is used to propose decisions on ingredients, quantities, and consolidated purchases from specific vendors. Other components of the system include financial forecasting, invoicing, accounting, and practically every other aspect of managing restaurants.

Part of a spreadsheet that helps decide whether or not to make an investment. The original calculation (top) yields a positive net present value (NPV); a correction in the expenses of the first year (middle) changes the return to negative; a change in the interest rate of the loan taken for the project (bottom) makes it profitable again.

	A	B	C	D	E	F
1	Year	1	2	3		
17						
18	Net Cashflow	(10,756,900)	877,880	12,078,900		
19	Interest Rate	6.50%				
20	NPV	673,122				
21						
22						
23						
24						
25						
26						

Sheet1 / Sheet2 / Sheet3 /

	A	B	C	D	E	F
1	Year	1	2	3		
17						
18	Net Cashflow	(11,556,900)	877,880	12,078,900		
19	Interest Rate	6.50%				
20	NPV	(78,052)				
21						
22						
23						
24						
25						
26						

Sheet1 / Sheet2 / Sheet3 /

	A	B	C	D	E	F
1	Year	1	2	3		
17						
18	Net Cashflow	(11,556,900)	877,880	12,078,900		
19	Interest Rate	5.50%				
20	NPV	120,882				
21						
22						
23						
24						
25						
26						

Sheet1 / Sheet2 / Sheet3 /

Agriculture

The Canadian government has sponsored the development of a series of DSSs for farmers, one of which is Prairie Crop Protection Planner, a system that helps farmers make decisions regarding weed, insect, and disease control on the Canadian prairie. When a farmer enters basic information about a particular crop and the pest problem—weeds, insects, or diseases—the Planner outlines options such as chemicals and ways to apply them. Farmers can describe their spraying equipment, size of the field, and current chemical prices from local suppliers, and the Prairie Crop Protection Planner calculates application rates, costs per acre, the amount of product the farmer will need to use in the sprayer's tank, and the amount of chemical needed to spray the field.

Government agencies offer decision support systems on the Web. For example, the U.S. Department of Agriculture provides several decision tools online for farmers. One of them uses three decades of historical temperatures to help farmers decide in which regions of Nebraska to plant grapevines, and which types, to avoid crop spoilage due to extreme temperatures. Part of the output is in the form of a color-coded map.

Tax Planning

Some applications that people may not think of as DSSs actually are. TurboTax, TaxCut, and other tax-preparation applications have been developed over the years to do much more than help fill out forms. They come with sophisticated formulas to help taxpayers plan the best strategy in selecting options, with the final purpose of minimizing the tax paid. For example, the

Decisions by Machines

Every year thousands of people are denied credit not because they are bad credit risks, but because of errors that lending institutions make. For example, a newly married woman might be denied credit because her credit history is still only under her maiden name. Errors in recording monthly payments are also a common reason for denying credit; it's possible for one late payment to deduct many points from one's credit score. For some banks, if your credit score is in the 500s or even 600s on a scale of 200–900, you are not considered a good credit risk. Some banks might agree to give you a loan with an interest rate that is higher than most people get.

A single late credit-card or mortgage payment could lower your credit score severely, but you might never know that, because the law does not require anyone to notify you. Many people do not even know that a credit score system exists, and that it is shared by all banks and other lenders. Chances are you will find out about your too-low score only when you apply for a loan and only if you ask for the reason of denial or higher offered interest rate. And when you find out and try to explain that there was a mitigating circumstance for the late payment, your explanation might not help you much. That's because American banks use computers for credit decisions. It is often a computer program that decides who will or will not receive credit. And the decision is final.

Chapter 9, "Challenges of Global Information Systems," pointed out the major differences between U.S. and European privacy laws. One of the areas in which the policies differ is automated decision making that affects individuals. There is no U.S. law that even addresses the issue, while the European Union (EU) restricts the use of automated decision making that affects individuals in its data protection directive.

- **European Protection.** The full title of the EU's directive is *Directive 95/46/EC of the European Parliament and of the Council of 24 October 1995 on the protection of individuals with regard to the processing of personal data and on the free movement of such data.* EU directives are akin to the U.S. Constitution; each member state may formulate its own laws within the framework of the directives. Practically speaking, this means member states may restrict organizations more and afford more protection than the directive requires, but not less.

  Article 15 of the directive is titled "Automated Individual Decisions." It grants every person the right "not to be subject to a decision which produces legal effects concerning him or

significantly affects him and which is based solely on automated processing of data intended to evaluate certain personal aspects relating to him, such as his performance at work, creditworthiness, reliability, conduct, etc."

- **Who Needs Protection?** To what extent should organizations rely on computer-based decision aids to make business decisions about individuals? Automated decision making is used routinely in the United States by banks, credit-card companies, mortgage companies, employers, and, to some extent, educational institutions. The affected individuals might be consumers, credit applicants, employees, job applicants, prospective students, applicants for membership in associations, and people who are evaluated by organizations in other capacities.

  Creditworthiness is determined by processing personal financial data in models that have been developed specifically to sort the good risks from the bad risks. A bad risk is a person or institution that is likely to default on a loan. Should credit-card companies, for instance, ask their officers to open a manila folder for every American adult and make a decision on creditworthiness only after leafing through the filed documents in it? Should they be banned from using an automated process that makes the decision for them based on the same criteria that the officers would use manually? And when employers sift through hundreds and thousands of digitized résumés of job applicants, should they be banned from using software that retrieves the résumés with keywords that suggest a good fit for the job, while eliminating those without them?

  The use of automated decision making offers not only added efficiency but also enhanced effectiveness. When using a DSS or an expert system, the user enjoys the knowledge and experience that have been accumulated by other people over many years. Thus, in addition to efficiency, automated decision making might be more effective than manual decision making.

- **Hidden Injustice.** On the other hand, shifting decision making to a machine might create injustices. Suppose your record is among several hundred records of applicants considered for a position. The records were obtained from a third party, a company that sells personal information. Your qualifications are excellent, but your record also indicates a law violation. The system removes you from the pool of eligible candidates, and you do not get the job. Had you seen your record before its processing, you could have told the company that this entry was an error: you were charged once but acquitted in court. If the company had contacted you, you could have ironed out the misunderstanding and possibly have gotten the job.

Is the EU directive excessive? Do American organizations overuse automated decision making? Is it practical, in the digital age, to give up the efficiency of automated decision making to determine an individual's creditworthiness or job performance? Does a little more justice in credit and employment justify giving up the greater efficiencies of automated decision making?

applications compare filing status and deduction options: which approach would result in a lower combined tax, filing as two individuals or joint filing as husband and wife? Itemizing deductions, or taking a standard deduction? Taking a smaller education credit, or a larger education deduction? Based on the taxable income and the combination of deductions taken, the applications warn users about their chances of being audited by the Internal Revenue Service and give them a chance to modify deductions. The applications also remind users of optional deductions, tell them what the deductions entail (e.g., if you take deduction X you may not take deduction Y or you increase the probability of being audited) and thereby make it easy for filers to make decisions. And when users complete their tax preparation for the past year, they can plan their tax for next year, based on their total income, type of income (wages, business, capital gains, and so forth), and make decisions on how much to contribute to pension funds, charity, and other purposes that serve as tax shields to reduce the tax owed next year.

Web Site Planning and Adjustment

Because so many companies use the Web as a marketing, selling, and customer support tool, decisions on how to design Web sites are extremely important. Some companies offer DSSs specifically designed to analyze shoppers' behavior at their sites based on captured data such as pages viewed, options clicked, and the sequence of pages shoppers view. For example, Datanautics, Inc. offers G2, a path analysis system that analyzes how visitors navigate through a site. Managers might be impressed that 30 percent of shoppers who follow a certain sequence of Web pages purchase an item. However, the software might reveal that another, unexpected sequence ends up with 90 percent of the shoppers buying something. This can lead to a decision to enhance those pages or eliminate certain pages between the home page and the last page before the purchase takes place.

Yield Management

You might be surprised to learn that the passenger sitting next to you on an airplane paid a third of what you paid for the same flight. This is the result of recommendations the airline receives from a DSS whose purpose is to maximize revenue. The concept is called **yield management** or *revenue management*. For each flight, revenue managers enter a myriad of data, including departure point and time, destination point and time of arrival, the number of airports in which the airplane stops, the airplane capacity, and information on utilized capacity from previous operations of the particular flight. They change pricing, or let the system change prices, according to the time a ticket is purchased, and how long before the passenger flies back. The dilemma is between offering low prices to fill up the plane, or upping the price and risking flying with some empty seats.

The purpose of yield management DSSs is to find the proper pricing to maximize the overall revenue from selling seats for each flight. The result is often price discrimination, which is legal and common practice in the airline industry: you might pay a different price depending on how far in advance you purchased the ticket, the fact that a companion flies with you, the number of days between departure and return, and several other variables. Typically, airlines double or triple the price of a ticket when it is purchased only a few days before departure, because usually the availability of seats on competitors' flights is limited. Airlines take advantage of this fact and the expectation that customers who make a late reservation usually do so because they have little flexibility in selecting the flight date. Other variables are less obvious, and therefore DSSs are used to model demand and sensitivity to prices.

Similar decision aids are used in the lodging industry. For example, Harrah's Entertainment, the operators of a chain of hotels and casinos, uses such a system to set room rates for its hotels and for offering different rates to different levels of members in its customer loyalty programs. Room rates might be lower, or even free, for customers who regularly spend a great deal of money on gambling. Like many other companies, the chain has a customer loyalty program called Total Rewards. Harrah's data analysis program, called Revenue Management System, recognizes a Total Rewards member's telephone number and allows reservation agents to offer lower prices for rooms during a busy weekend for a high-value customer—one who usually spends a lot—or to raise the price of a Saturday night stay for customers who don't yield much profit.

Financial Services

Manually deciding how much money to loan to which customer at what interest rate could delay the decision process to a point of losing the potential customer. Loan applicants are reluctant to wait more than a day or even a few hours for the bank's response. Automated decision aids can produce offers within minutes after a customer enters data. The DSS combines this data with data retrieved from credit history databases and preprogrammed rule models to create a rapid response.

Many banks use automated decision aids to determine creditworthiness of clients.

© Comstock Images/Getty Images

Consider DeepGreen Financial, an online home equity lender owned by LightYear Capital. This bank is actually a computer program. To apply for a mortgage loan, customers go to the company's site (www.deepgreenfinancial.com) and fill out an application, which takes no longer than 5 minutes. A DSS retrieves the customers' credit report, engages a scoring formula, accesses an online valuation of the property to be mortgaged, examines fraud and flood insurance conditions, and produces a decision on the loan (such as full amount requested or a smaller amount, with what down payment, and at what interest rate). Eighty percent of applicants receive a response within 2 minutes. The system also selects a local notary public. All that is left for the applicant is to select a closing date. Although many loan applicants still find it strange to think of an online information system as an equity lender, between 2000 (its inception year) and 2005, DeepGreen extended more than 57,000 loans totaling $4.5 billion.

An increasing amount of decision making in the financial services and many other industries are made this way: automatically and in real time. This saves many hours of labor and ensures speedy service for customers.

EXPERT SYSTEMS

It is not always possible to exploit expertise by coupling quantitative data from a database with decision models. In such cases, an expert system might be required. An **expert system (ES)** is developed to emulate the knowledge of an expert to solve problems and make decisions in a relatively narrow domain. A *domain* is a specific area of knowledge. For example, in medicine a domain is often a diagnosis of a specific disease or a family of related diseases, such as bacterial diseases. The purpose of ESs is to replicate the unstructured and undocumented knowledge of the few (the experts), and put it at the disposal of the many other people who need the knowledge, often novices or professionals in the same domain but with far less expertise. Because of the way ESs are formulated (based on the experience of experts), ESs cannot help users deal with events that are not considered by the experts during development. However, more advanced programs that include what are called neural networks (discussed later) can learn from new situations and formulate new rules in their knowledge bases to address events not originally considered in their development. Expert systems and neural networks are two techniques researched and implemented in a field called **artificial intelligence (AI)**. The field is so called because it focuses on methods and technologies to emulate how humans learn and solve problems.

POINT OF INTEREST

The Turing Test

Scientists continue the quest for software that will be at least as smart as humans, so that expertise can be enhanced and delivered through information technology. In 1950, Alan Turing, a British mathematician, published an article titled "Can Machines Think?" His own answer was yes. Today the Turing test is this: Let people present questions to a machine. If the answers fool the questioners into believing that they come from a person, then that machine is considered to be able to think. In 1990, Hugh Loebner offered to grant a gold medal and $100,000 to the first person who could build such a machine. At the annual competition, judges present the same questions to computers and people, but cannot see either. The communication is by text, similar to online chat. Competitors try to build software whose answers would be indistinguishable from those of humans. So far nobody has won.

As Figure 10.6 illustrates, the major difference between DSSs and ESs is in the "base" they use and how it is structured. DSSs use data from databases. An ES uses a **knowledge base**, which is a collection of facts and the relationships among them. An ES does not use a model module but an inference engine. The **inference engine** is software that combines data that is input by the user with the data relationships stored in the knowledge base. The result is a diagnosis or suggestion for the best course of action. In most ESs, the knowledge base is built as a series of IF-THEN rules. Figure 10.7 provides a simple illustration of how such rules are used to conclude which animal is examined. Obviously, one does not need an ES to figure out which animal one is looking at, but other diagnosis and decision making require expertise, which usually consists of many more rules, usually hundreds or thousands. In a mineral exploration, for example, such rules can be: IF the drilling depth is so many meters, AND IF the sample includes a certain percentage of carbon, and so forth, THEN there is a 90-percent probability that so many meters further down there is oil of commercial quality and quantity. Such rules are often not quantitative but qualitative, and therefore can only be stored as a knowledge base rather than a database.

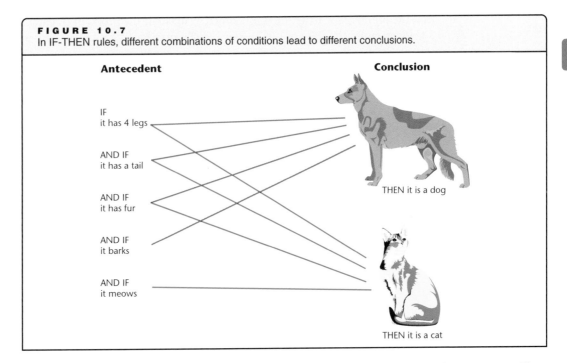

FIGURE 10.7
In IF-THEN rules, different combinations of conditions lead to different conclusions.

ES researchers continue to look for ways to better capture knowledge and represent it. They test the results of such efforts in highly unstructured problem-solving domains, including games. One such game that has intrigued both researchers and laypeople is chess. The game is a highly unstructured environment in which the number of possible moves is enormous, and hence, the player must be an expert to select the best move for every board configuration.

Rather than containing a set of IF-THEN rules, more sophisticated ESs use programs called **neural networks**, which are designed to mimic the way a human brain learns. An ES is constructed with a set of rules, but as data on real successes and failures of decisions is accumulated and fed into the system, the neural network refines the rules to accomplish a higher success rate.

Business applications have increasingly combined neural nets and ES technologies in software that monitors business processes and supply chain management. One example is an application called BizWorks, which was developed by InterBiz Solutions, a division of Computer

Associates International. It was installed at Myers Industries, an international manufacturer of plastic and rubber products for industrial, agricultural, automotive, commercial, and consumer markets. The application uses past production data so it can predict when molding machines are likely to produce defective products. It monitors data coming from the machines, looking for conditions similar to those resulting in defective products in the past. Using another technology called intelligent agents, which are discussed later, the software can alert customers. When BizWorks detects an imminent problem, it checks to see which customers ordered the products that the problematic machine is scheduled to make. If the problem threatens on-time delivery to a key customer, the sales and customer service managers receive an alert. They can then notify the customer.

Neural nets have been very effective in detecting fraud of many types. For example, 85 percent of credit-card issuers use a neural network product called Falcon from HNC Software, a subsidiary of the credit-rating firm Fair Isaac Corporation. The application uses large volumes of cardholder purchasing data and analyzes it to establish spending patterns. Deviations from these patterns trigger an investigation. Using mathematical algorithms, the software calculates, on a scale of 1–999, the likelihood that a transaction is fraudulent. For instance, if a cardholder historically has used his or her card once per week to purchase gasoline and groceries within a certain Pennsylvania zip code, the purchase of groceries in Vermont would trigger a low score of fraud likelihood. If the same card is suddenly used to purchase high-liquidity merchandise such as jewelry, the likelihood would be set at a much higher number. The low-risk pattern changes if the cardholder starts traveling often and makes purchases all over the country or in other countries.

Insurance companies use neural nets to detect fraudulent claims both from the insured party and from health-care providers. Empire Blue Cross Blue Shield has used the technology for many years and has saved millions of dollars. In one case, it caught a doctor who allegedly provided an annual respiratory test that normally is provided no more than twice per lifetime. In another case, it caught a doctor who filed a claim for a pregnancy test, but the software detected that the test was given to a man.

Expert Systems in Action

ESs have been implemented to help professionals in many different industries, such as health care, telecommunications, financial services, and agriculture. The following is a small sample.

Medical Diagnosis

Because medicine is one of the most unstructured domains, it is not surprising that many of the early ESs were developed to help doctors with the diagnosis of symptoms and treatment advice, as mentioned earlier. MYCIN (diagnosis of bacterial diseases), CADUCEUS (internal medicine diagnostics), and PUFF (diagnosis of pulmonary diseases) are only a few of these systems. The latter system includes instrumentation that connects to the patient's body and feeds various data about the patient's condition into the ES to be analyzed for pulmonary diseases.

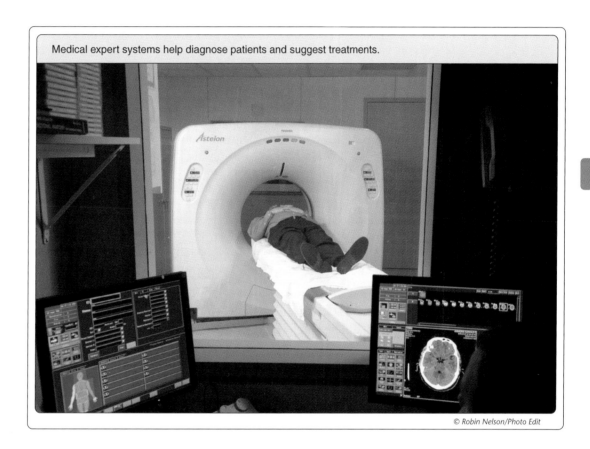

Medical expert systems help diagnose patients and suggest treatments.

© Robin Nelson/Photo Edit

More recently, German scientists developed an ES that enhances the accuracy in diagnoses of Alzheimer's disease, a disease that gradually destroys memory. The system examines positron emission tomography scans of the patient's brain. The scans provide images that can be reliably interpreted only by experienced physicians. Based on the expertise of such experts, the ES can detect Alzheimer's before the appearance of behavior typical of the disease. More than 4.5 million Americans suffer from Alzheimer's, and the proportion of the U.S. population that suffers from this yet cureless disease is growing. An early, accurate diagnosis helps patients and their families plan and gives them time to discuss care while the patient can still take part in decision making. When tested on 150 suspected patients, the ES did as well as the experts. Now it can serve any doctor in early diagnosis of the disease.

Medical Management

In addition to diagnostic ESs, some hospitals use systems that help discern which tests or other initial treatment a patient should receive. Some of the decisions might be administrative. For example, The University of Illinois at Chicago Medical Center uses an application called Discern Expert. It monitors patient data and events and recommends action, such as admission, transfer to another ward or hospital, discharge, or order of tests or treatments. For instance, a set of rules in the system can look like this:

IF: An order for a contrast-enhanced CAT SCAN is received

AND: The patient's BUN level is HIGH

AND: The patient's CREATININE level is HIGH

THEN: Send a message to the patient's physician via electronic mail indicating a possible adverse effect of contrast agent use in this setting.

Blood urea nitrogen (BUN) is caused by the breakdown of blood, muscle, and protein. High levels of it might indicate kidney disease. Creatinine is a protein produced by muscle tissue and released into the blood. High levels of it might indicate kidney failure. Discern Expert helps staff members prevent complications or unnecessary testing. Once a medical ES is composed, it can be used anywhere, bringing expertise to poor regions of the world, where expert doctors are in dire shortage.

Telephone Network Maintenance

Pacific Bell uses an ES to diagnose and fix network failures. The system consists of three parts: Monitor, Consultant, and Forecaster. Monitor constantly checks Pacific Bell's telephone network for errors. When a problem is detected, the system uses a synthesized voice to warn network specialists, who can then use Consultant to walk them through recommended troubleshooting and repair procedures to correct the problem. Before the company started using the ES, a small number of highly trained specialists did the troubleshooting, which is now done by employees with less training. Forecaster, the third part of the ES, checks system files and notifies personnel of problems likely to occur, based on previous experience, allowing the staff to prevent problems from occurring.

Credit Evaluation

Holders of American Express (AmEx) charge cards can potentially charge the card for hundreds of thousands of dollars per purchase. Obviously, most retailers and restaurateurs will not process a charge before they contact AmEx for approval. The AmEx clerk who considers the request uses an ES. The system requests data such as account number, location of the establishment, and amount of the purchase. Coupled with information from a database that contains previous data on the account, and a knowledge base with criteria for approving or denying credit, the ES provides a response.

Another expert system called FAST (Financial Analysis Support Techniques) helps with credit analysis. The system is used by more than 30 of the top 100 U.S. and Canadian banks, as well as some of the largest industrial and financial companies in the world. It gives a credit analyst access to the expertise of more experienced advisors, accelerating the training process and increasing productivity.

The system provides complex analysis of the data contained in applicants' financial reports. The expert system not only provides English-language interpretation of the historical financial output but also prepares the assumptions for annual projections and produces text output linkable to word-processing software. It eliminates much of the tedious writing of analytical reports, producing standard financial statement reviews.

Loan officers periodically update the knowledge base to customize it for a bank's current loan policy, as well as national and local economic forecasts and interest rate projections. The system consistently and reliably interprets the relationship of these variable factors and the levels of sensitivity that the loan officers associate with a particular financial statement.

Detection of Insider Securities Trading

Like other similar institutions, the American Stock Exchange (AMEX) has a special department to prevent insider trading of the securities under its supervision. Insider trading is the trading of stocks based on information available only to those affiliated with a company, not to the general public. This practice is a serious breach of U.S. federal law. To detect insider trading, the department receives information, from several sources, on unusual trading activity and uses this information to identify a stock it might want to investigate. Using an ES, the department's analysts access a large database of the stock's history and choose a time period of interest. The system provides questions that the analysts can answer with the information they received from the database. The questions are formulated to reflect the experience of expert investigators. After the analysts finish answering all the questions, the system provides two numbers: the probability that a further investigation is warranted, and the probability that it is not.

Detection of Common Metals

Metallurgists are experts, and their time is expensive. Also, they usually work in laboratories, which are expensive, too. General Electric Corp. developed an expert system that helps nonexperts to identify common metals and alloys outside laboratories. The user provides information on density, color, and hardness of the metal and results of simple chemical tests that can be performed by novices outside the laboratory setting. If the user provides sufficient information, the system will positively identify the metal or alloy. If there is insufficient information, the system will provide a list of possible metals in order of likelihood. Even such a list can be helpful in some situations, saving much time, labor cost, and the need to wait for lab testing.

Irrigation and Pest Management

Knowing the quantities of water and pesticides to use at different stages of peanut growing can save farmers millions of dollars. After much research, the National Peanut Research Laboratory of the U.S. Department of Agriculture developed an ES called EXNUT to help peanut growers make these decisions. Scientists produced a large knowledge base on plants, weather, soil, and other factors that affect the yield of peanut fields. Farmers feed EXNUT with data about the field throughout the growing season, such as minimum and maximum soil temperature and rainfall measures, and the program provides recommendations on irrigation, the application of fungicide, and the likelihood of pest conditions. It recommends that farmers withhold water during certain stages and that they use the highest and lowest soil temperatures as indicators of soil moisture and plant health.

The system was further developed, and its name was changed to EXNUT Irrigator Pro. Farmers who are not considered experts were able to increase their yield to quantities greater than those harvested by expert farmers, while using less water and fungicide. It costs a farmer $3.71 per acre to use the system, but the results are impressive: growers have increased yield by 200–300 pounds per acre with the help of the ES. The total yield of an acre is usually 5,000–6,000 pounds. The $3.71 cost gained additional revenue of $65.90 per acre.

A related ES, MNUT, helps farmers make sound marketing decisions. The system gives them an indication of the crop's market value, based on environmental conditions. It compares the farmer's predicted output to the predicted output of other farmers in his or her immediate area, state, or the entire country. MNUT also helps warn farmers against aflatoxin, a poisonous substance caused by a certain fungus that likes dry air. Federal law prohibits sale for human consumption of peanuts with 20 parts per billion of aflatoxin or more. Some of the peanut fields are irrigated, and some are not. If the system predicts that the unirrigated peanuts will contain an unacceptable level of the aflatoxin, farmers avoid mixing their irrigated and unirrigated crops, so that they can still sell the good peanuts for human consumption.

Diagnosis and Prediction of Mechanical Failure

Finding out what causes a failure in a system can be daunting. Therefore, it is not surprising that a great number of ESs help methodically diagnose what might cause a failure. For example, technicians at Cessna use the Cessna Diagnostic and Repair ES for the Citation X, an executive jet. If, say, the airplane's floodlight fails, the system starts the analysis with three possible situations. The technician clicks the menu item that describes the situation. In the bottom-left frame the ES lists the components that make up the failing assembly. When the technician clicks an item in the right frame, the ES displays a drawing of the relevant switches. The system contains many "maps" of switches as well as photos of different parts of the cockpit and drawings of electrical circuits. The final output is a set of instructions for fixing the problem.

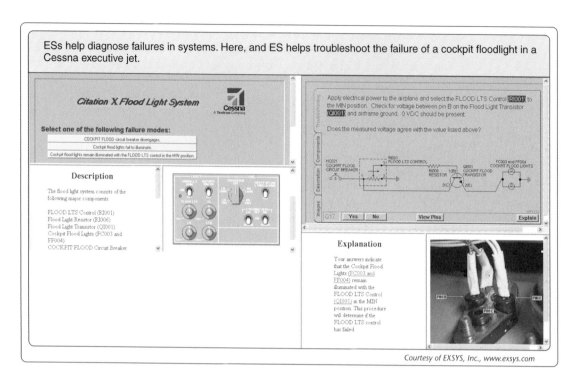

ESs help diagnose failures in systems. Here, and ES helps troubleshoot the failure of a cockpit floodlight in a Cessna executive jet.

Courtesy of EXSYS, Inc., www.exsys.com

A reliable way to predict the failure of diesel locomotive engines is to examine the oil from the engine. Experienced technicians at Canadian Pacific Railroad took many years to develop this expertise, which involves a technician analyzing a sample of lubrication oil for metal impurities, and a mechanic analyzing the data. The process not only takes years to learn, but is difficult to teach to novices, so Canadian Pacific decided to develop an ES for this purpose.

The system takes the spectrum data as input and uses the rules provided by the experts. A technician can use the output report, which details which components require service and which are likely to fail soon. The success of the system has been great. Analysis of more than 10,000 samples has yielded accurate predictions 98 percent of the time. The company saved money by replacing components before they failed. In some cases, the replacement of a single component saved more money than was spent on the development of the ES.

GEOGRAPHIC INFORMATION SYSTEMS

As mentioned in Chapter 5, some decisions can be made only when examining information on a map. Many business decisions concern geographic locations—as input, output, or both. For example, consider the process of choosing the best locations for new stores or determining how to deploy police forces optimally. For map-related decisions, **geographic information systems (GISs)** are often the best decision aids. GISs process location data and provide output. For instance, a GIS could be used to help a housing developer determine where to invest by tracking and displaying population changes on a map, highlighting in color increases of more than 10 percent over the past 3 years. With this information, a developer could easily decide where to invest on the basis of population growth trends. Other examples include the following:

- Delivery managers looking for the shortest distance a truck can travel to deliver ordered goods at the lowest cost.

- School district officials looking for the most efficient routes for busing school children to and from their homes.

- City planners looking to deploy services to better serve residents, which might include police officers deciding how to deploy their forces on the basis of precinct maps indicating levels of criminal activity.

- Health-care agencies analyzing which areas of a community need more or less attention and resources for treatment of certain diseases or injuries that result from criminal violence.

- Oil companies looking to determine drilling locations on the basis of geological tests.

- Hunters, fishers, hikers, and other people who enjoy outdoor recreation looking for suitable sites and trails for their activities based on their requirements, such as local fauna and trail length.

- Mapping concentrations of people at work and in shopping centers to help banks decide where to install new ATMs.

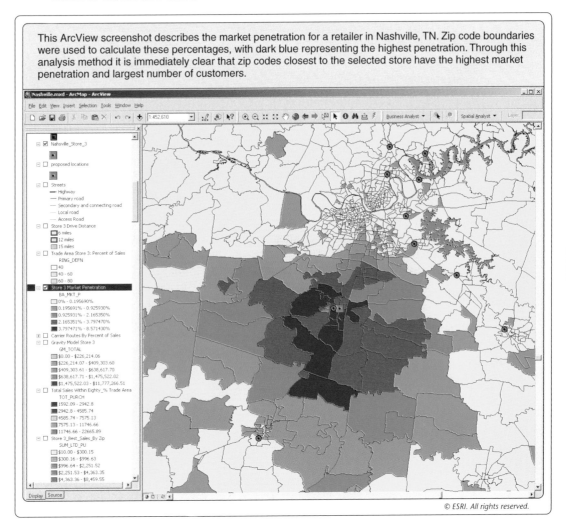

This ArcView screenshot describes the market penetration for a retailer in Nashville, TN. Zip code boundaries were used to calculate these percentages, with dark blue representing the highest penetration. Through this analysis method it is immediately clear that zip codes closest to the selected store have the highest market penetration and largest number of customers.

In Springfield, Massachusetts, for instance, health-care professionals integrated data collected for Hampden County with information from the area's two major medical centers and the health, planning, and police departments to use in combination with the region's map. They use models that help identify geographic areas and population groups that need health-care intervention in youth violence and late-stage breast cancer detection.

A typical GIS consists of (1) a database of quantitative and qualitative data from which information is extracted for display, (2) a database of maps, and (3) a program that displays the information on the maps. The digitized maps are produced from satellite and aerial photography. Displays might be in the form of easily understood symbols and colors or even of moving images. For instance, an oil exploration map might show different concentrations of expected crude oil deposits in different hues of red. Or, population density might be similarly displayed on a map using different hues of blue. A more sophisticated GIS might display, in colors or icons, concentrations of specific consumer groups by age, income, and other characteristics.

Web technology helps promote the use of GISs by private organizations and governments alike. Intranets allow employees to bring up thousands of maps from a central repository on their own PCs. HTML and XML, the primary languages used to compose and retrieve Web pages, support the presentation of pictures with marked areas, which makes them ideal for retrieval of marked maps. Clicking different areas of a map can zoom in and out as well as bring up related information in the form of other maps or text, utilizing the multimedia capabilities of the Web to the fullest.

 For example, sales managers can bring up maps of whole continents and see how past sales have performed over different territories. They can zoom in and zoom out on a territory. With the click of a mouse they can receive detailed information on who serves the territory and other pertinent information. Indeed, more and more retail chains adopt GISs for decision making. One of them is Pollo Tropical, a Hispanic-Caribbean restaurant chain. The company operates 64 restaurants in Florida and more than 20 franchised restaurants in Latin America and the Caribbean. Its managers used "gut feeling" to determine where to open new restaurants. Now they use a GIS with geodemographic data purchased from MapInfo, a leader in location intelligence software. The system helps them pinpoint where their best customers live and work in the company's effort to expand outside Florida.

In government work, a city clerk can bring up a map of the neighborhood of a resident, zoom in on the resident's house pictured on the map, click on the picture, and receive information such as real-estate taxes owed and paid over the past several years. Further information, such as whether a neighborhood uses septic tanks or a sewage system, might be rendered by different colors. The map can also show different zoning codes, such as land designated for residential, industrial, or commercial purposes.

A GIS tool enables law-enforcement officials to determine spatial patterns and hotspots for various types of crimes.

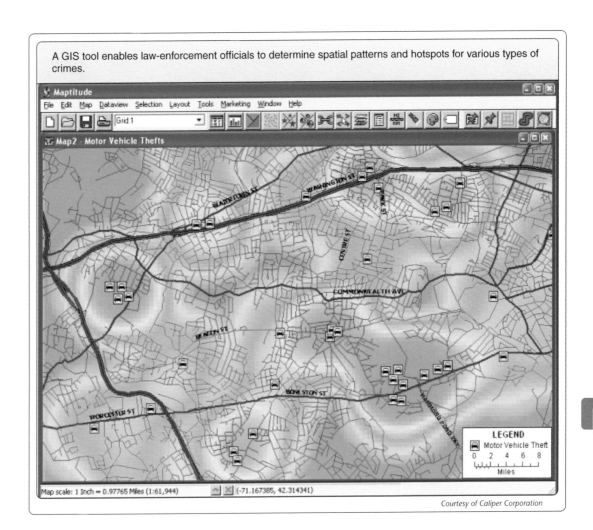

Courtesy of Caliper Corporation

- Decision aids include decision support systems, expert systems, geographic information systems, and any other software tool that helps with decision making automatically or on demand.

- The decision-making process comprises three major phases: intelligence, design, and choice. In the first phase, the data are collected from which relevant information will be gleaned. In the design phase, the manager organizes the data into useful information and uses models to analyze it and produce potential courses of action. In the final stage, the manager selects an alternative, that is, makes the decision.

- Problems span a continuum between two extremes: structured and unstructured. A structured problem is one for whose solution there is a proven algorithm. An unstructured problem is one for which there are multiple potential solutions.

- Most DSSs have three components. The data management module gives the user access to databases from which relevant information can be retrieved. The model management module selects, or lets the user select, an appropriate model through which the data are analyzed. The dialog module serves as an interface between the user and the other two modules. It allows the user to enter queries and parameters, and then presents the result in an appropriate or selected form, such as tabular or graphical.

- DSSs provide a quick way to perform sensitivity analysis. The user can change one or several parameters in the model and answer "what if" questions, called what if analysis.

- Powerful software tools such as electronic spreadsheets let users with little expertise in systems development create their own DSSs.

- Expert systems are developed to emulate the knowledge of an expert. Developers use artificial intelligence techniques.

- An expert system consists of a knowledge base, inference engine, and a dialog module.

- Neural network software is often integrated into an expert system to enable the system to learn and refine decision rules based on success or failure.

- Expert systems are used in narrow domains in which typical diagnosis and decisions are unstructured, such as health care, mineral exploration, stock investment, and weather forecasting.

- When decisions involve locations and routes, professionals can use geographic information systems (GISs). GISs provide maps with icons and colors to represent population concentrations, potential natural resources, deployment of police forces, pinpointing concentrations of diseases, and other factors that have to do with locations and routes.

- Computerized decision aids practically leave decision making to machines. When machines determine whom to hire, whom to accept for higher education, or to whom to give credit, the decision-making process could overlook important circumstances, in which case people might be done injustices.

DEBOER FARMS REVISITED

Carl DeBoer has been using an expert system to help manage pests on his farm. Such expert systems, as well as decision support systems, are increasingly used to assist the DeBoers and other farmers in their work.

decision making, monitoring, diagnosis, training, incidental learning, replication of expertise, timely response, and consistent solutions. Cite some examples of these contributions that the Pest-PRO system has made to DeBoer Farms.

What Would You Do?

1. Dr. Wildes told Carl that the PestPRO system took years to refine. Explain how the historical data and comparison with scientists' results can help computer systems "learn" through feedback.

2. The chapter illustrated nine contributions of expert systems to organizations: planning,

New Perspectives

1. Carl explored a decision support system that helps manage risk and an expert system to help handle infestations. What other types of decision support systems might help farm owners manage their businesses?

KEY TERMS

algorithm, 319
artificial intelligence (AI), 332
data management module, 322
decision support system
    (DSS), 321
dialog module, 325
expert system (ES), 332
geographic information system
    (GIS), 338

inference engine, 332
knowledge base, 332
model, 319
model management
    module, 323
neural network, 333
parameter, 319
semistructured problem, 320

sensitivity analysis, 327
structured problem, 319
unstructured problem, 319
what if analysis, 327
yield management, 330

REVIEW QUESTIONS

1. What is a decision? When does a person have to make a decision?

2. Calculating a complex trajectory of a spaceship to Mars is a structured problem, whereas diagnosing the cause of a rash on a person's skin is often unstructured. How so?

3. DSSs use models to process data. Explain what a model is. Give an example that is not mentioned in the chapter.

4. Many DSSs are not stand-alone anymore, but are embedded in other ISs. What are those ISs?

5. What is a sensitivity test? Give three examples.

6. The airline and lodging industries use DSSs for yield management. What is yield management, and what is the output of yield management DSS?

7. What is the purpose of an expert system? How can it serve as a competitive weapon?

8. Expert systems can distribute expertise. How so?

9. How could an ES be used to detect probable fraud committed by a bank employee?

10. What is the advantage of combining ES and neural net technologies?

11. What is a GIS? What purpose does it serve?

12. Two major elements are combined to make up a GIS. What are they?

DISCUSSION QUESTIONS

1. DSSs and ESs structure an often unstructured decision-making process. Explain this statement.

2. Bank officers use DSSs to decide to whom to extend and to whom to deny credit. Universities might use DSSs to decide which applicant to admit and which applicant to reject. Would you agree to using DSSs for such decisions without human intervention?

3. Some companies (such as Mrs. Fields Cookies) use DSSs to make decisions for their managers. The decisions are based on previous experience and on corporate policy. Would you prefer to work for a company that requires you to use a DSS for the decisions you have to execute, or would you rather work for a company that lets you make decisions on your own? Explain.

4. Some managers say that you should never accept the output of any computer-based decision aid without scrutiny. Do you agree? Explain.

5. Give three examples of a business decision for which you would not use a decision support system or any other software. Give three non-business examples. Explain.

6. Think of executives in human resources, finance, marketing, and information systems. In which of these areas could executives benefit the most from using GIS technologies? Explain.

7. Some DSSs allow the user to select a model for an analysis. Would you like to have the last say in determining which model would be used, or would you prefer to let the software use whatever model it chose for the analysis, and then produce a decision? Why?

8. How could you use a GIS for scheduling your classes? What would be the likely sources of information for such a system?

9. Some GISs are used for very small geographic areas, such as a campus or a single building. Can you think of how a GIS could help the maintenance department of a university campus?

10. As an increasing amount of decision making is carried out by software, do you think the demand for college-educated workers will diminish?

11. You noticed that the family doctor and the specialists that you see consult their PC and handheld computers for practically every diagnosis they make and for every prescription they give you. Does this make you trust these physicians less than physicians who do not consult their computers?

12. Many software packages offer expertise in a multitude of areas, such as investment, nutrition, and writing your own will. Do you trust the advice of such software?

13. "The more professionals use ESs, the less expertise they accumulate, because the less actual hands-on experience they gain. This is akin to a pilot who spends most of his flying time watching an autopilot system rather than flying the airplane with his own hands." Do you think that ESs can *decrease* real expertise for its users? Why or why not?

1. Make a list of six daily activities you perform. They might include preparing homework assignments, shopping, and other activities. Ensure that three of the activities call for decision making that is unstructured (or semistructured) and that three involve structured decision making. Prepare a one-page report listing the activities, stating what decision making is required, and explaining why the decision making is unstructured or structured.

2. Prepare a one-page report on the career you intend to pursue. Give at least four examples of activities involved in such a career that call for

problem solving. Explain which problem solving is structured and which is unstructured.

3. You are the head of a medical team that wants to learn about the spread of a new disease in your state. You decide to engage a company that designs GISs. List the types of data that would be needed for the system and which agencies are likely to have collected the data. Suggest visual effects to make it easy to identify concentrations of sick people and the spread of the disease.

HANDS-ON ACTIVITIES

1. Use an electronic spreadsheet such as Excel to design a DSS for solving the following problem. A publisher makes and sells books that have different titles but have the same format and are made of the same materials (paper, ink, binding, and so forth). Three types of costs are involved in the process:

   ■ *Fixed cost per title*: $15,000 for setting up the press, regardless of how many pages a title has or how many copies will be made of that title.

   ■ *Fixed cost per page*: Setting the plates for printing costs $2.00 per page, regardless of the number of books. (Thus, for a book of 324 pages, the per-page fixed cost would be $648.)

   ■ *Variable cost per page*: The printing and binding of each page of each copy of a title costs 7 cents.

   Assume that no other costs are involved (such as shipping and handling). Prepare a decision model that allows the publisher to decide the following:

   a. For a given number of copies, what should be the book's minimum retail price per copy to break even?

   b. For a given retail price, what is the break-even quantity of copies?

   Test your decision tool for a title that has 250 pages. If the publisher intends to sell 40,000 copies, what is the break-even price? If

the publisher decides to price the book at $18.00, what is the break-even quantity that must be sold?

E-mail your spreadsheet to your professor, attached to a message in which you answer the two test questions.

2. Use a spreadsheet or download a free ES shell for this assignment. Build a simple ES that determines the eligibility of an applicant for a bank loan of $50,000 for 30 years. Eligibility is determined by the number of points the applicant accumulates in several risk categories, based on the following:

Risk Category	Points
Age	
20 < age < 25	0
25 < age < 60	10
60 < age	0
Income (annual $) per household member	
income < 20,000	0
20,000 < income < 40,000	10
40,000 < income < 60,000	20
60,000 < income < 85,000	30
85,000 < income	40

Employment at current workplace

self-employed	10
less than 2 years	5
more than 2 years	10

Net worth (in $)

NW < 30,000	0
30,000 < NW < 50,000	10
50,000 < NW < 70,000	20
NW > 70,000	30

Loan size

No points are deducted for a $10,000 loan. Henceforth, 2 points are deducted from the total score for each additional $10,000 of the requested loan.

Loan life

No points are deducted for the first 5 years of the loan's life (years to repay the loan). Henceforth, 1 point is deducted for every 5 years.

Rule

If the applicant's total number of points is equal to or exceeds 60, grant the loan.

TEAM ACTIVITIES

1. Team up with two other students. Contact a local stockbroker. Ask the broker to give you a list of the most important points he or she considers when predicting appreciation of a stock. Ask how each point (such as last year's earnings per share, percentage of appreciation/depreciation over the past 6 months, and the like) affects the net result, as a percentage. Use the input to formalize the model in a spreadsheet application. Select a portfolio of 100 units of 10 traded stocks. Use the model to predict the increase in the price of each stock and the value of the entire portfolio a year into the future. If you know how to use macros, embellish your new DSS with a user-friendly dialog module.

2. Some decisions must be made by more than one person, perhaps a large group. Increasingly, the group must collaborate remotely through the Internet. Team up with another student. Your professor will give only one of you (student A) the pictorial description of a simple structure (e.g., an awning, a shed, or some other simple structure) that needs to be constructed. You and your teammate must be in two separate locations, not being able to see or hear each other. You may only set up the time when both of you will be at PCs with a certain IP number. Use NetMeeting to communicate. Student A should communicate to student B what's to be constructed. Both students should have a clear depiction of the structure (including measurements) and its color, and agree on it. When finished, meet face to face to see whether you agreed on the same features.

3. Obtain a digitized map of your campus. If you cannot copy one, you can use a scanner to digitize a paper map. Use a Web design application (such as FrontPage) to create a simple GIS. On the map page, mark 10 areas so that when clicked, another page comes up with additional information about the building or part of building you marked. Examples of marked areas that you could include: registrar's office, school of business building, the student union, and the PC lab. E-mail your GIS to your professor.

COMPANION CD QUESTIONS

1. Identify two customer relationship management (CRM) systems. What is the role of databases in these systems?

2. How can spreadsheets be used in decision support systems?

VIDEO QUESTIONS

1. What other sites could you combine with Google Maps to create new Web sites or products?

2. The video describes the merger of two Web sites: Craig's list and Google Maps. Give an example of two other sites that you'd like to see merged to create a new site, product, or service.

FROM IDEAS TO APPLICATION: REAL CASES

Minimize Credit Risks

Companies that extend credit want to be able to assess the risk of not being paid by their clients, with many of whom they have had no previous experience. While large companies often have their own risk assessment experts or use the expensive services of consultants, medium-size companies with revenues of $50–200 million per annum have traditionally found it difficult to assess the risk involved in doing business globally. One American company saw this as a business opportunity and decided to offer these firms the tools to reduce their exposure to credit risks, network security threats, ID theft, and other risks. The Web allowed it to offer expertise online.

American International Group, Inc. (AIG) is one of the world's largest insurance and financial services companies, with operations in 130 countries. The company offers its Web site TradeCredit.com (www.aigtradecredit.com), which provides up-to-the minute credit information about businesses that intend to buy goods and services from AIG's clients. Clients log on and can assess and monitor the buying power and repayment capabilities of a customer. AIG's system tracks, in real time, the financial standing of companies around the globe. This helps the seller—AIG's client—to set down payments and payment timetables that take into consideration the risk of not being paid in time or at all.

In addition, the system tracks and assesses country-specific risk variables, such as political instabilities and changes in trade laws. It also updates industry-specific risks, which are related to specific industries rather than the country in which a buyer operates. The risks are determined by experts who update the systems frequently.

AIG developed the original system in-house and implemented it in 1999. However, every time risk algorithms changed, programmers had to modify the code. The programming was time-consuming and costly. The IT department had to modify the original system so it would contain a structured credit algorithm that could be adapted to individual countries based on parameters that characterized business conditions and credit practices in each country. The idea was to separate the algorithms from tables that contain changing parameters. This way, managers can change parameters in country and industry tables, and the changes take effect in the algorithms automatically. This keeps the need to reprogram to a minimum.

Paul Narayanan, the manager of AIG's eBusiness Risk Solution Division, said that the major challenge was to transform the business rules into software code and design the software so that fine-tuning of those rules could be done without too much hassle. The system contains risk models shared by all countries, but in addition also special rules for each country and even regions within countries.

For the original DSS, experts developed complex risk models in Microsoft Excel. The models were eventually converted into Java for installation at AIG's Web site. The system became increasingly complex. After several years of operations the IT professionals realized that developing rules for additional countries took too long, about 2 months for each country. AIG purchased a financial risk DSS called Blaze Advisor from Fair Isaac, a credit assessment firm.

With the integration of Blaze Advisor, managers can change decision rules without involving programmers. Within the first 3 months of using the integrated system, AIG added 14 countries to the mere 2 that it covered before. The rules for a country that is already in the system can be updated with new rules within 8 hours. Risk models, rating criteria, and decision algorithms for new countries can be added in 5–14 days.

A subscriber to AIG TradeCredit.com logs on and enters the details identifying a company with which the subscriber wishes to do business. The subscriber receives real-time assessment of the potential buyer's ability to pay for goods and services. The subscriber can also receive the payment history of the company and make his or her own decisions. The system works so well that it is endorsed by the U.S. Chamber of Commerce for its members.

Sources: "Fair Isaac Blaze Advisor Business Rules Automate Risk Decisions for AIG TradeCredit.com," www.fairisaac.com, 2005; www.aig.com, 2005.

Thinking About the Case

1. Why is a system such as TradeCredit so important, especially in the era of e-commerce?

2. What are the advantages of using an online DSS such as this?

3. Why was the original software (developed in-house) merged with Blaze Advisor?

Modeling Health Care

How much of the physiology of the human body can be embedded in a computer program? How many diseases develop in a pattern that can be simulated in a software application? Apparently, a lot. Archimedes, named after the famous Greek mathematician and discoverer, is a medical decision-making application. What are the chances that a 31-year-old female with cancer and who smokes will respond better to one treatment than another? Ask Archimedes.

The unique decision support system was developed by David Eddy, the son and grandson of surgeons. Although he is a medical doctor, halfway through his residency he heard a different calling. He wanted to help patients via digitized medical modeling instead of a surgeon's scalpel. He obtained a Ph.D. in mathematics and developed a career in mathematical modeling to improve medical tests and treatments.

Eddy was dissatisfied with the shortcomings of medical treatment. When he set out to design his new system, the generally accepted patterns of diagnosis and treatment were simple: if a patient had a certain symptom, such as a lump in the chest, doctors would prescribe a certain treatment. There was little regard for the many other factors that might cause the situation as well as have an impact on the success of the treatment. Doctors rarely considered the treatment's chances of benefits and harms.

Eddy's system was developed by the Biomathematics Unit of Kaiser Permanente's Care Management Institute. The unit's head, Leonard Schlessinger, and his team used differential equations and algorithms to describe the anatomy, physiology, and progress of diseases. For example, based on epidemiological studies and clinical trials, they created a model of coronary artery disease. The model calculates the location and extent of the blockage and occurrence of symptoms. It then calculates the outcomes of the disease. Algorithms model the actions of patients and caregivers: patient behavior in seeking care, the performance of tests, and treatments by physicians. Before prescribing a treatment, physicians can try different treatments and change the process of care for a disease and then explore the effect that the system reports.

The starting point of modeling a disease and its treatment is a session with experts who know all about the disease. They describe the symptoms, impact on patients, and suggested treatments. Eddy and his team map out the symptoms associated with the progression of the disease. They add to the model equations that represent the symptoms and progression as well as the patient demographics. In all, there might be 50–100 variables that impact the progression of a disease.

Building a model for one disease takes over a year and costs $0.5–1 million. However, the rewards are impressive. Using Archimedes for proper drug prescriptions more than 10 years for just 10,000 patients with coronary artery disease can result in 4063 avoided heart attacks, 893 avoided deaths, and monetary savings of $44 million for Kaiser Permanente.

Physicians can use Archimedes to examine the impact of age, sex, race, income, employment, and eating habits—among other variables—on a person's health, as well as the effect of different treatment regimens. The application's accuracy is equal to that of doctors with tens of years of experience. It contains rules that researchers reach only after many years of clinical trials involving thousands of real patients. Medical trials that would take months or years can be simulated with Archimedes and take no more than 30 minutes.

The decisions doctors can make with Archimedes include the choice of tests, decision to hospitalize or not to hospitalize, medications, and the timing of treatments. The system also provides the cost of treatment and probable outcomes.

The system helps medical staffs and managers of medical centers plan better. It helps decide on which treatments to spend money. For example, it might show hospital managers that if they treat 1,000 patients who have angina pectoris (chest pains) with a certain treatment, the hospital can prevent 72 heart attacks and the cost of the treatment will be $6 million. Comparing the information with similar information about other treatments and alternative treatments of other diseases, managers can decide how best to can allocate resources. Thus, Archimedes addresses two purposes: medical treatment and medical management.

Sources: Wallace, P., "The Care Management Institute: Making the Right Thing Easier to Do," *The Permanente Journal*, Spring 2005, Volume 9 No. 2; Southwick, K., " 'Doctor Data' Digitizes Medical Care," *CIO Insight* (www.cioinsight.com), April 17, 2003; Care Management Institute, "Archimedes," www.kpcmi.org/media/archimedesqa.html, June 20, 2003.

Thinking About the Case

1. What are the data on which the Archimedes system relies?

2. A physician familiar with Eddy and his work admires the logic embedded in Archimedes but says it would be difficult to sell a system like this to other hospitals, because health care is an emotionally charged issue. Do you agree with the observation?

3. Does the system replace doctors? Why or why not?

Mapping Risk

The purpose of purchasing insurance is to pass risks to an insurance firm. However, insurance firms do not like risks any more than the individuals and businesses they insure. Therefore, insurance executives try to pinpoint the locations, or whole regions, with greater risks and those with lower risk. Knowing this helps them price their insurance policies better, or decide if they want to insure a certain asset at all. In addition, many insurance firms reinsure, which means they pay premiums to reinsurers, companies that reimburse the insurers if the insurers have to compensate their own clients.

Early in the 20th century many insurance companies refused to insure small properties, especially in certain urban areas. Therefore, in 1907, 150 owners of tenement houses on the East Side of New York City formed a trade association to protect their interests. They named it Greater New York Taxpayers Association. Over the years, the association turned into the GNY insurance company. GNY consists of Greater New York Mutual Insurance Company and Insurance Company of Greater New York. A.M. Best, the premier rater of insurance companies, granted the firm an A+ rating.

Greater New York Insurance Companies (GNY) has $200 million of direct insurance premiums. The terrible events of September 11, 2001, cost insurance companies $19 billion. After the 9/11 terrorist attacks, GNY found out that reinsurers were less willing to do business in the city. It could not reinsure as much of its business as it could before. One way of coping with the problem was to know the relationship between a location and its risks. Insurers want to know how much money they would have to pay in case of a total destruction of an asset. They call this total exposure. If the firm could show reinsurers total risks and total exposure relative to locations, they might be more comfortable taking the risks.

GNY executives wanted to be able to see all the risks they had by policy type and exposure within a certain radius from each pinpointed location, such as the Empire State Building. If the building were to be destroyed, what would be the total exposure: $2 billion? $5 billion? They decided to adopt mapping software. They considered products from MapInfo, CDS Business Mapping, Baseline Business Geographics, and Millbrook Inc.

After product demonstrations at the company's offices in East Brunswick, New Jersey, GNY decided to purchase MapInfo's system. MapInfo's programmers adapted the system to GNY's requirements. They installed a Web server in the company's New York offices so that the system could be available through an intranet to all employees. The data for the GIS came from policy, claim, and accounting information, all of which resided on an IBM AS/400 computer. The data is processed weekly through geocoding, that is, mapping it onto maps. The process involves 50,000–60,000 records and takes about 8 minutes. The result is an updated Access database that holds both the textual and numeric data and its relation to map locations.

Employees use Microsoft Internet Explorer to enter a location's address and a radius, usually 500 feet or greater. The system returns a map with icons, and a legend on the right-hand side lists the displayed content represented by each icon. When the search is for a product (that is, a certain type of insurance policy), a dot with a certain color represents each product. For example, if the search is by risk exposure (the maximum payment for a claim), red dots might represent $5 million and higher, blue dots might represent $2 million and higher, and so forth. Alternatively, the size of the dot can be changed for size of exposure.

If users so desire, they can obtain information such as agent code, construction code, product, protection class, and policy type for each insured asset on the map. Each information search can be performed by any three codes, including zip code. By clicking a link below the legend, search results can be exported into an Excel spreadsheet.

Management found that the investment was worthwhile. It paid $25,000 for the hardware and $64,000 for the software, training, and maintenance during the first year of operation. GNY has a maintenance contract with MapInfo, which costs $40,000 per year for the first 2 years. Now, underwriters do not need to use separate applications to associate risks with locations; they simply map the risks on a map. The underwriters are more comfortable with their decisions on whether to take a risk and insure an asset, and GNY's reinsurers are more comfortable with their own decisions when they see the risks drawn on a map.

Sources: www.gisdevelopment.net, 2005; www.gny.com, 2005; O'Donnell, A., "Mapping System Reassures Reinsurers," *Insurance & Technology* (www.insurancetech.com), March 3, 2003.

Thinking About the Case

1. Is the system described in the case really a GIS? If not, explain why not. If it is a GIS, explain what makes it one.

2. Is the system a DSS? Explain why or why not.

3. If you were a reinsurer's underwriter looking at information on this system, give an example of why you might refuse to insure an asset.

11

ELEVEN

Business Intelligence and Knowledge Management

LEARNING OBJECTIVES

As more and more business operations are managed using information from information systems and sometimes automatically *by* information systems, large amounts of data are collected and stored electronically. With proper software tools, data stored in databases and data warehouses enables executives to glean business intelligence, information that helps them know more about customers and suppliers, and therefore helps them make better decisions. Information technology also enables organizations to organize stored knowledge and garner knowledge from vast amounts of unstructured data.

When you finish this chapter, you will be able to:

- Explain the concepts of data mining and online analytical processing.

- Explain the notion of business intelligence and its benefits to organizations.

- Identify needs for knowledge storage and management in organizations.

- Explain the challenges in knowledge management and its benefits to organizations.

DEBOER FARMS:
Harvesting Technology's Benefits

Carl DeBoer looked out at the crowd. When Steve Jansson first asked him to talk about precision farming at a workshop for other farmers, Carl thought Steve was having a good joke at his expense. Carl was not exactly a technical genius. But Steve convinced Carl that he could serve as an example to others since DeBoer Farms had successfully implemented the system.

A New Type of Data

Carl looked down at his notes and began. "Precision farming is revolutionary not because it uses satellites and space age technology, but because it's an entirely new way to collect information about your farm, to manage that information, and to use it to help you make better decisions about how to increase your yield, reduce your risk, and increase profits.

"I had always monitored information, as you all do, on a per field basis. I took soil samples within a field, averaged the results, and then spread fertilizer uniformly over the field. I seeded the same way—evenly over the whole field. I measured my yield *per field*. Of course, I knew that there were differences within the field—I noticed that some parts of a field produced a better yield per acre than others and that some areas had more weeds. I knew there were differences *within* my fields, but until precision farming, there was no practical way to get meaningful information about these differences. There was no practical way to gather, store, or analyze this data, much less to customize the type and amount of fertilizer or seed to the different areas within a field. Precision farming has changed all that. It gathers and analyzes new data within a field and gives you detailed information on what to do about it."

Collecting Data for the Warehouse

"Okay, let's talk about how the system gathers this new data." Carl turned to his second page of notes. "Precision farming uses a geographic information system, or GIS, to make maps of your farm. You use data collection devices in the fields and handheld computers to enter the data and the GIS converts the data into yield, soil nutrients, topology, and weed maps.

"There are other kinds of data collection devices. We use an on-the-go weed detection system that relies on an optical camera, but I know other folks are using sensors that detect salt bands or grain protein.

"You can also enter data yourself. As you take soil samples, you use a handheld computer to record where exactly you took the sample from within the field. You can also record the patches of your field that have weeds. If you're taking insect counts, you can enter that information too.

"All this data you're collecting is used in two ways. First, it's used for all your current operations. If you've recorded a patch of weeds in a part of the field, you can program your tractor to spot spray that area the following day. Second, the data is collected into a data warehouse that stores all your input and output over the years. This is called historical data, and collecting and analyzing this type of data is what will really increase your yield."

Mining the Data

"Here's how it works," Carl continued. "Once you collected all this data into your warehouse, your program analyzes this data to find correlations. You might want to know what events lead to others. Has early planting led to insect infestation? Is crop rotation combating insect infestation? Your program can mine the data and answer these questions.

"Your program can also find clusters in your data, groups of data that you didn't know were related. For example, when the field floods, what part of the field will be nitrogen deficient as a result of runoff? Is there a pattern? If so, this program can detect it and you can program your tractor to fertilize those areas—without going through the trouble and expense of soil testing!

"The program also mines the data in the warehouse to make predictions. The program analyzes input factors like soil nutrients and seed density and output—crop production. You folks are probably all familiar with yield maps, maps that show crop production in a given season. This program generates a prescription map. After analyzing input and output correlations, the program generates recommendations regarding the types and amounts of fertilizers, seeds, and pesticides to use in each area of your field. The prescription map shows the amount of input factors, like fertilizer, pesticide, and seed, to use in different places. It shows the amount and type of input that will most likely produce the greatest output.

"There are a number of different software products that perform this analysis, but I know Sam Beatty is going to be speaking about the pros and cons of each of those systems later."

Implementing the System

"The next step is to implement the results of the analysis. For this, you need instruments that use variable rate technology, or VRT. You might have heard of a VRT sprayer or a VRT planter. These devices, mounted on a tractor, adjust the rate of application according to the prescription map that your software created. You can also use different seeds or fertilizer blends within a field. You can spot spray for weeds or insects and enter that information into the system and then view it later on the map."

Carl looked up from his notes. "Is all that clear?"

Laughter erupted from the audience. Then he noticed Fred Halpern raising his hand. "Go ahead, Fred," Carl said.

"Are you really saving money with this system?"

"Last year I saved $11 per acre. My yield improved, but I also used less seed, less pesticide, and less fertilizer. And you know what else, Fred? When you use less fertilizer, you have less runoff and that's better for the environment—and our groundwater."

"I'd heard that," Fred said. "But it really does sound a bit complicated."

"Well, we had to purchase new computer hardware, software, telecommunications equipment, and related high-tech field machinery. We had to spend time and money training so that we could figure out how to use data-logging software, field-mapping software, and VRT planters and sprayers. But, Fred, you know why they asked me to speak, don't you?" Carl paused to see if anyone would respond. "Well, if I can do it, anyone can!"

Carl heard some people laugh and saw others smile.

DATA MINING AND ONLINE ANALYSIS

Recall from our discussion in Chapter 7 that data warehouses are large databases containing historical transactions and other data. However, data warehouses in themselves are useless. To make data warehouses useful, organizations must use software tools to process data from these huge databases into meaningful information. Because executives can obtain significantly more information about their customers, suppliers, and their own organizations, they like to call information gleaned with such tools **business intelligence (BI)**. There are two main uses of these databases: data mining and online analytical processing.

Data Mining

Data warehouses could be regarded as a type of mine, where the data is the ore, and new useful information is the precious find. **Data mining** is the process of selecting, exploring, and modeling large amounts of data to discover previously unknown relationships that can support decision making. Data-mining software searches through large amounts of data for meaningful patterns of information.

While some tools help find predefined relationships and ratios, they do not answer the question that more powerful data-mining tools can answer: "What are the relationships we do not yet know?" This is because the investigator must determine which relationship the software should look for in the first place. To answer this question, other techniques are used in data mining, including artificial intelligence techniques, mentioned in Chapter 10.

To illustrate the difference between traditional queries and data-mining queries, consider the following examples. A typical traditional query would be: "What is the relationship between the amount of product X and the amount of product Y that we sold over the past quarter?" A typical data-mining query would be: "Discover two products most likely to sell well together on a weekend." The latter query lets the software find patterns that would otherwise not be detected through observation. While data has traditionally been used to see whether this or that pattern exists, data mining allows you to ask *what* patterns exist. Thus, some experts say that in data mining you let the computer answer questions that you do not know to ask. The combination of data-warehousing techniques and data-mining software makes it easier to predict future outcomes based on patterns discovered within historical data.

Data mining has four main objectives:

* *Sequence* or *path analysis*: Finding patterns where one event leads to another, later event.
* *Classification*: Finding whether certain facts fall into predefined groups.
* *Clustering*: Finding groups of related facts not previously known.
* *Forecasting*: Discovering patterns in data that can lead to reasonable predictions.

These techniques can be used in marketing, fraud detection, and other areas (see Figure 11.1). Data mining is most often used by marketing managers, who are constantly analyzing purchasing patterns so that potential buyers can be targeted more efficiently through special sales, product displays, or direct mail and e-mail campaigns. Data mining is an especially powerful tool in an environment in which businesses are shifting from mass-marketing a product to targeting the individual consumer with a variety of products that are likely to satisfy that person. Some observers call this approach "marketing to one."

Predicting Customer Behavior

Data mining is also used in banking, where it is employed to find profitable customers and patterns of fraud. It is also used to predict bankruptcies and loan payment defaults. For example, when Bank of America (BofA) looked for new approaches to retain customers, it used data-mining techniques. It merged various behavior patterns into finely tuned customer profiles. The data was clustered into smaller groups of individuals who were using banking services that didn't best support their activities. Bank employees contacted these customers and offered advice on services that would serve them better. The result was greater customer loyalty (measured in fewer accounts closed and fewer moves to other banks). The people who were contacted thought that the bank was trying to take good care of their money.

POINT OF INTEREST

Did You Really Buy It?

Many retailers will accept a returned item even if you cannot show a receipt. Some people take advantage of this and "return" stolen goods for cash. To minimize the phenomenon, some retailers have joined the Return Exchange, a program run by a company by the same name in Irvine, California. Now, when you return merchandise without a receipt to Staples, The Sports Authority, Guess, or another member retailer, you are asked to present a driver's license or other identification. The information is recorded and communicated to Return Exchange. The company uses statistical models to determine if certain "customers" engage in fraud. If the software determines that a person has defrauded retailers, the stores will stop accepting the person's returns. However, neither the retail chains nor the company disclose the criteria used to make the decision. Return Exchange does not allow retailers to share customer information.

FIGURE 11.1
Potential applications of data mining

DATA-MINING APPLICATION	*DESCRIPTION*
Consumer clustering	Identify the common characteristics of customers who tend to buy the same products and services from your company.
Customer churn	Identify the reason customers switch to competitors; predict which customers are likely to do so.
Fraud detection	Identify characteristics of transactions that are most likely to be fraudulent.
Direct marketing	Identify which prospective clients should be included in a mailing or e-mail list to obtain the highest response rate.
Interactive marketing	Predict what each individual accessing a Web site is most likely to be interested in seeing.
Market basket analysis	Understand what products or services are commonly purchased together, and on what days of the week.
Trend analysis	Reveal the difference between a typical customer this month and a typical customer last month.

Companies selling mobile phone services face a growing challenge of *customer churn* (switching to a competitor). Some surveys show that more than 50 percent of mobile phone users consider switching to a competitor at any given time, and 15 percent plan to switch to a competitor as soon as their contract expires. Mobilcom GmbH, a German company with 4.56 million customers and 1,100 employees, uses data mining to identify such customers and approach them with inducements to continue or renew their contract before they switch. The company uses an application called DB Intelligent Miner from IBM. The software periodically looks for patterns of customer churns, and assigns each customer a score representing the likelihood of canceling the contract. The software considers many variables, among which are the number of days to expiration and complaint history. Customer loyalty is extremely important because the cost of obtaining a new customer far exceeds the cost of retaining an existing one, especially in a highly competitive market such as mobile telephones.

To ensure a steady flow of customer data into their data warehouses, companies in almost every industry—from airlines through lodging, dining, and gambling—operate customer loyalty programs similar to the original frequent flier programs. Membership is often free, and customers leave a record every time they make a purchase even if they do not use a credit card to pay. In many cases mining such data provides business intelligence to target individual customers.

Utilizing Loyalty Programs

Loyalty programs such as frequent flier and consumer clubs help organizations amass huge amounts of data about their customers. Some grocery chains, for example, issue discount coupons only to the most loyal customers. Harrah's Entertainment Inc., the gambling and hotel chain, uses its data warehouse to target individual customers, rather than groups. The techniques—whose specifics the company refuses to disclose for obvious reasons—enables Harrah's to tailor lodging, dining, and gambling packages that are attractive to its customers. It helps discern the small spender from the big spender and decide how to price those services by individual spending patterns at the company's facilities. This is an example of yield management or revenue management, a concept introduced in Chapter 10. Harrah's relies heavily on its software applications to price-discriminate. It gives sales agents instructions to charge people who have a history of little spending on gambling higher per-night rates than they charge big gamblers.

Inferring Demographics

Some companies use data-mining techniques to try to predict what customers are likely to purchase in the future. As mentioned in previous chapters, Amazon.com is a leader in exploiting customer data. The company registered U.S. Patent Number 6,865,546, titled "Methods and systems of assisting users in purchasing items." The software developed by Amazon determines the age of the recipient of an item purchased by a customer. The age range is estimated based at least in part on a customer order history of gifts purchased for the recipient. The first gift is associated with the first "age appropriateness designation." The second gift is associated with a second age appropriateness designation. An age range associated with the recipient is estimated. The recipient's age progression is calculated, and the company uses it to offer the customer gifts for that person when the customer logs on to the site. So, if you purchase gifts from Amazon.com for your baby niece, do not be surprised if Amazon entices you to purchase items for a young girl, a young woman, and an older woman over the next few decades. Here is another example of what this data-mining tool can do: if you purchased perfume a week before Valentine's Day, it will infer that you bought the item as a Valentine's gift for a woman and offer certain colors for the wrapping paper.

Online Analytical Processing

Another type of application to exploit data warehouses might not be as sophisticated in terms of the analysis conducted, but is extremely fast in response and enables executives to make timely decisions: **online analytical processing (OLAP)**. Tables, even if joining data from several sources, limit the review of information. Often, executives need to view information in multiple combinations of two dimensions. For example, an executive might want to see a summary of the quantity of each product sold in each region. Then, she might want to view the total quantities of each product sold within each city of a region. And she might also want to view quantities sold of a specific product in all cities of all regions. OLAP is specially designed to answer queries such as these. OLAP applications let a user rotate virtual "cubes" of information, whereby each side of the cube provides another two dimensions of relevant information.

The Power of OLAP

Figure 11.2 shows the interface of a Web-based OLAP application, whose purpose is to provide information about federal employees. You can go to www.fedscope.opm.gov and receive information about federal personnel in almost any imaginable dimension for several years. Dimensions include region of employment, level of service, occupation, salary range, and many more. The middle table shows number of employees by department and region. Clicking the triangle left of "Department of Defense" produces more detailed information for that department, using the same dimension as before, but only for this department. You could also receive a similar data only for a particular branch of the military (bottom table). This would be an example of **drilling down**, a process by which one starts with a table that shows broad information and gradually retrieves tables of more specific information. The OLAP application lets you receive the information in numbers of employees or as their percentages in each region, department, or organizational units within the department.

 OLAP applications either operate on data that are organized especially for such use or process data from relational databases. A dynamic OLAP application responds to commands by composing tables "on the fly." To speed up response, databases can be organized in the first place as dimensional. In **dimensional databases**—also called **multidimensional databases**—the raw data is organized in tables that show information in summaries and ratios so that the inquirer does not have to wait for processing raw data. Many firms organize data in relational databases and data warehouses but also employ applications that automatically summarize that data and organize the information in dimensional databases for OLAP. Oracle, Cognos, Hyperion, and many other companies sell multidimensional database packages and OLAP tools to use them.

OLAP applications can easily answer questions such as, "What products are selling well?" or "Where are my weakest-performing sales offices?" Note that although the word "cube" is used to illustrate the multidimensionality of OLAP tables, the number of tables is not limited to six, which is the number of sides of a real cube. It is possible to produce tables showing relationships of any two related variables contained in the database, as long as the data exists in the database. OLAP enables managers to see summaries and ratios of the intersection of any two dimensions. As mentioned in Chapter 7, the data used by OLAP applications usually comes from a data warehouse.

OLAP applications are powerful tools for executives. For example, consider Figure 11.3. Executives of a manufacturing company want to know how the three models of their product have sold over the past quarter in three world regions. They can see sales in dollar terms (top table) and then in unit terms (second table). They can then drill down into summaries of a particular region, in this case North America, and see the number of units sold not only by model but by model and color, because each model is sold in three colors. This information might lead them to recommend to the dealer to stop selling Model 3 in blue in North America, because sales of blue units of this model are quite low in this region. While still investigating last quarter's sales in North America, the executives might want to examine the sales performance of each dealer in this region. It seems that Dealer 3 enjoyed brisk sales of Model 1, but not of Models 2 and 3. If the sales picture is the same for another quarter or two, they might decide to stop sales of these models through Dealer 3 and increase the number of units of Model 1 they provide to that dealer.

FIGURE 11.3
Using OLAP tables

Sales ($ 000)			
	Model 1	Model 2	Model 3
North America	115800	136941	53550
South America	72550	63021	25236
Asia	65875	53781	17136
Total	**254225**	**253743**	**95922**

Sales (Units)			
	Model 1	Model 2	Model 3
North America	4632	6521	2975
South America	2902	3001	1402
Asia	2635	2561	952
Total	**10169**	**12083**	**5329**

North America (Units)			
	Model 1	Model 2	Model 3
Red	2401	1785	2512
Blue	1766	527	52
White	465	4209	411
Total	**4632**	**6521**	**2975**

North America Dealerships (Units)			
	Model 1	Model 2	Model 3
Dealer 1	102	556	2011
Dealer 2	1578	2450	108
Dealer 3	2358	0	10
Dealer 4	20	520	57
Dealer 5	574	2995	789
Total	**4632**	**6521**	**2975**

In a similar manner, Ruby Tuesday, the restaurant chain, solved a problem at one of its restaurants. Managers who examined performance by location discovered that a restaurant in Knoxville, Tennessee, was performing well below the chain's average in terms of sales and profit. Analyzing the store's information revealed that customers were waiting longer than normally for tables, and for their food after they were seated. There could be many reasons for this: an inexperienced cook, understaffing, or slow waiters, to name a few.

Managers at headquarters decided to take a look at the average time between when a check was opened at the cash register and the time the customer paid. In the restaurant industry this is an indication of an important factor: how long it takes to move from one party to another at a given table. The shorter the time, the better. The average time "to close a check" at Ruby Tuesday's restaurants is 45 minutes. At this particular location it was 55–60 minutes. Examining additional information, management concluded that the reason for the longer wait was increased demand thanks to an economic boom in the region. The company sent people to change the layout of the kitchen, positions of the cooks, and the placement of food. Cooking took less time, serving was faster, and the wait time decreased by 10 percent. More customers could be served, and revenue went up.

OLAP applications are usually installed on a special server located between the user's computer and the server or servers that contain a data warehouse or dimensional databases (although OLAP might also process data from a transactional database). Since OLAP applications

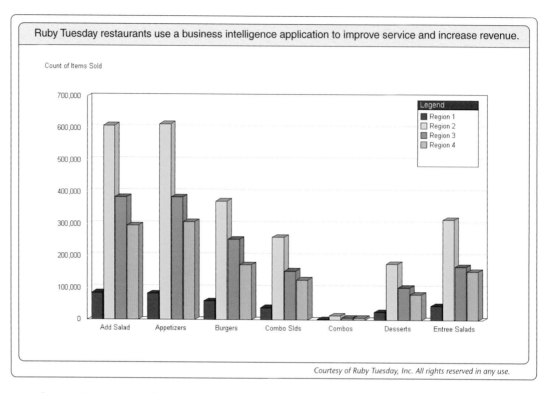

Ruby Tuesday restaurants use a business intelligence application to improve service and increase revenue.

Count of Items Sold

are designed to process large amounts of records and produce summaries, they are usually significantly faster than relational applications such as those using SQL (Structured Query Language) queries. OLAP applications can process 20,000 records per second. As mentioned before, when using pre-organized dimensional tables, the only processing involved is finding the table that corresponds to the dimensions and mode of presentation (such as values or percentages) that the user specified.

OLAP in Action

OLAP is increasingly used by corporations to gain efficiencies. For example, executives at Office Depot Inc. wanted to know how successful salesclerks and stores were at cross-selling certain items. A store succeeds in cross-selling when it convinces customers to buy paper when they buy pens, or to purchase computer peripherals when they purchase a computer. The company used OLAP on its data warehouse, which saves transactions from 1,020 stores and by more than 60,000 employees in 10 countries. Making the proper conclusions helped the company to increase annual sales revenues by $117 million. Management now knows better which items cross-sell with other items and therefore makes better decisions on placing items on shelves in proximity.

OLAP and similar techniques help managers and other users to analyze quickly what is happening in the business. Consider, for example, CVS, America's largest pharmacy chain with annual revenues exceeding $22 billion and more than 5,400 stores in 36 states. The company employs OLAP technology to let about 2,000 employees run analyses using more than 4 terabytes of data. Managers are able to quickly generate figures and ratios about store sales, inventory, profitability, category reviews, vendor scorecards, financials, clickstream activity at the company's Web site, and real-estate operations. CVS has a rich source of consumer data. Its customer loyalty program has more than 50 million members, the largest in the United States. Members use a CVS EasyCare card at each purchase to obtain cumulative discounts, and CVS is able to gather detailed data about customer purchases.

Managers in some companies now track information about their products from the purchasing of raw materials to the receipt of payment not only for operations but so they can learn more about their clients and their own business. For example, Ben & Jerry's, one of the largest U.S. ice cream makers, collects data about every container of ice cream it sells, starting with the ingredients. Each container is stamped with a tracking number, which is stored in a relational database. Using OLAP software, salespeople can track how fast new types of ice cream gain popularity, and which remain stagnant, on an hourly basis. Matching such information with about 200 telephone calls and e-mail messages the company receives weekly, managers can figure out which supplier's ingredients might have caused dissatisfaction with a certain product.

Employees who know very little about programming and report design are discovering that BI software is becoming easier and easier to use. Intelligent interfaces allow them to enter questions in free form or close to free form. A part of the application that is called the semantic layer parses the question, which has been written as if you were speaking to a person, translates it into instructions to the computer to access the appropriate data mart or the proper columns of a data warehouse, and produces the answer, which is a number of charts showing trends. In a few seconds a manager at Lands' End can find out which type of denim pants was the company's bestseller at Sears stores over the past six months. BI software has become so popular in large companies that Microsoft decided to integrate such software into its popular database management system, SQL Server.

More Customer Intelligence

Customer relationship management (CRM) has been discussed in several chapters. The major effort of most businesses, especially retail businesses, is to collect business intelligence about customers. Both data-mining and OLAP software are often integrated into CRM systems for this purpose. Since an increasing number of transactions are executed through the Web, managers can use data that is already in electronic form to analyze and strategize.

The challenge is to address the right customer, at the right time, with the right offer, instead of spending millions of dollars in mass marketing or covering numerous Web sites with ads. Many companies find that using only the data that they collect directly from consumers does not provide a full picture. They approach third parties, companies that specialize in collection and analysis of consumer data from multiple sources. The companies, such as DoubleClick, Engage, and Avenue A, use cookies and spyware (explained in Chapter 8) to track Web users' clickstreams.

By compiling billions of consumer clickstreams and creating behavioral models, these companies can determine individual consumers' interests from the sites they visited (what do they like?), the frequency of visits (are they loyal?), the times they surf (are they at work or at home?), and the number of times they click on ads or complete a transaction. Then, sites can display ads that match the typical interests at sites where the likely customers tend to visit. They can use software that will change the ad for each visitor by using cookies that identify the user.

Consider the challenge that was facing Drugstore.com, a Web-based drugstore headquartered in Bellevue, Washington. Management wanted to reach more customers who were likely to purchase its products, but they did not have the tools to discover who those people were. While Drugstore.com had plenty of information about customers—including name, address, and a list of past purchases—the company still did not know where exactly to find those customers on the Web or where to find more people who have the same buying habits. Management hired Avenue A | Razorfish Inc., a firm that specializes in consumer profiling. Avenue A managers say they know where 100 million Web users visit, shop, and buy. This information comes from data they have collected for several years, not for any specific client. During a previous marketing campaign for Drugstore.com, Avenue A had compiled anonymous information about every Drugstore.com customer who made a purchase during the campaign. Avenue A knew what specific ad or promotion a given customer had responded to, what that customer had browsed for on the Drugstore.com site, whether the customer had made a purchase, and how many times the customer had returned to purchase.

Using its Web Affinity Analysis software, Avenue A could track Drugstore.com's individual customers across more than 3,000 Web sites. Avenue A then constructed common themes in the customers' online behavior, such as the general Web sites they visited, visits to competing online drug retailers, and the likelihood that those individuals would click on ads. The company gave Drugstore.com a list of 1.45 million "high-quality prospects," shoppers with a high potential of purchasing from Drustore.com. Drugstore.com managers used the information to build a marketing strategy, assuming that those common characteristics and habits would be shared by as-yet-unconverted customers. (A converted customer is a shopper that is convinced to buy.) Using similar software helped Eddie Bauer, Inc. to decrease its marketing cost per sale by 74 percent over three months, and the Expedia Inc. travel site to cut its cost per sale by 91 percent over eight months.

Executive Dashboards

To make the use of BI tools convenient for executives, companies that develop BI tools create interfaces that help the executives to quickly grasp business situations. The popular name of such an interface is **dashboard**, because it looks something like a car dashboard. Car dashboards provide information in the form of clock-like indicators and scales. BI dashboards use similar visual images. They include speedometer-like indicators for periodic revenues, profits, and other financial information; plus bar charts, line graphs, and other graphical presentations whenever the information can be presented graphically. Figure 11.4 shows dashboards from Business Objects and XeoMatrix, providers of BI software. Similar dashboards are parts of BI tools offered by other vendors, including Siebel, Cognos, and SAS. ERP vendors, such as SAP and Oracle, also include dashboards in their applications. Dashboards are often designed to quickly present predefined business metrics such as occupancy ratios in hotels and hospitals, or inventory turns in retail.

Why You Should...
Learn About BI and KM Tools

Information technology has advanced from fast calculation machines to systems that produce useful information from structured data to software that turns unstructured information into knowledge. Knowing how to use BI tools will help you to independently produce highly useful information from data warehouses and other large data sources. In your work you will also need to use other peoples' knowledge. Much of this knowledge exists in the recorded work and in the minds of coworkers and experts outside your organization. Knowing how to use these tools will help you as well as others perform better. As a knowledge worker you will be able not only to use your own, limited knowledge but also augment it with the experiences of other people.

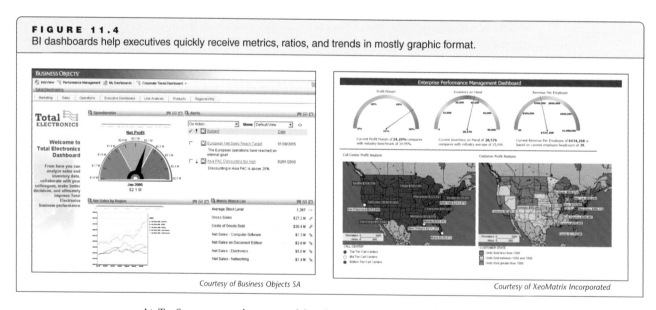

FIGURE 11.4

BI dashboards help executives quickly receive metrics, ratios, and trends in mostly graphic format.

Courtesy of Business Objects SA

Courtesy of XeoMatrix Incorporated

At TruServ, a member-owned hardware cooperative of 7,000 retailers worldwide, executives use dashboards to monitor revenue and sales of individual items. The cooperative operates stores under the names True Value, Grand Rental Station, Taylor Rental, Party Central, Home & Garden Showplace, and Induserve Supply. Using the dashboard to conduct analyses, managers can pinpoint trends and changes over time and receive alerts to help monitor, interpret, and make decisions. They can better track inventory. In the past, 20 percent of the cooperative's inventory was in the "red zone." Red zone inventory is either liquidated or sold for a loss after a promotion is ended. The executive dashboard was instrumental in helping TruServ reduce this loss inventory to 5 percent.

KNOWLEDGE MANAGEMENT

Imagine you work for a consulting firm. Your supervisor assigns you to a new client. As a smart professional, the first thing you want to check is whether your firm has had previous experience with this client and what knowledge has been accumulated about the experience. You heard that two ex-employees had contact with this client several years ago. It would be great to discuss it with them, but they are gone. Their knowledge was available to the firm, but it no longer is, because it is not recorded anywhere. The data recorded about the financial transactions with this client cannot provide the knowledge you are seeking: How easy or difficult was the interaction with the client's executives? What are the strengths and weaknesses of that organization? In engineering companies, engineers might want to see if colleagues have already encountered a problem they are trying to solve, and what the solution to that problem was then. IT professionals might want to know if their colleagues have encountered a similar repeating failure with a network management system.

POINT OF INTEREST

Chemical Mining

By some estimates, 85 percent of recorded corporate knowledge is in text files. Dow Chemical Co. maintains a BI center in Midland, Michigan. Using a software tool called ClearResearch from Clear Forest Corp., Dow's research staff has extracted useful information from various unstructured sources: abstracts of chemical patents registered over the past century, published research articles, and the company's own files. The software has reduced the time it takes Dow's researchers to decide what they need to read.

Source: Robb, D., "Text Mining Tools Take on Unstructured Data," *Computerworld* (www.computerworld.com), June 21, 2004.

An organization can learn much about its customers, sellers, and itself by mining data warehouses and using OLAP software, but such techniques still do not satisfy another important challenge: how to manage knowledge, expertise that is created within and outside the organization. As discussed in Chapter 10, expertise in narrow domains can be programmed in expert systems. However, there is much more knowledge that organizations would like to garner and manage. Effective management of knowledge can help both employees and customers.

Samuel Johnson, the author of an early English dictionary, said that one type of knowledge is what we know about a subject, and the other type is knowing where to find information about the subject. The purpose of knowledge management is mainly to gain the second type of knowledge. **Knowledge management** is the combination of activities involved in gathering, organizing, sharing, analyzing, and disseminating knowledge to improve an organization's performance.

Information that can be gleaned from stored data is knowledge, but there is much more knowledge that organizations would like to store that they currently do not. The knowledge that is not maintained in information systems is typically of the type that cannot be extracted from readily captured data at Web sites or other electronic means of transactions. It is accumulated through experience. Much of it is kept in people's minds, on paper notes, on discussion transcripts, and in other places that are not readily accessible to a company's employees. Therefore, knowledge management is a great challenge. Knowledge management is the attempt by organizations to put procedures and technologies in place to do the following:

- Transfer individual knowledge into databases.

- Filter and separate the most relevant knowledge.

- Organize that knowledge in databases that allow employees easy access to it or that "push" specific knowledge to employees based on prespecified needs.

Knowledge management (KM) software facilitates these activities. As the cost of storage media continues to decrease and database management packages are increasingly more sophisticated and affordable, storage and organization of unstructured information have been of a lesser challenge. The more difficult issue is development of tools that address the third challenge: quickly finding the most relevant information for solving problems.

Capturing and Sorting Organizational Knowledge

The research company IDC argues that almost half of the work that **knowledge workers** do in organizations has already been done, at least partially. This work includes researching a certain subject, preparing a report, and providing information as part of a consulting contract. It estimated that labor worth $3,000–5,000 per knowledge worker is wasted annually because workers try to solve the same problem that other workers have already solved. Organizations could save this duplication, or replication, by collecting and organizing knowledge that is gained by members of the organization.

To transfer knowledge into manageable online resources, some companies require workers to create reports of their finding. Others, especially consulting firms, require their employees to create reports about sessions with clients. However organizations collect information, the results might be several terabytes of potential knowledge, but the challenge for employees is to know how to find answers to specific questions. Some software tools have been developed to help.

Electronic Data Systems Corp. (EDS), an IT consulting firm, requires all of its 130,000 employees to fill out an online questionnaire about their activities once per year. With 20,000 of these employees EDS conducts surveys three times per year. Some of the questions provide multiple-choice answers, which make the input structured and easy to sort and analyze, but some of the most valuable input is in the form of free text. In the past, this part was forwarded to managers who learned and drew conclusions from it. Now, the company uses an automated system, PolyAnalyst from Megaputer Intelligence, Inc., to sort the text information and create links between topics. (See the Safety Net case study at the end of the chapter for more details about the software.)

Motorola, the giant manufacturer of communications equipment, has 4 terabytes of data managed by a knowledge management application. The application enabled engineers to query this huge resource. Still, unless a worker knew exactly where the proper data was or the names of people who were on a team that had solved the problem at hand, the worker could not find a proper answer. Motorola decided to implement Watson, an application developed by Intellext. Watson is installed on employees' PCs. It is embedded in Microsoft Word, PowerPoint, and Outlook. It analyzes an employee's document as it is being written, creates an automatic query about the subject, reaches out into the KM program, and pulls information that might be applicable to the task at hand.

Employee Knowledge Networks

While some tools build knowledge bases and help employees access them, others put the emphasis on directing employees to other employees who have a certain expertise. The advantage of this approach is that an expert can provide expertise that has not been captured in information systems (see Figure 11.5). Large companies, especially multisite ones, often waste money because employees in one organizational unit are not aware of the experience of employees in another unit. For example, one energy company spent $1 million on a product designed to work on oil rigs to prevent sediment from falling into wells. When the equipment was installed, it failed. The executives of another unit decided to purchase the same equipment, which, not surprisingly, failed in the other location. Then a third unit, elsewhere, purchased the equipment, which also failed. While one can justify the loss of the first $1 million as legitimate business expense in the course of trying a product, the other $2 million was lost because decision makers did not know that the equipment had already been tried and failed. To alleviate similar problems, some software companies, such as Tacit Systems Inc., AskMe Corporation, Participate Systems Inc., and Entopia Inc., have developed **employee knowledge networks**, tools that facilitate knowledge sharing through intranets. Recall that an intranet uses Web technologies to link employees of the same organization.

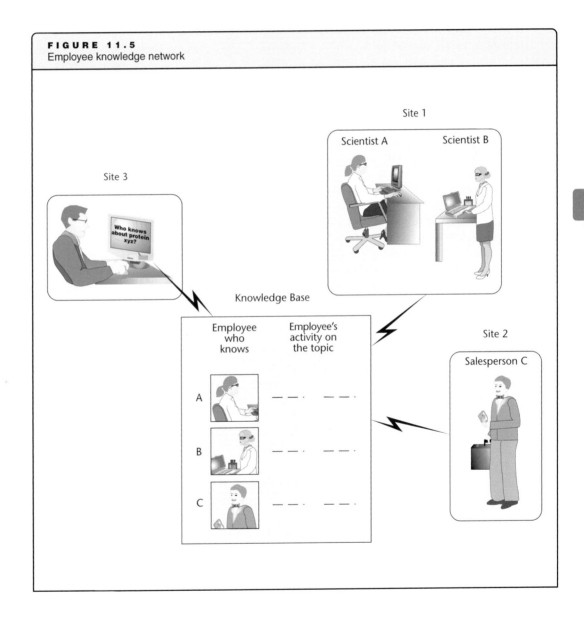

FIGURE 11.5
Employee knowledge network

Tacit Systems' ActiveNet tool continuously processes e-mail, documents, and other business communications and automatically "discovers" each employee's work focus, expertise, and business relationships. The tool "mines" this unstructured data to build a profile of each employee in terms of topics and interests. The goal is to ensure that two people who might benefit from creating a connection in a workplace do so, so that one can learn from the experience of another about a specific issue. By analyzing e-mail and documents, the tool

In the Middle Ages, Venice considered its expertise in making glassware not only a business trade secret but also a state secret. Divulging glassmaking knowledge to anyone outside the republic of Venice was punishable by death, because much of the state's economy depended on excluding other states and countries from such knowledge. Venice, like other states in that era, would never "offshore" any of the work to another country. Nowadays, matters are completely different. What was expertise a year ago has become routine work this year and will become automated next year. At that point, the expertise value in the product will have diminished, and to make a profit the organization that used to have a comparative advantage in producing the product will have to use the least expensive labor available. It will offshore manufacturing to a factory in a country were labor is cheaper. The industry in the original country will lose jobs.

Information technology helps create knowledge but also expedites the turning of knowledge into routine, automated processes that can be carried out elsewhere. IT also expedites the transfer of knowledge from countries that created it to countries that can quickly use it. Software used to be developed almost exclusively in the United States. Much of the software that the world uses now has been developed in Germany, India, Ireland, and Israel. A growing amount of the software developed for U.S. companies is developed in India and China. The programmers' expertise is similar, but the wages earned by programmers in those two countries are a fraction of what American programmers would be paid for the same work. This is a pivotal element in what is called *globalization*—moving from national economies to a global economy. Is this bad for countries such as the United States and good only for countries such as India and China? BI and KM software is developed mainly in the United States, Germany, and the United Kingdom. However, these systems are sold anywhere and can help companies in other countries compete with companies in those "developed" countries. This puts developing countries in position to gain knowledge much faster than before and compete better. Now, the competition is not only in the manufacturing and service areas but also in R&D.

In the United States, some observers view the issue in the following light: America used to be a world leader in manufacturing, but other countries now have a comparative advantage in manufacturing, and their workers have taken the jobs that American laborers used to perform. For some time Americans had an advantage in providing services, but many of these services are now provided over the Internet and telephone lines by workers in other countries, so the service sector's advantage has diminished. The United States is still great in innovation and creation of know-how, they say, but we are starting to see this advantage slipping away, too. And when other countries beat us in creation of knowledge, they ask, what's left with which to compete?

Should governments take measures—legal or otherwise—that protect their economic advantages? Should they penalize companies that offshore manufacturing jobs? Should they forbid the sale of know-how to other countries? Should they adopt the Venetian model? Or, should we look at the world as one large economy where each worker and each organization should compete for a piece of the pie regardless of national borders, so that consumers everywhere can enjoy products of the highest quality for the lowest price possible?

extracts the employee's interests and solutions to problems, and that information is added to the employee's profile. Other employees who seek advice can access the profile, but they cannot see the original e-mail or document created by the employee. This ensures uninhibited brainstorming and communication.

AskMe's software also detects and captures keywords from e-mail and documents created by employees. It creates a knowledge base that holds the names of employees and their interests. An employee can access a Web page at which the employee enters a free-form question. The software responds by listing the names of other employees who have created e-mail, text documents, or presentations on the subject, and the topics of their work. The employee can view the activity profiles of these people, and then contact them, via the Web site, by e-mail, instant messages, or paging. The responder can use the same Web site to respond and attach documents that might help the inquirer. AskMe's tool captures the communication, including attached documents, and adds them to the knowledge base. (Note that in this context the knowledge base is not organized as the knowledge bases in expert systems are.)

Knowledge from the Web

Consumers keep posting their opinions on products and services on the Web. Some do so at the site of the seller, others at general product evaluation sites such as epinions.com, and some on blogs. By some estimates consumer opinions are expressed in more than 550 billion Web pages. This information is difficult to locate and highly unstructured. If organizations could distill knowledge from it they could learn much more than they do from conducting market research studies, such as focus groups, both about their own products and those sold by competitors.

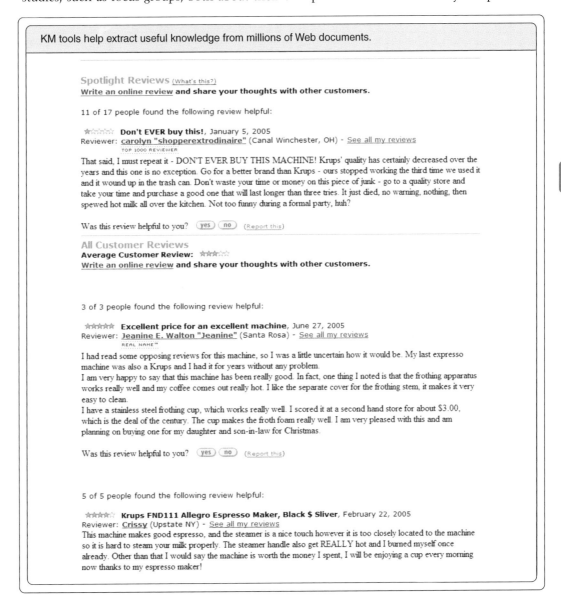

KM tools help extract useful knowledge from millions of Web documents.

Some companies have developed software tools that search for such information and derive valuable business knowledge from it. For example, Accenture Technology Labs, the technology research and development unit of the consulting firm Accenture, developed Online Audience Analysis. The tool searches thousands of Web sites daily and retrieves predetermined information about specific products and services. It then uses data-mining techniques to help organizations understand what consumers are saying about corporate brands and products.

Factiva, a subsidiary of Dow Jones & Reuters, promotes a software tool by the same name. Factiva, accessible through a Web site, gathers information online from over 9,000 sources—newspapers, journals, market data, and newswires—information that amounts to millions of documents. About 60 percent of the information is not accessible to the general public. It screens every piece of new information that is posted at any of these Web sites for information specified by a subscribing organization. The search can be more tailored and specific than searches performed through free search engines such as Google or Yahoo! The software helps organizations add to their knowledge base, especially in terms of what others say about their products and services. The tool takes into account factors such as the industry and context in which an inquirer works to select and deliver the proper information. For example, a key word such as "apple" means one thing to an employee of a hardware or software organization and something completely different to an employee in agriculture or a supermarket chain.

Autocategorization

To categorize knowledge into manageable data, companies use autocategorization software. Autocategorization automates the classification of data into categories for future retrieval. Practically all search engine sites, such as Google and Yahoo!, use autocategorization software, and continue to improve the software to provide more precise and faster responses to queries. Many companies have installed such software at their corporate Web sites.

For example, U.S. Robotics (USR), a large manufacturer of networking devices, operates in a market with narrow profit margins, and thus one call to the support personnel about a purchased item might wipe out the profit on that sale. Therefore, reducing support personnel labor is important. The firm's surveys showed that 90 percent of clients calling technical support had visited the USR Web site before calling. USR purchased autocategorization software from iPhrase Technologies, Inc. to help customers help themselves in searching for answers to their questions at the Web site so that customers would not have to telephone the support staff. The software improved the accuracy and responsiveness of the support database at USR's Web site. Consequently, support calls decreased by a third, saving the company more than $135,000 monthly.

Google, Yahoo!, and other companies in the search engine industry have developed applications that sift through documents both online and offline, categorize them, and help users bring up only links to the most relevant documents. These companies sell their products to corporations to use at their Web sites, intranets, and extranets.

Autocategorization and sophisticated search engines are important components of knowledge management. Firms continue to improve their online service to reduce the cost of product support.

Enter a question.

[   ]   **Search**   *iphrase* powered

(For Example: How do I find drivers for my USR5686E?) Search Tips

You Entered: "How do I connect USR5686E?"
We also tried related searches including USR5686E.

Results: **(See Also** Product Code Finder , Support , Products , Education **)**

Support   See all results in Support

USR5686E 56K V.92 External FaxmodemSupport Drivers, INFs, Firmware, Docs, Downloads and FAQs
　　　U.S. Robotics Support: **5686e** [products] **USR5686E** 56K V.92 External Faxmodem [**5686e**] Documents and FAQs Additional Support If the support information in this section doesn't help you solve your issue, you can contact a U.S. Robotics directly. Manuals and other Documents 56K Faxmodem Quick Installation Guide (PDF), , , , 56K Faxmodem User Guide (...
Tips for High Speed Connections using a V.FC/V.34 or Faster Modem
　　　...switch to rates as low as 4800 bps to compensate for these changes. If the loss of quality is extremely severe, the modem will drop the **connection** . Dropped v.FC **Connections** V.FC **connections** can only switch rates down to 14,400 bps. If you **connect** using v.FC, and line quality drops below that allowable for a 14,400 **connection** , the modem will ...
Connecting to the Router's Configuration Utility.
　　　...browser can read configuration pages inside your router. Launch your Web browser. Internet Explorer Users: 1. Click Tools , Internet Options , and then click the **Connections** tab. 2. Select Never dial a

WORLDWIDE HOST:
A Vision for the Future

Michael Lloyd, Worldwide Host's CIO, was convening a meeting with his TripExpert.com project staff. A few months had passed since he had been given the go-ahead to investigate development of the company's new travel Web site. He pointed to Worldwide's mission statement, which was posted on the boardroom wall:

Satisfying our guests' and employees' needs is the key to maintaining Worldwide Host's leading position in the global hospitality industry. We are dedicated to superior customer service and continued employee growth.

Michael spoke to the assembled team, composed of Worldwide Host and General Data Systems (GDS) employees. "As I've mentioned before, this statement is our guiding principle. Worldwide Host recognizes that information systems are central to its continued success. That's why we're here. We talked earlier about our need to look beyond our day-to-day IS issues, and I urged you all to rethink processes as we move ahead. We have an opportunity to reshape this company and its future—to look beyond our immediate technology needs to new technologies and processes that will allow future expansion and efficiency." With those initial words of encouragement, the team began to review the information they had gathered since their last meeting.

Investigating Existing Systems: Capabilities and Needs

Judith Kozak, GDS's top systems analyst, and her coworkers had been looking into the compatibility of Worldwide Host's existing reservations system with their airline and car-rental partners' systems. She noted that capabilities and systems differed: the airlines' reservation software needed to update flight information continually due to weather changes and equipment malfunctions, and airlines and car-rental companies both needed to track the whereabouts of their planes and cars to be sure that they were available where needed. In contrast, hotel systems are more static; properties themselves don't move, and cancellations occur much less frequently than in the airline industry. But the hotel systems needed information on each property that was more detailed—location of room, general appearance, type of beds, availability of meeting rooms, exercise facilities, and other details. In short, Worldwide Host's existing system didn't serve quite the same functions, or run on the same platform, as the other two systems. That made the prospect of tying the existing systems into a single system dubious.

Searching for System Alternatives

Corey Johnson, another team member from GDS, had been investigating online reservations systems such as Hotwire, Expedia, and Travelocity. The best ones were not available for sale or were too expensive. One developed by an airline had been used by travel agents for decades. But it couldn't easily be linked to the Web, and its use was not intuitive—the average Web surfer would have trouble with its user interface. Also, the system ran on an old, outdated mainframe system.

Finally, Corey located one new Web-based global reservations system whose owners, Reservations Technologies, licensed their product. Since it didn't have all the components TripExpert.com would need, GDS explored the possibility of tying it to part of Worldwide Host's existing reservations systems and working with the owners to develop additional functionalities. In the meantime, GDS hired Alana Pritchett, who had the expertise to migrate the data from their existing system into this new one.

Stalling Out on Database Development

Alana Pritchett had been heading up the database team. She and her two coworkers had been talking with Worldwide Host employees to gather information about their existing reservations system and to develop lists of new business needs for the TripExpert.com site. They thought they had covered every new function that the database needed to handle for Web site connections: aside from increased capacity, they noted that they'd need to display picture files to show Web shoppers sample rooms. The travel staff hadn't previously worried about graphics capabilities. They had also listed a requirement for the system to track TripExpert site reservations so that a small Web service fee would be added to the room rate. But what they and the Worldwide Host staff completely forgot about were the discounted room rates that were to be offered to last-minute Web shoppers. Within three weeks of a reservation date, the system needed to release a block of rooms to the Web site—rooms that were not already reserved by traditional means. Those rooms were to be made available at a discount to Web shoppers, enticing them to book last-minute stays. Worldwide Host hoped to fill more of its hotels by offering the Web discount and thus boosting profits.

The database team members were already making preliminary design plans when their omission came to light. They reported the slipup to Michael Lloyd with trepidation. They believed that incorporating the new features into the system's design could mean a delay of about 6 weeks, throwing the whole project behind schedule.

Getting Back on Track

Michael called in Judith Kozak, GDS's lead analyst, to find a solution—and quickly. Delays in the Trip-Expert system would mean that Worldwide Host would lose competitive ground since other sites were coming online. Judith had worked on Worldwide Host's existing reservations system and knew its capabilities well. She also knew GDS's analysts' skills.

"Michael, let me check Corey Johnson's schedule. He's been working on licensing the Web airline-reservation system for us. I think he is ahead of schedule in his investigation of the system's capabilities and his negotiations, so maybe we can borrow him for a while. Is that what your schedule shows? Good. Corey has worked under deadline pressure before and is an experienced analyst. If he and I put our heads together on this problem, I think we can straighten it out."

"Thanks, Judith. Let me know how it's looking as soon as you can. The database is critical to the site's functioning. If we don't get that component in place, we'll jeopardize the whole system. What good is the front end without the back?"

"Not much," she answered. "I'll call Corey right now to see whether he can meet with Alana's team and me tomorrow. In the meantime, try not to worry. We've hit bad stretches before but come out OK in the end."

PLANNING INFORMATION SYSTEMS

In recent years a growing number of corporations have implemented enterprise ISs such as ERP systems or their major components, SCM and CRM, or other sophisticated systems that serve the entire organization or many of its units. The investment of resources in such systems, both in financial and other terms, is great. The risk in implementing such large systems is also great. If the implementation is successful, the new system can significantly change the manner in which the organization conducts business and even the products or services it sells. For all these reasons it is necessary to plan the implementation of information systems, whether they are developed in-house, made to order by another company, or purchased and adapted for the organization. When planning, it is important to align IS strategies with the overall strategies of the organization. (Some organizations prefer to use the term "IT planning" rather than "IS planning." In this discussion the terms are used interchangeably.)

Steps in Planning Information Systems

IS planning includes a few key steps that are a part of any successful planning process:

- Creating a corporate and IS mission statement.
- Articulating the vision for IS within the organization.
- Creating IS strategic and tactical plans.
- Creating a plan for operations to achieve the mission and vision.
- Creating a budget to ensure that resources are available to achieve the mission and vision (see Figure 12.1).

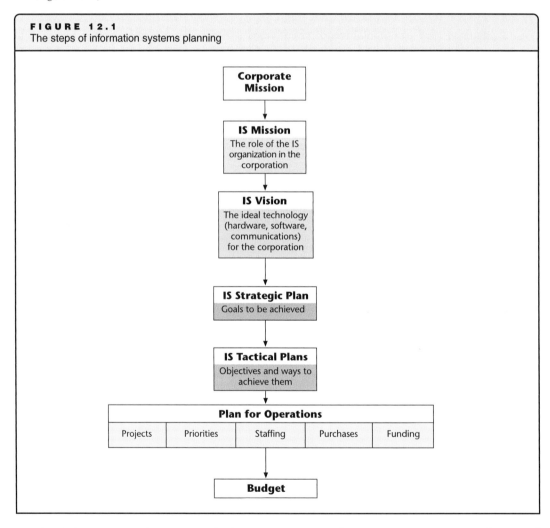

FIGURE 12.1
The steps of information systems planning

A *mission statement* is a paragraph that communicates the most important overarching goal of the organization for the next few years. Although the ultimate mission of any organization is to survive and—if it is a for-profit organization—to produce profit for its owners, mission statements rarely say just this. Rather, they say how the organization intends to survive and thrive. For example, in Amazon.com's early years, its mission was to brand itself as the most recognized retailer on the Web and to create the largest possible market share. Management pursued this mission, though it resulted in years of financial loss.

An important part of an organization's overall mission statement is an IS mission statement that is compatible with the larger mission. It is usually a paragraph, or several paragraphs, describing the role of IS in the organization. Often, the IS mission and IS vision are combined into one statement. The IS vision includes the ideal combination of hardware, software, and networking to support the overarching mission. For example, Amazon.com's management continues to recognize that innovative IT, especially Web and fulfillment technologies, is the most important resource for the organization's success.

The CIO, with cooperation of senior management as well as managers in the IT unit, devises a strategic plan for implementation of IT in the organization. The plan addresses what technology will be used and how employees, customers, and suppliers will use it over the next several years. Since IT advances so quickly, strategic IT plans are typically prepared for no longer than 5 years.

The goals laid out in the strategic plan are broken down into objectives, which are concrete details of how to accomplish those goals. The objectives typically include resources to be purchased or developed; timetables for purchasing, developing, adapting, and implementing those resources; training of employees to use the new resources; and other details to ensure timely implementation and transition.

The objectives are further broken down into specific operational details. For each project, management assigns a project manager and a team; vendors are selected from whom available components of hardware, software, and services will be purchased; and funding is requested. When the financial requests are approved, the corporate budget includes the money to be spent over several months or years on these projects.

POINT OF INTEREST

So Much for Planning

Many CIOs emphasize the need for IT planning and the importance of aligning the IT plan with their overall organization's business plan. However, a survey conducted by the professional group Financial Executives International and Computer Sciences Corp. revealed that this is hardly a common practice. Fewer than half of U.S. and Canadian companies have written IT plans, and even fewer believe that their plans are aligned with the goals of their CEOs. The same survey also showed that CIOs who do have a written IT plan and align their goals with business goals report a higher return on investment for every system in which their companies invested.

Source: "How to Get Your Money's Worth," *Baseline* (www.baselinemag.com), March 1, 2004.

IT planning is not much different from planning of any other acquisition of resources, starting with a vision of how the resources will be used to accomplish goals and breaking those ideas down into projects and the resources to be allocated to carry the projects to successful completion. In recent years, a growing proportion of IT funds have been spent on software, with most of the funds going to purchase and adapt software, rather than developing it in-house or assigning its development to another company.

The Benefits of Standardization in Planning

One major goal—and advantage—of planning is standardization. When management decides to adopt a certain IT resource for all its units, regardless of function or location, it standardizes its IT. Standardization results in several benefits:

- *Cost savings.* When the organization decides to purchase the same hardware or software for all its units, it has better bargaining power and therefore can obtain lower prices from vendors. This applies to purchasing or leasing computers of all classes—mainframe, midrange, and personal computers—as well as licensing software.

- *Efficient training.* It is easier to train employees how to use a small variety of software than to train them how to use a large variety. Less trainer time is required, and—more importantly—employees spend less time on training and more time on their regular assignments. This also saves cost in the form of fewer labor hours spent on training. Even if each employee only uses a single application, but the organization maintains several applications for the same purpose, training time is extended.

- *Efficient support.* Standardizing on a small number of computer models and software applications enables the IT staff to specialize in the hardware and software they have to support. The more focused skills make it easier for the organization to recruit support personnel, and results in more satisfactory service to users.

From Planning to Development

After planning a new IS or a set of ISs, management decides how to obtain the systems. In a great majority of cases, "systems" means software. For example, CRM and SCM systems rarely require specialized hardware. An increasing number of new systems are purchased and adapted for an organization's needs rather than developed in-house, although in-house development still takes place in many organizations. The approaches to systems development are the same regardless of who develops the system, the organization or its vendor.

There are generally two approaches to systems development: the systems development life cycle (SDLC) and nontraditional methods, among which are many grouped under the umbrella of agile methods. SDLC is the more traditional approach and has been used for several decades. There are circumstances under which it should still be used. Agile methods developed out of prototyping, an application development approach that emerged in the 1980s aimed at cutting costs and time. **Prototyping** involves fast development of an application based on initial user requirements and several cycles of user input and developer improvements. Using the philosophy of prototyping—that coding should start as soon as possible and that users should be involved throughout the process—led to several methods of software development called agile methods. The following sections discuss both approaches.

Why You Should...

Understand the Principles of Systems Development

By and large, organizations have recognized the need to let non-IT managers play major roles in systems development. You might be called on to participate in this process, not just to provide input here and there but as a member of a development team. The IT professionals on the team need your insight into the business activities you run. They need your advice on ways to improve these activities through the use of new or improved ISs. One approach to development, agile methods, actually views the users as sharing at least half of the responsibility for the effort.

Software developers count on you and your coworkers to provide them with proper requirements and feedback. You had better be knowledgeable, active, and assertive in software development projects, because you will have to live with the products of these efforts. Also, when your organization decides to discard one IS and adopt a new one, your understanding of the conversion process and proper cooperation will be highly valuable.

THE SYSTEMS DEVELOPMENT LIFE CYCLE

Large ISs that address structured problems, such as accounting and payroll systems and enterprise software applications, are usually conceived, planned, developed, and maintained within a framework called the **systems development life cycle (SDLC)**. The approach is also called "waterfall" development, because it consists of several distinct phases that are followed methodically, and the developers complete the phases sequentially. The developers do not deliver pieces of the systems before the entire system is fully completed. Although different textbooks might refer to the different phases and subphases of the SDLC by different names, or organize them slightly differently, in general, the process follows the same steps. While the SDLC is a powerful methodology for systems development, organizations are sometimes forced to take shortcuts, skipping a step here or there. Sometimes, time pressures, funding constraints, or other factors lead developers to use different approaches to systems development.

The SDLC approach assumes that the life of an IS starts with a need, followed by an assessment of the functions that a system must have to fulfill that need, and ends when the benefits of the system no longer outweigh its maintenance costs, at which point the life of a new system begins. Hence, the process is called a *life cycle*. After the planning phase, the SDLC includes four major phases: analysis, design, implementation, and support. Figure 12.2 depicts the cycle and the conditions that can trigger a return to a previous phase. The analysis and design phases are broken down into several steps, as described in the following discussion.

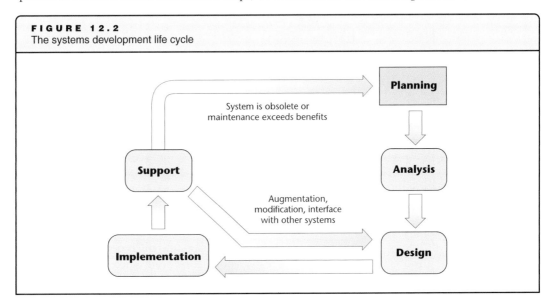

FIGURE 12.2
The systems development life cycle

Analysis

The **systems analysis** phase is a five-step process (summarized in Figure 12.3) that is designed to answer these questions:

Investigation

- What is the business process that the system is to support?
- What business opportunity do you want the system to seize, what problems do you want it to solve, or what directive must you fulfill?

Technical Feasibility Study

- Is there technology to create the system you want?

Economic Feasibility Study

- What resources do you need to implement the system?
- Will the system's benefits outweigh its costs?

Operational Feasibility Study

- Will the system be used appropriately by its intended users (employees, customers, suppliers)?
- Will the system be used to its full capacity?

Requirements Definition

- What features do you want the system to have?
- What interfaces will the system have with other systems?

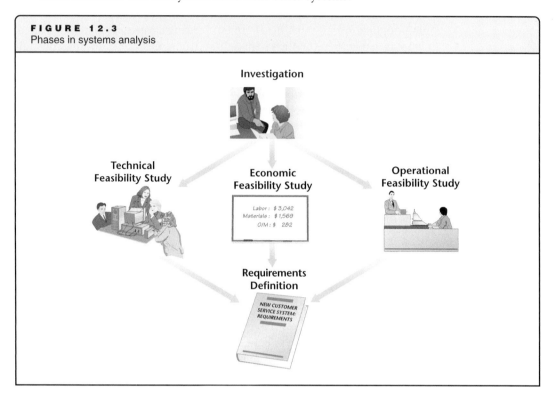

FIGURE 12.3
Phases in systems analysis

Investigation

Technical Feasibility Study

Economic Feasibility Study

Labor : $ 3,042
Materials : $ 1,569
O/M : $ 282

Operational Feasibility Study

Requirements Definition

NEW CUSTOMER SERVICE SYSTEM: REQUIREMENTS

Investigation

The first step in systems analysis is investigation, which determines whether there is a real need for a system and whether the system as conceived is feasible. Usually, a small *ad hoc* team—consisting of a representative of the sponsoring executive, one or two systems analysts, and representatives of business units would use the new system or be affected by it—is put together to perform a quick preliminary investigation.

The team spends time with employees at their workstations to learn firsthand about the way they currently carry out their duties, and interviews the workers about problems with the current system. This direct contact with users gives workers the opportunity to express their ideas about the way they would like a new IS to function to improve their work. The investigative team prepares a written report summarizing the information gathered. The team members also forward their own opinions on the need for a new system. They will not necessarily agree that a new system is justified.

If the preliminary report concludes that the business situation warrants investment in a new IS, a more comprehensive investigation might be authorized. The sponsoring executive selects members for a larger analysis team. Usually, members of the original team are included in this augmented group to conduct **feasibility studies**. The objective of the larger investigation team is to determine whether the proposed system is feasible technically, economically, and operationally.

The Technical Feasibility Study

A new IS is technically feasible if its components exist or can be developed with available tools. The team must also consider the organization's existing commitments to hardware, software, and telecommunications equipment. For example, if the company recently purchased hundreds of units of a certain computer, it is unlikely that management will approve the purchase of computers of another model for a single new application. Thus, the investigators must find out whether the proposed system can run properly on existing hardware.

The Economic Feasibility Study

Like any project, the development of a new IS must be economically justified, so organizations conduct an economic feasibility study. That is, over the life of the system, the benefits must outweigh the costs. To this end, the analysts prepare a **cost/benefit analysis**, which can be a spreadsheet showing all the costs incurred by the system and all the benefits that are expected from its operation.

The most accurate method of economic analysis is the fully quantitative **return on investment (ROI)**, which is a calculation of the difference between the stream of benefits and the stream of costs over the life of the system, discounted by the applicable interest rate, as shown in Figure 12.4. To find the ROI, the net present value of the system is calculated by combining the net present value of the costs of the system with the net present value of the benefits of the system, using calculations based on annual costs and benefits and using the appropriate interest rate. If the ROI is positive, the system is economically feasible, or cost justified. Remember that during the time the system is developed, which might be several years, there are no benefits, only development costs. Operational costs during the system's life include software license fees, maintenance personnel, telecommunications, power, and computer-related supplies (such as hardware replacement, software upgrades, and paper and toner purchases). If the system involves a Web site, the cost of revising and enhancing the site by Webmasters and other professionals must also be included.

FIGURE 12.4
Estimated benefits and costs of an IS ($000)

Year	2007	2008	2009	2010	2011	2012
Benefits						
Increase in sales			56,000	45,000	30,000	10,000
Reduction in staff			20,000	20,000	20,000	20,000
Total Benefits	0	0	76,000	65,000	50,000	30,000
Costs						
Analysis	15,000					
Design	37,500					
Implementation	0	56,000				
Hardware	0	20,000				
Operation and maintenance	0	0	5,000	5,000	5,000	5,000
Total Costs	52,000	76,000	5,000	5,000	5,000	5,000
Difference	(-52,000)	(-76,000)	71,000	60,000	45,000	25,000
Discounted at 5%	(-49,524)	(-68,934)	61,332	49,362	32,259	18,657
Net present value for six years	43,152					

Figure 12.4 presents a simplified example of a cost/benefit spreadsheet and analysis for a small system. Since the net present value of the system is positive ($43,152,000), and therefore the benefits exceed the investment, the development effort is economically justified. In the figure, in the year 2012, the net present value starts to diminish. As this value continues to diminish, the organization should consider creating a new system. If the system is not replaced or significantly upgraded, the existing system will become a drain on the organization over time.

Often, it is difficult to justify the cost of a new IS because too many of the benefits are *intangible*, that is, they cannot be quantified in dollar terms. Improved customer service, better decision making, and a more enjoyable workplace are all benefits that might eventually increase profit but are very difficult to estimate in dollar amounts. This inability to measure benefits is especially true when the new IS is intended not merely to automate a manual process but to support a new business initiative or improve intellectual activities such as decision making. For example, it is difficult to quantify the benefits of business intelligence (BI) and knowledge management (KM) systems. Software vendors often promote fast ROI as a selling point, and express it in terms of the short period of time over which the adopting organization can recoup the investment. Still, such claims are difficult, if not impossible, to demonstrate. Therefore, the economic incentive for investing in a new IS is often "we must use it because our competitors use it" and a general expectation that the new IS will benefit the organization in at least one way.

The Operational Feasibility Study

The purpose of the operational feasibility study is to determine whether the new system will be used as intended. More specifically, this analysis answers the following questions:

- Will the system fit into the culture of this organization?
- Will all the intended users use the system to its full capacity?
- Will the system interfere with company policies or statutory laws?

Organizational culture is an umbrella term referring to the general tone of the corporate environment. This includes issues such as tendency to share or not to share information among units and people, willingness to team-play, and the proclivity of employees to experiment with new ideas and technologies. The development team must consider culture to ensure that the new system will fit the organization. For example, if the system will be used by telecommuters, the organization must be open to telecommunications via the Internet. The analysts must find out whether this need would compromise information security and confidentiality.

Another point the team considers is compliance with statutory regulations and company policy. For example, the record-keeping system the staff wants to use might violate customer privacy or risk the confidentiality of government contracts with the company. If these issues cannot be overcome at the outset, then the proposed system is not operationally feasible.

Requirements Definition

When the analysts determine that the proposed system is feasible, the project team is installed. Management or the consulting firm nominates a project leader who puts together a project team to develop the system until it is ready for delivery. The team includes systems analysts, programmers, and, often, representatives from the prospective group of users.

One of the first pieces of information the analysts need to know is the system requirements. **System requirements** are the functions that the system is expected to fulfill and the features through which it will perform its tasks. In other words, system requirements are what the system should be able to do and the means by which it will fulfill its stated goal. This can be done through interviews, questionnaires, examination of documents, and on-the-job observations.

Once facts are gathered, they are organized into a document detailing the system requirements, and the managers of the business unit, or business units, for which the system is to be developed often sign the document as a contract between them and the developers. This formal sign-off is a crucial milestone in the analysis process; if the requirements are not well defined, resources will be wasted or underbudgeted, and the completion of the project will be delayed.

Design

With a comprehensive list of requirements, the project team can begin the next step in systems development, designing the new system. The purpose of this phase is to devise the means to meet all the business requirements detailed in the requirements report. As indicated in Figure 12.5, **systems design** comprises three steps: a description of the components and how they will work, construction, and testing. If the decision is to purchase ready-made software, the description of components becomes a description of how certain components will be adapted for the particular needs of the purchasing organization, and construction is the actual changes in programming code.

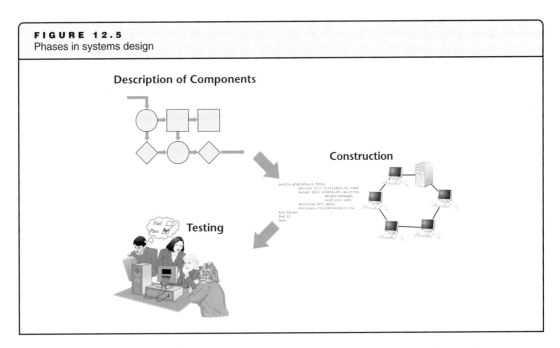

FIGURE 12.5
Phases in systems design

Description of Components

Construction

Testing

To communicate ideas about data, processes, and information gleaned from data, systems analysts and programmers use conventions of symbols. The advantage of such conventions is that visual information can be grasped much faster and more accurately than text, much as a blueprint for a building conveys specifications more efficiently than the equivalent text. One such convention is the data flow diagram.

Data Flow Diagrams

A **data flow diagram (DFD)** is used to describe the flow of data in a business operation, using only four symbols for these elements: external entities, processes, data stores, and the direction in which data flows (see Figure 12.6). *External entities* include individuals and groups of people who are external to the system, such as customers, employees, other departments in the organization, or other organizations. A *process* is any event or sequence of events in which data are either changed or acted on, such as the processing of data into information or the application of data to decision making. A *data store* is any form of data at rest, such as a filing cabinet or a database. Data flows from an external entity to a process, from a process to a data store, from a data store to a process, and so on. Thus, a carefully drawn DFD can provide a useful representation of a system, whether existing or planned.

The use of only four symbols and the simplicity of DFDs are their great advantage. Often, systems analysts produce several levels of DFDs for a system. The highest level contains the least number of symbols and is the least detailed. A lower level is more detailed; what might be represented only as a general process in the higher level is exploded into several subprocesses and several databases. The lowest-level diagram explodes some processes further and is the most detailed; it shows every possible process, data store, and entity involved. Usually, the first- and second-level diagrams are presented to non-IS executives, and the lowest-level DFD is considered by the IS professionals while they analyze or develop the system.

The DFD in Figure 12.7 shows a process of calculating a sales bonus. A salesclerk is an entity entering data (in this case, salespeople's ID numbers), which flows into a process, namely, the bonus calculation, which also receives data from the salespeople database (in this case, the dollar amount each salesperson sold over the past year). The result of the process, the bonus amount for each salesperson, is information that flows into a bonus file. Later, the company's controller will use the information to generate bonus checks.

DFD symbols are suitable for describing any IS, even if it is not computer based. A DFD of the existing system helps pinpoint its weaknesses by describing the flow of data graphically and allowing analysts to pinpoint which processes and databases can be automated, shared by different processes, or otherwise changed to strengthen the IS. If a new IS is needed, a DFD of the conceptualized new system is drawn to provide the logical blueprint for its construction.

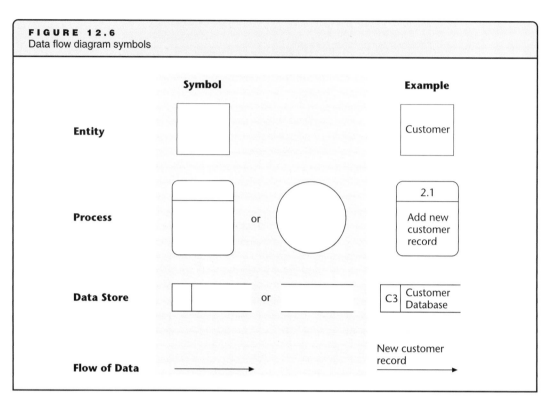

FIGURE 12.6
Data flow diagram symbols

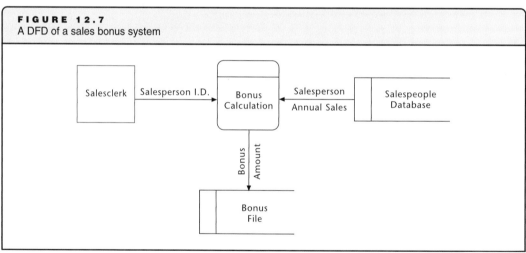

FIGURE 12.7
A DFD of a sales bonus system

While DFDs are easy to learn and use, they have shortcomings—like any diagramming method—and cannot describe a system completely. For example, they do not specify computations within a process or timing relationships among data flows. A payroll DFD, for instance, cannot specify whether employee timesheets are checked as they are submitted or at the end of the week. Such details usually accompany DFDs as text comments.

Unified Modeling Language (UML)

As an increasing number of developed applications became object oriented, a new way to describe desired software was needed. Several diagramming sets were developed by the 1970s, but in the late-1990s a *de facto* standard emerged: UML. **Unified Modeling Language (UML)** is a graphical standard for visualizing, specifying, and documenting software. It helps developers to communicate and logically validate desired features in the design phases of software development projects. It is independent of particular programming languages, but it does provide standard visual symbols and notations for specifying object-oriented elements, such as classes and procedures. It also provides symbols to communicate software that is used for constructing

Web sites and Web-based activities, such as selecting items from an online catalog and executing online payments.

UML consists of diagrams that describe the following types of software: use case, class, interaction, state, activity, and physical components. A use case is an activity that the system executes in response to a user. A user is referred to as an "actor." Use case diagrams communicate the relationships between actors and use cases. Class diagrams describe class structure and contents and use the three-part symbol for class: name, attributes, and methods (see the example in Chapter 5, Figure 5.4). Interaction diagrams describe interactions of objects and the sequence of their activities. State charts communicate the states through which objects pass, as well as the objects' responses to signals (called stimuli) they receive. Activity diagrams represent highly active states that are triggered by completion of the actions of other states; therefore, they focus on internal processing. Physical diagrams are high-level descriptions of software modules. They consist of components diagrams, which describe the software, including source code, compilation, and execution; and deployment diagrams, which describe the configuration of software components when they are executed. Figure 12.8 shows an example of modeling in UML.

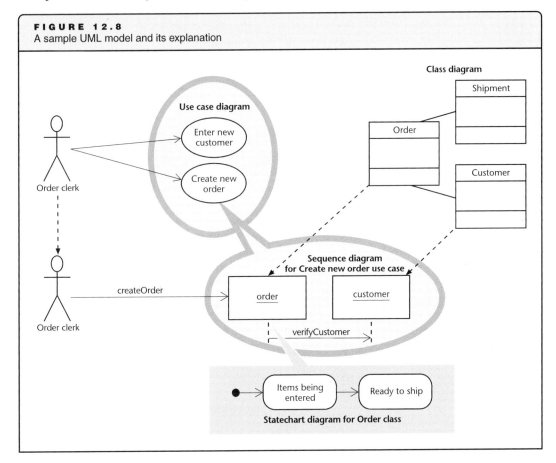

FIGURE 12.8
A sample UML model and its explanation

Construction

Once the software development tools are chosen, the construction of the system begins. System construction is predominantly programming. Professional programmers translate input, output, and processes, as described in data flow diagrams, into programs. The effort often takes months or even years (in which case the users might not be served well due to changes in business needs). When a program module is completed, it is tested. Testing is performed by way of walk-through and simulation.

In a walk-through, the systems analysts and programmers follow the logic of the program, conduct processes that the system is programmed to execute when running, produce output, and compare output with what they know the results should be. In simulation, the team actually runs the program with these data. When all the modules of the application are completed and successfully tested, the modules are integrated into one coherent program.

System Testing

Although simulation with each module provides some testing, it is important to test the entire integrated system. The system is checked against the system requirements originally defined in the analysis phase by running typical data through the system. The quality of the output is examined, and processing times are measured to ensure that the original requirements are met.

Testing should include attempts to get the system to fail, by violating processing and security controls. The testers should try to "outsmart" the system, entering unreasonable data and trying to access files that should not be accessed directly by some users or—under certain circumstances—by any user. This violation of typical operating rules is a crucial step in the development effort, because many unforeseen snags can be discovered and fixed before the system is introduced for daily use. If the new system passes the tests, it is ready for implementation in the business units that will use it.

Testing tends to be the least respected phase in systems development. Too often project managers who are under time pressure to deliver a new IS either hasten testing or forgo it altogether. Because it is the last phase before delivery of the new system, it is the natural "victim" when time and budget have run out. This rush has caused many failures and, eventually, longer delays than if the system had undergone comprehensive testing. A thorough testing phase might delay delivery, but it drastically reduces the probability that flaws will be discovered only after the new system is delivered.

Implementation

The **implementation** of a new IS, also called delivery, consists of two steps: conversion and training. Although training might precede conversion, if training is done on the job it can occur after conversion. **Conversion** takes place when an operation switches from using an old system to using a new system. Conversion can be a difficult time for an organization. Operators need to get used to new systems, and even though the system might have been thoroughly tested, conversion can hold some unpleasant surprises if certain bugs or problems have not been discovered earlier. Services to other departments and to customers might be delayed, and data might be lost. There are four basic conversion strategies to manage the transition (see Figure 12.9).

Parallel Conversion

In **parallel conversion**, the old system is used along with the new system for a predetermined period of time. This duplication minimizes risk because if the new system fails, operations are not stopped and no damage is caused to the organization. However, parallel conversion is costly because of the expenses, especially labor costs, associated with running two systems.

Phased Conversion

ISs, especially large ones, can often be broken into functional modules and phased into operation one at a time, a process called **phased conversion**. For example, conversion of an accounting IS can be phased, with the accounts receivable module converted first, then the accounts payable, then the general ledger, and so on. A supply chain management system might be implemented one module at a time: first, the customer order module, then the shipment module, then the inventory control module, and so on, up to the collection module. This phased approach also reduces risk, although the benefits of using the entire integrated system are delayed. Also, users can learn how to use one module at a time, which is easier than learning the entire system at once. However, when parts of both systems are used, there might be data inconsistencies between the two.

Cut-Over Conversion

In a **cut-over conversion**, also called **flash cut conversion**, the old system is discarded and the new one takes over the entire business operation for which it was developed. This strategy is highly risky, but it can be inexpensive, if successful, because no resources are spent on running two systems in parallel, and the benefits of the entire new system are immediately realized.

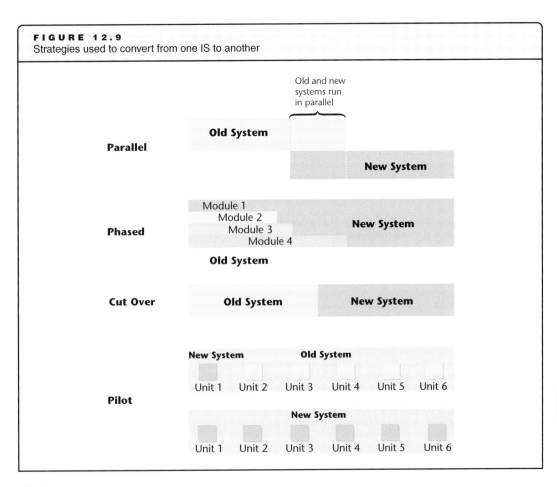

FIGURE 12.9
Strategies used to convert from one IS to another

Pilot Conversion

If the new system is to be used in more than one business unit, it might first be introduced for a period of time in a single unit, where problems can be addressed and the system can be polished before implementing it in the other business units. This trial conversion is also possible for systems shared by many departments and disparate sites, as is increasingly the case due to the growing popularity of intranets and extranets. Obviously, piloting reduces risks because it confines any problems to fewer units. It is especially useful for determining how comfortable staff members and other users, such as suppliers and customers, are with a new system, a lesson that can be applied to the later units. As with the parallel strategy, the pilot strategy means that benefits of the full implementation of the system are delayed.

When a system is developed by a software vendor for a wide market rather than for a specific client, conversion often takes place at beta sites. A beta site is an organization whose management agrees to test the new system for several months and provide feedback.

Support

The role of IT professionals does not end with the delivery of the new system. They must support it and ensure that users can operate it satisfactorily. Support includes two main responsibilities: maintenance and user help. Maintenance consists of postimplementation debugging and updating (making changes and additions), including adding features that were originally desired but later postponed so budget and time limits could be met. Usually, updating is the greater effort.

Debugging is the correction of bugs or problems in programs that were not discovered during tests. Updating is revising the system to comply with changing business needs that occur after the implementation phase. For example, if a company collects personal data for market analysis, managers might want to use the new IS to collect more data, which might require new fields in the databases.

Although maintenance is viewed by IS professionals as lacking in glamour, it should not be taken lightly or left to less-experienced professionals. Company surveys show that up to 80 percent of IS budgets is spent on maintenance, the cost of which varies widely from system to system. The major reason for this huge proportion is that support is the longest phase in a system's life cycle. While development takes several months to about 3 years, the system is expected to yield benefits over many years.

Efficient and effective system maintenance is possible only if good documentation is written while the system is being developed, and if the code is written in a structured, easy-to-follow manner. Documentation consists of three main types: paper books, electronic documents, and in-program documentation. The latter covers nonexecutable comments in the code, seen only when reviewing the application's source code. You can see this type of documentation when you retrieve the source code of many Web pages. In-program documentation briefly describes what each module of the program does and sometimes who developed it. Printed and electronic documentation is prepared both for programmers, who can better understand how to revise code, and for users who want to learn about the various features of the application.

AGILE METHODS

While the full approach of the SDLC or similar waterfall methods are used to develop ISs, it is widely recognized that these methods are lengthy, expensive, and inflexible. Systems developed on the SDLC model are often unable to adapt to vague or rapidly changing user requirements. To overcome these challenges, alternative methods have emerged that are collectively called **agile methods**. As Figure 12.10 illustrates, agile methods treat software development as a series of contacts with users, with the goal of fast development of software to satisfy user requirements, and improving the software shortly after users request modifications. Agile methods make extensive use of iterative programming, involving users often, and keeping programmers open to modifications while the development is still under way. The better known methods are Extreme Programming (XP), Adaptive Software Development (ASD), Lean Development (LD), Rational Unified Process (RUP), Feature Driven Development (FDD), Dynamic Systems Development Method (DSDM), Scrum, and Crystal. XP is by far the most documented and best known of these methods.

The differences among the methods are outside the scope of this discussion. However, the major advantage of all agile methods is that they result in fast development of applications so that users can have them within weeks rather than months or years. Users do not have to wait long for modifications of the systems, whether the modifications are required because of programmer errors or because users have second thoughts about some features.

However, the benefits of agile methods do not come without risks. First, the analysis phase is minimal or is sometimes eliminated completely. Reducing or skipping a thorough formal analysis increases the risk of incompatibilities and other unforeseen mishaps. Also, the developers devote most of their time to construction and little time to documentation, so modification at a later date can be extremely time consuming, if not impossible. Because of the inherent risks, there are times when agile methods are appropriate and others when they are not (see the discussion later in this section).

Software developers who espouse the approach usually subscribe to the *Manifesto for Agile Software Development*, which expresses priorities: individuals and interactions over processes and tools; working software over comprehensive documentation; customer collaboration over contract negotiation; and responding to change over following a plan. You can find the full Manifesto at http://agilemanifesto.org/principles.html. The software developed should primarily satisfy users, not business processes, because users must be satisfied with the applications they use even if that means changing processes. While program documentation is important, it should not come at the expense of well-working software, especially when time is limited and the programmers must decide how to allot their time, on better software or on better documentation. The customers of software development, the users, are not an adverse party and should not be negotiated with but regarded as codevelopers and co-owners of the software. Plans are good but might stand in the way of necessary changes. Responding to changing user requirements is more important than following a plan. If there is a development plan at all, it is fine to change it often.

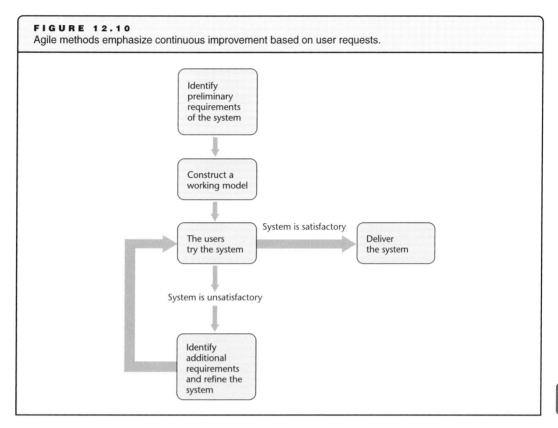

FIGURE 12.10
Agile methods emphasize continuous improvement based on user requests.

Identify
preliminary
requirements
of the system

Construct a
working model

The users
try the system

System is satisfactory → Deliver the system

System is unsatisfactory

Identify
additional
requirements
and refine the
system

All agile methods aim to have "light but sufficient" development processes. Therefore, project teams avoid use of formal project management plans, financial spreadsheets for budgeting, task lists, or any other activity that does not directly contribute to development of a functioning application.

POINT OF INTEREST

It Takes Two

Agile methods have some innovative approaches to software development. For example, Extreme Programming (XP) requires programmers to work in pairs, each pair sharing a computer and working together on the same code. The main purpose is to improve code review—the process of finding and fixing programming mistakes. Sharing the same monitor and keyboard also improves communication between the two programmers. The practice helps fix all errors as the code is developed rather than at a later testing. Thus, an application of high quality can be developed within a short time.

While the SDLC or any other waterfall approach requires users to sign off on their requirements and then wait for the system to be completed, agile methods encourage users' involvement throughout the process and encourage developers to change requirements in response to user input if needed. The purpose of agile methods is not to conform to a static contract with the users but to ensure that the users receive an application with which they are happy. To avoid costly redesign, agile methods encourage developers to test each module as soon as it is complete.

For example, Extreme Programming (XP) includes the following principles: produce the initial software within weeks (rather than months) to receive rapid feedback from users; invent simple solutions so there is less to change and necessary changes are easy to make; improve design quality continually, so that the next "story" is less costly to implement; and test constantly to accomplish earlier, less expensive defect detection. (A *story* is a requirement or set of requirements delivered by the users.) Instead of formal requirements, the developers encourage the users to give examples of how they would like to use the application in a certain business situation. Communication with users is highly informal and takes place on a daily basis.

Unlike more traditional methods, agile methods encourage two programmers to work on the same module of code on the same computer. This fosters constructive criticism and feedback. This is a major feature in XP. The constant communication between the two coders is meant to ensure cross-fertilization of ideas and high-quality software. The idea is that two minds working on the same code create synergy, and that two pairs of eyes are more likely to spot bugs than a single pair.

Critics of agile programming in general and XP in particular argue that the relaxed approach to planning and ceding decision making and accountability to clients (users) might result in disasters, especially if such methods are applied to large, complex projects. The critics cite the DaimlerChrysler payroll system (Chrysler Comprehensive Compensation, known as C3). C3 was the first large application developed with the XP method and was eventually canceled. The software never delivered more than one-fourth of the features it was supposed to have.

On the other hand, supporters give examples of success. One is a system developed for Domino's Pizza. When the company needed a new sales-tracking system, its CIO realized the project was too big and the time allotted for it—9 months—too short. He hired the services of experienced XP consultants and programmers. The clients described each feature—a story in XP parlance—on an index card. Each feature was coded in less than a week. The software was ready on time and with full functionality. It links point-of-sale registers with applications that track orders at the chain's 7,000 stores, which sell 400 million pizzas annually. Management now can analyze sales by toppings, crusts, sizes, delivery address, and soda sold with the pies.

When to Use Agile Methods

Agile methods are an efficient approach to development when a system is small, when it deals with unstructured problems, and when the users cannot specify all the requirements at the start of the project. They are also useful when developing a user interface: the developers can save time by quickly developing the screens, icons, and menus for users to evaluate instead of forcing the users to provide specifications.

When a system to be developed is small in scale, the risk involved in the lack of thorough analysis is minimal, partly because the investment of resources is small. (A small system is one that serves one person or a small group of employees. A large system is one that serves many employees, who might be accessing the system via a network from different sites.) If the small-system development takes longer than planned, the overall cost is still likely to be smaller than if a full SDLC were performed.

When users cannot communicate their requirements, either because they are not familiar with technological developments or because they find it hard to conceptualize the system's input and output files, processes, and user interface, developers have no choice but to use agile methods. In this case the users are often able to communicate their requirements as the development proceeds. For example, it is easier for marketing personnel to evaluate Web pages designed for a new electronic catalog and promotion site than to describe in detail what they want before seeing anything. Without being shown actual examples, users often can offer little guidance beyond "I will know it when I see it." It is easier for future users to respond to screens, menus, procedures, and other features developed by IT professionals than to provide a list of requirements for them.

When Not to Use Agile Methods

Agile methods might not be appropriate for all systems development. If a system is large or complex, or if it is designed to interface with other systems, using agile methods might pose too great a risk because the methods skip feasibility studies. Some experts do not recommend the use of agile methods for large systems because such systems require a significant investment of resources; therefore, system failure could entail great financial loss. The systematic approach of the SDLC is recommended if the system is complex and consists of many modules, because extra care must be applied in documenting requirements and the manner in which components will be integrated, to ensure smooth and successful development.

For the same reasons, use of agile methods should be avoided when a system is to be interfaced with other systems. The system requirements and integration must be analyzed carefully, documented, and carried out according to a plan agreed on by the users and developers before the design and construction phases start. This early consensus reduces the risk of incompatibility and damage to other, existing systems. Therefore, accounting ISs, large order-entry systems, and payroll systems as whole systems are rarely developed under agile methods. Other factors that should encourage use of waterfall methods are the size of the development team, how often the application is expected to be modified, how critical it is in terms of affecting people's lives and critical organizational goals, and how tight the development budget is.

Figure 12.11 summarizes factors in deciding when and when not to use agile methods.

FIGURE 12.11
When and when not to use agile methods

When to use Agile Methods	When not to use Agile Methods
Small-scale system	Large-scale system
System solving unstructured problems	Complex system
When it's difficult for users to specify system requirements	System with interfaces to other systems
When the development team is small and co-located	When the team is large or distributed in multiple sites
System requirements are dynamic	System requirements are fairly static
System will not put people and critical organization goals at risk	System will significantly affect people's well-being and critical organizational goals
Development project budget is tight	Development is well-funded

SYSTEMS INTEGRATION

Firms often must wrestle with highly distributed, heterogeneous environments populated with applications for special tasks, which cannot be accessed by systems used for other tasks. Often, the disparate systems cannot "talk to each other" because they run on different operating systems (or, as IS professionals say, on different platforms).

Much of what IT professionals do is systems integration, rather than analysis and development of a stand-alone IS. Systems integration looks at the information needs of an entire organization, or at least of a major division of it. The analysts consider the existing, but often disparate, ISs and then produce a plan to integrate them so that data can flow more easily among different units of the organization and users can access different types of data via a single interface. Consequently, many IS service companies call themselves systems integrators. Systems integration has become increasingly important mainly because more and more ISs are linked to Web sites, because more legacy databases are integrated into new enterprise applications such as SCM and ERP systems, and because of the growing linking of ISs between organizations (see Figure 12.12). *Legacy systems* are old systems that organizations decide to continue to use because the investment in a new system would not justify the improved features or because the old systems have some advantage that cannot be obtained from newer systems.

Systems integration is often more challenging than systems development. In fact, some IT professionals regard systems development as a subspecialty of systems integration because the integrator must develop systems with an understanding of how data maintained in disparate systems can be efficiently retrieved and used for effective business processes, and because legacy systems must often be interfaced with recently acquired systems.

For example, marketing managers can have richer information for decision making if they have easy access to accounting and financial data through their own marketing IS. The better the integration, the better they can incorporate this information into their marketing information.

Should IS Professionals Be Certified?

When organizations commit millions of dollars to developing systems, they count on IT professionals to provide high-quality systems that will fulfill their intended purposes without harming their businesses, their employees, or their consumers. But the products of IT professionals often fail and cause serious damage. Some people argue that because of the high investment and high risk usually associated with systems development and operation, IT professionals, like other professionals, should be certified. These people argue that certification would minimize problems caused by ISs. Others argue that certification might stifle free competition and innovation, or even create a profession whose members will make it difficult to pass certification examinations so that current members can continue to enjoy high income.

Certification is meant to guarantee that the experts have passed tests that ensure their skills. The government or other authorized bodies are expected to license experts, thereby certifying which people have knowledge and skills in a particular discipline that are significantly greater than those of a layperson. Proponents of the measure argue that certification could reduce the malfunctioning of ISs.

Certification Pros. Some experts say certification could minimize the number and severity of IS malfunctions. Civil engineers must be certified to plan buildings and bridges. Doctors pass rigorous exams before they receive their licenses and begin to practice without supervision. Public accountants must be licensed to perform audits. Lawyers must pass the bar exams to practice. Why, these people ask, should IS professionals be allowed to practice without licensing?

Software experts do possess all the characteristics of professionals. They work in a field that requires expertise, and the public and their clients usually are not qualified to evaluate their skills. Certification could help the following groups in their relationships with IT specialists:

- *Employers* often hire software professionals without knowing what they are getting. They count on the information included in the candidate's résumé and, sometimes, on letters of recommendation. Mandatory certification might protect potential employers against charlatans. Also, certification would provide potential employers with information on a candidate's suitability for different levels of performance. For example, a professional might be qualified to participate in a systems development team but not to head the project team.

- *Clients* could benefit from mandatory certification even more. While employers can learn, in time, of the real capabilities of their personnel, businesses that hire consultants have no previous employment experience on which to rely.

- *Society* might enjoy fewer software-related failures. Only those who are qualified would be allowed to engage in development and maintenance of information systems, thereby improving the overall integrity of ISs. Certification is especially needed for those holding key development positions for systems whose impact on society is significant, such as medical ISs and software embedded in weapons systems.

Certification Cons. Two arguments are raised against mandatory certification:

- It is difficult, if not impossible, to devise a way to measure software development competence. For instance, there are many different methods for developing applications, and there is no proven advantage of one. A computer professional might be very experienced in one method but not in others. It would be unfair to disqualify that individual merely on this basis.

- Some argue that mandatory certification might create a "closed shop" by using a single entry exam designed to admit very few people. In such a scenario, the status and income of those admitted would be enhanced at the expense of those excluded. With little fear of competition within the closed group, there is often little incentive to improve skills.

Where We Operate Now. Currently, there is no mandatory certification of IT professionals. In fact, there isn't even agreement about who should be considered an IT professional. Some organizations, such as the Institute for Certification of Computer Professionals (ICCP), test and certify people who voluntarily take their tests. (About 50,000 people have been certified by ICCP globally, out of millions who consider themselves IT professionals.) Some software companies certify analysts and programmers to install their companies' tools. However, there are no certification regulations for IT professionals in the United States or anywhere else that are similar to those for many other professions.

FIGURE 12.12

Situations calling for systems integration

- Linking existing ISs to Web sites

- Linking databases to Web sites

- Interfacing legacy systems with new systems

- Linking legacy databases with enterprise applications

- Sharing information systems among organizations

Systems integrators must also be well versed in hardware and software issues, because different ISs often use incompatible hardware and software. Often, overcoming incompatibility issues is one of the most difficult aspects of integration. Consider business intelligence systems, which were discussed in Chapter 11. The concept of extracting business intelligence from large data warehouses involves integration of several ISs. The challenges are great, and by some estimates more than half of all BI projects are never completed or fail to deliver all the expected features and benefits.

Systems integration has become increasingly complex because it now involves the ISs not only of a single organization but of several organizations. In the era of extranets, the challenge is many times more difficult because IT professionals must integrate systems of several different companies so that they can communicate and work well using telecommunications. Imagine how difficult it is to integrate disparate legacy systems of several companies. For this reason, companies often contract with highly experienced experts for such projects.

POINT OF INTEREST

Want to be Certified?

If you are willing to take the test, you can add one or several of the following titles to your name: CCP, CBIP, CDMP, ISA, ACP, I.S.P. The Institute for Certification of Computer Professionals tests IT professionals and provides them with certificates. To see the goals of this not-for-profit organization and how the certification process is carried out, as well as what these acronyms stand for, visit www.iccp.org.

- IT planning is important especially because investing in IT is typically great and because of the high risk in implementing enterprise applications.

- Standardization is often an important part of IT planning. Standardization helps save costs, provides efficient training, and results in efficient support.

- The systems development life cycle (SDLC) and other waterfall methods consist of well-defined and carefully followed phases: analysis, design, implementation, and support.

- The purpose of systems analysis is to determine what needs the system will satisfy.

- Feasibility studies determine whether developing the system is possible and desirable from a number of viewpoints. The technical feasibility study examines the technical state of the art to ensure that the hardware and software exist to build the system. The economic feasibility study weighs the benefits of the system against its cost. The operational feasibility study determines whether the system will fit the organizational culture and be used to full capacity.

- System requirements detail the features the users need in the new system.

- In systems design, developers outline the systems components graphically and construct the software. Tools such as data flow diagrams and the Unified Modeling Language (UML) are used to create a model of the desired system.

- When the system is completed, it is implemented. Implementation includes training and conversion from the old system to the new system. Conversion can take place by one of several strategies: parallel, phased, cut-over, or piloting.

- The systems life cycle continues in the form of support. The system is maintained to ensure operability without fault and satisfaction of changing business needs.

- Agile methods are a popular alternative to the traditional systems development life cycle. Agile methods place great emphasis on flexible requirements and frequent interaction with users. These methods skip detailed systems analysis and aim at delivering a new application in the shortest possible time.

- Systems integration is often much more complicated than systems development because it requires the IT professionals to make different applications communicate with each other seamlessly. The complexity is multiplied when integrating ISs of several organizations that must work together over the Web.

- Because of the great responsibility of IS professionals, the question of whether certification is needed has come up. If doctors, civil engineers, lawyers, and public accountants are subject to mandatory certification, many people argue that IS professionals should be, too.

WORLDWIDE HOST REVISITED

Worldwide Host's TripExpert.com project team has been busy investigating opportunities for development of the new Web site. They are keeping strategic planning issues in mind as they learn more about options for the site.

What Would You Do?

1. The case at the beginning of the chapter lists Worldwide Host's corporate mission statement. From that statement, information given in the opening case, and the examples in the chapter, write a possible IS mission statement for Worldwide Host. Be sure to include information on IS's place in the organization and its chief contributions.

2. In what ways has the TripExpert.com team been dealing with systems integration, instead of systems development? Cite examples of systems that Worldwide Host is trying to integrate.

WORLDWIDE HOST REVISITED, CONTINUED

New Perspectives

1. The TripExpert.com site is facing a time crunch. The chapter discussed agile methods as ways to speed development of information systems. Would these techniques work for the TripExpert.com project? Why or why not?

2. The database team overlooked a key new requirement for the database system. Could this mistake have been prevented? If so, how and at what stage of the systems development life cycle?

KEY TERMS

agile method, 398
beta site, 397
conversion, 396
cost/benefit analysis, 391
cut-over conversion (flash cut conversion), 396
data flow diagram (DFD), 393
feasibility study, 390
implementation, 396

organizational culture, 392
parallel conversion, 396
phased conversion, 396
piloting, 397
prototyping, 388
return on investment (ROI), 391
support, 397
system requirement, 392

systems analysis, 389
systems design, 392
systems development life cycle (SDLC), 388
systems integration, 401
Unified Modeling Language (UML), 394

REVIEW QUESTIONS

1. Why is IT planning so important?

2. As part of their IT planning many organizations decide to standardize. What does standardization mean in this context, and what are its potential benefits?

3. Why is traditional systems development referred to as a "cycle"? What determines the cycle's end?

4. Systems developers often use the term "application development" rather than "systems development." Why?

5. What are the benefits using data flow diagrams?

6. SDLC is usually recommended for developing an IS that will be interfaced to other ISs. Give two examples of an IS that is interfaced with at least two other ISs.

7. Recall the discussion of IT professionals in Chapter 1. Of the following professionals, who does the majority of the systems construction job: the CIO, systems analyst, the database administrator (DBA), or the programmer? Why?

8. What are the advantages of agile methods over waterfall development methods, such as the traditional SDLC? What are the risks?

9. Why are agile methods so helpful when users cannot define system requirements?

10. An increasing number of IS professionals prefer to call the end users of their creations "customers," even if the developers and users are employees of the same organization. Why?

11. What is systems integration?

12. Why is systems integration more complicated in the Web era than before?

13. The emergence of the Web as a vehicle for business increased the need for systems integration. How so?

1. The modern view of systems development is that it should be a continuation of IS planning. Why?

2. Consider a new chain of shoe stores. The marketing department of the corporation would like to know the customers and their preferences. What questions would you ask before developing an IS for data collection and analysis?

3. The analysis phase of systems development includes fact-finding. Suggest ways to find facts, other than the ways mentioned in this chapter.

4. In data flow diagrams, a process is always labeled with an action, while entities and data stores are labeled with nouns. Why? Give two examples for each of these elements.

5. You are asked to recommend a conversion strategy for a new accounts receivable system. The system will be used only by the controller's office. Which strategy will you recommend, and why?

6. You are asked to recommend a conversion strategy for a new ERP system that includes accounting, sales, purchasing, and payroll modules. Which strategy will you recommend, and why?

7. What are the elements that make the responsibilities of IT professionals similar to those of other professionals?

8. Do you support mandatory certification of IT professionals? Why or why not? If you do, which IT professionals (analysts, programmers, DBAs) would you require to pass tests? Why?

9. Many IT professionals say that trying to certify all specialists in this profession is impractical. Why?

10. Many software companies (such as Microsoft, Oracle, and SAP) certify people as consultants for their products. For instance, you might become a certified SAP R/3 Technical Consultant. Is this type of certification the same, in principle, as the certification of a physician, lawyer, or certified public accountant (CPA)? Explain.

11. Suppose you are the IT director for a hospital. You have a small crew that helps the medical and administrative staffs with their computers and applications, but when a new system must be developed, you must hire IT professionals. How would you conduct your search for reliable IS developers? Whom would you contact, and what questions would you ask?

12. You are the CIO for a large university hospital. The medical staff of the oncology ward would like to build an expert system for diagnosis. Your preliminary review shows that the financial investment would be great. What questions do you ask (of both the doctors and your staff) to decide whether to use a thorough SDLC or agile methods to develop the system? List and explain your questions.

13. You are trying to explain to your supervisor the general details of a proposed IS. The IS involves a server connecting many PCs. Your supervisor is not an IS professional and has no idea what a DFD is. How would you prefer to communicate your ideas: verbally; in writing, but without diagrams; with a DFD; or with a combination of some or all of these means? Explain your choice.

14. During development of a new IS, professional jargon might facilitate communication among IS professionals, but it might be detrimental when used to communicate with users. Explain.

1. Prepare a 10-minute software-based presentation (use PowerPoint or another application) to make a presentation on the topic: "Factors that have made IS planning difficult over the past 5 years." Include in your presentation developments in hardware, software, and telecommunications; globalization; the Internet; the IT labor force; and any other area that has had an impact on IT planning.

2. You were hired as an IS consultant by a small chain of stores that rents domestic appliances. Partly because operations are run with paper records, one store does not know what is going on in the other stores. The president of this

small company thinks that the chain doesn't utilize its inventory efficiently. For example, if a customer needs a lawnmower and the appliance is not available in store A, the salespeople cannot tell the customer if the mower is available at another outlet or offer to bring it for the customer from another outlet. The president would like an IS that would allow the chain to serve the customers better and that would help with tracking and billing, too. She would like to take advantage of the Web to help both employees and customers. Both should know what is available for rent and at which store at any given time. List the questions you would ask in your fact-finding effort and indicate who in the organization would be asked each question.

3. Assume you are the leader of a team that has just completed construction of a Web site that provides information but also allows online purchasing of your company's products. Enumerate and explain the steps you would take to test the system. Prepare a software-based presentation (using PowerPoint or a similar application) to explain all the testing steps and why each must be taken. (*Hint*: Keep in mind different operating systems, Web browsers, screen sizes, and so forth.)

HANDS-ON ACTIVITIES

1. Prepare a DFD that describes the following application:

Gadgets, Inc., sells its items through traveling salespeople. When a salesperson receives a signed contract from a client, he or she enters the details into a notebook computer. The salesperson later transmits the record to the company's mainframe computer at its headquarters. The program records the details in four files: sales, shipping, accounts receivable, and commissions. If the buyer is a new customer (one who is not yet in the customer database), the program enters the customer's record into the customer database and generates a thank-you letter. The program also calculates the 5 percent commission, which is recorded in the commission file with the salesperson's code.

At the end of the month, the program produces a paper report with the records of all the new customers. In addition, if the total monthly sales of the salesperson exceed $100,000, the program generates a congratulatory letter showing that total. If the total is less than $5,000, the program produces a letter showing the total and the sentence: "Try harder next month."

2. Prepare a DFD that communicates the following business walk-up car rental scenario:

When a customer approaches the counter at Buggy Car Rental, a serviceperson asks the customer for the details of the desired car. He or she then checks in a computerized database to see whether a car with these features is available. If a car is available, the serviceperson collects pertinent information from the customer (including an imprint of the customer's credit card), fills out a contract, and has the customer sign the contract. The customer is then given a key and is told where to find the car in the parking lot. The serviceperson indicates in the database that the car is no longer available. If a car with the desired specifications is not available, the serviceperson offers a car of a higher category at no extra charge. If such a car is not available either, the service person offers an available car of a lower category. The customer either rents it or refuses to rent it.

When the car is returned, the customer pays by check or by charging the credit card and returns the keys. The serviceperson gives the customer a copy of the signed contract, indicates in the database that the car is now available, and records its new mileage.

1. Team up with another student. Each of you should select a different agile method from the list appearing in this chapter. Each should write a one-page summary of the principles, benefits, and shortcomings of the method. Then, sit together and write a one-page summary of the differences between the two methods along the three points.

2. Team up with another student to search the Web for tools that facilitate software development and choose three tools. List the features provided in each of the tools. Assume that the vendors' claims are true. Which phases and activities of the systems development life cycle does each tool support? Which would you prefer to use in systems development? Why? Prepare a 5-minute software-based presentation (using PowerPoint or a similar application) to present your findings and explain your recommendations.

1. Use presentation software to create a presentation outlining the steps in IT project management.

2. Use spreadsheet software to re-create the table shown in Figure 12.4, but change the amounts shown. Be sure your spreadsheet uses formulas where applicable.

1. Visit Basecamp (http://www.basecamphq.com/). Give an example of a project for which you could use this tool.

2. How does this online project management tool compete with stand-alone project management software. Create a table comparing the features of Basecamp with at least two stand-alone project management programs.

FROM IDEAS TO APPLICATION: REAL CASES

Choice's Choices

In Chapter 8 you learned about Choice Hotels International B2B Web site as a successful enterprise. The company owns and franchises hotels in the United States and other countries: Comfort Inn, Quality, Clarion, Sleep Inn, EconoLodge, Rodeway Inn, and MainStay Suites. In 1999 the company established ChoiceBuys.com, a Web site through which the independent hotel operators can purchase supplies. The combined purchasing power of $1.5 billion per year reduces costs for each hotel and adds a commission to Choice Hotels' coffers.

Things look bright now, but the road to success was paved with difficulties. Choice had to purchase, develop, and redesign the Web site's software several times. Custom software development and customization of an existing application proved to be quite a challenge.

ChoiceBuys.com was based on software developed by a startup, and that software used to crash often. In 2000, a team of developers was formed to redevelop much of the software. The team used Macromedia ColdFusion, a software tool for developing Web applications. The team experienced problems when the Web application could not properly access the SQL Server database. The system was unstable, performed slowly, and was inflexible. The developers then switched to a set of development tools from Rational Software Corp. (Rational Software was later purchased by IBM.) The Java application was to run on a UNIX server.

At this point the development team consisted of 15 contract programmers. Brad Douglas, Choice's vice president of emerging businesses, knew that to maintain the systems, more programmers would be required. He also recognized that his company was not a software development house but a hotel chain and franchisor. Therefore, he elected to find a software package that was ready to meet Choice's business needs. The team's leader, Nikole Smith, used the system requirements that the team had developed as the platform for a request for quotation from software vendors. Of the 24 vendors considered, one, Comergent, had a software package that met 85 percent of Choice's requirements.

Even so, the software was not geared toward the type of relationship Choice had with its franchisees. It was developed to serve manufacturers who needed to support resellers of their products. The Web site functions more like an internal purchasing mechanism than

a site to attract independent hotels that might choose to make their purchases through it. Choice's chief technology officer now admits that the Web site should have been better tailored to the needs of the clients rather than those of Choice.

In 2002, when the new software was launched at the Web site, Choice's revenue from it dropped slightly, from $12 million in 2001 to $11.8 million. The company hired Catalyst Design Group, a consulting firm, to investigate what was wrong with the site. The consulting firm sent representatives to 5 franchisees. They interviewed the owners and staff of 5 hotels, and watched purchasing officers as they were using the site. The consultants recorded their difficulties. The officers often got lost when looking for certain options.

Because the site's software generates a separate order for each supplier, the Web site software was designed to accommodate this mode of operations. To the hotels' purchasing staffs it seemed as if they were using a separate shopping cart for each item they wanted to order. They had grown used to the standard implemented by Amazon.com and other retailers: select and drop as many items as you want into the same shopping cart. Upon the consultants' recommendation, users now see a single shopping cart. The ordered items are then split internally into different orders for different suppliers.

There were other features to fix. The search mechanism did not filter inquiries well enough. Entering "shampoo" resulted in a long list that included both hair shampoos and carpet shampoos. The site needed software that could help users better define and find the items they were seeking. There was no straightforward mechanism to comparing prices of products of different manufacturers. Comergent and Choice placed an emphasis on helping the hotels create lists of frequently ordered items to shorten the selection process, but the emphasis on this feature overshadowed other features and actually distracted users when they wanted to browse and search.

Redesigning the site's software yielded positive results. The number of hotels using the site rose 13 percent from 2003 to 2004, and the number of orders increased by 14 percent. Despite the challenges with the software, the idea of establishing a Web site for the Partner Services Division proved itself. In 1998, before the site was established, the division's revenue from commissions was $6.4 million. In 2004 it was $14 million.

Counting on the successful Web site, management decided to start selling its e-commerce expertise. To this end management established PrimarySource.com, a subsidiary that offers hotels outside it franchise chain access to the same purchasing system. Partner Services Technology is the division that operates the site. The first client outside Choice's chain was VGM Club, an organization that makes purchases for 3,000 golf and country clubs. This would almost double the buying power of the enterprise, which already serves 3,800 hotels.

Sources: Carr, D. F., "Choice Hotels: Supplies and Demand," *Baseline* (www.baselinemag.com), May 23, 2005; www. primarysource.com, 2005; www.comergent.com/customers/customer2/choice_hotels.cfm, 2005.

Thinking About the Case

1. Did Choice follow the SDLC method of software development? Did it use an agile method? Explain.

2. Knowing now what has happened during the period 1999–2004, what would you do differently in designing the implementing the Web site?

3. If you were Choice's CIO, would you decide to purchase software (as the company did twice), or would you have it custom-developed? Why?

4. Do you think Choice could have done what Catalyst did with the same effectiveness?

5. Should Choice have hired a company such as Catalyst at an earlier time (say, 1999, before the Web site was launched)? Why or why not?

Back to Low Tech

When an organization commissions development of an innovative system that succeeds, everybody sings songs of praise for the IT professionals involved in the project. When the software fails, everybody points fingers. We then hear that the project was "too ambitious" and its leaders "irresponsible." In June 2005, after a decade-long effort, a software development project that cost $230 million was canceled. Had it succeeded, United Airlines and Denver International Airport (DIA) would probably be praised as having the world's most advanced baggage handling system.

The modern DIA, owned by the City of Denver, was supposed to open in October 1993. It was planned to have the world's most advanced baggage handling system, fully computerized and using software especially developed for the system. Because the system was not ready by the planned opening time, United Airlines, which is the major user of the airport and the party that originally requested the system, agreed with the city of Denver to take over the management of this project. The airport opened for business in February 1995, but the computerized baggage handling system did not work as planned.

The system was designed and constructed by BAE Automated Systems Inc., a company whose assets were acquired in 2003 by G&T Conveyor Co. The system consisted of a network of PCs communicating with thousands of remotely controlled carts that carried baggage on a 21-mile underground track. The carts were equipped with wireless communication equipment to communicate with the PCs. The PCs kept track of every bag's current location. The carts carried bags from check-in counters to sorting areas where their bar-code tags were scanned. Then they were routed to the proper flight gates. Baggage handling at DIA was supposed to be fully automatic and highly accurate.

The system could never process baggage of arriving flights. After several years of effort, the only components that did work properly were those handling luggage destined out of Denver on United Airlines and for some baggage transfers between flights. All other handling continued to be manual. The system failed often. The software occasionally misidentified a bag's destination, and the conveyor sometimes crushed bags. The entire system stopped functioning often. When that happened, bags had to be handled manually, flights were delayed, and many bags were not on the same planes with their owners. United's mishandling ratio at DIA was higher with the system than at airports where baggage was handled manually. At Denver the ratio was 12.4 bags per 1,000. At San Francisco, United's mishandling ratio was 6.1 per 1,000.

The system was supposed to save labor and therefore, cost. The results were quite the opposite. Before the airport was built, United had signed a 30-year contract with Denver to pay $60 million annually for the system's space and equipment. The company continued to pay this sum despite the fact that the system did not work properly. It also paid $12 million annually to a contractor to operate and maintain the system. The decision to handle baggage manually saved the airline $1 million per month. Had the system worked properly, other airlines using the airport would use it. Since it failed, none except United Airlines even tried it.

United's executive said that the main reason for switching to manual handling was not to save cost but to improve customer service. However, scrapping the system would save the maintenance cost and also the cost of compensating customers for lost and misrouted bags. Reportedly, the airline also negotiated with the city of Denver to reduce or eliminate the annual fee for equipment that is no longer used.

Consultants not involved in the project criticized the airline's management for waiting so many years before pulling the plug, especially in light of the fact that the airline had filed for bankruptcy protection in 2002. The airline should have canceled the project several years sooner, they said, especially because this was a leading-edge system that required great resources. Perhaps this is a human tendency: a refusal to admit failure, accept the loss, and move on.

Sources: Weiss, T., "United Axes Troubled Baggage System at Denver Airport," *Computerworld*, June 10, 2005; Yamanouchi, K., Leib, J., "United to Shed Dreary Baggage," DenverPost.com, June 8, 2005; Associated Press, "United Abandons Denver Baggage System," June 7, 2005.

Thinking About the Case

1. Should executives avoid trying to commission cutting-edge systems that rely on IT? Why or why not?

2. Critics say United Airlines should have canceled the project years before it actually did. Suppose it is 1996. Tens of millions of dollars have been spent on the project so far. You have the power to stop the project. What is your decision and why?

3. One observer said that had the project succeeded, United's executives would be considered heroes and all other airlines would adopt the technology. Why do you think these executives decided to continue to try to make the system operable?

13

THIRTEEN

Choices in Systems Acquisition

LEARNING OBJECTIVES

Developing systems in-house or commissioning a software development firm is the most expensive way to acquire ISs. Other alternatives might be less expensive and offer different benefits. Some of the alternatives have been mentioned in previous chapters, but they are discussed in more depth here and will provide a deeper understanding of systems acquisition.

When you finish this chapter, you will able to:

- Explain the differences among the alternatives to tailored system development: outsourcing, licensing ready-made software, contracting with an application service provider, and encouraging users to develop their own applications.

- List the business trade-offs inherent in the various methods of acquiring systems.

- Describe which systems acquisition approach is appropriate for a particular set of circumstances.

- Discuss organizational policies on employee computer use.

WORLDWIDE HOST:
Tapping Others' Expertise

Worldwide Host is a leader in the hotel industry, not in software development. CIO Michael Lloyd had convinced his executive team long ago that it made better financial sense for the hotel chain to contract with a software firm to develop or upgrade its information systems while he and his staff concentrated on hardware and day-to-day support. It took time, many interviews, and the review of several proposals to find a firm that fit well with Worldwide's unique needs, but General Data Systems (GDS) fit the bill. That firm was a top-notch software developer with a long track record in the industry, and it provided the technical expertise that Worldwide needed to keep abreast of ever changing technology. The partnership between the two firms allowed Worldwide to keep its IT staffing low and use GDS for help with new business needs and problems. The TripExpert.com Web site project was just the latest in the two firms' collaboration.

Adding Another Firm to the Mix

Michael was meeting with GDS analysts Judith Kozak and Corey Johnson to go over some decisions for the TripExpert.com Web site. Corey began reporting on his latest information concerning their plans to purchase a license from Reservations Technologies for an existing reservation system developed for the Web.

"We ran benchmark tests on the system's performance, and it did provide the transaction response time we need on the Web. Its scalability is also good—it can handle projected peak customer demand. We repeated the tests several times with different sets of data, and it performed well. So, that system seems to be a good option for us," he said.

Michael interrupted. "How long has this company been in business, and who else has used their system? I want to be sure they're reliable since we're staking a big part of Worldwide's future on the TripExpert site."

"They've been around for about 9 years—not long for a software company overall—but pretty old for a Web software firm. I checked the background of some of their technical staff, and they received advanced degrees in computer science, artificial intelligence, and electrical engineering from Stanford, MIT, and the University of Illinois. Plus, they gained practical experience at other companies before launching their firm. They are well respected in the field," reported Corey.

"What about their clients?" Michael persisted.

"They've worked with quite a few airlines— GlobalAir, Svenska, Universal Airlines. North Trans, one of your airline partners, recommended them to me. We could set up a time to review some of their operations on-site, if that would make you feel more comfortable."

"Great. I'd like to hear firsthand from their customers. Let's set that up in the next couple of weeks. I have some travel coming up over the next few months, so the sooner, the better."

Fitting It All Together

Judith asked, "What about the additional functionalities that we need for TripExpert? Will GDS have to hire programmers for that purpose or will Reservations Technologies take care of it?"

"Their system was designed flexibly to allow easy modifications. They'll create the additional functionalities. The company also offers technical assistance as part of a licensing agreement, if we need their help in modifying the system to tie into our existing reservations system," Corey responded.

"Speaking of the hotel reservation component, Judith, how are we coming on Worldwide's new system? Are we back on track after the database glitch?" Michael asked.

"We lost 5 weeks overall after we pulled additional staff in to work on the room rate-discounting component. We'll keep trying to gain back a day or two wherever we can. But we need to maintain our quality standards. Also, we need to begin planning our training sessions for your travel division. I've been putting some materials together as we go."

Michael laughed. "Another task to add to my list—can't wait."

OPTIONS AND PRIORITIES

In Chapter 12 you learned about software development and that few companies develop their own ISs in-house. Recall, also, that "systems" almost always means "applications," and therefore the terms will be used interchangeably in this chapter, as in Chapter 12. There are generally four alternatives to in-house development, as illustrated in Figure 13.1: outsourcing, licensing, using the service of an application service provider (ASP), and having users develop the system. If an application of the desired features and quality can be obtained from more than one of these sources, then the major factor left to be considered is usually cost. The preference then would be to license, because of immediate availability and low cost. If the application cannot be licensed, the next choice would usually be to obtain use of the system from an ASP because the system is immediately available for use and the organization does not have to lay out a large sum up front for such use. If ASPs do not offer the desired IS and non-IT employees can develop it, then this would usually be the chosen alternative. If non-IT employees cannot develop the IS, the choice might then be to outsource the development of the IS. However, as you will see, outsourcing is a concept that might encompass more than just commissioning the development of an application.

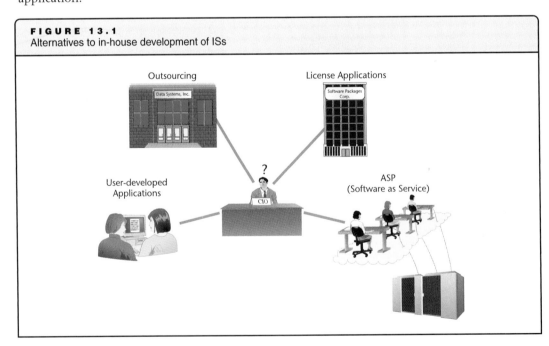

FIGURE 13.1
Alternatives to in-house development of ISs

There are many factors to be considered in addition to quality and cost. Therefore, these alternatives are not fully comparable, and often cannot be prioritized as simply as they have been here. The purpose of this discussion is to clarify the advantages and disadvantages of these options. As you will see, there are many factors that drive organizations to decide how they acquire ISs and the service that supports the maintenance and use of the systems.

OUTSOURCING

Outsourcing in general means hiring the services of another organization or individual to perform some of the work that otherwise would be performed by you or your employees. In the IT arena **outsourcing** has two meanings. One is to commission the development of an application to another organization, usually a company that specializes in the development of this type of application. The other is to hire the services of another company to manage all or parts of the services that otherwise would be rendered by an IT unit of the organization. The latter concept might not include development of new applications.

Outsourcing Custom-Designed Applications

Often, an organization has a need that no existing software can satisfy. For example, if the cost-accounting procedures of a particular company are so specific that no commercially available software can perform them, the company must develop **custom-designed**, or **tailored, software**. In recent years fewer and fewer companies have developed applications in-house. The majority of custom-designed applications are developed by companies that specialize in providing consulting and software development services to other businesses.

While custom-designed applications are more expensive than purchased ones, they have several advantages (see Figure 13.2).

- *Good fit to need*: The organization enjoys an application that meets its needs exactly, rather than settling for the near fit of a ready-made program.

- *Good fit to culture*: When custom developing a system, developers are more sensitive to the organizational culture. Employees enjoy an application that fits their work. When licensing a packaged application, employees sometimes must change their work to accommodate the software.

- *Dedicated maintenance*: Because the programmers are easily accessible to the company, they are familiar with the programs and can provide customized software maintenance. Maintenance includes modification for business changes (including mergers with and acquisition of other organizations) and upgrading of the software when new technologies become available.

- *Smooth interface*: When a system is custom-made for an organization, special care can be taken to ensure that it has proper interfaces with other systems. The new system can communicate smoothly with those systems.

- *Specialized security*: Special security measures can be integrated into the application. Because the program is custom designed, security measures are known only to the organization.

- *Potential for strategic advantage*: Recall from the discussion in Chapter 2, "Strategic Uses of Information Systems," that companies gain a strategic advantage when they can employ an IS that their competitors do not have. A unique application might give a business a strategic advantage because it is the only business that can enjoy the application. For example, no CRM application can do for a business what an enterprise application that was developed specifically to serve its customers in a unique way can do.

The greatest disadvantage of tailored applications is their high cost. Tailored software development requires an organization to fund all development costs; in contrast, costs of developing off-the-shelf and other ready applications are distributed over a larger number of expected purchasers. Another disadvantage of custom-designed development is that the production schedule can be delayed because IS personnel might not be available for long periods.

FIGURE 13.2
Advantages and disadvantages of custom-designed applications

Advantages

◆ Good fit of features to business needs

◆ Good fit of features to organizational culture

◆ Personnel available for maintenance

◆ Smooth interfaces with other information systems

◆ Availability of special security measures

◆ Potential for a strategic advantage

Disadvantages

◆ High cost

◆ Long wait for development if IS personnel are busy with other projects

◆ Application may be too organization-specific to interface with systems of other organizations

Another important downside is that custom-designed software is less likely to be compatible with other organizations' systems. If organizations with different tailor-made systems decide to link their systems, they might incur significant cost to modify one or both of the systems.

Clients of outsourced software development should also be aware of an inherent conflict of this option: on one hand they want the developing firm to conform to a contract that includes specific requirements of the software. On the other hand, specific requirements make the development effort inflexible and potentially costly: if the client company needs to change requirements as the development goes on, the developers might either refuse to deviate from the original requirements or might agree to make the changes for hefty additional charges. Contracts for outsourced software development might also be incompatible with some development methods, such as agile methods, discussed in Chapter 12. The essence of such methods is the clients' ability to request modified or new features as the development goes on, which might stand in stark contrast to the contract.

Many North American and European countries have outsourced development of well-defined applications to professionals in other countries, an act often referred to as **offshoring**. Programmers in India, China, and the Philippines earn a fraction of their colleagues in Western countries while often mastering the same level of skills. This might reduce the cost of development significantly. Offshoring has caused layoffs of programmers in clients' countries and created much bitterness among those professionals and supporters of local labor. However, this is part of the growing scope of economic globalization.

POINT OF INTEREST

Global Competition

India enjoys 44 percent of the global market of outsourced software development and back-office services (such as taking orders and tax preparation). India's income from these activities was $17.2 billion in the fiscal year ended in March 2005. It is not surprising that so many North American and West European countries outsource software development to India: the hourly rate of a software developer in India is $18–26 while the hourly rate in the United States and Europe is $55–65.

Sources: Associated Press, June 2005; neoIT (www.neoit.com), June 2005.

Outsourcing IT Services

A large number of businesses have turned to IT companies for long-term services: purchasing and maintaining hardware; developing, licensing, and maintaining software; installing and maintaining communications networks; developing, maintaining, and operating Web sites; staffing help desks, running IT daily operations, managing customer and supplier relations, and so on. An organization might use a combination of in-house and outsourced services. It might outsource the development of an IS, but then put its own employees in charge of its operation, or it might outsource both the development and operation of the system. When a business outsources only routine business processes, such as customer order entry or human resource transactions, the practice is sometimes called *business process outsourcing*. Note, however, that this term includes outsourcing many activities, whereas this discussion is limited to only IT services.

In considering whether to outsource IT services, management should ask the following questions:

- What are our core business competencies? Of the business we conduct, what specialties should we continue to practice ourselves?

- What do we do outside our specialties that could be done better for us by organizations that specialize in that area?

- Which of our activities could be improved if we created an alliance with IT organizations?

- Which of our activities should we work to improve internally?

Many companies have come to realize that IT is not their core competency and should not be a focus of their efforts. In addition, the pace of developments in IT might require more expertise than is available within many organizations.

A growing portion of corporate IS budgets is allocated for purchased (outsourced) services. IT companies that made their reputation by providing hardware and software, such as IBM and Unisys, have seen the revenue from the outsourcing service portion of their business grow faster than the revenue from hardware and software sales. Among the largest IT service providers are IBM, EDS, Accenture, Computer Sciences Corp. (CSC), Unisys, First Data, AT&T, Capgemini, Perot Systems, and Hewlett-Packard. For the sake of simplicity and clarity here, such companies are called vendors, and the organizations to which they outsource are called clients. (Note that some trade journals prefer to refer to vendors as outsourcers.) Outsourcing is typically a long-term contractual relationship in which the vendor takes over some or all of the client's IT functions. Typical outsourced functions are listed in Figure 13.3.

FIGURE 13.3
Typical outsourced IT services

- ◆ Application development and software maintenance

- ◆ Hardware purchasing and hardware maintenance

- ◆ Telecommunications installation and maintenance

- ◆ Help desk services

- ◆ Web site design and maintenance

- ◆ Staff training

IT outsourcing contracts are typically signed for long periods of time, usually for 7 to 10 years. The sums of money involved are very large, some reaching billions of dollars. For example, in March 2003 Motorola signed a 10-year, $1.6 billion contract with CSC to handle its IT infrastructure. Until May 1, 2003, when the contract became effective, Motorola handled all of its IT needs in-house. CSC now handles Motorola's worldwide midrange computers, desktop computers, telecommunications, and data centers. IBM signed a 10-year, $2.5 billion outsourcing contract with Deutsche Bank to take care of the bank's IT needs in eight European countries. In January 2003 IBM signed a 7-year, $5 billion contract to satisfy most of JPMorgan Chase's IT needs.

In July 2005 Perot Systems took over several IT services of Metaldyne for a period of 10 years. Metaldyne is a designer and supplier of automotive components. Perot Systems provides network management, service desk help, and data center operations.

There is a peculiar—and paradoxical—aspect to IT outsourcing: while contracts are signed for long periods of time, they typically involve rapidly changing technologies. Vendors often agree to sign outsourcing contracts only if the period is at least 5 years because of the human resource commitment they have to make, but strategic IT plans—as discussed in Chapter 12—are for only 3–5 years. As a result, clients sometimes find themselves bound by contracts that no longer satisfy their needs. They then try to renegotiate the contract. For example, in July 2001 Tenet Healthcare Corporation extended its outsourcing relationship with Perot Systems before its contract expired. The companies signed the original contract in 1995 for 7 years. This time, the operator of 114 acute care hospitals nationwide wanted the vendor to focus on enhancing the infrastructure and applications for a wide array of Web-based applications to support communication among employees and with insurance companies. It therefore asked to renegotiate the contract before the original termination date of 2002. The new contract was for 10 years and was worth $550 million.

Renegotiation of outsourcing contracts is not unusual. Several companies that signed long-term contracts have found that the financial burden was too heavy or that the expected benefits had not materialized. In April 2004 Sears, Roebuck and Co. signed a 10-year, $1.6 billion outsourcing contract with CSC. Eleven months later, in May 2005, Sears terminated the agreement, claiming that CSC failed to perform some of its obligations. At this writing, the case is being prosecuted in court.

Why You Should...

Understand Alternative Avenues for the Acquisition of Information Systems

As an increasing number of business activities are supported and enhanced by ISs, it is extremely important for organizations to acquire systems that best fit their needs and are available as soon as possible, and to minimize the cost of systems acquisition and maintenance of the systems. As explained in Chapter 12, employees should involve themselves in the process of deciding which ISs will be introduced into their business units and what features they will have. Since there are several ways to obtain ISs, professionals like you must understand the advantages and disadvantages of each. If you have a concern with a certain approach to acquire the system you need, you should voice it and be able to propose other options.

Advantages of Outsourcing IT Services

Clients contract for IT services to offload in-house responsibility and to better manage risks. When a client outsources, management knows how much the outsourced services will cost; thus, the risk of miscalculation is eliminated. But there are additional advantages that make the option attractive:

- *Improved financial planning*: Outsourcing allows a client to know exactly what the cost of its IS functions will be over the period of the contract, which is usually several years. This allows for better financial planning.

- *Reduced license and maintenance fees*: Professional IS firms often pay discounted prices for CASE (computer-aided software engineering) tools and other resources, based on volume purchases; they can pass these savings on to their clients.

- *Increased attention to core business*: Letting outside experts manage IT frees executives from managing it. They can thus concentrate on the company's core business—including developing and marketing new products.

- *Shorter implementation cycles*: IT vendors can usually complete a new application project in less time than an in-house development team can, thanks to their experience with development projects of similar systems for other clients. (However, they are not likely to use less time if they lack experience with such systems, or if they insist on a waterfall development process rather than an agile method.)

- *Reduction of personnel and fixed costs*: In-house IS salaries and benefits and expensive capital expenditures for items such as CASE tools are paid whether or not the IS staff is productive. IS firms, on the other hand, spread their fixed and overhead costs (office space, furnishings, systems development software, and the like) over many projects and many clients, thereby decreasing the expense absorbed by any single client.

- *Increased access to highly qualified know-how*: Outsourcing allows clients to tap into one of the greatest assets of an IT vendor: experience gained through work with many clients in different environments.

- *Availability of ongoing consulting as part of standard support*: Most outsourcing contracts allow client companies to consult the vendor for all types of IT advice, which would otherwise be unavailable (or only available from a highly paid consultant). Such advice might include guidance on how to use a feature of a recently purchased application or on how to move data from one application to another.

As you can see, cost savings is only one reason to outsource IS functions. In fact, studies show that saving money is not the most common reason for outsourcing. Surveys have shown that executives expected several benefits from an outsourcing relationship. Figure 13.4 shows the most cited expectations, such as access to technological skills and industry expertise. To many executives, these expected benefits are more important than cost savings, especially in light of reports that in many cases outsourcing did not save the client money.

FIGURE 13.4
Expected benefits from IT outsourcing

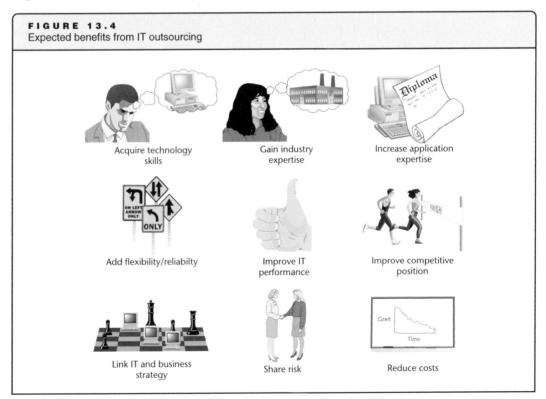

Acquire technology skills

Gain industry expertise

Increase application expertise

Add flexibility/reliabilty

Improve IT performance

Improve competitive position

Link IT and business strategy

Share risk

Reduce costs

Risks of Outsourcing IT Services

Despite its popularity, outsourcing is not a panacea and should be considered carefully before it is adopted. There are conditions under which organizations should avoid outsourcing. The major risks are as follows:

- *Loss of control*: A company that outsources a major part of its IS operations will probably be unable to regain control for a long time. The organization must evaluate the nature of the industry in which it operates. While outsourcing can be a good option in a relatively stable industry, it is highly risky in one that is quickly changing. Although the personnel of an IS service company might have the necessary IS technical skills, they might jeopardize the client's core business in the long run if they cannot adapt to constantly changing business realities in the client's industry. Sometimes when this problem becomes clear, the client might have disposed of all personnel who could react properly to such developments. Moreover, even if the client organization still employs qualified IT professionals, the vendor might object to their involvement in activities that, according to the outsourcing contract, are outside their jurisdiction.

- *Loss of experienced employees*: Outsourcing often involves transferring hundreds, or even thousands, of the organization's employees to the IS vendor. For example, as part of the outsourcing contract between Motorola and CSC in 2003, CSC absorbed 1,300 of Motorola's IT employees, and when the Wall Street company JPMorgan outsourced its IT functions to IBM in 2003, IBM hired its client's 4,000 IT employees. The organization that absorbs the workers can usually employ them with lower overhead expenses than their former employer and use their skills more productively. The client gets rid of this overhead cost, but it also gives up well-trained personnel. In addition, if most of the vendor's personnel serving the client are the same employees that the client maintained until the outsourcing contract was signed, the company's ability to gain new expertise from outsourcing could be compromised.

- *Risks of losing a competitive advantage*: Innovative ISs, especially those intended to give their owners a competitive advantage, should not be outsourced. Outsourcing the development of strategic systems is a way of disclosing trade secrets. Confidentiality agreements can reduce, but never completely eliminate, the risk. A competitor might hire the same vendor to build an IS for the same purpose, thereby potentially eliminating the first client's advantage. In addition, assuming that these systems incorporate new business or technical concepts, vendors will bring less than their usual level of experience—and therefore fewer benefits—to the project. Outsourcing strategic or core business ISs incurs more risk than outsourcing the routine tasks of operational ISs (see Figure 13.5).

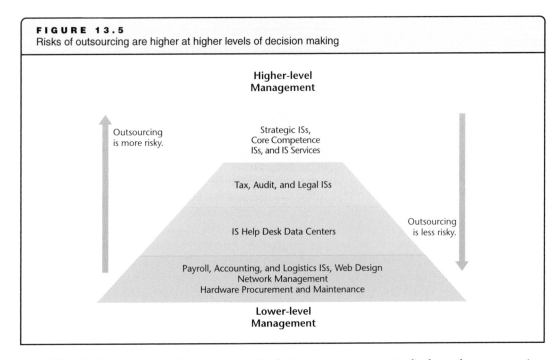

FIGURE 13.5
Risks of outsourcing are higher at higher levels of decision making

Higher-level
Management

Outsourcing
is more risky.

Strategic ISs,
Core Competence
ISs, and IS Services

Tax, Audit, and Legal ISs

IS Help Desk Data Centers

Outsourcing
is less risky.

Payroll, Accounting, and Logistics ISs, Web Design
Network Management
Hardware Procurement and Maintenance

Lower-level
Management

- *High price*: Despite careful precontract calculations, some companies find out that outsourcing costs them significantly more than they would have spent had they taken care of their own ISs or related services. Several clients have pressured vendors to renegotiate their outsourcing contracts or have found a way to terminate the contract because executives believed they could enjoy the same level of service, or higher-quality service, by maintaining a corporate IT staff. To minimize such unpleasant discoveries, the negotiating team must clearly define every service to be included in the arrangement, including the quality of personnel, service hours, and the scope and quality of services rendered when new hardware and software are adopted or when the client company decides to embark on new ventures, such as e-commerce initiatives or establishment of an intranet.

The most important element of an outsourcing agreement for both parties, but mostly for the client, is what professionals call the **service-level agreement**. The negotiators for the client must carefully list all the types of services expected of the vendor as well as the metrics to be used to measure the degree to which the vendor has met the level of promised services. Clients should not expect vendors to list the service level and metrics; the *clients* must do it. It is in the client's interest to have as specific a contract as possible, because any service that is not included in the contract, or is mentioned only in general terms, leaves the door open for the vendor not to render it, or not to render it to a level expected by the client.

POINT OF INTEREST

Outsourcing SOX

After several corporate scandals, the United States Congress passed the Sarbanes-Oxley Corporate Governance Act in 2005. Corporations were given ample time to take the necessary steps to comply, some of which involve software that helps to prevent fraud and ensure accurate financial filings. The law, named after its authors, is popularly known as SOX. U.S. corporations spent $5.5 billion in 2004, and were likely to spend another $5.8 billion in 2005, to comply with the new law. About a quarter of this sum was spent on software development and modification. Indian software companies have benefited tremendously. Apparently, much of the software engineering work is outsourced to companies in this country, which specialize in SOX-related software.

Source: Bellman, E., "A Cost of Sarbanes-Oxley: Outsourcing to India," *Wall Street Journal*, July 14, 2005.

LICENSING APPLICATIONS

Businesses can select from a growing list of high-quality packaged software, from office applications that fit on a CD to large enterprise applications. Therefore, purchasing prepackaged software should be the first alternative considered when a company needs to acquire a new system. Recall that "purchased" software is almost always *licensed* software. The purchaser actually purchases a license to use the software, not the software itself. Thus, here the term "licensing" means purchasing a license to use. Unless an IS must be tailored to uncommon needs in an organization, licensing a prepackaged system might well be the best option.

Ready-made software can be classified into two groups: one is the relatively inexpensive software that helps in the office, such as Microsoft Office and similar suites, including software that supports more specific tasks such as project management and tax preparation. Such software usually costs tens of dollars to several hundred dollars for a single user or thousands of dollars for a company with many employees. The other group includes large software applications that support whole organizational functions, such as human resource management and financial management, or enterprise applications that span the entire organization. Such packages include ERP, SCM, and CRM applications and typically cost millions of dollars.

Software Licensing Benefits

When licensing a software package, the buyer gains several benefits: immediate system availability, high quality, low price (license fee), and available support. Immediate availability helps shorten the time from the decision to implement a new system and the actual implementation. If the company maintains an IT staff that develops applications, purchasing software frees the staff to develop the systems that must be specifically tailored to its business needs.

High-quality software is guaranteed through purchase partly because the software company specializes in developing its products and partly because its products would not survive on the market if they were not of high quality. Large developers often distribute prerelease versions, called **beta versions**, or simply betas, of software to be tested by companies (called beta sites) that agree to use the application with actual data for several months. The beta sites then report problems and propose improvements in return for receiving the fully developed software free or for a reduced license fee. By the time the software is released to the general market, it has been well tested.

Because software companies spread product development costs over many units, the price to a single customer is a fraction of what it would cost to develop a similar application in-house or to hire an outside company to develop it. Also, instead of tying up its own personnel to maintain the software, the buyer can usually contract for long-term service and be notified of new, advanced versions of the application. All software development companies provide after-the-sale support. Often, buyers enjoy a period of 3 months to 1 year of free service.

Even large companies that could afford to develop ISs on their own often elect to purchase when they can find suitable software. For example, CMS Energy, a $9 billion energy producer in Jackson, Michigan, decided to install a Web-based supply chain management system to link with the company's equipment suppliers. The company's information technologists wanted to build the system themselves. The executive vice president and chief financial and administrative officer, whose professional background is in IT, nixed that idea. He estimated that the cost of a homegrown system—about $20 million—would be greater than the savings it would deliver in its first few years of operation. Instead, he suggested the company use packaged software. The alternative cut the cost of the system in half.

You might be more familiar with off-the-shelf applications than with larger, more complex packaged applications. However, in recent years, enterprise applications have constituted a far larger part of IT expenditures on packaged software. As mentioned earlier, enterprise applications are complex applications that serve many parts of an organization, often several departments. They consist of several modules, each of which can be interfaced with another module from the same vendor.

Organizations cannot simply purchase such large applications and install them; they must employ professionals who specialize in the installation of the software, which might take months. Within limits, the providers of these large applications agree to customize part of the applications to the specific needs of a client. However, such customization is very expensive and is often risky; in some cases, customization has taken significantly longer than planned and was not completed to the full satisfaction of the client.

Software Licensing Risks

Although licensing a ready-made application is attractive, it has its risks:

- *Loose fit between needs and features*: Ready-made software is developed for the widest common denominator of potential user organizations. It might be useful to many, but it will be optimal for few. Companies must take extra care to ensure that ready-made software truly complies with company needs, including organizational culture. Obtaining input from many potential users in the selection process reduces this risk.

- *Difficulties in modifications*: Many companies find that they must have packaged software such as ERP and SCM applications modified to meet their specific needs, and too many of them find that the vendor does a poor job. For example, in 2000 and 2001 Nike spent $400 million to have i2 Technologies implement i2's SCM software. In 2001, Nike claimed that the software did not work properly, causing shortages of high-demand products and overstocks of less demanded items. Nike's management said that the software, which was supposed to streamline communication with suppliers and buyers and lower operating costs, failed both in performance and functionality. i2 blamed difficulties on customizing the software and Nike's inappropriate implementation of the software according to i2's suggested methods. Nike found those methods too rigid and did not implement them. Apparently, the mishap reduced Nike's sales in the first quarter of 2001 by $100 million. Apparently, "just do it" did not suffice. "Do it right" would have been a better approach.

- *Bankruptcy of the vendor*: If the vendor goes out of business, the purchaser is left without support, maintenance service, and the opportunity to purchase upgrades to an application to which it is committed. Except for checking the financial strength of potential vendors, there is not much the purchaser can do to reduce this risk.

- *High turnover of vendor personnel*: Turnover among IS professionals is significantly higher than in other occupations. If a substantial number of employees involved in application development and upgrading leave a vendor, support is likely to deteriorate, and upgrades will be of poor quality. Purchasers can do little to reduce this risk.

Steps in Licensing Ready-Made Software

When selecting a particular software package, companies invest a lot of money and make a long-term commitment to conducting their business in a particular manner. Factors such as the complexity of installation, cost of training, and quality and cost of after-sale service must be considered in addition to the demonstrable quality of the software. Once a company decides that it will purchase a ready-made application, a project management team is formed to oversee system implementation and handle all vendor contact. The project management team has the following responsibilities (see Figure 13.6):

- *Identifying the problem or opportunity*: This step is similar to the initial inquiry and fact-finding step in the systems development life cycle (SDLC), discussed in Chapter 12. The inquiry results in the identification of gross functional requirements and key integration points with other systems. The report generated often serves as a basis for a request for information from potential vendors.

- *Identifying potential vendors*: On the basis of information in trade journals (printed and on the Web) and previously received promotional material, as well as client references, vendors who offer applications in the domain at hand are identified. In addition to these sources, IS people might gather information at trade shows, from other organizations that have used similar technology, and from colleagues.

- *Soliciting vendor information*: The project manager sends a **request for information (RFI)** to the vendors identified, requesting general, somewhat informal information about the product.

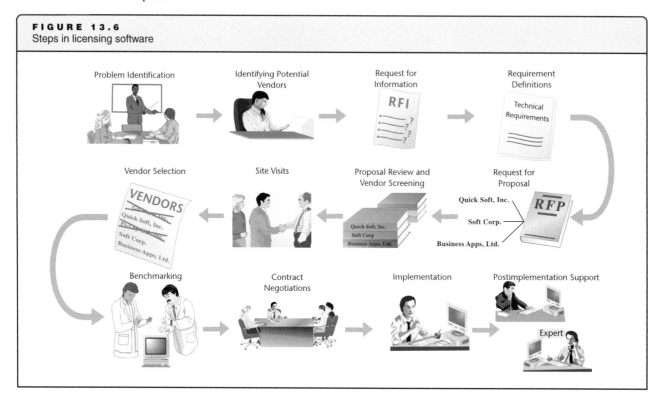

FIGURE 13.6
Steps in licensing software

- *Defining system requirements*: The project manager lists a set of functional and technical requirements and identifies the functional and technical capabilities of all vendors, highlighting the items that are common to both lists, as well as those that are not. The project management team involves the users in defining system requirements to ensure that the chosen application will integrate well with existing and planned systems.

- *Requesting vendor proposals*: The team prepares a **request for proposal (RFP)**, a document specifying all the system requirements and soliciting a proposal from each vendor contacted. The response should include not only technical requirements but also a detailed description of the implementation process as well as a timetable and budget that can be easily transformed into a contractual agreement. The team should strive to provide enough detail and vision to limit the amount of precontract clarification and negotiation.

- *Reviewing proposals and screening vendors*: The team reviews the proposals and identifies the most qualified vendors. Vendor selection criteria include functionality, architectural fit, price, services, and support.

- *Visiting sites*: The complexity of the RFP responses might make evaluation impossible without a visit to a client site where a copy of the application is in use. The team should discuss with other clients the pros and cons of the application.

- *Selecting the vendor*: The team ranks the remaining vendors. The selection factors are weighted, and the vendor with the highest total points is chosen for contract negotiation. Sometimes make-or-break factors are identified early in the process to eliminate vendors that cannot provide the essential service. By now, the team has gathered enough information on the functionality of the various systems.

- *Benchmarking*: Before finalizing the purchasing decision, the system should be tested using **benchmarking**, which is comparing actual performance against specific quantifiable criteria. If all other conditions are the same for all the bidders, the vendor whose application best meets or exceeds the benchmarks is selected.

- *Negotiating a contract*: The contract should clearly define performance expectations and include penalties if requirements are not met. Special attention should be given to the schedule, budget, responsibility for system support, and support response times. Some clients include a clause on keeping the source code in escrow. If the vendor goes out of business, the client will receive the source code, without which the system cannot be maintained. The client should tie all payments to completion of milestones by the vendor and acceptance of deliverables.

- *Implementing the new system*: The new system is introduced in the business units it will serve. Training takes place.

- *Managing postimplementation support*: Vendors expect buyers of their large applications to request extensive on-site postimplementation support. Unexpected lapses or unfamiliarity with the system might require fine-tuning, additional training, and modification of the software. It is best to develop an ongoing relationship with the vendor because a solid relationship will foster timely service and support.

When choosing a vendor, organizations look for the quality and reliability of the product, but there are additional factors, such as quality of service and support, vendor's support for industry standards, and vendor financial soundness, that are extremely important. In surveys, IS managers have almost invariably revealed the importance of factors considered in selecting a vendor as shown in Figure 13.7 (in descending order). Product quality and reliability stand well ahead of the price/performance ratio.

FIGURE 13.7
How IT managers rank the importance of product purchase factors

FACTOR	RATING
Quality and reliability	_____
Product performance	_____
Quality of after-sale service and support	_____
Trustworthiness of vendor	_____
Price/performance ratio	_____
Ease of doing business with vendor	_____
Vendor's support for industry standards	_____
Openness of future strategies and plans	_____
Vendor financial stability	_____

SOFTWARE AS A SERVICE

The option to use software applications through the Web was introduced in 1998. An organization that offers the use of software through communication lines is called an **application service provider (ASP)**. The concept is called **software as a service (SaaS)** or *software by subscription*. CSC, IBM Global Services, USinternetworking (USi), Oracle Corp., Corio, and Salesforce.com are among the better known players in this industry, but many other companies offer such services.

An ASP does not install any software on a client's computers. Rather, the application is installed at the ASP's location, along with the databases and other files that the application processes for the client. However, clients can choose to save all the files produced by the application on their own local storage devices. The clients' employees access the application through the Web. They call up the application, enter data, process the data, produce reports online and on paper, and in general use the application the same way they would had it been installed at their location.

ASPs do not necessarily rent their own software packages. They often rent software developed by other companies. For example, USinternetworking rents enterprise packages that were developed and are often installed by Oracle. Rent is usually several hundred dollars per month per user, depending on the software rented.

As Figure 13.8 shows, there are several benefits to renting and using software through the Web, as well as risks. As in any time-limited rental, the client does not have to commit large sums of money up front. No employees have to devote time to learning how to maintain the software, nor to maintaining it once it is installed. No storage hardware is required for the applications and associated data, because the vendor uses its own hardware. And the software is usually available significantly sooner than if installed at the client's location; while it might take years to install and test enterprise applications on-site, an online renter can use the same application 3 to 6 weeks after signing a contract. And even if an organization is willing to pay for the software, it might not find skilled personnel to install and maintain the software.

FIGURE 13.8
Benefits and risks of ASP services

Benefits

- No need to learn to maintain the application

- No need to maintain the application

- No need to allocate hardware for the installation

- No need to hire experts for installation and maintenance

- Timely availability

Risks

- Possible long transaction response time on the Internet

- Security risks, such as interception by competitors

For many small companies this option is clearly the best. Holden Humphrey Co. is a lumber wholesaler in Chicopee, Massachusetts. It has 24 employees. The company's president decided it made no financial sense to hire IT personnel or pay for licensed software. The company pays $1,000 per month to an ASP, which enables 9 of the employees to remotely access inventory management, accounting, and CRM applications.

The "software on demand" approach seems to attract a growing clientele. Clients are mainly small and medium corporations, but some large ones also prefer this option. Salesforce.com, which specializes in CRM software, has grown very fast. The company was established in 2000, and by 2005 had 308,000 subscribers.

The obvious risk is that the client cedes control of the systems, the application, and possibly its related data, to another party. Although some vendors are willing to make minor changes to suit the client's needs, they will not make all that are requested. Some experts argue that by renting, clients have less control over their systems, and that it is better to retain the ability to modify applications in-house. Response time might become a problem as well, because neither the ASP nor the client has full control over traffic on the Internet. Also, as with all activities through a public network, there are security risks, such as interception of information by a competitor.

For this reason, some clients prefer to use a leased line rather than the Internet to connect to the ASP. For instance, Simpson Industries, a manufacturer of auto parts in Plymouth, Michigan, uses an ERP system offered by IBM Global Services. But employees use the application through a leased line (a line that only Simpson can use) to connect directly to IBM's service center in

Rochester, New York. When considering using a leased line, IS managers should consider the cost. While a DSL or cable link costs $30 to $50 per month, a leased line with the same capacity costs $1,000 to $2,000 per month. Organizations should also consider the type of application and data their company is about to use.

POINT OF INTEREST

Slow But Steady Growth

The software-as-a-service industry has been notorious for several years because many ASPs operated on financially shaky ground. Many could not deliver the quality of service they promised. In recent years hundreds of these companies either closed shop or were absorbed into larger companies. As the industry matures, a growing number of corporations use ASPs. According to International Data Corp. (IDC), U.S. companies spent $2.3 billion on hosted software in 2003, a 35 percent increase from the previous year. In 2004 the figure reached $4.2 billion. The firm predicted annual increases of 21 percent to $10.7 billion in 2009.

Source: International Data Corp., 2005.

Caveat Emptor

In recent years faster links to the Internet and a more stable ASP industry have made SaaS an attractive option. However, even with reputable providers, some subscribers were disappointed because the scope of services and level of reliability were not what they had expected when they signed the contract. Managers in organizations considering ASPs should heed the following "commandments":

1. *Check the ASP's history.* Ask the provider for a list of references, and contact these customers to ask about their experience. Ask how soon the provider switched to a new version of the application they rented.
2. *Check the ASP's financial strength.* Request copies of the ASP's financial reports. Ensure that it has enough funds or secured funding to stay in business for the duration of your planned contract.
3. *Ensure you understand the price scheme.* Ask whether the price changes when you decide to switch to using another application. Ask whether the price includes help desk services.
4. *Get a list of the provider's infrastructure.* Ask to see a list of the ASP's hardware, software, and telecommunication facilities. Ask who the ASP's business partners are that provide hardware, software, and telecommunication services. Ask how data, including sensitive data such as credit-card account numbers, are stored and protected. Ask about security measures.
5. *Craft the service contract carefully.* Ensure that the contract includes penalties the ASP will pay if services are not rendered fully. Ensure that your organization will not have to pay penalties for early termination.

One important point to check when examining the list of facilities is uptime. **Uptime** is the proportion of time that the ASP's systems and communication links are up. Since no provider can guarantee 100 percent uptime, ASPs often promise 99.9 percent ("three nines," in professional lingo) uptime, which sounds satisfactory, but it might not be. Three nines mean that downtime might reach 500 minutes per year. This is usually acceptable for customer relationship management systems. Human resource managers or sales representatives, who typically use ISs less than 50 hours per week, might settle even for two nines (99 percent guaranteed uptime). However, experts recommend that organizations look for ASPs that can guarantee five nines—99.999 percent uptime—for critical applications. This high percentage of uptime ensures downtime of no more than 5 minutes per year. There are firms that specialize in monitoring the uptime of ASPs. One such company is Towers Perrin, a management consulting firm that monitors the uptime of 200 Web-based applications.

Who hires the services of ASPs? Although you will find a variety of companies among ASP clients, the majority of the clients fall into four categories:

- Companies that are growing fast and rely on software for deployment of their operations.

- Small companies that do not have the cash to pay up front, but who must use office, telecommunications, and basic business operations applications.

- Medium-sized companies that need expensive software, such as enterprise applications, for their operations but cannot afford the immediate payment of large sums (examples are ERP applications from companies such as SAP and PeopleSoft).

- Organizational units at geographical sites where it is difficult to obtain desired software or personnel to install and maintain the software. These sites are typically located far away from a regional headquarters in a less-developed country. The office at that site can then use applications from a more developed country.

In 2001, a new type of service provider, similar to an ASP, started to catch the attention of businesses in need of IT services: the **storage service provider (SSP)**. An SSP does not rent software applications, but rents storage space. Instead of spending money on the purchase of magnetic disks, a company can contract with an SSP and have all or some of its files stored remotely on the SSP's storage devices. The storage and retrieval are executed through communication lines, in most cases the Internet.

USER APPLICATION DEVELOPMENT

If an adequate application is not available on the market, or if an organization does not wish to take the risks discussed earlier with purchasing or renting, and if the application is not too complex, there is another alternative to software development: **user application development**, in which nonprogrammer users write their own business applications. Typically, user-developed software is fairly simple and limited in scope; it is unlikely that users could develop complex applications such as ERP systems. If end users do have the necessary skills, they should be allowed to develop small applications for immediate needs, and when they do, such applications can be maintained by the end users (see Figure 13.9). They should be encouraged to develop applications that will be used for a brief time and then discarded. End users should not develop large or complex applications, applications that interface with other systems, or applications that are vital for the survival of the organization. They should also be discouraged from developing applications that might survive their own tenure in the organization.

FIGURE 13.9
Guidelines for end-user development of applications

End users should develop if...	*End users should not develop if...*
End users have the necessary skills	The application is large or complex
The application is small	The application interfaces with other systems
The application is needed immediately	The application is vital for the organization's survival
The application can be maintained by the users	The application will survive the user's tenure
The application will be used briefly and discarded	

Managing User-Developed Applications

The proliferation of user-developed applications poses challenges to managers, both in IT units and other business units. In addition to the rules outlined in Figure 13.9, management must cope with the following challenges:

- *Managing the reaction of IT professionals*: IT professionals often react negatively to user development because they perceive it as undermining their own duties and authority. To solve this problem, management must set clear guidelines delineating what types of applications end users may and may not develop.

Computer Use Policies for Employees

The increasing numbers of PCs and the pervasive use of e-mail and the Web in businesses have exposed more and more people to ISs. The U.S. Census Bureau found that over 60 percent of workers' jobs involved computer use for all or part of the workday. This enables workers to be more productive, but computers are often used for unproductive, or even destructive, activities. If an employee uses a company car without permission, the act is obviously wrong. But if an employee uses a company computer to store private files, is that wrong? Accessing a company's intranet is legitimate and encouraged. Accessing another employee's file might be wrong. However, some employees might not be aware of the differences. What are the appropriate personal uses of company computers? Is the answer to this question already covered in existing laws? Should companies have policies that define the appropriate uses of their IT resources? Do we need new laws to ensure a law-abiding workforce? The answers to these questions vary.

- **When There Is No Corporate Policy.** Although unauthorized use of computers might be considered theft, authorities usually do not deal with it as such. Perhaps this is why most state statutes do not specifically address unauthorized use of computers. There is, however, one exception: California law states that an employee might use an employer's computer services for his or her own purpose without permission if no damage is caused and if the value of supplies and computer services does not exceed $100.

  If someone from outside a company accessed the company's computer without authorization and used it for any purpose whatsoever, the act would clearly be criminal under the laws of many countries and of almost every state in the United States. However, if an *employee* uses the same company computer after hours to prepare a homework assignment for a college class, the act might not be considered unethical, let alone criminal, unless the organization has a clear policy against such activity. What about creating a résumé or writing a letter as part of a job search? Without a company policy, the answer to this question is not clear.

  Widespread access to the Web makes the issues even more complicated. Employees have been fired for surfing the Web for their own personal purposes during work time. Some have

been fired for surfing the Web during lunch breaks or after work hours; while they did not waste company-paid time, management objected to the specific sites they accessed, mostly those displaying pornographic images.

- **Company Policies Work.** To avoid misunderstanding, employers should provide clear guidelines, stating that any computer use not for the company's direct benefit, without the prior approval of the company, is forbidden. One simple measure that some organizations have taken is to have a written policy that is conspicuously posted, signed by employees upon hiring, or both. The notice could read as follows:

  "Company policy forbids any employee, without prior authorization of the employee's supervisor, to (a) access or use any equipment or data unless such access is work-related and required to fulfill that employee's duties, or (b) alter, damage, or destroy any company computer resource or property, including any computer equipment, system, terminal, network, software, data, or documentation, including individual employee computer files. Any such act by an employee might result in civil and criminal liability under federal, state, and local laws."

Many companies do not object to recreational or educational use of their computers by employees outside of company time. If this is the case, the policy should say so. Without a policy, companies should not be surprised when their employees' interpretation of reasonable personal use differs from their employers'. However, if there is no clear policy, employees should always remember that a PC is a work tool that their employer put at their disposal for responsible use as part of their job. It is not there to help their own business or entertain them either during or outside of paid time. Thus, for example, they should not use e-mail or instant messaging to chat with their friends or browse the Web for their enjoyment. Yet, is sending a personal e-mail message during lunch break really much different from using a company pen to write a personal note during lunch break? Perhaps the best way to avoid misunderstanding is to simply ask your employer if what you intend to do is objectionable.

The proliferation of desktop computers and easier-to-use development tools in the workplace has been a major stimulus in application development by users.

© AP/Wide World Photos

- *Providing support*: To encourage users to develop applications, IS managers must designate a single technical contact for users. It is difficult to provide IT support for user-developed applications, because the IT staff members are usually unfamiliar with an application developed without their involvement. Yet, IT staff should help solve problems or enhance such applications when end users think their own skills are not adequate.

- *Compatibility*: To ensure compatibility with other applications within an organization, the organization's IT professionals should adopt and supply standard development tools to interested users. Users should not be allowed to use nonstandard tools. Note that compatibility in this context is for the purpose of transferring data among end users; interfacing user-developed applications with other organizational systems should be discouraged.

- *Managing access*: Sometimes, users need to copy data from organizational databases to their own developed spreadsheets or databases. If access to organizational databases is granted at all for such a purpose, access should be tightly controlled by the IT staff to maintain data integrity and security. Users should be forewarned not to rely on such access when developing their own applications if this is against the organization's policy.

Advantages and Risks

There are several important advantages to user development of applications:

- *Shortened lead times*: Users almost always develop applications more quickly than IS personnel, because they are highly motivated (they will benefit from the new system); their systems are usually simpler in design; and they have a head start by being totally familiar with the business domain for which they are developing the application.

- *Good fit to needs*: Nobody knows the users' specific business needs better than the users themselves. Thus, they are apt to develop an application that will satisfy all their needs.

- *Compliance with culture*: User-developed software closely conforms to an individual unit's subculture, which makes the transition to a new system easier for employees.

- *Efficient utilization of resources*: Developing software on computers that are already being used for many other purposes is an efficient use of IT resources.

- *Acquisition of skills*: The more employees there are who know how to develop applications, the greater an organization's skills inventory.

- *Freeing up IS staff time*: User-developers free IS staff to develop and maintain an organization's more complex and sophisticated systems.

However, with all the pros, there are also cons to application development by users. They must be considered seriously. The risks are as follows:

- *Poorly developed applications*: User-developers are not as skilled as IS personnel. On average, the applications they develop are of lower quality than systems developed by professionals. Users are often tempted to develop applications that are too complex for their skills and tools, resulting in systems that are difficult to use and maintain.

- *Islands of information*: An organization that relies on user development runs the risk of creating islands of information and "private" databases not under the control of the organization's IS managers. This lack of control might make it difficult to achieve the benefits of integrated ISs.

- *Duplication*: User-developers often waste resources developing applications that are identical or similar to systems that already exist elsewhere within the organization.

- *Security problems*: Giving end users access to organizational databases for the purpose of creating systems might result in violations of security policies. This risk is especially true in client/server environments. The creation of "private databases" known only to the individual user is risky. The user might not be aware that the information he or she produces from the data is "classified" under an organization's policy.

- *Poor documentation*: Practically speaking, "poor documentation" might be a misnomer. Usually, users do not create any documentation at all because (1) they do not know how to write documentation, and (2) they develop the application on their own to have it ready as soon as possible, and they don't want to take the time to document it. Lack of documentation makes system maintenance difficult at best and impossible at worst. Often, applications are patched together by new users, and pretty soon nobody knows how to iron out bugs or modify programs.

- There are several alternatives to having applications developed in-house: outsourcing, licensing ready-made software, using the services of an ASP, and user application development.

- Outsourcing has two meanings in IT: commissioning the development of a tailored application to an IT company, and assigning all or some of the IT services of the organization to a vendor of IT services.

- Outsourcing custom-designed applications might afford the organization good fit of the software to need, good fit to culture, dedicated maintenance, smooth interface, specialized security, and potential for strategic advantage.

- The potential advantages of outsourcing IT services include improving cost clarity and reducing license and maintenance fees, freeing the client to concentrate on its core businesses, shortening the time needed to implement new technologies, reducing personnel and fixed costs, gaining access to highly qualified know-how, and receiving ongoing consulting as part of standard support. However, outsourcing IT services has some potential risks: loss of control, loss of experienced employees, loss of competitive advantage, and high price. To ensure that the client enjoys all the expected services and their quality, a detailed service-level agreement must be signed with the IT service vendor.

- When an organization purchases a license to use ready-made software, it enjoys high-quality software that is immediately available at low price (license fee). However, licensed ready-made software has some potential risks: loose fit between needs and the software features, difficulties in modifications, bankruptcy of the vendor, and high turnover of the vendor's employees.

- Using the services of an ASP has become popular. The concept is also known as software by subscription or software as a service (SaaS). The client pays monthly fees based on the type of application used and the number of users, and its employees use the applications via a network, mostly through the Internet. ASP clients enjoy availability of applications, avoid the costs of storage hardware and large IT staffs, and do not have to make a long-term commitment of capital to software that might become obsolete in 2 or 3 years. The downsides of using an ASP are the loss of control over applications, the potentially low speed of interaction, and the security risks associated with using an IS via a public network.

- There are several advantages to user application development: a short lead time, good fit of application capabilities to business needs, good compliance with organizational culture, efficient utilization of computing resources, acquisition of skills by users, and the freeing of IS staff to deal with the more complex challenges of the systems. Disadvantages of user-developed applications include the risk of poorly developed applications, undesirable islands of information and private databases, duplications of effort, security problems, and poor documentation. Thus, user development of applications needs to be managed. IS managers need to determine the applications that users should and should not develop and dictate the tools that should be used.

- Well over half of America's office workers now have rich computer resources at the tips of their fingers. Often, employees do not know which activities are welcomed and which are not. If an organization lacks a clear policy, employees are not discouraged from abusing computers. This abuse is especially true when employees access Web sites that are objectionable to their employer or when employees use e-mail for purposes not intended by the employer. If no policy has been established, the simple rule is that employees should not use their computers for anything but work.

WORLDWIDE HOST REVISITED

Worldwide Host has developed a solid partnership with General Data Systems, using the software firm to develop new systems or upgrade existing systems. Take a closer look at some of the relationships firms establish in today's marketplace—the ways they are established and their advantages and disadvantages.

What Would You Do?

1. Worldwide Host has outsourced its software development to General Data Systems. What are some advantages that the hotel chain receives from this arrangement? Make a list of those advantages. What are some possible risks?

2. In the opening case, Michael Lloyd seems concerned about the qualifications of Reservations Technologies, the firm from which Worldwide plans to license the reservation system. He's asked you to help him develop a list of questions. Prepare a set of questions for him to ask both the company and its clients.

New Perspectives

1. The chapter mentions application service providers as an option to acquire software. Do some research about ASPs to see whether any of them offer systems such as the ones Worldwide Host needs to use. Could Worldwide Host use an ASP for any of its needs? If so, which specific needs could be satisfied?

2. Several years in the future Worldwide Host replaces its reservation system with one customized for it by a software development firm. A competitor approaches Worldwide's management and offers to pay an attractive annual fee for a license to use the system. Should management agree? Why or why not?

KEY TERMS

application service provider
   (ASP), 425
benchmarking, 424
beta versions, 422
custom-designed (tailored)
   software, 415
offshoring, 416

outsourcing, 415
request for information
   (RFI), 424
request for proposal (RFP), 424
service-level agreement, 421
software as a service
   (SaaS), 425

storage service provider
   (SSP), 428
uptime, 427
user application
   development, 428

REVIEW QUESTIONS

1. List and explain all the various options now available for an organization to enjoy the services of an IS. What does the organization own and for how long? What doesn't it own but can use?

2. Few organizations would develop an application in-house or pay another company to develop it if a similar application can be licensed. Why?

3. What are the benefits and risks of outsourcing IT services?

4. The major hardware and software makers, such as IBM and Hewlett-Packard, derive an increasing portion of their revenue from outsourcing contracts. Try to analyze why they direct more of their efforts in this direction.

5. What might cause a client to ask for renegotiating a long-term outsourcing contract?

6. You are the CIO of a large manufacturing company. A software vendor approaches you with an offer to have your company serve as a beta site for a new human resource application. What would you do before making a decision?

7. What is an RFI? What is the difference between an RFI and an RFP? The ideal response to an RFP is one that can be easily transformed into a contract. Why?

8. What is the purpose of benchmarking? Often, benchmarking involves visiting other organizations that have applied the system under consideration. Why?

9. What would you benchmark in a system whose purpose is to enter customer orders and accept customer credit-card account numbers for payment?

10. When purchasing an off-the-shelf application, to which phase of SDLC is the postimplementation support and service equivalent?

11. Some organizations charge the purchase price of an application that serves only a particular organizational unit back to the unit. Why does the existence of a charge-back system create an incentive to have users develop their own applications?

12. Why don't users usually document the applications they develop? Why is poor documentation a problem?

13. List and explain the benefits and risks of using the services of an ASP.

14. Some companies use ASPs because they want to concentrate on core competencies. What is a core competency?

15. What is a storage service provider (SSP)? How is it different from an ASP?

DISCUSSION QUESTIONS

1. Some outsourcing clients have devised contracts with vendors that give the vendors an incentive to develop new, innovative ISs for the client. What elements would you include in a contract like this if you were a manager for an outsourcing (client) company?

2. Vendors like to market themselves as "partners" with their outsourcing clients. Why?

3. Do you think that development of ISs by end users should be encouraged? Do the benefits of the practice outweigh its risks?

4. Will ready-made software applications ever meet all the needs of all businesses? Explain.

5. The volume of business in the ASP industry was predicted to reach about ten times what it is now. What do you think are the reasons for the much less brisk business of ASPs?

6. If you were in a position to make the decision to rent an enterprise financial software package through an ASP or to rent and install it at your organization's location, would you use an ASP?

What elements would you consider (about the vendor and your own organization) before you made the decision?

7. A CIO said that while he would not use a public network such as the Internet with an ASP for some types of ISs, he would use the Web for other types. He said that he would let employees use an accounting application through the Web. Give three examples of applications that you would recommend not to use through the Web and three that you would recommend to use through the Web. Explain your choices.

8. Do you think using applications through ASP services on the Web will increase in popularity or fizzle as an option for acquiring applications? Explain.

9. Explain why you agree or disagree with the following statement: "Employees are smart enough to know what they should and should not do with their computers. A conduct policy will not prevent wrongdoing."

10. Should employees be allowed to use their employers' e-mail for private communication at all? Outside of paid time?

11. When using the services of an ASP, the client gains an important element that is often overlooked: support service. Considering only support service, would you prefer to have the rented software installed on your own company's hardware or leave it installed at the vendor's site? Explain.

12. What are the risks of renting through the Web that you foresee that are not mentioned in the chapter?

13. Recall the discussions of telecommunications and the Internet in Chapters 6 and 8. What developments might encourage more organizations to use services of ASPs?

14. Assume that you are the CEO of a company that provides computers and access to e-mail and the Web to almost all of its employees. You are about to circulate a new IT use policy in the company. List and explain your "ten commandments" (or fewer, or more) for employees' use of software, e-mail, and the Web.

APPLYING CONCEPTS

1. You are a manager for a new company that is about to start selling textbooks to college bookstores via the Web. Several firms specialize in software that supports transactions and data collection on the Web. Prepare an RFI for an application to support your new company's effort on the Web, including posted catalogs, orders, shipment tracking, payment, and data collection for future marketing.

   Submit the list of questions you want prospective bidders to answer, and be ready to give your professor an explanation for including each of the questions.

2. Find an organization that purchased a software application 3 to 6 months ago. The application might be in any business area: accounting, payroll, inventory control, financial management, manufacturing, human resources, or an integrative enterprise application. Interview the person who recommended the purchase, and summarize the reasoning behind his or her decision. Then interview one or two daily users and summarize the pros and cons they discuss. What, if anything, would you do differently before deciding to purchase this application?

HANDS-ON ACTIVITIES

1. In recent years several companies experienced either a total failure or major mishaps when trying to have vendors implement enterprise applications. Consider "failure" as inability to complete the project or a project that ended up costing the client significantly more than expected, including lost revenue. Find at least three sources about the case. Synthesize, list, and explain what happened and why. Conclude with your own recommendations of what could be done to avoid or minimize the damage. The recommendations should be written so that potential clients of such projects could take proper precautions. Your report should be about 2,500 words long.

2. In recent years a growing amount of software has been outsourced by U.S. companies to other countries, such as India and China. Research the Web and write a two-page paper that lists and explains the benefits and the disadvantages of offshoring application development.

1. Every online retailer (e-tailer) uses a virtual shopping cart application. Team up with another student, research the Web for companies that sell such applications, and write a 2,000-word report that summarizes the following points: (a) Who are the major companies that sell these applications? (b) What are the prices of these packages? (c) How long does it take to install the applications? (d) How is the relationship with the bank processing the credit-card payments established? (e) Are there ASPs that rent the use of such systems over the Internet (namely, the e-tailer uses a shopping cart application installed at the ASP's location)? (f) If there are ASPs that rent such systems, what are the payment schemes?

2. Throughout this book, many organizations that provide information and advice on IT have been mentioned. Explore the Web sites of these organizations and the Web sites of IT-related magazines to find the latest statistics on the different alternatives for obtaining ISs. Use PowerPoint to answer the following questions and express your answers in pie charts:

   a. What was the dollar amount spent on IT in your country in each of the past 3 years, and what percentage of this amount was spent on software acquisition?

   b. How was the amount spent on software distributed among in-house development, purchased ready-made software, and outsourced development?

1. Research database software applications. Under circumstances should a company (a) purchase an off-the-shelf package, (b) develop its own package, or (c) use an application service provider?

2. Use a spreadsheet package to create a table containing the information you found for Question 1.

1. Have you downloaded or traded or shared software illegally? Why did you do it? After watching the clip, would you do it again?

2. What methods are software manufacturers using to prevent software piracy?

FROM IDEAS TO APPLICATION: REAL CASES

Wawa Flying High

Like so many executives, Wawa's CIO Neil McCarthy wanted his organization to have an enterprise application that helps make effective and timely decisions. He wanted all his organization's departments to have access to all the pertinent data in the same format, so they would not erroneously perceive different information from the same data, as often happened. But Wawa did not have the software tools to ensure that until 2004.

Headquartered in Pennsylvania, many years ago Wawa was just a dairy. After some years the privately held firm established convenience stores in which it sold its dairy products. The variety of items kept growing over the years. Wawa's coffee became famous. The chain grew from one location in Pennsylvania to 550 stores in 5 states: Pennsylvania, Delaware, New Jersey, Maryland, and Virginia. The stores are operated by 16,000 "associates." In the early 2000s Wawa started opening its own gas stations, and, of course, each gas station has a Wawa store. The company's logo, a Canada goose (Wawa, as the Native Americans called it), appears on more convenience stores as the chain grows. Wawa's 2004 revenue was $3 billion.

McCarthy realized that unit managers could not slice and dice a given set of data in the same way because they were using different applications. Business units saw data in different formats, which often led to decisions based on different information. McCarthy wanted the entire organization to have a unified view of any data, and therefore the same information for decision making, whether the information was produced by the marketing, accounting, or real-estate department. McCarthy wanted to give all units access to information that would enable managers to decide which products to continue to carry and which to discontinue, which price to increase and which to decrease depending on demand trends. He needed a good retail enterprise software package.

To meet the new goal, Wawa decided to implement an ERP system. Management approached SAP and Retek. At the time, SAP and Oracle were engaged in a fierce bid to acquire Retek, a company that developed and sold an ERP and business intelligence software package called ProfitLogic. Eventually, Oracle won the bid and purchased Retek. Unrelated to Oracle's new acquisition, Wawa selected SAP as its supplier of ERP software.

Wawa believed that SAP's upgrades would be less complicated than Retek's. McCarthy's opinion was that with Retek, every upgrade is like starting implementation of the software from scratch, and that Retek approached each upgrade as if it were a customized installation. McCarthy found that SAP's "out of the box" software met all of Wawa's initial needs, so very little customization would be required, if at all. Unlike some retailers who carry hundreds of thousands of different items, Wawa sells only 5,000. Thus, the IT staff believed that Wawa could pretty well "grow with the system," namely scale and modify the software relatively easily if the need arose.

Wawa also uses Oracle software. Shouldn't that have tipped the choice toward Oracle? McCarthy did not think so. He cited the company's use of Microsoft operating systems, but that did not mean that the company should also adopt other Microsoft products, such as SQL Server.

The company agreed to pay SAP a sum between $5 million and $9 million for the license. (Wawa disclosed only the amount's range.) McCarthy hired a consulting firm, The Lakewest Group, to prepare a business case, including an ROI (return on investment) calculation. He presented it to his fellow corporate executives. They liked the business case for the system.

The IT department did not rush to begin the system's implementation. The plan was to deploy the modules in phases over 4 to 5 years. First, the financial modules were to be deployed. The human resource and data warehousing modules would be last to be implemented. The long deployment was one reason why McCarthy preferred the SAP system, which would not require much modification and upgrading. His 18-year experience taught him that such upgrades are a distraction. Since the SAP applications were not expected to require radical upgrades, he believed that the SAP system would allow less disruptive modifications to the software.

Apparently, Retek's software is richer in features, and this is why it needs to be more customized for each client. However, when customized, it fits business needs better than SAP's "plain vanilla" retail software package. Joe Polonski, Retek's vice president of enterprise strategy, was disappointed to lose Wawa's business. He said that Wawa's decision to adopt software that required fewer upgrades made business sense if the company settled for what SAP offered and was inclined to change business processes to fit the software, rather than the other way around.

Sources: Schuman, E., "Wawa CIO: Upgrade Fear Dictated Multimillion-Dollar SAP Purchase," *CIO Insight* (www.cioinsight. com), May 20, 2005; www.wawa.com, 2005.

Thinking About the Case

1. McCarthy could probably prepare an ROI calculation with his own staff, or with other staff from Wawa. How could hiring an external consulting firm help his case convincing management to acquire the system?

2. What is the risk in frequent modification to licensed software?

3. If you were Wawa's CIO, which alternative would you prefer: software with more features that fit more business needs but requires more modifications, or software that provides fewer features and requires fewer modifications?

Let Them Run Our Daily Business

Al Etterman, the CIO of JDS Uniphase, has a simple view about IT. He says his company's IT falls into two categories: technology that *advances* the business and technology that *runs* the business. He sees no reason to use his own company's staff to develop or maintain technology that runs the business.

JDS Uniphase (JDSU), headquartered in San José, California, is the product of a 1999 merger of two companies, JDS Fitel and Uniphase, two organizations that specialized in innovative fiber optic networking technologies. In 2000, just before the Internet bubble burst, management wanted to start using an ERP system.

That year, the telecommunications equipment industry suffered a great drop in demand. JDSU, like Cisco and other companies in the industry, started to face hard times. Its 2004 revenue of $636 million was less than half its 2000 revenue. Its 2004 staff of 5,500 was a third of its 2000 staff. During 2000 the company acquired several companies. Cash was tight. Rather than pay for and manage its own ERP software, as most companies still do, the company decided to use an ASP. Oracle was chosen. Oracle calls its software-as-a-service business *On Demand*.

In fact, JDSU uses Oracle not only as an ASP. It has outsourced many of its IT services to Oracle. Every JDSU employee anywhere in the world can access the company's database and ERP software via the Internet. The software is hosted at an Oracle facility in Austin, Texas. Letting Oracle manage its ERP operations as well as its database enabled JDSU to reduce its IT staff by about a third. Oracle now handles all routine operations, such as processing customer orders, financial data, and human resources transactions, and other common operations. As Etterman puts it, he would

rather spend on "business-facing" resources than database administration. By business-facing he and other executives mean activities that advance the organization, and that nobody else can do better for the organization.

The company feels that the arrangement has served it well, especially in light of rapidly changing market conditions. Several years ago it developed and sold only devices that were installed in optical networks. As an increasing number of these devices became commodities—items manufactured by many companies for low prices—JDSU moved to develop other products, such as components for big screen television sets, paint that changes color by viewing angle, and forgery-proof identification marks for money bills and packaged drugs. Fifty percent of its revenue now comes from these products. The arrangement with Oracle accommodated both the downscaling in sales and the sales of a larger variety of items. JDSU did not have to spend money on adapting the software.

JDSU operates 14 facilities in several countries, including a manufacturing plant in Shenzhen, China. Management sees an advantage in using a single central database and hosted ERP system that serves all the facilities. Etterman gives an example: workers at the Shenzhen plant started production of a new product without training. They used specifications that were designed and posted at the central system by engineers in California. Should the company start growing again—and signs are that it will—new locations can immediately use the data and applications online.

JDSU did not outsource all its IT activities, though. In 2002 it internally built a data warehouse and applications for finance and order processing, for which the company uses Oracle's database management systems. Oracle also hosts all the data for JDSU. When Oracle upgraded its DBMS to version 11i, JDSU operations were not affected, and its systems experienced no downtime. Upgrading the systems for JDSU was carried out over one weekend for all its locations.

The arrangement with Oracle has worked well. Yet, there are some functions that JDSU would not outsource. One such activity is business systems analysis, performed by JDSU professionals. Etterman sees these people as a bridge between workers and the IT they need, and he wants to keep this intelligence in-house. When new needs arise, these professionals communicate them to Oracle.

For example, one IT professional suggested that order information be accessible to customers online so they can check order status. The purpose was to provide faster service and reduce the number of phone calls. Oracle made the information accessible, and customers can now use an order status function online. Etterman continues to seek ways to support business opportunities by using hosted software.

Sources: Cone, E., "Take My Software. Please." *CIO Insight* (www.cioinsight.com), January 5, 2005; www.jdsu.com, 2005.

Thinking About the Case

1. What is the IT philosophy of JDSU? Do you agree or disagree with it? Why or why not?

2. Is JDSU using Oracle as an ASP, an outsourcing vendor, or both? Explain.

3. Do you see any risks to JDSU in its arrangement with Oracle? If not, why not? If you do, what are the risks?

14

FOURTEEN

Risks, Security, and Disaster Recovery

LEARNING OBJECTIVES

As the use of computer-based information systems has spread, so has the threat to the integrity of data and the reliability of information. Organizations must deal seriously with the risks of both natural and manmade menaces. A computer expert once noted: "The only truly secure system is powered off, cast in a block of concrete, and sealed in a lead room with armed guards. And even then I have my doubts." Indeed, there is no way to fully secure an information system against every potential mishap, but there are ways to significantly reduce risks and recover losses.

When you finish this chapter, you will be able to:

- Describe the primary goals of information security.

- Enumerate the main types of risks to information systems.

- List the various types of attacks on networked systems.

- Describe the types of controls required to ensure the integrity of data entry and processing and uninterrupted e-commerce.

- Describe the various kinds of security measures that can be taken to protect data and ISs.

- Outline the principles of developing a recovery plan.

- Explain the economic aspects of information security.

WORLDWIDE HOST:
Battling Back from Attacks

Worldwide Host's TripExpert.com site was fulfilling its promise. The site had been up for 10 months now. CIO Michael Lloyd thought back to the end of the Web site's development project, when he had congratulated the General Data Systems staff for their hard work in getting the site up and running. At the time he did not pay much attention to the fact that the system was linked to a public network. Soon, he realized that such a link requires special consideration. The first event to draw his attention was a prank.

Web Site Defaced

Michael's Webmaster, Susan O'Donnell, rushed into his office one day to report that someone had defaced the TripExpert home page. Since the site was so important to Worldwide, she checked it daily to ensure that it was running smoothly. She was shocked at what she saw on the site when she logged on in the morning. Someone had placed offensive images and language on the page, so she immediately took the site offline.

"It'll probably take us until early afternoon to get the site up again," she said. "Fixing the home page takes only a few minutes, but ensuring that this doesn't happen again will take longer. We're working on it right now as our top priority."

Michael responded, "I'm coming down now to see for myself. We get transactions of about $90,000 an hour from that site. We've got to get it back online as soon as possible."

Michael and Susan hurried down to the information center, waved their badges in front of the radio ID scanner, entered their codes, and opened the door. Inside, two IS staff members were working to clear the Web page of the intruder's messages. All four worked furiously to find the hole that allowed the intruder to deface the home page. They quickly replaced the page with a backup copy. After several hours of hard work, they patched the server software with code that they believed would eliminate the security hole and brought the site back online.

Attacks Continue

Five weeks after the defacement incident, Worldwide Host received a second blow: its site was among several that were hit with a denial-of-service attack. Requests were swamping Worldwide's servers. Michael and his IS security chief decided to disconnect the servers from the Net. Michael knew this meant a loss of profit of thousands of dollars, but there was nothing else he could do.

They turned the site on after an hour. Apparently, the attack had subsided, but Michael was worried that the attacker had also tried to damage databases or steal information.

"What is the extent of the problem, Jason? Did they breach any of our internal systems?"

"Doesn't look like it, but they were trying to get into our database. The secure servers that we use for transactions withstood the attempt to penetrate the customer database."

Michael sighed with relief. "Our security firm said that secure servers were critical to keeping our transactions private. Our system depends on the safety of our customers' information."

"Well, the security people were right. I'll keep running my diagnostics on the damaged software," said Jason. "I'll probably have to reformat the hard drives, reinstall the operating systems, and then the applications. That'll take some time."

"Susan is preparing a statement to post on the Web site to reassure our customers. We need to get that up fast. What else can we do to prevent denial-of-service attacks?"

"Since traffic load is the critical issue, we could add more servers to handle both the attacks and legitimate transactions. But the cost of those extra servers might be high."

"Let's look into it. We need to keep our site online."

GOALS OF INFORMATION SECURITY

In June 2005, hackers invaded the databases of CardSystems Solutions, a company that processes credit-card transactions. Data from about 200,000 subscribers of MasterCard, Visa, and other credit card issuers was stolen. Had the hackers wanted, they could have used the same security breach to steal data from another 40 million accounts. Apparently, CardSystems Solutions did not comply with the data security policies that its clients required. The company paid a heavy toll: in July 2005 Visa and American Express stopped using the organization for their transaction processing. Visa and American Express gave merchants who used CardSystems' services ample time to switch to one of another several hundred companies that provide similar service.

As you have already seen, the development, implementation, and maintenance of ISs constitute a large and growing part of the cost of doing business; protecting these resources is a primary concern. The increasing reliance on ISs, combined with their connection to the outside world through a public network, the Internet, makes securing corporate ISs increasingly challenging. The role of computer controls and security is to protect systems against accidental mishaps and intentional theft and corruption of data and application, as well as to help organizations ensure that their IT operations comply with the law and with expectations of employees and customers for privacy. The major goals of information security are to:

- Reduce the risk of systems and organizations ceasing operations.
- Maintain information confidentiality.
- Ensure the integrity and reliability of data resources.
- Ensure the uninterrupted availability of data resources and online operations.
- Ensure compliance with policies and laws regarding security and privacy.

To plan measures to support these goals, organizations first must be aware of the possible risks to their information resources, which include hardware, applications, data, and networks; then, they must execute security measures to defend against those risks.

In recent years the U.S. Congress passed several laws that set standards for the protection of patient and customer privacy and compliance with corporate internal controls. They include the Health Insurance Portability and Accountability Act (HIPAA), Gramm-Leach-Bliley Act (GLBA), and Sarbanes-Oxley Act (SOX). These laws have an important effect on securing information and, therefore, on securing information systems. Other countries have similar laws that have similar implications for information security. However, corporate concern should not be focused only on complying with the law. It should ensure that information resources are secure to minimize situations that might practically take them out of business.

RISKS TO INFORMATION SYSTEMS

In recent years, especially because of the growth of online business, corporations have considered protection of their IS resources an increasingly important issue, for good reasons. **Downtime**, the time during which ISs or data are not available in the course of conducting business, has become a dreaded situation for almost every business worldwide. By some estimates, U.S. businesses lose $4 billion annually because of downtime. An online airline reservation business can lose $90,000 per hour of downtime; an online retail business loses an average of $900,000; a credit-card company could lose $2.6 million; and an online brokerage house might lose up to $6.5 million per hour of downtime. The estimates by type of application for all industries are also mind-boggling. According to the Standish Group, the cost per minute of CRM applications not being available is typically about $2,500. E-commerce applications typically have a downtime cost per minute of about $7,800. The following section discusses the most pervasive risks to IS operations.

Risks to Hardware

While stories about damage to ISs by malicious Internet attacks grab headlines, the truth about risks to ISs is simply this: the number one cause of systems downtime is hardware failure. Risks to hardware involve physical damage to computers, peripheral equipment, and communications media. The major causes of such damage are natural disasters, blackouts and brownouts, and vandalism.

Natural Disasters

Natural disasters that pose a risk to ISs include fires, floods, earthquakes, hurricanes, tornadoes, and lightning, which can destroy hardware, software, or both, causing total or partial paralysis of systems or communications lines. Floodwater can ruin storage media and cause short circuits that burn delicate components such as microchips. Lightning and voltage surges cause tiny wires to melt and destroy circuitry. In addition, wildlife and human error occasionally destroy communications lines; animals gnaw cables, and farmers occasionally cut wires inadvertently while tending their crops.

Blackouts and Brownouts

Computers run on electricity. If power is disrupted, the computer and its peripheral devices cannot function, and the change in power supply can be very damaging to computer processes and storage. **Blackouts** are total losses of electrical power. In **brownouts**, the voltage of the power decreases, or there are very short interruptions in the flow of power. Power failure might not only disrupt operations, but it can also cause irreparable damage to hardware. Occasional surges in voltage are equally harmful, because their impact on equipment is similar to that of lightning.

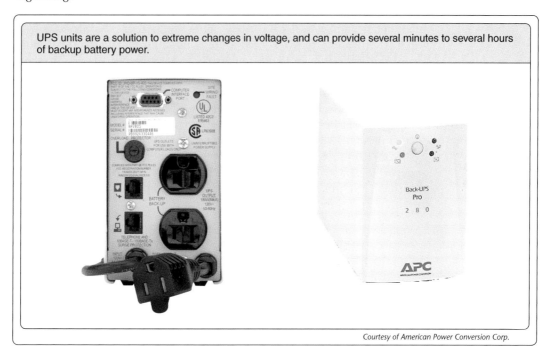

UPS units are a solution to extreme changes in voltage, and can provide several minutes to several hours of backup battery power.

Courtesy of American Power Conversion Corp.

The popular way of handling brownouts is to connect a voltage regulator between computers and the electric network. A voltage regulator boosts or decreases voltage to smooth out drops or surges and maintains voltage within an acceptable tolerance.

To ensure against interruptions in power supply, organizations use **uninterruptible power supply (UPS)** systems, which provide an alternative power supply for a short time, as soon as a power network fails. The only practical measure against prolonged blackouts in a public electrical network is to maintain an alternative source of power, such as a generator that uses diesel or another fuel. Once the general power stops, the generator can kick in and produce the power needed for the computer system.

Vandalism

Vandalism occurs when human beings deliberately destroy computer systems. Bitter customers might damage ATMs, or disgruntled employees might destroy computer equipment out of fear that it will eliminate their jobs or simply to get even with their superiors. It is difficult to defend computers against vandalism. ATMs and other equipment that are accessible to the public are often encased in metal boxes, but someone with persistence can still cause severe damage. In the workplace, the best measure against vandalism is to allow access only to those who have a real need for the system. Sensitive equipment, such as servers, should be locked in a special room. Such rooms usually are well equipped with fire suppression systems and are air-conditioned, and thus protect also against environmental risks.

Risks to Data and Applications

The primary concern of any organization should be its data, because it is often a unique resource. Data collected over time can almost never be recollected the same way, and even when it can, the process would be too expensive and too time consuming to recover the business from its loss. The concern for applications, especially if the applications are not tailor-made, should come second. All data and applications are susceptible to disruption, damage, and theft. While the culprit in the destruction of hardware is often a natural disaster or power spike, the culprit in damage to software is almost always human.

Theft of Information and Identity Theft

Sometimes the negligence of corporations and the careless use of technology, especially on public links to the Internet, create security "holes" or vulnerabilities. In one case, a young man named Juju Jiang installed a program called Invisible KeyLogger Stealth on public-use computers in 14 Kinko's stores, where customers can access the Internet. (Such Internet-connected PCs are also available in public libraries and airports.) **Keystroke logging** software records individual keystrokes. For one year, his software secretly recorded more than 450 usernames and passwords, which he used to access existing bank accounts and create new ones. Jiang was caught when he used an application called GoToMyPC. Subscribers to the GoToMyPC service can use an application by the same name to link to a PC from another PC and fully control the remote one as if they were sitting in front of it. Using the application, he remotely accessed and used one of his victims' PCs. Using the PC at home, this person noticed that the cursor was moving "by itself." The cursor opened files and subscribed to an online payment transfer service. Jiang pled guilty in court.

In 2005 keystroke logging was put to work online by a criminal ring on a massive scale. As discussed in Chapter 8, spyware software is used for several purposes. This time spyware was used to install a keystroke logging application that recorded communication with the victim's bank, insurance company, or other financial institutions. The collected data included credit-card

Natural disasters are a serious threat to hardware.

details, Social Security numbers, usernames, passwords, Instant messaging chat sessions, and search terms. Some of the data was then saved in a file hosted on a server in the United States that had an offshore-registered domain name. Sunbelt, a company that develops and sells antispam and security software, managed to obtain access to a victim's computer and track what the spyware did. The company reported that the online thieves obtained confidential financial details of customers of 50 international banks. The keystroke logging software was small (26 KB), and took advantage of Internet Explorer browsers. For example, it accessed the browser's Protected Storage area, in which users often save their usernames and passwords for convenient automatic logins. Sunbelt recommended disabling this feature.

POINT OF INTEREST

Like the Weather

A survey by Gallup and Experian conducted in August 2005 found that 1 in every 5 Americans has fallen victim to identity theft. The survey also showed that Americans are concerned about the growing menace but, by and large, are reluctant to do anything about it.

Source: Gallup, August 16, 2005.

In some cases it is employees who unwittingly give away important information such as access codes. Con artists use tricks known as **social engineering**. They telephone an employee who has a password to access an application or a database, introduce themselves as service people from a telephone company, or the organization's own IT unit, and say they must have the employee's password to fix a problem. Employees are often tempted to provide their password. The "social engineers" then steal valuable information.

Once criminals have a person's identifying details, such as a Social Security number, driver's license number, or credit-card number, they can pretend to be this person. This crime is called **identity theft**. The imposter can easily withdraw money from the victim's bank accounts, put charges on the victim's credit card, and apply for new credit cards. Since an increasing number of applications for such instruments as well as financial transactions are executed online, identity theft has become a serious problem. According to Gartner Group, 9.4 million U.S. adults were identity theft victims between May 2003 and April 2004, and their financial losses were $11.7 billion.

Courtesy of AP/Wide World Photos; J. Messerschmidt/CORBIS

Understand Risks, Security, and Disaster Recovery Planning

As explained and demonstrated throughout this book, information is the lifeblood of any modern organization. Practically every aspect of business depends on the currency of processed data and the timely provision of information. This fluent process can be achieved only if information systems are protected against threats. As a professional, you must be aware of what might happen to the ISs upon which you and your colleagues or subordinates depend. You must protect the systems against events that threaten their operation and make it impossible to carry out critical business activities. When a new system is developed, you should ask the developers to provide a system that not only supports the functions of your business unit but also incorporates controls that will minimize any compromise of the system. And to be prepared for a disaster, you should know how to implement your part of the business recovery plan to help restore operations as soon as possible.

Both social engineering and breaking access codes to steal data from online databases have caused huge damage to corporations. Connecting databases to the Internet is necessary for proper operation of multisite organizations and organizations that must share data remotely with business partners. The only way to minimize hacking into such systems is to improve security measures.

In recent years identity theft has been more prevalent as part of *phishing*, a crime discussed in Chapter 8. Crooks spam millions of recipients with bogus messages, supposedly from legitimate companies, directing them to a site where they are requested to "update" their personal data including passwords. The sites are ones constructed by the criminals who steal the personal data and use it to charge the victim's credit account, apply for new credit cards, or—in the worst situations—also apply for other documents such as driver's license and apply for loans online.

Data Alteration, Data Destruction, and Web Defacement

Alteration or destruction of data is often an act of mischief. Data alteration is not a new phenomenon. In 1983, a group of Milwaukee teenagers accessed a computer system at Sloan-Kettering Cancer Center in New York via a modem and altered patients' records just for "fun." An alert nurse noticed a double—and lethal—dose of a medication in a patient's record and called a doctor. She saved the patient's life.

As mentioned before, an organization's data is often the most important asset it owns, even more important than its hardware and applications. Even if data is altered or destroyed as a prank, the damage to the organization is great. The effort to reinstate missing or altered records from a backup copy might entail expensive labor. Even if the actual damage is not great, IT staff must spend a lot of time scanning the data pools to ascertain the integrity of the entire resource, and they must also figure out how the perpetrator managed to circumvent security controls. This activity itself wastes the time of high-salaried employees.

Often, the target of online vandals is not data but the organization's Web site. Each day, some organizations find their Web sites have been defaced. Defacement causes several types of damage: first-time visitors are not likely to stay around long enough or revisit to learn about the true nature of the site, and they might associate the offensive material with the organization; frequent visitors might never come back; and shoppers who have had a good experience with the site might leave it forever because they no longer trust its security measures.

 To deface a Web site, an intruder needs to know the site's access code or codes that enable the Webmaster and other authorized people to work on the site's server and update its pages. The intruder might either obtain the codes from someone who knows them or use special "brute force" software that tries different codes until it succeeds in accessing the pages.

Web site defacing is done to embarrass an organization or as an act of protest. In June 2005 Microsoft's United Kingdom Web site was defaced with a banner "FREE RAFA—HACK IS NOT A CRIME". The banner referred to Rafael Nunez-Aponte, who had been arrested in the United States for attacks on U.S. government Web sites. Zohn-h, an Estonian security firm that tracks Web site attacks, recorded 392,545 attacks on Web sites, of which 322,188 were for the mere purpose of defacement, in 2004. The firm estimated that 2,500 Web servers are successfully attacked daily.

The best measure against defacement, of course, is software that protects against unauthorized access, or as it is more commonly known, hacking. However, since such software might fail, the public damage can be minimized by ensuring that members of the organization monitor the home page and other essential pages frequently. When the defacement is detected shortly after it occurs, the defaced pages can be replaced with backups before too many visitors have seen the rogue pages. An increasing number of Web sites are restored within hours or even minutes from the defacement.

The cure to any unauthorized entry to an IS is for the organization to find the hole in its security software and fix it with the appropriate software. Such software is often called a "patch." Software companies that sell server management applications often produce patches and invite clients to download and install them.

To combat hackers organizations use honeytokens. A **honeytoken** is a bogus record in a networked database that neither employees nor business partners would ever access for legitimate purposes. When the intruder copies the database or the part of the database that contains that record, a simple program alerts security personnel, who can start an investigation. The program that detects the incident might also reside on a router or another communications device that is programmed to send an alert as soon as it detects the honeytoken. To entice the intruder to retrieve the honeytoken when only searching for individual records, the honeytoken might be a bogus record of a famous person, such as a medical record of a celebrity in a medical database or the salary of the CEO in a payroll database.

To learn of security holes and methods of unauthorized access, organizations can establish honeypots. A **honeypot** is a server that contains a mirrored copy of a production database (a database that is used for business operations), or one with invalid records. It is set up to make intruders think they have accessed a production database. The traces they leave educate information security officers of vulnerable points in the configuration of servers that perform valid work. In some cases security people followed an intruder's "roaming" in the honeypot in real time. Note, however, that different sources have different definitions of the terms honeypot and honeytoken. For example, some define honeypot as any trap set for abusers, including a physical computer, and a honeytoken as a special case where the trap is only data.

Computer Viruses, Worms, and Logic Bombs

Computer **viruses** are so named because they act on programs and data in a fashion similar to the way viruses act on living tissue: computer viruses easily spread from computer to computer. Because so many computers are now connected to one another and many people share files, people unknowingly transmit to other computers viruses that have infected their own files. Once a virus reaches a computer, it damages applications and data files. In addition to destroying legitimate applications and data files, viruses might disrupt data communications: the presence of viruses causes data communications applications to process huge numbers of messages and files for no useful purpose, which detracts from the efficiency of transmitting and receiving legitimate messages and files. The only difference between a computer virus and a worm is that a **worm** spreads in a network without human intervention. A worm attacks computers without the need to send e-mail or open any received files. Most people refer to both types of rogue code as viruses, as does this book.

Almost as soon as e-mail became widespread, criminal minds used it to launch viruses. The Melissa virus of 1999 was an early demonstration of why you should be suspicious of e-mail messages even when they seem to come from people or organizations you know. In the Melissa case, an innocent-looking e-mail message contained an attached Microsoft Word document that, when opened, activated a macro that sent an infected message to the first 50 entries in the victim's Microsoft Outlook address book. Many other viruses spread in a similar way: the recipient is tempted to open—and thereby activate—a file that is attached to a message. The program in that file then destroys files, slows down operations, or does both, and uses vulnerabilities in the operating system and other applications to launch copies of itself to other computers linked to the Internet. Since Melissa, there have been thousands of virus and worm attacks, and millions of computers continue to be infected.

Some viruses do not affect any files, but the speed at which they spread and their repeated attacks slow down network traffic to an intolerable crawl. According to researchers at the University of California and other institutions, in January 2003 the Slammer worm struck more than 75,000 computers in just 10 minutes. The number of infected computers doubled every 8.5 seconds. According to MessageLabs Inc., which scans e-mail for viruses, in August 2003 its software detected more than 1 million copies of the "F" variant of the Sobig virus within 24 hours of its first detection. Many organizations had to shut down their e-mail services because of the Sobig virus. At the University of Wisconsin at Madison, information security staff removed 30,000 infected e-mail messages per hour until the system was totally clean.

There are many more viruses waiting for victims. CERT/CC (Computer Emergency Response Team/Coordination Center), operated by Carnegie Mellon University, works for the U.S. government and is one of the major distributors of information on new viruses, worms, and other threats to computer security. It estimated that there are at least 30,000 computer viruses somewhere on public networks at any given time; other sources estimate the number at 40,000. CERT says that about 300 new ones are created each month.

One way to protect against viruses is to use **antivirus software**, which is readily available on the market from companies that specialize in developing this kind of software, such as Symantec and McAfee. Subscribers can regularly update the software with code that identifies and deletes or quarantines new viruses, or choose automatic updates, in which virus definitions are updated automatically when the computer is connected to the Internet. However, if a new virus is designed to operate in a way not yet known, the software is unlikely to detect it. Most virus-detection applications allow the user to automatically or selectively destroy suspect programs. Another way to minimize virus threats is to program network software, especially e-mail server software, to reject any messages that come with executable files that might be or contain viruses. Some e-mail applications, such as Microsoft Outlook, are programmed to reject such files.

Some viruses are called **Trojan horses**, analogous to the destructive gift given to the ancient Trojans. In their war against Troy, the Greeks pretended they were abandoning the city's outskirts and left behind a big wooden horse as a present. The Trojans pulled the horse into the city. When night fell, Greek soldiers hidden within the horse jumped out and opened the gates for thousands of their comrades, who conquered the city. In computer terms, a Trojan horse is any virus disguised as legitimate software or useful software that contains a virus. Many people also refer to spyware that comes with useful software as Trojan horse software.

A growing number of viruses and worms take advantage of vulnerable features of operating systems, most notably Microsoft Windows. Most attack this company's operating systems because the large majority of organizations worldwide use Microsoft operating systems to run their servers and computers. In the same way software vendors provide patches against direct intrusion into computer systems, they also distribute security patches against viruses and worms. However, it is up to security professionals and network administrators to implement those patches as soon as they become available. Six months before the SQL Slammer worm attack,

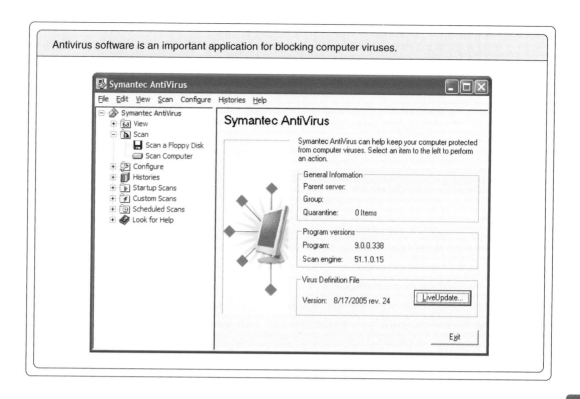

Antivirus software is an important application for blocking computer viruses.

Microsoft distributed patches to fix the vulnerability that the worm exploited. Unfortunately, many companies did not apply the patch. On January 25, 2003, the worm attacked 300,000 servers worldwide. Within 14 minutes, servers with the popular database software SQL Server started to crash on five continents. The 911 response system in Seattle was crippled, Continental Airlines was forced to cancel some flights because of problems with electronic check-in, and operations of some mobile phone services in South Korea as well as many ATMs owned by Bank of America were disabled.

Some rogue computer programs do not spread immediately like a virus but are often significantly more damaging to the individual organization that is victimized. A **logic bomb** is software that is programmed to cause damage at a specified time to specific applications and data files. It lies dormant until a certain event takes place in the computer or until the computer's inner clock reaches the specified time; the event or time triggers the virus to start causing damage. Logic bombs are usually planted by insiders, that is, employees of the victimized organization. In one case, a man named Timothy Lloyd was convicted of planting a logic bomb on Omega Engineering's computer system after he found out he was about to be fired. Lloyd, who had worked for the company for 11 years, planted six destructive lines of code on a company network server. He had tested the bomb and then reconstructed all the files. Twenty days after he left the company, the bomb erased all of the company's contracts, designs, and production programs, as well as proprietary software used by the company's manufacturing machines. The 31-year-old man's act cost the company an estimated $12 million, led to laying off 80 employees, and diminished its competitive position in the electronic manufacturing market. A plant manager for the company who testified at Lloyd's trial said the company would never recover from this sabotage. Lloyd was sentenced to 41 months in prison.

Nonmalicious Mishaps

Unintentional damage to software occurs because of poor training, lack of adherence to simple backup procedures, or simple human error. Although unintentional damage rarely occurs in robust applications, poor training might result in inappropriate use of an application so that it ruins data, unbeknownst to the user. For instance, when faced with an instruction that might change or delete data, a robust application will pose a question such as: "Are you sure you want to delete the record?" or issue a warning such as "This might destroy the file." More common damage is caused by the failure to save all work and create a backup copy. Destruction of data often happens when using a word-processing program to create text files and when updating databases.

Unauthorized downloading and installation of software that might cause damage can be controlled by limiting administration rights to employees. Many organizations instruct operating systems to deny such rights to most employees. They program ISs to accept new software installation only when the proper access codes are entered.

RISKS TO ONLINE OPERATIONS

The massive movement of operations to the Internet has attracted hackers who try to interrupt such operations daily. In addition to unauthorized access, data theft, and defacing of Web pages, there has been a surge in denial-of-service attacks and hijacking of computers.

Denial of Service

In February 2005, people who tried to access the Web sites of the Japanese prime minister and cabinet office could not do so because the sites were victims of a denial-of-service attack. **Denial of service (DoS)** occurs when someone launches a frequent and unusually large number of information requests to a Web site. The mere logging in to a site is such a request. The intention of such log-in requests is to slow down legitimate traffic on the site's server; business can slow to a halt. The server's or servers' frantic efforts to handle the massive amount of traffic denies legitimate visitors and business partners access to the site.

Such attacks are usually perpetrated from multiple computers, in which case they are called **distributed denial-of-service (DDoS)** attacks. In most such attacks, the perpetrator launches software that uses other people's computers for the attack—unbeknownst to them. Professionals call the computers used in these attacks "zombies." Zombie computers not only exacerbate the volume of calls but also make it impossible to track down the generator of the DDoS. Practically all DoS attacks now are of the DDoS type.

Because it is impossible to stop anyone from trying to log on to a Web site, there is no full cure for a DDoS attack, but equipment is available that can filter most of the illegitimate traffic targeting a site. The equipment detects repeated requests that come from the same IP numbers at an abnormal frequency and blocks them, and it can be programmed to block all incoming communication from suspected servers. The equipment can filter about 99 percent, but using the equipment slows down communication, so the site's response is slowed. In addition, blocking requests might also deny access to legitimate visitors from suspected servers, especially if the server is used by an ISP who provides Internet access to thousands of people and organizations. One way to mitigate DoS attacks is for an organization to use multiple servers, which is a good idea anyway to handle times of legitimate traffic increases.

No organization is immune to DDoS. Some of the most visible Web sites have been attacked, including those of eBay, Amazon, CNN, and the U.S. White House. All had to shut down their sites for several hours. Amazon, eBay, and other sites have lost revenue as a result. Even CERT has been forced to shut down its site. A DDoS attack sent information into its Web site at rates several hundred times higher than normal. One report from the University of California at San Diego estimated that there are 4,000 DDoS attacks somewhere in the world each week.

Computer Hijacking

You might not be aware of it, but there is a good chance your networked computer has been hijacked. No, nobody would remove it from your desk, but if it is connected to the Internet, it is used by other people. **Hijacking** a computer means using some or all of the resources of a computer linked to a public network without the consent of its owner. As you have seen, this has been done for DDoS, but it is also done for other purposes.

Hijacking is carried out by surreptitiously installing a small program called a *bot* on a computer. Like many viruses, these programs are downloaded unwittingly by people who use chat rooms and file-sharing networks. When your computer is hijacked, your Internet connection might slow to a crawl. The damage to corporations in the form of reduced productivity can be great. The main purpose of hijacking computers is spamming: using hijacked computers to send unsolicited commercial e-mail to large numbers of people, often millions of addresses. Spammers do so for two reasons: they hide the real source of the e-mail so that they cannot be identified and pursued, and they take advantage of the hijacked machines' computer resources— CPU time, memory, and communications link—to expedite the distribution of spam.

POINT OF INTEREST

Big Rewards and a Light Sentence

Because so many viruses attack operating systems developed by Microsoft, in 2003 the company started offering monetary rewards of $250,000 each for informants who help arrest and convict criminals who launch such viruses. Two informants helped to arrest and convict Sven Jaschan, a German teenager who launched the Sasser worm in May 2004. Sasser exploited a flaw in Windows 2000 and Windows XP and caused hundreds of thousands of PCs to crash and reboot. The two informants shared the $250,000 reward. The 19-year old Jaschan was sentenced to 21 months of suspended arrest for a probation period of 3 years. While on probation, he had to provide 30 hours of community service either at a hospital or a retirement home.

Source: Evers, J., "Sasser Author Gets Suspended Sentence," CNET News.com (http://news.com.com/), July 8, 2005.

Antivirus software vendor McAfee estimated that from April to June 2005, 13,000 additional computers were hijacked, an increase of 63 percent from the same period in the previous year. In all, Symantec—another antivirus vendor—estimated that hundreds of thousands of computers were infected with bots. Other experts estimate the number in the millions. The main targets are corporate and household computers with fast Internet connections shared by two or more computers.

To hijack computers, spammers exploit security holes in operating systems and communications software, and then surreptitiously install e-mail forwarding software, much as one would install a virus. Most users do not notice the extra work their computers do. One precaution is to check why a computer continues activity (such as hard disk work) when the owner does not use it. Computer owners can also install special software that detects e-mail forwarding applications.

Computer hijacking is also done to turn computers into zombies to help a DDoS. Instead of exploiting the computers to send e-mail, they are used to send repeated service requests to Web servers. The MSBlast worm was programmed to launch a DDoS attach against the Microsoft Windows Update site on the 16th of each month starting in August 2003. Microsoft posted a patch against the bot and later reported that by April 2004 its update system had removed the virus from 9.5 million computers.

CONTROLS

Controls are constraints and other restrictions imposed on a user or a system, and they can be used to secure systems against the risks just discussed or to reduce damage caused to systems, applications, and data. Figure 14.1 lists the most common controls. Controls are implemented not only for access but also to implement policies and ensure that nonsensical data is not entered into corporate databases.

FIGURE 14.1
Common controls to protect systems from risks

- Program robustness and data entry controls

- Backup

- Access controls

- Atomic transactions

- Audit trail

Program Robustness and Data Entry Controls

A computer program is said to be "robust" if it is free of bugs and can handle unforeseen situations well. Robust applications can resist inappropriate usage, such as incorrect data entry or processing. The most robust programs consider every possible misuse or abuse. A highly robust program includes code that promptly produces a clear message if a user either errs or tries to circumvent a process. For example, a Web site invites users to select a username and password, and the operators want passwords that are not easy to guess. The application should be programmed to reject any password that has fewer than a certain number of characters or does not include numerals. A clear message then must be presented, inviting the user to follow the guidelines.

Controls also translate business policies into system features. For example, Blockbuster Video uses its IS to implement a policy limiting debt for each customer to a certain level. When a renter reaches the debt limit and tries to rent another DVD, a message appears on the cash register screen: "Do not rent!" Thus, the policy is implemented by using a control at the point of sale. Similar systems do not allow any expenditures to be committed unless a certain budgetary item is first checked to ensure sufficient allocation. A spending policy has been implemented through the proper software.

Backup

Probably the easiest way to protect against loss of data is to automatically duplicate all data periodically, a process referred to as data **backup**. Storage media suitable for routine backup were discussed in Chapter 4. Many systems have built-in automatic backup programs. The data might be duplicated on inexpensive storage devices such as magnetic tapes. Manufacturers of storage devices also offer Redundant Arrays of Independent Disks (RAID) for this purpose. **RAID** is a set of disks that is programmed to replicate stored data to provide a higher degree of reliability.

Of course, backing up data is not enough. The disks or tapes with backed up data must be routinely transported off-site, so that if a business site is damaged by a disaster, the remote storage can be used since it is likely to be spared. In the past, many companies had a truck haul backup disks and tapes to the storage location at the end of every business day, and some might still do so. However, due to the great developments in telecommunications in recent years, most corporations prefer to back up data at a remote site through communications lines. Often, the backup disks or tapes reside thousands of miles away from the organization's business offices. For additional protection, backup disks or tapes are locked in safes that can withstand fire and floods.

Companies can also use the services of firms that specialize in providing backup facilities. The vendor maintains a site with huge amounts of disk space linked to the Internet. The online data backup service typically provides client organizations with an application that copies designated files from the client's systems to the remote disks. For obvious reasons, some professionals call this type of service "e-vaulting." One company that provides the service is AmeriVault (www.amerivault.com).

Access Controls

Unauthorized access to information systems, usually via public networks such as the Internet, does not always damage IT resources. However, it is regarded as one of the most serious threats to security because it is often the prelude to the destruction of Web sites, databases, and other resources, or theft of valuable information.

Access controls are measures taken to ensure that only those who are authorized have access to a computer or network or to certain applications or data. One way to block access to a computer is by physically locking it in a facility to which only authorized users have a key or by locking the computer itself with a physical key. However, in the age of networked computers, this solution is practical only for a limited number of servers and other computers. Therefore, these organizations must use other access controls, most of which rely on software.

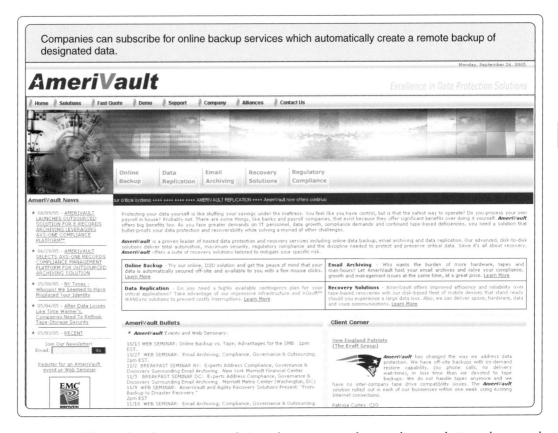

Companies can subscribe for online backup services which automatically create a remote backup of designated data.

Experts like to classify access controls into three groups: what you know, what you have, and who you are. "What you know" includes access codes such as user IDs, account numbers, and passwords. "What you have" is some kind of a device, such as a security card, which you use directly or which continuously change coordinated access codes and display them for you. "Who you are" includes your unique physical characteristics.

The most common way to control access is through the combination of a user ID and a password. While user IDs are usually not secret, passwords are. IS managers encourage users to change their passwords frequently, which most systems easily allow, so that others do not have time to figure them out. Some organizations have systems that force users to change their passwords at preset intervals, such as once a month or once every 3 months. Some systems also prevent users from selecting a password that they have used in the past, to minimize the chance that someone else might guess it, and many require a minimum length and mix of characters and numerals. Access codes and their related passwords are maintained either in a special list that becomes part of the operating system or in a database that the system searches to determine whether a user is authorized to access the requested resource.

A more secure measure than passwords is security cards, such as RSA's SecureID. The device is distributed to employees who need access to confidential databases, usually remotely. Employees receive a small device that displays a 6-digit number. Special circuitry changes the number both at the server and the device to the same new number every minute. To gain access, employees enter at least one access code and the current number. The device is small enough to be carried on a key chain or in a wallet. This two-factor access control increases the probability that only authorized people gain access. This is an example of using both what you know and what you have.

In recent years, some companies have adopted physical access controls called biometrics. A **biometric** characteristic is a unique physical, measurable characteristic of a human being that is used to identify a person. Characteristics such as fingerprints, retinal pictures, or voiceprints can be used in biometrics. They are in the class of "who you are." When a fingerprint is used, the user presses a finger on a scanner or puts it before a digital camera. The fingerprint is compared against a database of digitized fingerprints of people with authorized access. A growing number of laptop computers have a built-in fingerprint scanner for the same purpose. The procedure is similar when the image of a person's retina is scanned. With voice recognition, the user is instructed to utter a word or several words. The intonation and accent are digitized and compared with a list of digitized voice samples.

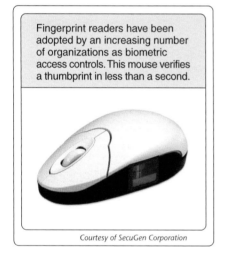

Fingerprint readers have been adopted by an increasing number of organizations as biometric access controls. This mouse verifies a thumbprint in less than a second.

Courtesy of SecuGen Corporation

Several manufacturers of computer equipment offer individual keyboard-embedded and mouse-embedded fingerprint devices. For example, SecuGen Corporation offers EyeD Mouse, a mouse that includes a fingerprint reader on the thumb side of the device. It verifies a fingerprint in less than a second. Using biometric access devices is the best way not only to prevent unauthorized access to computers but also to reduce the workload of Help desk personnel. Up to 50 percent of the calls Help desk personnel receive come from employees who have forgotten their passwords.

Atomic Transactions

As you know, in an efficient IS, a user enters data only once, and the data is recorded in different files for different purposes, according to the system's programmed instructions. For instance, in a typical order system, a sale is recorded in several files: the shipping file (so that the warehouse knows what to pack and ship), the invoice file (to produce an invoice and keep a copy in the system), the accounts receivable file (for accounting purposes), and the commission file (so that the salesperson can be compensated with the appropriate commission fee at the end of the month). As indicated in Figure 14.2, a system supports atomic transactions when its code only allows the recording of data if they successfully reach all their many destinations. An **atomic transaction** (from the Greek *atomos*, indivisible) is a set of indivisible transactions that are either all executed or none are—never only some. Using atomic transactions ensures that only full entry occurs in all the appropriate files.

For instance, suppose the different files just mentioned reside on more than one disk, one of which is malfunctioning. When the clerk enters the sale transaction, the system tries to automatically record the appropriate data from the entry into each of the files. The shipping, accounts receivable, and invoice files are updated, but the malfunctioning commission file cannot accept the data. Without controls, the sale would be recorded, but unknown to anyone, the commission would not be updated, and the salesperson would be deprived of the commission on this deal. However, an atomic transaction control mechanism detects that not all four files have been updated with the transaction, and it doesn't update any of the files. The system might try to update again later, but if the update does not go through, the application produces an appropriate error message for the clerk, and remedial action can be taken.

FIGURE 14.2

Atomic transactions ensure updating of all appropriate files. Either all files are updated, or none are updated and the control produces an error message.

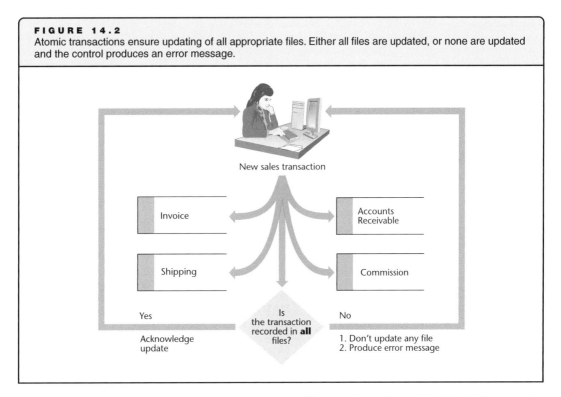

Note that this is a control not only against a malfunction but also against fraud. Suppose the salesperson collaborates with the clerk to enter the sale only in the commission file, so he or she can be rewarded for a sale that has never taken place—and then plans to split the fee with the clerk. The atomic transactions control would not let this happen.

Audit Trail

In spite of the many steps taken to prevent system abuse, it nonetheless occurs. Consequently, further steps are needed to track transactions so that (1) when abuses are found, they can be traced, and (2) fear of detection indirectly discourages abuse. One popular tracking tool is the **audit trail**: a series of documented facts that help detect who recorded which transactions, at what time, and under whose approval. Whenever an employee records a transaction, such a system prompts the employee to provide certain information: an invoice number, account number, salesperson ID number, and the like. Sometimes an audit trail is automatically created using data, such as the date and time of a transaction or the name or password of the user updating the file. This data is recorded directly from the computer—often unbeknownst to the user—and attached to the record of the transaction.

The laws and regulations of many countries require certain policy and audit trail controls, and since so many operations are performed using ISs, the controls must be programmed into software. In the United States, the Sarbanes-Oxley Act of 2002 requires corporations to implement audit trails and other measures in their systems.

Audit trail information helps uncover undesirable acts, from innocent mistakes to premeditated fraud. The information helps determine who authorized and who made the entries, the date and time of the transactions, and other identifying data that are essential in correcting mistakes or recovering losses. The audit trail is the most important tool of the **information systems auditor** (formerly known as the electronic data processing auditor), the professional whose job it is to find erroneous or fraudulent cases and investigate them.

SECURITY MEASURES

As you've seen so far in this chapter, the great increase in the number of people and organizations using the Internet has provided fertile ground for unauthorized and destructive activity. This section describes several ways that organizations can protect themselves against such attacks, including using firewalls, authentication and encryption, digital signatures, and digital certificates.

Firewalls and Proxy Servers

The best defense against unauthorized access to systems over the Internet is a **firewall**, which is hardware and software that blocks access to computing resources. Firewalls are routinely integrated into the circuitry of routers, as discussed in Chapter 6. Firewall software screens the activities of a person who logs on to a Web site; it allows retrieval and viewing of certain material, but blocks attempts to change the information or to access other resources that reside on the same computer or computers connected to it.

It is important to note that while firewalls are used to keep unauthorized users out, they are also used to keep unauthorized software or instructions away, such as computer viruses and other rogue software. When an employee uses a company computer to access external Web sites, the firewall screens for viruses and active attempts to invade company resources through the open communications line. It might also be programmed to block employee access to sites that are suspected of launching rogue programs, or to sites that provide no useful resources. The firewall then prohibits the user from logging on to those sites.

As Figure 14.3 illustrates, a firewall controls communication between a trusted network and the "untrusted" Internet. The firewall can be installed on a server or on a router. Network professionals use firewall software to check which applications can access the Internet and which servers might be accessed from the organization's network.

To increase security, some companies implement the **DMZ** (demilitarized zone) approach. The DMZ is a network of computers that are connected to the company's trusted network (such as an intranet) at one end and the untrusted network—the public Internet—at the other end. The DMZ includes resources to which the organization allows direct access from the Internet. It might include a Web site and computers from which people can download files. A DMZ provides a barrier between the Internet and a company's organizational network, which is usually an intranet. The connection between the DMZ and the organization's trusted network is established by using a proxy server.

A **proxy server** "represents" another server for all information requests from resources inside the trusted network. However, a proxy server can also be placed between the Internet and the organization's trusted network when there is no DMZ. For example, this might be the arrangement when the organization establishes its Web site as part of its trusted network. The proxy server then retrieves Web pages for computers requesting them remotely through the Internet. Thus, external computers requesting Web pages never come in direct touch with the computer

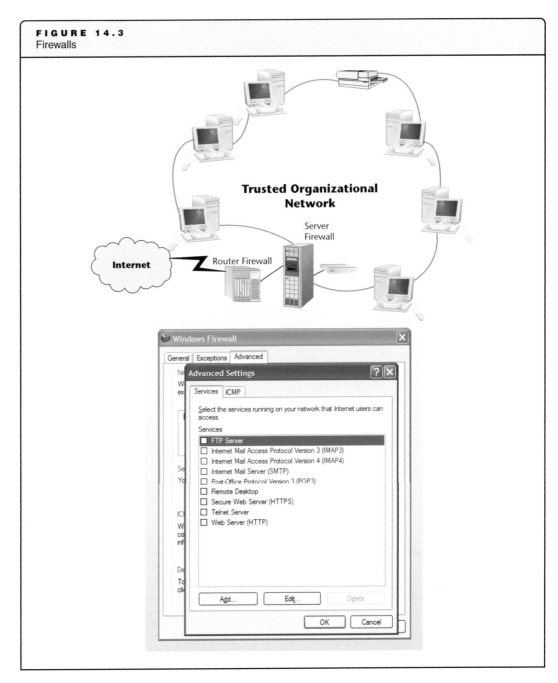

FIGURE 14.3
Firewalls

hosting the Web pages. When a business hires the services of an ISP, the proxy server is often the one operated by the ISP.

Both the organizational network server and proxy server employ firewalls. In Figure 14.3, the firewalls would be installed on the server of the organizational network and the router. The router is often called a "boundary router." The double firewall architecture adds an extra measure of security for an intranet.

Authentication and Encryption

With so much Web-based commerce and other communication on the Internet, both businesses and individuals must be able to authenticate messages. That is, they must be able to tell whether certain information, plain or encrypted, was sent to them by the party that was supposed to send it. Note that the word "message" is used here for any type of information, not only text. It might be images, sounds, or any other information in digital form.

Authentication is the process of ensuring that the person who sends a message to or receives a message from you is indeed that person. Authentication can be accomplished by senders and receivers exchanging codes known only to them. Once authentication is established, keeping a message secret can be accomplished by transforming it into a form that cannot be read by anyone who intercepts it. Coding a message into a form unreadable to an interceptor is called **encryption**. Authentication often occurs also when an encrypted message is received, because the recipient needs to ensure that the message was indeed encrypted and sent by a certain party.

Both authentication and secrecy are important when communicating confidential information such as financial and medical records. Authentication and secrecy are also essential when transacting business through a public network. For example, millions of people now buy and sell shares of stock and other financial products on the Web, businesses and individuals make purchases through the Web and use credit-card account numbers for payment, and medical clinics use the Web to transmit patient records to insurance companies and prescriptions to pharmacies. All must authenticate the recipient and keep the entire communication confidential.

To authenticate the users and maintain secrecy, the parties can use encryption programs. Encryption programs scramble information transmitted over the network so that an interceptor only receives unintelligible data. The original message is called **plaintext**; the coded message is called **ciphertext**. Encryption uses a mathematical algorithm, which is a formula, and a key. The key is a unique combination of bits that must be used in the formula to decipher the ciphertext. As indicated in Figure 14.4, the receiving computer uses the key to decipher the ciphertext back into plaintext.

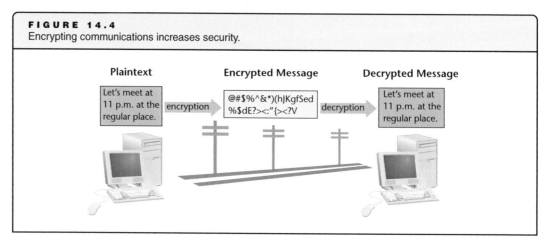

FIGURE 14.4
Encrypting communications increases security.

To illustrate the use of encryption algorithms and keys, here is a simple example. Suppose you send a secret message that you want the recipient to decipher. Remember that each character in your digital message is represented by a byte, which is a combination of eight bits. The byte can be expressed as a numeric value. For instance, the character represented by 00010101 has a decimal value of 21. So, each character in your message has a numeric value. To decipher it, you might devise the following algorithm: $y = x + k$, where x is the original value of the character, k is the key, and y is the new (encrypted) value of the byte. The value of k is secret and known only to you and to the recipient. Suppose you and the recipient agree that the key's value is 00101000 (decimal 40). Now, each original character is first manipulated through the algorithm before transmittal. For example, the byte 00010101 (decimal 21) will now be transmitted as 00111101 (decimal 61), and 10111001 (decimal 185) will be transmitted as 11100001 (decimal 225). The result of any manipulation of text by this algorithm is a string of characters that makes no sense to anyone who cannot figure out the algorithm and the key. In reality, the algorithms are usually known to many people, or can be figured out relatively easily; it is the key that cannot be so easily deduced. In this case, the key is an addition of 40 in decimal (expressed as 00101000 in binary) to each byte (character). Since the recipient knows the key, he or she can use the algorithm, along with the key, to decipher your message into readable text. Note that this is an extremely simple example. In reality, encryption algorithms are significantly more complex. Also note that the key used in this example is a combination of eight bits, which is quite easy to figure out. It would be significantly more difficult to figure out a key consisting of 128, 256, 512, or 1024 bits, which are commonly used in Internet communication. When keys that long are used, even with the latest hardware and most sophisticated code-breaking software the average time to decipher an encrypted message is so long that the probability of success is extremely small.

Public-Key Encryption

As Figure 14.5 indicates, when both the sender and recipient use the same secret key (which is the case in the earlier example), the technique is called **symmetric encryption**. However, symmetric encryption requires that the recipient have the key before the encrypted text is received. Therefore, the key is referred to simply as a *secret key* or *private key*. While it is fairly simple to keep the secrecy of a message when the sender and recipient have the same key beforehand, it is impractical in daily transactions on the Internet. For example, a retail Web site would not be able to function if every time a new buyer would require a secret key to ensure confidentiality. Therefore, in such communication, there must be a way for the sender to communicate the key to the recipient before the message is sent. To this end, the parties use an **asymmetric encryption** comprising two keys: one is public, and the other is private. It is clear why this type of encryption is also called "public-key" encryption.

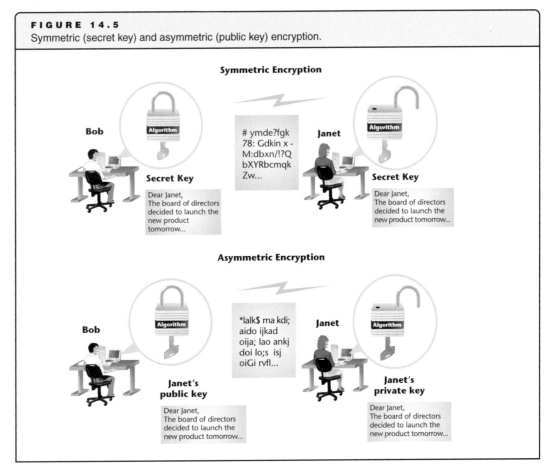

FIGURE 14.5
Symmetric (secret key) and asymmetric (public key) encryption.

A public key is distributed widely and might be known to everyone; a private key is secret and known only to the recipient of the message. When the sender wants to send a secure message to the recipient, he uses the recipient's public key to encrypt the message. The recipient then uses her own private key to decrypt it. There is a mathematical relationship between the public and private keys. The public and private keys are related in such a way that only the public key can be used to encrypt messages, and only the corresponding private key can be used to decrypt them. It is virtually impossible to deduce the private key from the public key. All applications that use public keys and private keys use the same principles. What differentiates them from one another is the different encryption algorithm each uses.

Online businesses often switch site visitors to a secure server when visitors are asked to provide secret information such as credit-card account numbers or other personal information. The secure server provides the visitor's Web browser with the site's public key. The browser uses it to encrypt the credit-card number and any other personal information. The secure server uses the private key to decrypt the information. Once an encrypted exchange is established, the server can send the visitor's browser a secret key that both can use. Moreover, the server can change that key often during the session to make decryption more difficult.

Transport Layer Security

A protocol called **Transport Layer Security (TLS)** is used for transactions on the Web. TLS is the successor of Secure Socket Layer (SSL) and works following the same principles as SSL with some improvements that are outside the scope of this discussion. It is part of virtually all current Web browsers. Current versions of browsers use TSL with a 128-bit key. TLS uses a combination of public key and symmetric key encryption. It works as follows:

1. When a visitor connects to an online site, the site's server sends the visitor's browser its public key.
2. The visitor's browser creates a temporary symmetric (secret) key of 128 bits. The key is transmitted to the site's server encrypted by using the site's public key. Now both the visitor's browser and the site's server know the same secret key and can use it for encryption.
3. The visitor can now safely transmit confidential information.

How safe is a 128-bit key? It would take 250 PCs working simultaneously around the clock an estimated 9 trillion times the age of the universe just to decrypt a single message. This is the reason why practically all financial institutions use 128-bit encryption, and if you want to bank online, you must use a browser that supports this key length. However, how long it takes an interceptor to decipher depends on current speed of hardware and sophistication of code-breaking software. As hardware becomes faster and software becomes more sophisticated, standard keys usually are set longer.

When you log on to secure servers you might notice that the "HTTP://" in the URL box at the top of the browser turns into an "HTTPS://" and a little closed padlock appears on the bottom of the browser. It is advisable not to transfer any confidential information through the Web when these two indications do not appear. **HTTPS** is the secure version of HTTP, discussed in Chapter 8. HTTPS encrypts communication using SSL or TSL. Luckily, all this encryption and decryption is done by the browser. When you access a secure area of a Web site, the communication between the site's server and your Web browser is encrypted. The information you view on your screen was encrypted by the software installed on the site's server and then decrypted by your browser.

Digital Signatures

A **digital signature** is a way to authenticate online messages, analogous to a physical signature on a piece of paper, but implemented with public-key cryptography. The digital signature authenticates the identity of the sender of a message and also guarantees that no one has altered the sent document; it is as if the message were carried in an electronically sealed envelope.

When you send an encrypted message, two phases are involved in creating a digital signature. First, the encryption software uses a hashing algorithm (a mathematical formula) to create a message digest from the file you wish to transmit. A **message digest** is akin to the unique fingerprint of a file. Then, the software uses your private (secret) key to encrypt the message digest. The result is a digital signature for that specific file.

How does it work? Follow the flowchart in Figure 14.6. Suppose you want to send the draft of a detailed price proposal to your business partner. You want to be certain that the document you intend to send is indeed the one she receives. She wants the assurance that the document she receives is really from you.

1. You attach the price proposal file to an e-mail message. The entire communication is essentially one message, indicated as "Plain message" in Figure 14.6.
2. Using the hashing software, your computer creates a message hash, the message digest, which is a mathematically manipulated file of the message and is not readily readable by a human.
3. You then use a private key that you have previously obtained from the public-key issuer, such as a certificate authority, to encrypt the message digest. Your computer uses your private key to turn the message digest into a digital signature.

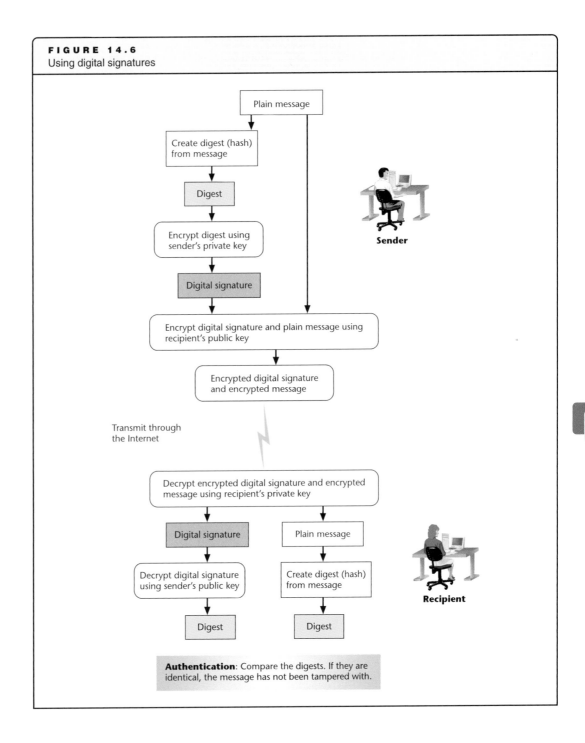

FIGURE 14.6
Using digital signatures

Plain message

Create digest (hash) from message

Digest

Encrypt digest using sender's private key

Digital signature

Sender

Encrypt digital signature and plain message using recipient's public key

Encrypted digital signature and encrypted message

Transmit through the Internet

Decrypt encrypted digital signature and encrypted message using recipient's private key

Digital signature

Plain message

Decrypt digital signature using sender's public key

Create digest (hash) from message

Recipient

Digest

Digest

Authentication: Compare the digests. If they are identical, the message has not been tampered with.

4. The computer also uses your private key to encrypt the message in its plain (unhashed) form. Your computer sends off both files.

5. Your business partner receives the encrypted files: the digital signature (which is an encrypted message digest) and the encrypted message, which usually come as one file.

6. Your business partner's computer uses her private key (which is mathematically related to her public key, which you used) to decrypt both your digital signature and your encrypted unhashed message.

7. The decrypted digital signature becomes the message digest. Hashing the decrypted unhashed message turns this message into a digest, too.

8. If the two message digests are identical, the message received is, apparently, the one you sent, unchanged.

Since the message digest is different for every message, your digital signature is different each time you send a message. As described here, senders of encrypted messages obtain the public key of the recipient from an issuer of such keys. In most cases, the issuer is a certificate authority, and the recipient's public key is included in the recipient's digital certificate, which is discussed next.

Digital Certificates

To authenticate a digital signature, both buyers and sellers must use digital certificates (also known as digital IDs). **Digital certificates** are computer files that serve as the equivalent of ID cards by associating one's identity with one's public key. An issuer of digital certificates is called a **certificate authority (CA)**, an organization that serves as a trusted third party. A CA certifies the identity of anyone who inquires about a party communicating on the Internet. Some CAs are subsidiaries of banks and credit-card companies and others are independent. American Express CA, Digital Signature Trust Co., VeriSign Inc., and GlobalSign NV are just a few of the numerous companies that sell digital certificates. To view a long list of CAs you can go to www.pki-page.org. A CA issues the public (and private) keys associated with a certificate.

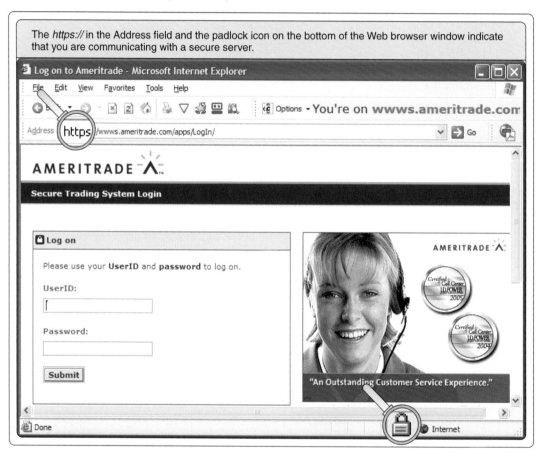

A digital certificate contains its holder's name, a serial number, expiration dates, and a copy of the certificate holder's public key (used to encrypt messages and digital signatures). It also contains the digital signature of the certificate authority so that a recipient can verify that the certificate is real. To view the digital certificate of a secure online business, click the padlock icon in the lower-right corner of your browser. Figure 14.7 shows the certificate window that you would open (left). Click the Details tab to view the version, serial number, signature encryption method, issuer name, and other details of the certificate (right).

Digital certificates are the equivalent of tamperproof photo identification cards. They are based on public-key encryption techniques that verify the identities of the buyer and seller in electronic transactions and prevent documents from being altered after the transaction is completed. Consumers have their own digital certificates stored on their home computers' hard disks. In a transaction, a consumer uses one digital key attached to the certificate that he or she

FIGURE 14.7
A digital certificate

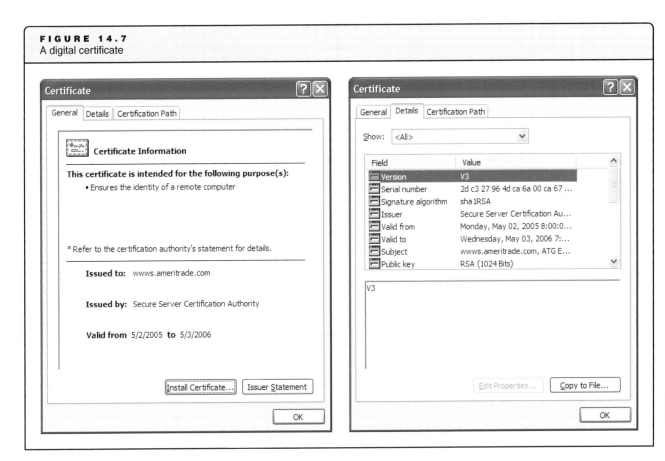

sends to the seller. The seller sends the certificate and his own digital key to a certificate authority, which then can determine the authenticity of the digital signature. Completed transaction documents are stored on a secure hard disk maintained by a trusted third party.

The recipient of an encrypted message uses the certificate authority's public key to decode the digital certificate attached to the message, verifies it as issued by the certificate authority, and then obtains the sender's public key and identification information held within the certificate. With this information, the recipient can send an encrypted reply.

When using the Web, encryption and authentication take place automatically and are transparent to the users. However, there is an indication in the browser's window if the communication is secure. In Microsoft Internet Explorer and Firefox, a small padlock appears in the lower-right corner. In Netscape, an open padlock appears in the lower-right corner if the site you reached is not secure, and a closed padlock appears if it is secure. You might see these signs as soon as the page requiring your password appears in your browser. If you double-click the padlock, a window opens with details on the digital certificate that the site uses, such as the certificate issuer's name, the date it was issued, and the date it expires.

The Downside of Security Measures

Security measures—especially passwords, encryption applications, and firewalls—have a price that relates to more than money: they slow down data communications, and they require user discipline, which is not always easy to maintain. Employees tend to forget their passwords, especially if they must replace them every 30 or 90 days.

Employees are especially annoyed when they have to remember a different password for every system they use; in some companies, there might be four or five different systems, each with its own access control. A simpler solution is an approach called **SSO (single sign-on)**. With SSO, users are required to identify themselves only once before accessing several different systems. However, SSO requires special software that interacts with all the systems in an organization, and the systems must be linked through a network. Not many organizations have installed such software.

CIOs often cite SSO as an effective way to bring down the amount of work their subordinates must do. Such was certainly the case at Philadelphia Gas Works (PGW), a utility company with a staff of 1,700 serving over half a million customers. The IT staff received about 20,000 calls per year from employees, about half of which were about forgotten passwords. The IT staff had to reset these passwords. Since SSO was implemented, the number of calls of this nature decreased to about 10,000 per year.

Encryption slows down communication because the software must encrypt and decrypt every message. Remember that when you use a secure Web site, much of the information you view on your screen is encrypted by the software installed on the site's server and then decrypted by your browser. All this activity takes time, and the delay only exacerbates the Internet's low download speed during periods of heavy traffic. Firewalls have the same slowing effect; screening every download takes time, which affects anyone trying to access information, including employees, business partners, and consumers.

IT specialists must clearly explain to managers the implications of applying security measures, especially on systems connected to the Internet. The IT specialists and other managers must first determine which resource should be accessed only with passwords and which also require other screening methods, such as firewalls. They must tell employees what impact a new security measure will have on their daily work, and if the measure will adversely affect their work, the specialists must convince the employees that the inconvenience is the price for protecting data. The IT specialists should also continue to work on methods that minimize inconvenience and delays.

Recall the discussion of virtual private networks (VPNs), which enable employees to access ISs using special security software involving passwords and encryption. This approach allows employees to access an intranet only from computers equipped with the proper VPN software and only if they remember passwords. When Wawa Corporation—the convenience store chain discussed in a case in Chapter 13—implemented a new SAP ERP system, the CIO implemented a one-time keyfob such as SecurID®. The password changes frequently and the user does not have to remember it, because it appears automatically on the keyfob. There is no need to use VPN software. If someone steals a password, the thief cannot use it for more than a few seconds because it then changes. This enables Wawa employees to access the intranet from any computer in the world.

RECOVERY MEASURES

Security measures might reduce undesirable mishaps, but nobody can control all disasters. To be prepared for disasters when they do occur, organizations must have recovery measures in place. Organizations that depend heavily on ISs for their daily business often use redundancy; that is, they run all systems and transactions on two computers in parallel to protect against loss of data and business. If one computer is down, the work can continue on the other computer. Redundancy makes the system fault tolerant. However, in distributed systems, doubling every computing resource is extremely expensive, so other measures must be taken.

The Business Recovery Plan

To prepare for mishaps, either natural or malicious, many organizations have well-planned programs in place, called **business recovery plans** (also called *disaster recovery plans, business resumption plans,* or *business continuity plans*). The plans detail what should be done and by whom if critical systems go down. In principle, the systems do not have to be ISs. However, most of the attention and resources in recovery plans are devoted to measures that should be taken when ISs go down or if IS operations become untrustworthy.

The 2005 Hurricane Katrina in the U.S. Gulf Coast was a wakeup call for many executives, reminding them in terrible terms of the need for recovery planning. Concern about disaster recovery has spread beyond banks, insurance companies, and data centers, the traditional disaster recovery fanatics. Many customer service and retail firms realize that they can easily lose customers if they don't deliver services and products in a timely manner, which is why the terms "business recovery," "business resumption," and "business continuity" have caught on in some circles. In interactive computing environments, when business systems are idle, so are the people who bring in revenue. Employees cannot do their work, customers cannot purchase, and suppliers cannot accept requests for raw materials and services. In addition, companies' reputations can be harmed, and competitive advantage and market share lost.

Experts propose nine steps to develop a business recovery plan:

1. *Obtain management's commitment to the plan.* Development of a recovery plan requires substantial resources. Top management must be convinced of the potential damages that paralysis of information systems might cause. Once management is committed, it should appoint a business recovery coordinator to develop the plan and execute it if disaster occurs.

2. *Establish a planning committee.* The coordinator establishes a planning committee comprising representatives from all business units that are dependent on computer-based ISs. The members serve as liaisons between the coordinator and their unit managers. The managers are authorized to establish emergency procedures for their own departments.

3. *Perform risk assessment and impact analysis.* The committee assesses which operations would be hurt by disasters, and how long the organization could continue to operate without the damaged resources. This analysis is carried out through interviews with managers of functional business areas. The committee compiles information regarding maximum allowable downtime, required backup information, and the financial, operational, and legal consequences of extended downtime.

4. *Prioritize recovery needs.* The disaster recovery coordinator ranks each IS application according to its effect on an organization's ability to achieve its mission. **Mission-critical applications**, those without which the business cannot conduct its operations, are given the highest priority. The largest or most widely used system might not be the most critical. Applications might be categorized into several classes, such as:

   - *Critical*: Applications that cannot be replaced with manual systems under any circumstances.
   - *Vital*: Applications that can be replaced with manual systems for a brief period, such as several days.
   - *Sensitive*: Applications that can be replaced with acceptable manual systems for an extended period of time, though at great cost.
   - *Noncritical*: Applications that can be interrupted for an extended period of time at little or no cost to the organization.

5. *Select a recovery plan.* Recovery plan alternatives are evaluated by considering advantages and disadvantages in terms of risk reduction, cost, and the speed at which employees can adjust to the alternative system.

6. *Select vendors.* If it is determined that an external vendor can better respond to a disaster than in-house staff and provide a better alternative system, then the most cost-effective external vendor should be selected. Factors considered should include the vendor's ability to provide telecommunications alternatives, experience, and capacity to support current applications.

7. *Develop and implement the plan.* The plan includes organizational and vendor responsibilities and the sequence of events that will take place. Each business unit is informed of its responsibilities, who the key contacts are in each department, and the training programs available for personnel.

8. *Test the plan.* Testing includes a walk-through with each business unit, simulations as if a real disaster had occurred, and (if no damage will be caused) a deliberate interruption of the system and implementation of the plan. In mock disasters, the coordinator measures the time it takes to implement the plan and its effectiveness.

9. *Continually test and evaluate.* The staff must be aware of the plan at all times. Therefore, the plan must be tested periodically. It should be evaluated in light of new business practices and the addition of new applications. If necessary, the plan should be modified to accommodate these changes.

The plan should include the key personnel and their responsibilities, as well as a procedure to reinstitute interactions with outside business partners and suppliers. Because an organization's priorities and environment change over time, the plan must be examined periodically and updated if necessary. There will be new business processes or changes in the relative importance of existing processes or tasks, new or different application software, changes in hardware, and new or different IS and end users. The plan must be modified to reflect the new environment, and the changes must be thoroughly tested. A copy of the plan should be kept off-site, because if a disaster occurs, an on-site copy might not be available. Many companies keep an electronic copy posted at a server many miles away, so that they can retrieve it from wherever their officer can have Internet access.

Although the threat of terrorism has increased awareness for the need of recovery plans, CIOs often find the tasks of earmarking funds for disaster recovery programs difficult because they cannot show the return on investment (ROI) of such an "investment." Most companies institute recovery programs only after a disaster or near disaster occurs. Usually, the larger companies have such programs. Even at companies that do have recovery plans, experts estimate that most of those plans are never tested. Worse, some experts observed that one out of five recovery plans did not work well when tested.

Recovery Planning and Hot Site Providers

Companies that choose not to fully develop their own recovery plan can outsource it to companies that specialize in either disaster recovery planning or provision of alternative sites. Strohl Systems, EverGreen Data Continuity, and other companies provide both planning and software for disaster recovery. The software helps create and update records of key people and procedures. Fewer companies provide alternative sites—hot sites—chief among them IBM and SunGard Availability Services, a division of SunGard. They provide backup and operation facilities to which a client's employees can move and continue operations in case of a disaster.

For example, IBM maintains a business continuity and recovery center in Sterling Forest, New York. The center is equipped with desks, computer systems, and Internet links. Customers can use the duplicate databases and applications maintained for them. The company also provides hotel rooms and air mattresses for people who need to work long hours. As soon as the power went out in the summer of 2003, the center's diesel-powered generators started up, and it was ready to take in clients' employees. Some clients had secured online systems but no light in the offices. These clients operated the systems from links at the center.

More than 90 percent of U.S. businesses are within 35 miles of a SunGard center. When the blackout of August 2003 occurred, about 100 of the company's clients notified it that they might use the centers, and 61 declared their situations disasters. In the following days, the centers served 2,000 people in 8 centers in Jersey City, Cleveland, Detroit, Long Island, and other places. Worldwide, the company maintains redundant facilities totaling 279,000 square meters (3 million square feet), equipped with software and networking facilities to enable a client organization to resume business within hours.

THE ECONOMICS OF INFORMATION SECURITY

Security measures should be dealt with in a manner similar to purchasing insurance. The spending on measures should be proportional to the potential damage. Organizations also need to assess the minimum rate of system downtime and ensure that they can financially sustain the downtime.

Terrorism and PATRIOTism

Information technology can help track down criminals and terrorists, but it also helps criminals and terrorists in their efforts. The technology can help protect privacy and other civil rights, but it can also help violate such rights. The growing danger of terrorism and the continued effort of governments to reduce drug-related and other crimes led to controversial use, or abuse, of IT. In the United States, one particular law with a long name includes controversial provisions that have worried civil libertarians since October 2001. Uniting and Strengthening America by Providing Appropriate Tools Required to Intercept and Obstruct Terrorism Act of 2001, the PATRIOT Act, as it is popularly known, gives law enforcement agencies surveillance and wiretapping rights they did not have before that year. The law permits the FBI to read private files and personal Internet records without informing the suspected citizen and without need for a law enforcement agency to present to the court a probable cause. "Our constitutional freedoms are in jeopardy. Now is the time to restore real checks and balances to the worst sections of the Patriot Act" called a Web posting of the American Civil Liberties Union (ACLU) in 2005, when the law was reconsidered by the U.S. Congress. On the contrary, said many members of Congress, the law should be enhanced to give the FBI even freer hand.

The Electronic Privacy Information Center (EPIC) explains the major concerns with the Act, which made changes to 15 existing laws. The Act gives more power than before to law enforcement agencies in installing pen registers and trap and trace devices. A pen register is any device that records outgoing phone numbers. A trap and track device—a caller ID device, for instance—captures and records incoming telephone numbers. Similarly, the Act extends the government's authority to gain access to personal financial information and student information, even if the subject of the investigation is not suspected of wrongdoing. Agents only have to certify that the information likely to be obtained is relevant to an ongoing criminal investigation. In the past, the government had to show to a judge probable cause—a reasonable suspicion that the subject of an investigation is committing or is about to commit a crime. If a government attorney "certifies" that the information collected is likely to be relevant, the judge must grant permission to install the device and collect the information.

The previous federal law referred only to telephones, but the new Act expanded communication tapping to the Internet, because it redefined a pen register as "a device or process which records or decodes dialing, routing, addressing, or signaling information transmitted by an instrument or facility from which a wire or electronic communication is transmitted." This practically allows law enforcement agencies to record, without probable cause, e-mail addresses and URLs. Some jurists opine that this actually allows the agencies to record not only e-mail sender and recipient addresses and Web addresses but also the content of e-mail messages and Web pages.

Even before adoption of the PATRIOT Act, the FBI used "packet sniffing" devices connected to the servers operated by Internet service providers (ISPs). Until 2002 the agency used a custom-built device known as Carnivore, and later started using commercial devices that reportedly perform the same way. The devices are supposed to monitor e-mail traffic of suspects. However, millions of other subscribers use the same servers and therefore are subject to the same surveillance. When tapping communications, law enforcement agencies need the cooperation of a third party, such as a telephone company or an ISP. In the past, the law limited the definition of such third parties. Now, there is no limitation. Therefore, if a university, public library, municipality, or an airport provides access to the Internet—such as through a hotspot—all users of these services are subject to surveillance. Furthermore, that third party is prohibited from notifying anyone, including unsuspected users, of the surveillance.

Proponents of the Act want to leave all its provisions in place beyond 2005 and add two provisions. They would like to allow the FBI to demand records without first obtaining an approval from a prosecutor or a judge. Some would also amend the law to require the U.S. Postal Service to let FBI agents copy information from the outside of envelopes in the mail.

Again, we are faced with an old dilemma: How far should we allow our governments to go in their efforts to protect us against crime and terrorism? At what point do we start to pay too much in terms of privacy and civil rights for such protection? And when terrorists strike or threaten to strike, should we give up our liberties for more security?

How Much Security Is Enough Security?

From a pure cost point of view, how much should an organization spend on data security measures? There are two types of costs that must be considered to answer this question: the cost of the potential damage, and the cost of implementing a preventive measure. The cost of the damage is the aggregate of all the potential damages multiplied by their respective probabilities, as follows:

$$Cost\ of\ potential\ damage = \sum_{i=1}^{n} Cost\ of\ disruption_i \times Probability\ of\ disruption_i$$

Where i is a probable event, and n is the number of events.

Experts are usually employed to estimate the cost and probabilities of damages, as well as the cost of security measures. Obviously, the more extensive the preventive measures, the smaller the damage potential. So, as the cost of security measures goes up, the cost of potential damage goes down. Ideally, the enterprise places itself at the optimum point, which is the point at which the total of the two costs is minimized, as Figure 14.8 illustrates.

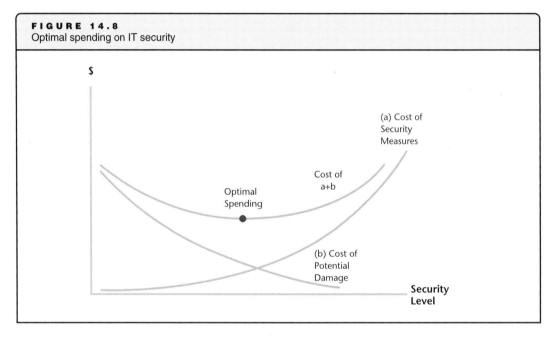

FIGURE 14.8
Optimal spending on IT security

When budgeting for IT security, managers need to define what they want to protect. They should focus on the asset they must protect, which in most cases is information, not applications. Copies of applications are usually kept in a safe place to replace those that get damaged. They should also estimate the loss of revenue from downtime. Then, they should budget sums that do not exceed the value of what the measures protect—information and potential revenues. Even the most ardent IT security advocates agree that there is no point spending $100,000 to protect information that is worth $10,000.

Calculating Downtime

All other factors being equal, businesses should try to install ISs whose downtime is the lowest possible, but if obtaining a system with a higher uptime adds to the cost, they should consider the benefit of greater uptime against the added cost. Mission-critical systems must be connected to an alternative source of power, duplicated with a redundant system, or both. Often, such systems must be up 24 hours per day, 7 days per week.

When the service that the business provides depends on uninterrupted power, the systems are often connected to the grids of two utility companies and an alternative off-grid power source, such as generators. For example, Equinix, a company in Newark and Secaucus, New Jersey, that maintains data centers for large companies uses such an arrangement. Both facilities receive power from two power stations. In the August 2003 blackout, when both utility companies stopped supplying electricity, the company's systems were automatically powered by batteries, and shortly after that by diesel generators. Clients continued to transmit and receive data as if nothing happened.

Recall the discussion of system uptime in Chapter 8. Experts can provide good estimates of the probability systems will fail, both in terms of power failure in a certain region and for particular applications. Experience in operating certain systems, such as ERP and SCM systems, can teach the IT staff for how many minutes or seconds per year the system is likely to fail. For example, if the uptime of a system is 99 percent ("two nines"), it should be expected to be down 1 percent of the time, and if "time" means 24 × 7, downtime expectancy is 87.6 hours per year (365 days × 24 hours × 0.01). This might be sufficient for a system supporting some human resources operations, but not an airline reservation system or an SCM system of a global company. For these systems, the number of nines must be greater, such as 99.999 percent, in which case there would be only 5.256 minutes of downtime expected per year (365 × 24 × 60 × 0.00001).

More and more ISs are now interfaced with other systems, which makes them a chain or cluster of several interdependent systems. For example, if system A is connected to system B, B depends on A, and the uptime of the systems are 99 percent and 99.5 percent, respectively; the probability of uptime for B is the multiplication of these probabilities, or 98.505 percent. Therefore, you could expect the systems to be down 0.01495 of the time, about 131 hours per year. This is a greater downtime than if system B operated independently. The greater the number of interdependent systems, the greater the expected downtime.

Redundancies, on the other hand, reduce expected downtime. For example, if two airline reservation systems operate in parallel, each can serve all the transactions, and the probabilities of their failures are 2 percent and 3 percent, the probability that the reservation service will be down is 0.06 percent (0.03 × 0.02), just 0.0006 of the time. This downtime is significantly smaller than the downtime of a service based on either system individually. This is why so many companies rely on redundant power sources and systems, such as duplicate databases, mirrored servers, and duplicate applications, especially when much of their operations are executed online, and even more so when the operations depend on constant online interaction with customers.

There might be no point in spending much money to increase the "nines" of uptime for every system. For example, if the only purpose of an IS is to help access a data warehouse to glean business intelligence (recall the discussions in Chapters 7 and 11), spending thousands of dollars to increase its number of nines from 99 to 99.999 is probably not a wise choice. For a data warehouse, if an analysis cannot be performed immediately, it can usually be performed later without serious ramifications.

- The purpose of controls and security measures is to maintain the functionality of ISs, the confidentiality of information, the integrity and availability of data and computing resources, the uninterruptible availability of data resources and online operations, and compliance with security and privacy laws.

- Risks to ISs include risks to hardware, risks to data and applications, and risks to networks.

- Risks to hardware include natural disasters, such as earthquakes, fires, floods, and power failures, as well as vandalism. Protective measures run the gamut from surge protectors to the maintenance of duplicate systems, which make ISs fault tolerant.

- Risks to data and applications include theft of information, identify theft, data alteration, data destruction, defacement of Web sites, computer viruses, worms, and logic bombs, as well as non-malicious mishaps such as unauthorized downloading and installation of software.

- Risks to online operations include denial of service and computer hijacking.

- To minimize disruption, organizations use controls. Controls include program robustness and constraints on data entry, periodic backup of software and data files, access controls, atomic transactions, and audit trails.

- Access controls also include information that must be entered before information resources can be used: passwords, synchronized numbers, and biometrics. Biometric technologies are growing in popularity because they do not require memorization of passwords, which employees tend to forget.

- Atomic transactions are an important control that ensures information integrity: either all files involved in a transaction are updated, or none is.

- To protect resources that are linked to the Internet, organizations use firewalls, which are special hardware and software to control access to servers and their contents.

- Encryption schemes scramble messages at the sending end and descramble them at the receiving end. Encryption is also used to authenticate the sender or recipient of a message, verifying that the user is indeed the party he or she claims to be and to keep messages secret.

- To encrypt and decrypt messages the communicating parties must use a key. The larger the number of bits in the key, the longer it takes to break the encryption. In symmetric encryption, both users use a private, secret key. In asymmetric key encryption, the parties use a public and a private key.

- The public-private key method does not require both parties to have a common secret key before the communication starts. To encrypt, the sender needs the recipient's public key; to decrypt, the recipient uses his or her private key. This system is a useful feature that lets consumers and organizations transact business confidentially on the Web.

- TLS and HTTPS are encryption standards specially designed for the Web. They are embedded in Web browsers.

- Organizations can purchase public and private keys along with an associated digital certificate from a certificate authority. Digital certificates contain the certificate holder's public key and other information, such as the issue and expiration date of the certificate.

- Many organizations have business recovery plans that are developed and periodically tested by a special committee. The plans identify mission-critical applications and prescribe steps that various employees should take in a disaster.

- A growing number of companies also use the services of organizations that specialize in providing alternative sites, hot sites, to continue operations in case of a disaster, such as a massive terror attack, natural disaster, or power outage.

- When considering how much to invest in security measures, organizations should evaluate the dollar amounts of the potential damage on one hand, and the cost of security on the other hand. The more that is spent on security, the smaller the potential loss. Organizations should spend the amount that brings the combined costs to a minimum.

- A system that depends on other systems for input has a greater downtime probability than if it is used independently of other systems. Redundant systems significantly reduce downtime probability.

- Governments are obliged to protect citizens against crime and terrorism and therefore must be able to tap electronic communication of suspects. Such practices often collide with individuals' right to privacy.

WORLDWIDE HOST REVISITED

Worldwide Host's Web site has been up and running for several months now. In that time, the TripExpert site has been defaced, experienced a denial-of-service attack, and has been hit with an attempt to invade the customer database. Putting its system on the World Wide Web has certainly introduced challenges to Worldwide's IS staff. Let us look at some computer security issues in more depth.

3. The chapter discussed controls on information systems to help secure them. From the description in the opening case, you know that Worldwide Host uses secure servers and physical access controls for its information systems. What other types of controls should it be using to safeguard its systems? Develop a list for Michael Lloyd and his security chief.

What Would You Do?

1. Jason Theodore, Worldwide Host's IS security chief, informs Michael Lloyd that there have been a growing number of Trojan horse attacks that target specific businesses. The perpetrators send e-mails to specific employees who have access to important financial information. The senders disguise themselves as a colleague and ask the employee to go to a Web site or open an attachment that installs a virus that is able to send sensitive financial information back to the perpetrator. Develop a list of recommendations for Michael Lloyd to distribute to employees to help safeguard Worldwide Host.

2. Severe weather is always a concern for IS personnel. If a flood or power outage hit Worldwide Host's offices, it could take down its entire operations. Michael Lloyd has asked you to help him develop a disaster recovery plan. What measures would you recommend Worldwide Host take to prepare for and recover from a disaster?

New Perspectives

1. Worldwide Host handles thousands of transactions involving customers' credit cards. The TripExpert.com employees are complaining that the response time for the new system is much slower than their old reservations system. Michael Lloyd knows that this is the result of security measures—use of passwords, encryption and decryption, and screening of transactions. He is meeting with the travel staff to explain the security-response trade-off. Prepare an outline of his speech for him, which discusses the pros and cons of the security measures.

2. Michael Lloyd has been approached by a vendor that provides disaster recovery services at an alternative site. Should Worldwide Host consider use of such a service? If so, for what systems and business functions?

KEY TERMS

access controls, 453
antivirus software, 448
asymmetric (public key)
    encryption, 459
atomic transaction, 454

audit trail, 455
authentication, 458
backup, 452
biometric, 454
blackout, 443

brownout, 443
business recovery plan, 464
certificate authority (CA), 462
ciphertext, 458
controls, 451

denial of service (DoS), 450
digital certificate, 462
digital signature, 460
distributed denial of service
    (DDoS), 450
DMZ, 456
downtime, 442
encryption, 458
firewall, 456
hijacking, 450
honeypot, 447
honeytoken, 447

hot site, 466
HTTPS, 460
identity theft, 445
information systems
    auditor, 456
keystroke logging, 444
logic bomb, 449
message digest, 460
mission-critical application, 465
plaintext, 458
proxy server, 456
RAID, 452

social engineering, 445
SSO (single sign-on), 463
symmetric (secret or private
    key) encryption, 459
Transport Layer Security
    (TLS), 460
Trojan horse, 448
uninterruptible power supply
    (UPS), 443
virus, 447
worm, 447

REVIEW QUESTIONS

1. What are the goals of security measures for ISs? Explain.

2. All the data of your company is concentrated in two databases. All employees use PCs or laptop computers. All use a corporate network. You are to prioritize protection of the following elements of your company: PCs and laptops, the databases, the corporate network. Which is the element about which you are most concerned, and why?

3. Data alteration and destruction are dreaded by many IS managers more than any other mishap. Why? Is the threat of Web site defacement as severe as data destruction or alteration? Why or why not?

4. Some companies still make a duplicate copy of disks or tapes and transport them to a remote site as a precaution against loss of data on the original storage media. What is the preferred way of keeping secured copies of data nowadays? Give at least two benefits and one possible drawback of the new way.

5. Comment on the following statement: If your computer is connected to an external communication line, anyone with a similar link can potentially access your systems.

6. What is a honeytoken and how is it used by companies?

7. What is a honeypot and how is it used by businesses?

8. What is the difference between a virus and a worm? Which is potentially more dangerous and why?

9. Why is encryption that uses the public-key method so important in electronic commerce?

10. Assume that you are charged with developing an application to record baseball performance statistics. What limits would you include to ensure that the information entered is reasonable?

11. What is an audit trail? What audit trail information would you have for a shipping record?

12. This chapter gives an example of an atomic transaction. Give another example from any business area.

13. What is the difference between authentication and confidentiality?

14. What are biometric access controls? How are they better than passwords?

15. What is a firewall, and how does it work?

16. What is a DDoS? How is it executed, and what is the purpose of zombies in a DDoS? What can organizations do to prevent a DDoS attack?

17. What is the purpose of business recovery plans?

18. A growing number of companies have implemented business recovery plans, but there are still many without such plans. Why?

1. Companies that process credit-card transactions for merchants have their computers vaulted behind concrete walls, iron bars, and heavy steel doors. Employees must enter a code into a keypad to enter the vaults. Yet, every so often information on millions of credit-card accounts is stolen without any physical break-in. How so?

2. In the Blockbuster example of system controls, the cash register displays the message "Do not rent!" when a patron reaches the maximum debt allowed. However, the customer service representative might still rent a videotape to the customer. What would you do to better enforce the chain's policy?

3. A military officer in Colorado orders an item whose part number is 7954. The clerk at the supply center hundreds of miles away receives the order through his computer and ships the item: a ship's anchor, not realizing that Colorado is located hundreds of miles from any ocean. Apparently, the officer wanted to order item number 7945, a fuel tank for a fighter aircraft, but he erred when entering the item's number. What controls would you implement both at the entry system and at the systems employed at the supply center to prevent such mistakes?

4. The average loss in a bank robbery is several thousand dollars, and the culprit has an 85 percent chance of being caught. The average damage in a "usual" white-collar fraud is several tens of thousands of dollars. The average amount stolen in computer fraud is several hundreds of thousands of dollars, and it is extremely hard to find the culprit. Why is the amount involved in computer fraud so high, and why is it difficult to find the culprits?

5. To prevent unauthorized people from copying data from a database, some companies forbid their employees to come to work with USB flash memory devices and subject them to body searches. Is this an effective measure? Why or why not?

6. The majority of criminals who commit computer fraud are insiders, that is, employees. What measures would you take to minimize insider fraud through ISs?

7. Would you prefer that your identity be verified with a biometric (such as your palm or fingerprint, or your cornea picture), or with a password? Why?

8. Explain in an intuitive way why the downtime probability of a system that depends on another system is greater than if it were operating independently.

9. Employees often complain about the hurdles they have to pass whenever they need to access data and the slow response of ISs because of firewalls and encryption measures. As a CIO, how would you explain the need for such measures to employees? Would you give them any say in the decision of how to balance convenience and protection of data and applications?

10. Organizations often use firewalls to block employee access to certain Web sites. Do you agree with this practice, or do you think it violates employee privacy?

11. Firewalls might keep track of Web pages that employees download to their PCs. Do you think this practice violates employee privacy?

12. When financial institutions discover that their ISs (especially databases) have been broken into, they often do not report the event to law enforcement officers. Even if they know who the hacker is, they do what they can to avoid publicity. Why? Should they be forced to report such events?

13. When hackers are caught, they often argue that they actually did a service to the organization whose system they accessed without permission; now, they say, the organization knows its system has a weak point, and it can take the proper steps to improve security. Do you agree with this claim? Why or why not?

14. A CIO tells you, "We regularly review all of the potential vulnerabilities of our information systems and networks. We implement hardware, software, and procedures against any potential event, no matter the cost." What do you say to this executive?

15. Is the potential for identity theft growing? Explain.

16. Encryption helps individuals and organizations to maintain privacy and confidentiality, thereby helping protect civil liberties. However, encryption also helps terrorists and criminals hide their intentions. Some governments have laws that forbid nongovernment agencies to use strong encryption software. The idea is to allow people to encrypt their communication, but not enough to prevent the government from decrypting the communication in surveillance of suspected criminals and terrorists. Do you favor such laws, or do you advocate that everybody have access to the strongest encryption software possible? Explain.

APPLYING CONCEPTS

1. Search the Web for the full text of HIPAA. Assume you are the CIO of a health insurance company. List and explain five controls that you must implement in your organization's ISs as a result of this law.

2. Research the impact of the Sarbanes-Oxley Act on ISs. Write a two-page report explaining the major controls corporations must incorporate in their ISs to satisfy the Act.

3. Log on to a secure Web site. Figure out which icon you have to click to receive information on the security measures used in the session. Send your professor an e-mail message detailing the site's URL and all the information you obtained: the length of the key that is used for encryption, the type of digital certificate used, the issuer of the digital certificate, the date it was issued and its expiration date, and so forth. Explain each item.

HANDS-ON ACTIVITIES

 Use Excel or another spreadsheet application to show your work when solving the following problems:

1. A company uses three information systems that are linked sequentially: System A feeds System B, and System B feeds System C. Consider the following average uptimes: System A, 98 percent; System B, 97 percent; System C, 95 percent. What is the average expected downtime (as a percentage) of System C?

2. To reduce chances of failure, a company has connected all of its vital information systems to electric power from two different utility firms. The probability of failure of electric power from one utility firm is 2 percent. The probability of failure of electric power from the other utility firm is 1.5 percent. What is the probability that these information systems will receive no electric power at all?

3. A CIO states, "Our online transaction system has availability of five nines. However, we hired the services of an ASP for using our human resources information systems. Our HR system has availability of only three nines."

   a. Calculate the minutes of downtime per week for each of these systems.

   b. Explain why the company must have such a high number of nines for one system but can settle for a significantly lower number of nines for the other system.

TEAM ACTIVITIES

1. Team up with another student. Research the Web for recovery planning expenditures in your country or worldwide over the past 5 years. Prepare a table showing the expenditure amounts. Add an analysis that explains the reasons for changes in the expenditures.

2. Your team should evaluate the business recovery plan of your school. If there is none, write a business recovery plan for the school. If there is one in place, evaluate its weaknesses and make suggestions for improvement. Prepare a 10-minute, software-based presentation of your findings and suggestions.

COMPANION CD QUESTIONS

1. Do you run antivirus software on your home computer? Is it up to date? If not, why not?

2. What security measures have you implemented to protect your home computer? Will you do anything differently after reading this chapter?

VIDEO QUESTIONS

1. Under what circumstances would you use system restore?

2. Have you used system restore? If not, would you?

FROM IDEAS TO APPLICATION: REAL CASES

Planning for the Worst

Executives at FleetBoston Financial were not happy when they finished evaluating the company's disaster recovery plan. Their conclusion was clear: had a disaster occurred, the bank would not be able to do business for two full days. It would take that long to recover data and information systems to a level that allows proper service and no further loss of revenue. This was unacceptable. To complicate matters, the bank was also in the midst of a merger with Bank of America.

FleetBoston Financial is the seventh largest financial holding company in the United States. It provides a variety of financial services to 20 million customers in more than 20 countries. Headquartered in Boston, Massachusetts, the company has assets worth $192 billion and employs more than 50,000 employees worldwide. Its services include retail banking, corporate banking, and investments banking. In the Northeast region of the United States it maintains more than 1,500 branches and over 3,700 ATMs. In Latin America it has 250 offices.

Management used two important metrics to evaluate disaster recovery planning. One is Recovery Time Objective (RTO), which is the maximum length of time that a business process can be allowed to be unavailable. This is the time that elapses from the start of a disaster to the time when all systems are up and running normally. The other metric is Recovery Point Objective (RPO), which is the amount of work in progress that can be lost. That is, the value of all the work processes that were disrupted when the disaster occurred. If all this work must be recovered, an organization must have a plan that will bring RPO down to zero. All work must be recovered and processed fully. When an organization can tolerate the loss of a day's work, for instance, the assumption is that the work can be redone by interviewing employees and by other measures. FleetBoston management decided to have an RTO of 24 hours and an RPO of zero.

Senior vice president of technology Lari Sue Taylor carried a frightening finding in mind when supporting the zero RPO goal. A Gartner Group analysis found that 93 percent of businesses that suffered a major data loss went out of business within 5 years.

At the time, FleetBoston used magnetic tapes to back up data. However, because tapes are slow, it would take 24 hours to copy the data back to magnetic disks. The company decided to use vaulting services. It contracted with SunGard's Electronic Vaulting Services and also implemented a remote backup arrangement called Symmetrix Data Remote Facility (SDRF). Data can be copied to disks at a remote location without delaying operations. When data must be recovered, hundreds of terabytes can be copied back to the bank's disks within hours.

Each transaction used to be duplicated at the bank's data center. It was that data center that had to be backed up for disastrous events. A duplicate data center was established at a SunGard location, 120 miles from the bank's data center. A combination of hardware and networking devices was used to ensure satisfactorily fast duplication of every transaction. There is a delay of only a few seconds between recording at the data center and at the SunGard site.

From 48 hours, the company's RTO decreased to less than 1 hour for critical systems, those that must continue to run to sustain the most important business. Sometime after the recovery mechanism was established, the bank experienced an emergency. No data was accessible at the data center. The remote site kicked in without any problems. Taylor said that the investment in the recovery measure was fully paid back by this single event. Had FleetBoston had the old method of tape backup, the bank would have suffered a major loss of revenue.

Management is happy with the recovery measures. However, the procedures are under constant review to improve. For example, so far all the data saved on the mainframe computers at the data center has been automatically saved and accumulated over the years. The company is now considering the possibility of implementing information life cycle management. In life cycle management, old data is discarded if not required by law or for backup while new data is saved. This way a smaller amount of data is maintained at any given time.

Sources: Robb, D., "Case Study: Improving Disaster Recovery Without Breaking the Bank," StorageForum.com (www.enterprisestorageforum.com), May 10, 2004; www.fleet.com, 2005; www.business.com, 2005.

Thinking About the Case

1. If you were the CIO of a large bank and had to convince management to invest in recovery measures such as FleetBoston's, what would be your single most convincing argument?

2. Describe the two key evaluation factors, RTO and RPO. Is one more important than the other? Explain.

3. If you were an executive for FleetBoston, would you pursue an information life cycle management effort, or would you recommend continuing to accumulate data, albeit perhaps for other purposes than backup? For what purpose could data be accumulated over many years?

The Tester

The case studies in this book usually revolve around organizations. This story is about a person, a "soldier" in the war against cybercriminals. Meet Mark Seiden, security tester extraordinaire. "Tell me which information your bank keeps most secret," he challenged a top bank executive 2 years ago, "and I'll get it anyway." The executive complied. He told Seiden he wanted the identities of clients who were negotiating secret deals, so secret that many people inside the bank referred to them by code names. He also wanted the financial details of some mergers and acquisitions in which his bank was involved. The executive knew that those two types of information were kept under strict electronic locks by the bank.

A week later Seiden visited the executive again in his office. He gave him a printout of the secret information. He also gave the man photocopies of the floor plans of each bank office and a suitcase filled with backup tapes from which Seiden could reconstruct all the files maintained on the bank's computers. Seiden spent 2 weekend nights to obtain the information.

Seiden, with 35 years of experience in computer programming, is one of a small group of professional intruders, experts who are paid by corporations to find security loopholes, both in physical facilities and software. Companies hire Seiden to help improve security systems and procedures to protect their ISs and other sensitive corporate assets.

Business is booming for Seiden and his colleagues. As hackers increase their invasion of corporate databases and steal information from a growing number of organizations, executives are learning fast why it pays to hire the services of such people. Experts say that in the early days of the Internet, breaking into corporate ISs was mainly a matter of showing off one's prowess. Now, it has become a crime of greed. The main targets are personal information and credit-card account numbers. In a survey conducted by the FBI in 2005, 87 percent of the polled corporations said they had routine security audits, an increase from 82 percent in 2004. An analyst for the Gartner Group said that North American corporations spent more than $2 billion on security consultants in 2004, an increase of 14 percent from 2003.

Much of the work such consultants do has nothing to do with hacking. Seiden has a wardrobe of uniforms and other corporate garbs. They include a uniform the FedEx drivers wear, and a windbreaker that Iron Mountain workers wear when they drive their vans to pick up backup files for credit card-processing firms. He also holds a set of tools that help him pick locks, at which he is adept. If you ask, he will tell you that the easiest way to enter a locked room is through the plenum space between the hard ceiling and the tiles underneath, space used for wiring and ventilation. Remove a tile, and you are in a safe room that is no longer so safe.

So how did Seiden get that precious information about the bank? The bank maintains some of the best security software, so Seiden did not even try to crack it. He obtained a badge that the bank often handed out to outside consultants. Wearing the badge he could enter the room where the bank's computers were housed at headquarters. He noticed that the master keys to the building as well as the building's floor plans were stored in a file cabinet that took him only 2 minutes to pick. Roaming freely in "safe" rooms, he also found the backup tapes.

He then used social engineering to obtain information. Pretending he was a bank employee, he telephoned the accounting department and asked whom he should contact for assigning a code name to a project. Equipped with the name of the clerk who assigned code names, he went to her office and noticed that she placed sheets with code names in a folder and locked the folder in a file cabinet. Since the office was in a locked area, she had no reason to lock the file cabinet (which Seiden could pick anyway, if he needed to). He later explored the folder and obtained the code names of secret clients and information about confidential mergers and acquisitions that the bank was negotiating.

Seiden agrees that corporations cannot defend themselves against every intrusion, physical or otherwise. He agrees with the analogous construction of a house without windows: it can be built, but nobody would want to live in it. What corporations should do, he says, is ensure that when an intrusion occurs they know about it and take measures to ascertain that this type of intrusion does not happen again.

Sources: Rivlin, G., "The Sniffer vs. the Cybercrooks," *New York Times*, Section 3, p. 1, col. 2, July 31, 2005; www.msbit.com/mis.html, 2005.

Thinking About the Case

1. The case mentions three different ways of obtaining information illegally. What are they?

2. Why do you think corporations are spending increasing amounts of money on the services of security testers? Can you cite some recent mishaps that would prompt a corporation to do so?

3. Refer to the analogy of "a house without windows." You are the CEO of a large corporation. Give an example of a measure you would never take even if it enhanced security.

access controls—Hardware and software measures, such as user IDs and passwords, used to control access to information systems.

access point (AP)—An arrangement consisting of a device connected to the Internet on one end and to a router on the other end. All wireless devices link to the Internet through the router.

affiliate program—An arrangement by which a Web site promotes sales for another Web site through a link to the seller's site, and for which the affiliate is compensated. There are various schemes of compensation to affiliates.

agile methods—Software development methods that emphasize constant communication with clients (end users) and fast development of code, as well as modifications as soon as they are needed.

algorithm—An sequence of steps one takes to solve a problem. Often, these steps are expressed as mathematical formulas.

antivirus software—Software designed to detect and intercept computer viruses.

applet—A small software application, usually written in Java or another programming language for the Web.

application—A computer program that addresses a general or specific business or scientific need. General applications include electronic spreadsheets and word processors. Specific applications are written especially for a business unit to accommodate special activities.

Application Service Provider (ASP)—A firm that rents the use of software applications through an Internet link.

application software—Software developed to meet general or specific business needs.

application-specific software—A collective term for all computer programs that are designed specifically to address certain business problems, such as a program written to deal with a company's market research effort.

Arithmetic Logic Unit (ALU)—The electronic circuitry in the central processing unit of a computer responsible for arithmetic and logic operations.

artificial intelligence (AI)—The study and creation of computer programs that mimic human behavior. This discipline combines the interests of computer science, cognitive science, linguistics, and management information systems. The main subfields of AI are robotics, artificial vision, natural language processors, and expert systems.

assembly languages—Second-generation programming languages that assemble several bytes into groups of characters that are human-readable to expedite programming tasks.

asymmetric (public key) encryption—Encryption technology in which a message is encrypted with one key and decrypted with another.

atomic transaction—A transaction whose entry is not complete until all entries into the appropriate files have been successfully completed. It is an important data entry control. (Atom = Indivisible)

audit trail—Names, dates, and other references in computer files that can help an auditor track down the person who used an IS for a transaction, legal or illegal.

authentication—The process of ensuring that the person who sends a message to or receives a message from another party is indeed that person.

autocategorization—Automatic sorting and indexing of information that is executed by specialized knowledge management software.

B2B—Business-to-business, a term that refers to transactions between businesses, often through an Internet link.

B2C—Business-to-consumer, a term that refers to transactions between a business and its customers, often through an Internet link.

backbone—The network of copper lines, optical fibers, and radio satellites that supports the Internet.

backup—Periodic duplication of data in order to guard against loss.

backward compatibility—Compatibility of a device with another device that supports only an older standard. For example, USB 2.0 is backward-compatible with computers that support only USB 1.1 devices.

bandwidth—The capacity of the communications channel, practically its speed; the number of signal streams the channel can support, usually measured as number of bits per second. A greater bandwidth also supports a greater bit rate, i.e., transmission speed.

banners—Advertisements that appear on a Web page.

baseband—A communications channel that allows only a very low bit rate in telecommunications, such as unconditioned telephone twisted pair cables.

benchmarking—The measurement of time intervals and other important characteristics of hardware and software, usually when testing them before a decision to purchase or reject.

beta site—An organization that agrees to use a new application for a specific period and report errors and unsatisfactory features to the developer in return for free use and support.

bill of materials (BOM)—A list showing an explosion of the materials that go into the production of an item. Used in planning the purchase of raw materials.

biometric—A unique, measurable characteristic or trait of a human being used for automatically authenticating a person's identity. Biometric technologies include digitized fingerprints, retinal pictures, and voice. Used with special hardware to uniquely identify a person who tries to access a facility or an IS, instead of a password.

bit—Binary digit; either a zero or a one. The smallest unit of information used in computing.

bits per second (bps)—The measurement of the capacity (or transmission rate) of a communications channel.

blackouts and brownouts—Periods of power loss or a significant fall in power. Such events may cause computers to stop working, or even damage them. Computers can be protected against these events by using proper equipment, such as UPS (uninterruptible power supply) systems.

bleeding edge—The situation in which a business fails because it tries to be on the technological leading edge.

blog—A contraction of Web log. A Web site where participants post their opinions on a topic or set of related topics; these postings are listed in chronological order.

Bluetooth—A personal wireless network protocol. It enables wireless communication between input devices and computers and among other devices within 10 meters.

brainstorming—The process of a group collaboratively generating new ideas and creative solutions to problems.

brick-and-mortar—A popular term for companies that use physical structure for doing business directly with other businesses and consumers, such as stores. Often used to contrast with businesses that sell only online.

bridge—A device connecting two communications networks that use similar hardware.

broadband—High-speed digital communication, sometimes defined as at least 200 kbps. T1, Cable modem, and DSL provide broadband.

Broadband over Power Lines (BPL)—A broadband service provided over electric power lines.

bus—The set of wires or soldered conductors in the computer through which the different components (such as the CPU and RAM) communicate. It also refers to a data communications topology whereby communicating devices are connected to a single, open-ended medium.

business intelligence (BI)—Information gleaned from large amounts of data, usually a data warehouse or online databases; a BI system discovers not-yet-known patterns, trends, and other useful information that can help improve the organization's performance.

business model—The manner in which businesses generate income.

business planning—The general idea or explicit statement of where an organization wishes to be at some time in the future in terms of its capabilities and market position.

business recovery plan—Organizational plan that prepares for disruption in information systems, detailing what should be done and by whom, if critical information systems fail or become untrustworthy; also called business recovery plan and disaster recovery plan. Also known as business continuity plan.

byte—A standard group of 8 bits.

C2C—Consumer-to-consumer business. The term usually refers to Web-based transactions between two consumers via the servers of an organization, such as auctions and sales. eBay is an example of a C2C site.

CASE (Computer-Aided Software Engineering)—Software tools that expedite systems development. The tools provide a 4GL or application generator for fast code writing, facilities for flowcharting or data-flow diagramming, data-dictionary facility, word-processing capability, and other features required to develop and document the new software. The term is much less popular now than it was in the 1980s and early 1990s.

cash management system (CMS)—Information system that helps reduce the interest and fees that organizations have to pay when borrowing money and increases the yield that organizations can receive on unused funds.

central processing unit (CPU)—The circuitry of a computer microprocessor that fetches instructions and data from the primary memory and executes the instructions. The CPU is the most important electronic unit of the computer.

certificate authority (CA)—An organization that issues digital certificates, which authenticate the holder in electronic business transactions.

character—The smallest piece of data in the data hierarchy.

chief information officer (CIO)—The highest-ranking IS officer in the organization, usually a vice president, who oversees the planning, development, and implementation of IS and serves as leader to all IS professionals in the organization.

chief security officer (CSO)—Also called chief information security officer (CISO), the highest-ranking officer in charge of planning and implementing information security measures in the organization, such as access codes and backup procedures.

chief technology officer (CTO)—A high-level corporate officer who is in charge of all information technology needs of the organization. Sometimes the CTO reports to the chief information officer, but in some companies this person practically serves as the CIO.

ciphertext—A coded message designed to authenticate users and maintain secrecy.

circuit switching—A communication process in which a dedicated channel (circuit) is established for the duration of a transmission; the sending node signals the receiving node; the receiver acknowledges the signal and then receives the entire message.

clickstream tracking—The use of software to record the activities of a person at Web sites. Whenever the person clicks a link, the activity is added to the record.

clock rate—The rate of repetitive machine cycles that a computer can perform; also called frequency. Measured in GHz.

closed system—A system that stands alone, with no connection to another system.

coaxial cable—A transmission medium consisting of thick copper wire insulated and shielded by a special sheath of meshed wires to prevent electromagnetic interference. Supports high-speed telecommunication.

co-location—The placement and maintenance of a Web server with servers of other subscribers of the service provider. The servers are co-located in the same facility.

competitive advantage—A position in which one dominates a market; also called strategic advantage.

compiler—A program whose purpose is to translate code written in a high-level programming language into the equivalent code in machine language for execution by the computer.

composite key—In a data file, a combination of two fields that can serve as a unique key to locate specific records.

computer-aided design (CAD)—Special software used by engineers and designers that facilitates engineering and design work.

computer-aided manufacturing (CAM)—Automation of manufacturing activities by use of computers. Often, the information for the activity comes directly from connected computers that were used for engineering the parts or products to be manufactured.

Computerized Numeric Control (CNC)—Control by computers that take data and create instructions that tell robots how to manufacture and assemble parts and products.

conclusion—The *then* component of an *if-then* rule in knowledge representation.

consumer profiling—The collection of information about individual shoppers in order to know and serve consumers better.

control unit—The circuitry in the CPU that fetches instructions and data from the primary memory, decodes the instructions, passes them to the ALU for execution, and stores the results in the primary memory.

controls—Constraints applied to a system to ensure proper use and security standards.

conversion—The process of abandoning an old information system and implementing a new one.

conversion rate—In marketing, the proportion of shoppers who end up buying from the organization. The term also applies to online shopping.

cookie—A small file that a Web site places on a visitor's hard disk so that the Web site can remember something about the visitor later, such as an ID number or username.

cost/benefit analysis—An evaluation of the costs incurred by an information system and the benefits gained by the system.

CRT (cathode-ray tube)—A display (for a computer or television set) that uses an electronic gun to draw and paint on the screen by bombarding pixels on the internal side of the screen.

custom-designed (tailored) software—Software designed to meet the specific needs of a particular organization or department; also called tailored software.

customer relationship management (CRM)—A set of applications designed to gather and analyze information about customers.

cut-over conversion (flash cut conversion)—A swift switch from an old information system to the new.

dashboard—A graphic presentation of organizational performance. Dashboards display in an easy-to-grasp visual manner metrics, trends, and other helpful information that is the result of processing of business intelligence applications.

data—Facts about people, other subjects, and events. May be manipulated and processed to produce information.

data dictionary—The part of the database that contains information about the different sets of records and fields, such as their source and who may change them.

data flow diagram (DFD)—A graphical method to communicate the data flow in a business unit. Usually serves as a blueprint for a new information system in the development process. The DFD uses four symbols for entity, process, data store, and data flow.

data integrity—Accuracy, timeliness, and relevance of data in a context.

data management module—In a decision support system, a database or data warehouse that allows a decision maker to conduct the intelligence phase of decision making.

data mart—A collection of archival data that is part of a data warehouse, usually focusing on one aspect of the organization such as sales of a family of products or daily revenues in a geographic region.

data mining—Using a special application that scours large databases for relationships among business events, such as items typically purchased together on a certain day of the week, or machinery failures that occur along with a specific use mode of the machine.

Instead of the user querying the databases, the application dynamically looks for such relationships.

data modeling—The process of charting existing or planned data stores and flows of an organization or one of its units. It includes charting of entity relationship diagrams.

data processing—The operation of manipulating data to produce information.

data redundancy—The existence of the same data in more than one place in a computer system. Although some data redundancy is unavoidable, efforts should be made to minimize it.

data warehouse—A huge collection of historical data that can be processed to support management decision making.

data warehousing—Techniques to store very large amounts of historical data in databases, especially for business intelligence.

data word—The number of bits that a CPU retrieves from memory for processing in one machine cycle. When all other conditions are equal, a machine with a larger data word is faster.

database—A collection of shared, interrelated records, usually in more than one file. An approach to data management that facilitates data entry, update, and manipulation.

database administrator (DBA)—The individual in charge of building and maintaining organizational databases.

database approach—An approach to maintaining data that contains a mechanism for tagging, retrieving, and manipulating data.

database management system (DBMS)—A computer program that allows the user to construct a database, populate it with data, and manipulate the data.

debugging—The process of finding and correcting errors in software.

decision support system (DSS)—Information system that aids managers in making decisions based on built-in models. DSSs comprise three modules: data management, model management, and dialog management. DSSs may be an integral part of a larger application, such as an ERP system.

dedicated hosting—An arrangement in which a Web hosting organization devotes an entire server to only the Web site of a single client organization, as opposed to having multiple clients' sites share one server.

denial of service (DoS)—The inability of legitimate visitors to log on to a Web site when too many malicious requests are launched by an attacker. Most DoS attacks are distributed (DDoS).

dialog module—The part of a decision-support system, or any other system, that allows the user to interact with the application. Also called interface.

dial-up connection—A connection to the Internet through a regular telephone and modem. Dial-up connections are slow, as opposed to broadband connections.

digital certificates—Computer files that serve as the equivalent of ID cards.

digital signature—An encrypted digest of the text that is sent along with a message that authenticates the identity of the sender and guarantees that no one has altered the sent document.

digital subscriber line (DSL)—Technology that relieves individual subscribers of the need for the conversion of digital signals into analog signals between the telephone exchange and the subscriber jack. DSL lines are linked to the Internet on a permanent basis and support bit rates significantly greater than a normal telephone line between the subscriber's jack and the telephone exchange.

digital video disc (DVD)—A collective term for several types of high-capacity storage optical discs, used for data storage and motion pictures. Also called digital versatile disc.

dimensional database—A database of tables, each of which contains aggregations and other manipulated information gleaned from the data to speed up the presentation by online processing applications. Also called multidimensional database.

direct access—The manner in which a record is retrieved from a storage device, without the need to seek it sequentially. The record's address is calculated from the value in its logical key field.

direct access storage (DAS)—Any data storage device that is directly connected to a computer as opposed to being connected via a communications network. When a disk is contained in the computer box or externally but directly linked to it, it is considered DAS.

disaster recovery plan—*See* business recovery plan.

distributed denial of service (DDoS)—Multiple log-in requests from many computers to the same Web site, so that the Web site is jammed with requests and cannot accept inquiries of legitimate visitors.

DMZ—Demilitarized zone, a network of computers and other devices connected to the Internet where visitors are not allowed direct access to other resources connected to the DMZ. DMZs are used to serve visitors while minimizing risk of unauthorized access.

DNS (Domain Name System)—Hardware and software making up a server whose purpose is to resolve domain names (converting them back to IP numbers) and routing messages on the Internet.

domain name—The name assigned to an Internet server or to a part of a server that hosts a Web site.

dot-matrix printer—A printer on which the print head consists of a matrix of little pins; thus, each printed character is made up of tiny dots.

downloading—The copying of data or applications from a computer to your computer, for example from a source on the Internet to your PC.

downstream—The movement of data bits from another computer to your computer via the Internet. Downstream speed of Internet connection services is usually greater than the upstream speed.

downtime—The unplanned period of time during which a system does not function.

drilling down—The process of finding the most relevant information for executive decision making within a database or data warehouse by moving from more general information to more specific details, such as from performance of a division to performance of a department within the division.

driver—The software that enables an operating system to control a device, such as an optical disc drive or joystick.

dynamic IP number—The IP number assigned to a computer that is connected to the Internet intermittently for the duration of the computer's connection.

dynamic Web page—A Web page whose contents change while the visitor watches it.

e-commerce—Business activity that is electronically executed between parties, such as between two businesses or between a business and a consumer.

economic order quantity (EOQ)—The optimal (cost-minimizing) quantity of a specific raw material that allows a business to minimize overstocking and save cost without risking understocking and missing production deadlines.

effectiveness—The measure of how well a job is performed.

efficiency—The ratio of output to input; the greater the ratio, the greater the efficiency.

electronic funds transfer (EFT)—The electronic transfer of cash from an account in one bank to an account in another bank.

electronic product code (EPC)—A product code embedded in a radio frequency identification (RFID) tag. Similar to the older UPC.

employee knowledge network—Software that facilitates search of relevant knowledge within an organization. The software points an employee with need for certain information or expertise to coworkers who might have such information or expertise.

encryption—The conversion of plaintext to an unreadable stream of characters, especially to prevent a party that intercepts telecommunicated messages from reading them. Special encryption software is used by the sending party to encrypt messages, and by the receiving party to decipher them.

enterprise applications—Applications that fulfill a number of functions together, such as inventory planning, purchasing, payment, and billing.

enterprise resource planning (ERP) system—An information system that supports different activities for different departments, assisting executives with planning and running different interdependent functions.

entity—Any object about which an organization chooses to collect data.

entity relationship diagram (ERD)—One of several conventions for graphical rendition of the data elements involved in business processes and the logical relationships among the elements.

ergonomics—The science of designing and modifying machines to better suit people's health and comfort.

Ethernet—The design, introduced and named by Xerox, for the contention-based data communications protocol.

European Article Number (EAN)—A European standard of product code, similar to UPC but containing more information.

expert system (ES)—A computer program that mimics the decision process of a human expert in providing a solution to a problem. Current expert systems deal with problems and diagnostics in narrow domains. An ES consists of a knowledge base, an inference engine, and a dialog management module.

external data—Data that are collected from a wide array of sources outside the organization, including mass communications media, specialized newsletters, government agencies, and the Web.

external memory—Any non-RAM memory, including internal and external hard disks, flash memory, and optical discs.

extranet—A network, part of which is the Internet, whose purpose is to facilitate communication and trade between an organization and its business partners.

feasibility studies—A series of studies conducted to determine if a proposed information system can be built, and whether or not it will benefit the business; the series includes technical, economic, and operational feasibility studies.

field—A data element in a record, describing one aspect of an entity or event. Referred to as attribute in relational databases.

File Transfer Protocol (FTP)—Software that allows the transfer of files over communications lines.

firewall—Hardware and software designed to control access by Internet surfers to an information system, and access to Internet sites by organizational users.

first mover—A business that is first in its industry to adopt a technology or method.

fixed wireless—A network of fixed transceivers to facilitate connection to the Internet. Requires line of sight between transceivers.

flash drive—A storage device containing flash memory. Flash drives are used in numerous electronic devices and often are designed to connect to a computer through a USB port.

flash memory—A memory chip that can be rewritten and can hold its content without electric power. Thumb drives, as well as ROM, are made of flash memory.

foreign key—In a relational database: a field in a table that is a primary key in another table. Foreign keys allow association of data between the two files.

frame relay—A high-speed packet switching protocol used on the Internet.

fulfillment—Picking, packing, and shipping after a customer places an order online.

general-purpose application software—Programs that serve varied purposes, such as developing decision-making tools or creating documents; examples include spreadsheets and word processors.

geographic information system (GIS)—Information system that exhibits information visually on a computer monitor with local, regional, national, or international maps, so that the information can easily be related to locations or routes on the map. GISs are used, for example, in the planning of transportation and product distribution, or the examination of government resources distributed over an area.

Gigabit Ethernet—A network protocol often used in local area networks (LANs) supporting up to 1 Gbps.

global information system—Any information system that crosses national borders.

Global Trade Item Number (GTIN)—A number that uniquely identifies products and services. The GTIN is a global standard succeeding the EAN and UPC.

glocalization—The planning and designing of global Web sites so that they also cater to local needs and preferences.

groupware—Any of several types of software that enable users of computers in remote locations to work together on the same project. The users can create and change documents and graphic designs on the same monitor.

hard disk—A stack of several rigid aluminum platters coated with easily magnetized substance to record data. Usually installed in the same box that holds the CPU and other computer components, but may be portable.

hardware—All physical components of a computer or computer system.

hijacking—In the context of networks, computers that are remotely taken advantage of by people who were not authorized to do so by the lawful owner. The computer is "hijacked" after a controlling application was surreptitiously installed on the computer's hard disk. Hijacked computers are exploited to participate in spamming or DDoS attacks.

honeypot—A duplicate database on a server connected to the Internet to trace an intruder. The server is dedicated specifically for detection of intrusions and is not productive. The honeypot is there to be attacked in lieu of a productive server. The traces can be used to improve security measures and possibly catch the intruder.

honeytoken—A bogus record in a database on a honeypot or productive server that is likely to draw an intruder's attention. If the intruder changes the record, the security officers know that the server has been attacked and can fix vulnerabilities.

host—A computer that contains files and other resources that can be accessed by "clients," computers linked to it via a network.

hot site—A location where a client organization hit by a disaster can continue its vital operations. The structure—often underground—is equipped with hardware and software to support the client's employees.

hotspot—An area, usually of 300-feet radius, in which a wireless device can connect to the Internet. The hotspot is created by installing an access point consisting of a device connected to the Internet on one end and to a router on the other end. All wireless devices link to the Internet through the router.

HTTPS—The secure version of HTTP.

hub—In networking, a device connecting several computers or other electronic devices.

Hypertext Markup Language (HTML)—A programming language for Web pages and Web browsers.

Hypertext Transfer Protocol (HTTP)—Software that allows browsers to log on to Web sites.

Hypertext Transfer Protocol Secure—*See* HTTPS.

identity theft—The criminal practice of obtaining enough personal information to pretend to be the victim, usually resulting in running up that person's credit cards or issuing new credit cards under that person's name.

GLOSSARY

IEEE 802.11—A standard for wireless communication. Several other IEEE 802.x standards have been approved by the Institute of Electrical and Electronics Engineers.

imaging—The transformation of text and graphical documents into digitized files. The document can be electronically retrieved and printed to reconstruct a copy of the original. Imaging has saved much space and expense in paper-intensive business areas.

impression—In Web advertising, the event of an ad displayed on a surfer's monitor.

inference engine—The part of an expert system that links facts and relationships in the knowledge base to reach a solution to a problem.

information—The product of processing data so that they can be used in a context by human beings.

information system (IS)—A computer-based set of hardware, software, and telecommunications components, supported by people and procedures, to process data and turn it into useful information.

information technology (IT)—Refers to all technologies that collectively facilitate construction and maintenance of information systems.

ink-jet printer—Inexpensive type of printer that sprays ink to create the printed text or pictures of a computer-generated document.

input—Raw data entered into a computer for processing.

input device—A tool, such as a keyboard or voice recognition system, used to enter data into an information system.

instant messaging (IM)—The capability for several online computer users to share messages in real time; also called chatting online.

intelligent agent—A sophisticated program that can be instructed to perform services for human beings, especially on the Internet.

internal memory—The memory circuitry inside the computer, communicating directly with the CPU. Consists of RAM and ROM.

Internet Protocol (IP) number—A unique number assigned to a server or another device that is connected to the Internet for identification purposes. Consists of 32 bits.

Internet service provider (ISP)—An individual or organization that provides Internet connection, and sometimes other related services, to subscribers.

interpreter—A programming language translator that translates the source code, one statement at a time, and executes it. If the instruction is erroneous, the interpreter produces an appropriate error message.

intranet—A network using Web browsing software that serves employees within an organization.

join table—In relational database manipulation, a table created by linking—that is, joining—data from multiple tables.

just-in-time (JIT)—The manufacturing strategy in which suppliers ship parts directly to assembly lines, saving the cost of warehousing raw materials, parts, and subassemblies.

key—A field in a database table whose values identify records either for display or for processing. Typical keys are part number (in an inventory file) and Social Security number (in a human resources file).

keystroke logging—Automatically recording the keystrokes of a computer user. The logging is done by special software, usually surreptitiously with the intention of later using secret access codes.

knowledge base—The collection of facts and the relationships among them that mimic the decision-making process in an expert's mind and constitute a major component of an expert system.

knowledge management—The combination of activities involved in gathering, sharing, analyzing, and disseminating knowledge to improve an organization's performance.

LAN (local area network)—A computer network confined to a building or a group of adjacent buildings, as opposed to a wide area network.

late mover—An organization that adopts a technology or method after competitors have adopted it.

liquid crystal display (LCD)—A flat-panel computer monitor in which a conductive-film-covered screen is filled with a liquid crystal whose molecules can align in different planes when charged with certain electrical voltage, which either blocks light or allows it to pass through the liquid. The combination of light and dark produces images of characters and pictures.

load balancing—The transfer of visitor inquiries from a busy server to a less busy server.

logic bomb—A destructive computer program that is inactive until it is triggered by an event taking place in the computer, such as the deletion of a certain record from a file. When the event is a particular time, the logic bomb is referred to as a time bomb.

machine cycle—The steps that the CPU follows repeatedly: fetch an instruction, decode the instruction, execute the instruction, and store the result.

machine language—Binary programming language that is specific to a computer. A computer can execute a program only after the program's source code is translated to object code expressed in the computer's machine language.

magnetic disk—A disk or set of disks sharing a spindle, coated with an easily magnetized substance to record data in the form of tiny magnetic fields.

magnetic tape—Coated polyester tape used to store computer data; similar to tape recorder or VCR tape.

magnetic-ink character recognition (MICR)—A technology that allows a special electronic device to read data printed with magnetic ink. The data are later processed by a computer. MICR is widely used in banking. The bank code, account number, and the amount of a check are printed in magnetic ink on the bottom of checks.

mainframe computer—A computer larger than a midrange computer but smaller than a supercomputer.

management information system (MIS)—A computer-based information system used for planning, control, decision making, or problem solving.

manufacturing execution system—An information system that helps pinpoint bottlenecks in production lines.

manufacturing resource planning (MRP II)—The combination of MRP with other manufacturing-related activities to plan the entire manufacturing process, not just inventory.

many-to-many relationship—In databases, a relationship between two tables whereby every record in a table can be associated with several records in the other table.

master production schedule (MPS)—The component of an MRP II system that specifies production capacity to meet customer demands and maintain inventories.

material requirements planning (MRP)—Inventory control that includes a calculation of future need.

m-commerce—Mobile commerce, enabled by advances in technology for mobile communications devices.

metadata—Information about the data in a database, often called data dictionary.

microcomputer—The smallest type of computer; includes desktop, laptop, and handheld computers.

microprocessor—An electronic chip that contains the circuitry of either a CPU or a processor with a dedicated and limited purpose, for example, a communications processor.

microwaves—Short (high frequency) radio waves. Used in telecommunications to carry digital signals.

midrange computer—A computer larger than a microcomputer but smaller than a mainframe.

migration—The move from old hardware or software to new hardware or software. Migrating a legacy system is the process of adapting the old system to work more efficiently or more effectively, especially when interfacing it with other systems.

MIPS—Millions of instructions per second; an inaccurate measure of computer speed.

mirror—An Internet server that holds the same software and data as another server, which may be located thousands of miles away.

mission-critical applications—Applications without which a business cannot conduct its operations.

Mobile Broadband Wireless Access (MBWA)—IEEE 801.20 standard to support continuous wireless connection while moving in vehicles.

model—A representation of reality.

model management module—A collection of models that a decision-support system draws on to assist in decision making.

modem (modulator/demodulator)—A communications device that transforms digital signals to analog telephone signals, and vice versa, for data communications over voice telephone lines. The term is widely used for all devices that connect a computer to a wide area network, such as the Internet, even if the device does not modulate or demodulate.

modulation—The modification of a digital signal (from a computer) into an analog signal (for a phone line to transmit).

multidimensional database—*See* dimensional database.

multimedia software—Software that processes and displays various forms of information: text, sound, pictures, and video.

multiprocessing—The mode in which a computer uses more than one processing unit simultaneously to process data.

multitasking—The ability of a computer to run more than one program seemingly at the same time; it enables the notion of windows in which different programs are represented.

multithreading—Computer technology that allows more than one stream (thread) of processing at the same time.

network—A combination of a communications device and a computer or several computers, or two or more computers, so that the various devices can send and receive text or audiovisual information to each other.

network administrator—The individual who is responsible for the acquisition, implementation, management, maintenance, and troubleshooting of computer networks throughout the organization.

network interface card (NIC)—Circuitry embedded or installed in a computer to support proper linking of the computer to a network.

network-attached storage (NAS)—An arrangement of storage devices linked to computers through a network.

neural network—An artificial intelligence computer program that emulates the way in which the human brain operates, especially its ability to learn.

node—A device connected to at least one other device on a network.

nonimpact printer—A printer that creates an image on a page without pressing any mechanism against the paper; includes laser, ink-jet, electrostatic, and electrothermal printers.

notebook computer—A computer as small as a book, yet with computing power similar to that of a desktop microcomputer.

object code—Program code in machine language, immediately processable by the computer.

object-oriented database—A database, in which data are part of an object, that is processed using object-oriented programs.

object-oriented programming (OOP) language—A programming language that combines data and the procedures that process the data into a single unit called an "object," which can be invoked from different programs.

OC (optical carrier)—A family of several very high-speed technologies using optical fibers. Usually, the standard is marked as OC-3, OC-12, OC-48, etc.

offshoring—Outsourcing work to employees in other countries.

one-to-many relationship—In a database, a relationship between two tables such that each record in the one table can be associated with several records in the other table but each record in the other table can be associated with only one record in the first table.

online analytical processing (OLAP)—A type of application that operates on data stored in databases and data warehouses to produce summary tables with multiple combinations of dimensions. An OLAP server is connected to the database or data warehouse server at one end and to the user's computer at the other.

open source software—Software whose source code can be accessed by the general public.

open system—A system that interfaces and interacts with other systems.

operating system (OS)—System software that supports the running of applications developed to utilize its features and controls peripheral equipment.

optical disc—A disc on which data are recorded by treating the disc surface so it reflects light in different ways; includes CD and DVD.

optical tape—A storage device that uses the same principles as a compact disc.

organizational culture—An umbrella term referring to the general tone of a corporate environment.

output—The result of processing data by the computer; usually, information.

output device—A device, usually a monitor or printer, that delivers information from a computer to a person.

outsourcing—Buying the services of an information service firm that undertakes some or all of the organization's IS operations.

packaged software—General-purpose applications that come ready to install from a magnetic disk, CD, or file downloaded from a vendor's Web site.

packet—Several bytes that make up a part of a telecommunicated message.

packet switching—A telecommunications method whereby messages are broken into groups of fixed amounts of bytes, and each group (packet) is transmitted through the shortest route available. The packets are assembled at the destination into the original message.

PAN (personal area network)—A network of devices typically within a small radius that enables a user to use two or more devices wirelessly, such as wireless keyboard and mouse.

parallel conversion—Using an old information system along with a new system for a predetermined period of time before relying only on the new one.

parallel processing—The capacity for several CPUs in one computer to process different data at the same time.

parameters—The categories that are considered when following a sequence of steps in problem solving.

peer-to-peer file sharing—Software applications that enable two Internet users to send and receive to each other. The technology is highly objectionable to organizations that sell copyrighted materials because the software promotes violation of copyrights.

peer-to-peer LAN—A local area network (LAN) in which no central device controls communications.

personal digital assistant (PDA)—A small handheld computer. Many PDAs require the use of a special stylus to click displayed items and to enter handwritten information that is recognized by the computer. An increasing number of PDAs also serve as mobile phones, music players, and GPS devices.

phased conversion—Implementing a new information system one module at a time.

phishing—The criminal practice of luring Internet users to provide their personal information via e-mail or the Web. Phishing almost always results in fraud or identity theft.

piloting—A trial conversion in which a new information system is introduced in one business unit before introducing it in others.

pixel—The smallest picture element addressable on a monitor, short for "picture element." In an LCD monitor, it is a triad of three transistors controlling the colors of red, green, and blue that can be switched on and off and kept on with varying amounts of electricity to produce various colors and hues. In a CRT monitor, the triad is made of phosphorous dots that are excited by an electron gun.

plaintext—An original message, before encryption.

plug-and-play—The ability of an operating system to recognize a new attachment and its function without a user's intervention.

podcasting—The practice of posting sound files at a Web site for automating downloading and playing by subscribers.

port—A socket on a computer to which external devices, such as printers, keyboards, and scanners, can be connected. Also, software that enables direct communication of certain applications with the Internet.

primary key—In a file, a field that holds values that are unique to each record. Only a primary key can be used to uniquely identify and retrieve a record.

process—Any manipulation of data, usually with the goal of producing information.

productivity—Efficiency, when the input is labor. The fewer labor hours needed to perform a job, the greater the productivity.

programming—The process of writing software.

programming languages—Sets of syntax for abbreviated forms of instructions that special programs can translate into machine language so a computer can understand the instructions.

project management—The set of activities that is performed to ensure the timely and successful completion of a project within the budget. Project management includes planning activities, hiring and managing personnel, budgeting, conducting meetings, and tracking technical and financial performance. Project management software applications facilitate these activities.

proprietary software—Software owned by an individual or organizations. The owner can control licensing and usage terms of the software. Nonproprietary software is not owned by anyone and is free for use.

protocol—A standard set of rules that governs telecommunication between two communications devices or in a network.

prototyping—An approach to the development of information systems in which several analysis steps are skipped, to accelerate the development process. A "quick and dirty" model is developed and continually improved until the prospective users are satisfied. Prototyping has evolved into agile development methods.

proxy server—A computer that serves as an intermediary between two servers on the Internet, often for the purpose of security or filtering out certain information.

public-key encryption—Encryption technology in which the recipient's public key is used to encrypt and the recipient's private key is used to decrypt.

pure-play—A business operating with clients only via the Web, as opposed to operating via stores or other physical facilities.

radio frequency identification (RFID)—Technology that enables identification of an object (such as product, vehicle, or living creature) by receiving a radio signal from a tag attached to the object.

RAID (Redundant Array of Independent Disks)—A set of magnetic disk packs maintained for backup purposes. Sometimes RAIDs are used for storing large databases.

RAM (random access memory)—The major part of a computer's internal memory. RAM is volatile; that is, software is held in it temporarily and disappears when the machine is unplugged or turned off, or it may disappear when operations are interrupted or new software is installed or activated. RAM is made of microchips containing transistors. Many computers have free sockets that allow the expansion of RAM.

rapid prototyping—Using software and special output devices to create prototypes to test design in three dimensions.

reach percentage—The percentage of Web users who have visited a site in the past month, or the ratio of visitors to the total Web population.

record—A set of standard field types. All the fields of a record contain data about a certain entity or event.

reengineering—The process by which an organization takes a fresh look at a business process and reorganizes it to attain efficiency. Almost always, reengineering includes the integration of a new or improved information system.

relational database model—A general structure of database in which records are organized in tables (relations) and the relationships among tables are maintained through foreign keys.

relational operation—An operation that creates a temporary table that is a subset of the original table or tables in a relational database.

repeater—A device that strengthens signals and then sends them on their next leg toward their next destination.

request for information (RFI)—A request to vendors for general, somewhat informal, information about their products.

request for proposal (RFP)—A document specifying all the system requirements and soliciting a proposal from vendors who might want to bid on a project or service.

resolution—The degree to which the image on a computer monitor is sharp. Higher resolution means a sharper image. Resolution depends on the number of pixels on the screen and the dot pitch.

return on investment (ROI)—A financial calculation of the difference between the stream of benefits and the stream of costs over the life of an information system; often used as a general term to indicate that an investment in an information system is recouped or smaller than the cost the system saves or the increase in revenue it brings about.

reverse auction (name-your-own-price auction)—An online auction in which participants post the price they want to pay for a good or service, and retailers compete to make the sale; also called a name-your-price auction.

RFI (radio frequency interference)—The unwanted reception of radio signals that occurs when using metal communication lines. Optical fibers are not susceptible to RFI.

ROM (read-only memory)—The minor part of a computer's internal memory. ROM is loaded by the manufacturer with software that cannot be changed. Usually,

ROM holds very basic system software, but sometimes also applications. Like RAM, ROM consists of microchips containing transistors.

router—A network hub, wired or wireless, that ensures proper routing of messages within a network such as a LAN and between each device on that network and another network, such as the Internet.

RSS—Really Simple Syndication, a type of application using XML for aggregating updates to blogs and news posted at Web sites.

Safe Harbor—A list of U.S. corporations that have agreed to conform to European Union data protection laws with regard to EU citizens. The arrangement enables the corporations to continue to do business with European companies.

scalability—The ability to adapt applications as business needs grow.

schema—The structure of a database, detailing the names and types of fields in each set of records, and the relationships among sets of records.

search advertising—Placing ads at search engine Web sites.

semistructured problem—An unstructured problem with which the decision maker may have had some experience. Requires expertise to resolve.

sensitivity analysis—Using a model to determine the extent to which a change in a factor affects an outcome. The analysis is done by repeating *if-then* calculations.

sequential storage—A file organization for sequential record entry and retrieval. The records are organized as a list that follows a logical order, such as ascending order of ID numbers, or descending order of part numbers. To retrieve a record, the application must start the search at the first record and retrieve every record, sequentially, until the desired record is encountered.

server—A computer connected to several less powerful computers that can utilize its databases and applications.

service-level agreement—A document that lists all the types of services expected of an outsourcing vendor as well as the metrics that will be used to measure the degree to which the vendor has met the level of promised services. Usually, the client makes the list.

shared hosting—An arrangement by which the Web sites of several clients are maintained by the hosting vendor on the same server.

social engineering—Deceptive methods that hackers use to entice people to release confidential information such as access codes and passwords. Often, the crooks misrepresent themselves as technicians who need one's password for fixing a problem in a network.

software—Sets of instructions that control the operations of a computer.

software as a service (SaaS)—An alternative to developing or licensing software, which enables the client to rent the software through communication lines, usually over the Internet, from an application service provider (ASP).

solid state disk (SSD)—Flash memory that serves as external storage medium as if it were a hard disk.

source code—An application's code written in the original high-level programming language.

source data input device—A device that enables data entry directly from a document without need for human keying. Such devices include bar-code readers and optical character readers.

speech recognition—The process of translating human speech into computer-readable data and instructions.

spyware—A small application stored surreptitiously by a Web site on the hard disk of a visitor's computer. The application tracks activities of the user, including visits to Web sites, and transmits the information to the operator's server.

SSO (single sign-on)—Enabling employees to access several information systems by using a single password.

static IP number—An Internet Protocol number permanently associated with a device.

storage—The operation of storing data and information in an information system.

storage area network (SAN)—A device that enables multiple networked computers to save data on a group of disks located in a special area.

storage service provider (SSP)—A firm that rents storage space for software through an Internet link.

strategic advantage—A position in which one dominates a market; also called competitive advantage.

strategic information system—Any information system that gives its owner a competitive advantage.

structured problem—A problem for whose solution there is a known set of steps to follow. Also called a programmable problem.

Structured Query Language (SQL)—The data definition and manipulation language of choice for many developers of relational database management systems.

stylus—A penlike marking device used to enter commands and data on a computer screen.

subsystem—A component of a larger system.

suite—A group of general software applications that are often used in the same environment. The strengths of the different applications can be used to build a single powerful document. Current suites are usually a combination of a spreadsheet, a word processor, and a database management system.

supercomputer—The most powerful class of computers, used by large organizations, research institutions, and universities for complex scientific computations and the manipulation of very large databases.

supply chain—The activities performed from the purchase of raw material to the shipping of manufactured goods and collecting for their sale.

supply chain management (SCM)—The coordination of purchasing, manufacturing, shipping, and billing operations, often supported by an enterprise resource planning system.

support—The maintenance and provision for user help on an information system.

switching costs—Expenses that are incurred when a customer stops buying a product or service from one business and starts buying it from another.

symmetric (secret or private key) encryption—Encryption technology in which both the sender and recipient of a message use the same key for encryption and decryption.

synergy—From Greek "to work together." The attainment of output, when two factors work together, that is greater or better than the sum of their products when they work separately.

system—An array of components that work together to achieve a common goal or multiple goals.

system clock—Special circuitry within the computer control unit that synchronizes all tasks.

system requirements—The functions that an information system is expected to fulfill and the features through which it will perform its tasks.

system software—Software that executes routine tasks. System software includes operating systems, language translators, and communications software. Also called "support software."

systems analysis—The early steps in the systems development process, to define the requirements of the proposed system and determine its feasibility.

systems analyst—An IT professional who analyzes business problems and recommends technological solutions.

systems design—The evaluation of alternative solutions to a business problem and the specification of hardware, software, and communications technology for the selection solution.

systems development life cycle (SDLC)—The oldest method of developing an information system, consisting of several phases of analysis and design, which must be followed sequentially.

systems integration—Interfacing several information systems.

systems thinking—The approach of thinking of an organization in terms of its suborganizations or systems; a framework for problem solving and decision making.

table—A set of related records in a relational database.

tablet computer—A full-power personal computer in the form of a thick writing tablet.

targeted marketing—Promoting products and services to the people who are most likely to purchase them.

TCP/IP (Transmission Control Protocol/Internet Protocol)—A packet-switching protocol that is actually a set of related protocols that can guarantee packets are delivered in the correct order and can handle differences in transmission and reception rates.

technology convergence—The combining of several technologies into a single device, such as mobile phone, digital camera, and Web browser.

telecommunications—Communications over a long distance, as opposed to communication within a computer, or between adjacent hardware pieces.

throughput—A general measure of the rate of computer output.

time to market—The time between generating an idea for a product and completing a prototype that can be mass-manufactured; also called engineering lead time.

touch screen—A computer monitor that serves both as input and output device. The user touches the areas of a certain menu item to select options, and the screen senses the selection at the point of the touch.

trackball—A device similar to a mouse, used for clicking, locking, and dragging displayed information; in this case, the ball moves within the device rather than over a surface.

track pad—A device used for clicking, logging, and dragging displayed information; the cursor is controlled by moving one's finger along a touch-sensitive pad.

transaction—A business event. In an IS context, the record of a business event.

transaction processing system (TPS)—Any system that records transactions.

transmission rate—The speed at which data are communicated over a communications channel.

Transport Layer Security (TLS)—The successor of Secure Sockets Layer (SSL), the software in the Web browser responsible for secure communication.

Trojan horse—A malicious piece of software hidden with a benign and legitimate software that one downloads or agrees to otherwise accept and install on one's computer. The Trojan horse then causes damage.

twisted pair cable—Traditional telephone wires, twisted in pairs to reduce electromagnetic interference.

Unicode—An international standard to enable the storage and display of characters of a large variety of languages—such as Asian, Arabic, and Hebrew—on computers.

Unified Modeling Language (UML)—An extensive standard for graphically representing elements of programming, specifically accommodating programming in object-oriented languages and Web technologies.

Uniform Resource Locator (URL)—The address of a Web site. Always starts with *http://* but does not have to contain *www*.

uninterruptible power supply (UPS)—A device that provides an alternative power supply as soon as a power network fails.

Universal Product Code (UPC)—A code usually expressed as a number and series of variable width bars that uniquely identifies the product by scanning.

universal serial bus (USB)—A ubiquitous socket that enables the connection of numerous devices to computers.

unstructured problem—A problem for whose solution there is no pretested set of steps, and with which the solver is not familiar—or is only slightly familiar—from previous experience.

upstream—The movement of data from your computer to another computer via a network, usually the Internet. Upstream speed through the services of Internet providers is typically lower than the downstream speed.

uptime—The percentage of time (so much time per year) that an information system is in full operation.

USB drive—Any storage device that connects to a computer through a USB socket, but especially flash drives.

user application development—Development of corporate applications by employees rather than IT professionals.

utilities—Programs that provide help in routine user operations.

value-added network (VAN)—A telecommunications network owned and managed by a vendor that charges clients periodic fees for network management services.

videoconferencing—A telecommunication system that allows people who are in different locations to meet via transmitted images and speech.

virtual memory—Storage space on a disk that is treated by the operating system as if it were part of the computer's RAM.

virtual private network (VPN)—Hardware and software installed to ensure that a network path that includes the Internet enables employees of the same organization or employees of business partners to communicate confidentially. The hardware and software create an impression that the entire communication path is private.

virtual private server—Part of a server that serves as an Internet server for a client of a Web hosting company, while other clients share the same physical server.

virtual reality (VR)—A set of hardware and software that creates images, sounds, and possibly the sensation of touch that give the user the feeling of a real environment and experience. In advanced VR systems, the user wears special goggles and gloves.

virus—Destructive software that propagates and is activated by unwary users; a virus usually damages applications and data files or disrupts communications.

visual programming language—A programming language that provides icons, colors, and other visual elements from which the programmer can choose to speed up software development.

VoIP (Voice over Internet Protocol)—Technologies that enable voice communication by utilizing the Internet instead of the telephone network.

Web hosting—The business of organizations that host, maintain, and often help design Web sites for clients.

Web page authoring tools—Software tools that make Web page composition easier and faster than writing code by providing icons and menus.

Webmaster—The person who is in charge of constructing and maintaining the organization's Web site.

what if analysis—An analysis that is conducted to test the degree to which one variable affects another; also called sensitivity analysis.

wide area network (WAN)—A network of computers and other communications devices that extends over a large area, possibly comprising national territories. Example: the Internet.

Wi-Fi—A name given to the IEEE 802.11 standards of wireless communication. Wi-Fi technologies are used in hotspots and in home and office networks. Wi-Fi is usually effective for a radius of 300 feet.

WiMAX—The IEEE 802.16 standard for wireless networking with a range of up to 50 km (31 miles). (WiMAX stands for the organization that promotes that standard, Worldwide Interoperability for Microwave Access.)

wireless LAN (WLAN)—A local area network that uses electromagnetic waves (radio or infrared light) as the medium of communication. In recent years almost all WLANs have been established using Wi-Fi.

workstation—A powerful microcomputer providing high-speed processing and high-resolution graphics. Used primarily for scientific and engineering assignments.

worm—A rogue program that spreads in a computer network.

XHTML—A standard that combines HTML standards and XML standards.

XML (Extensible Markup Language)—A programming language that tags data elements in order to indicate what the data mean, especially in Web pages.

yield management—Software that helps maximize the capacity of airline seats and hotel rooms by analyzing which variables affect purchasing of such services and in what way.

A

Access (Microsoft), 57, 155, 217, 225, 226, 227, 228
access controls, 453–454, 470
  biometrics, 454
  defined, **453**
  fingerprints, 454
  managing, 430
  passwords, 453–454, 463, 470
  radio frequency identification, 205
  retinal picture, 454
  user IDs, 453
access points (APs), **193**
accounting systems, 72–74
  accounts payable, 72, 73
  accounts receivable, 72, 73
  agile methods, 401
  auditor functions, 73
  budgets, 74
  business function interdependence, 72–74
  cash flow management, 72
  cash management systems, 74
  cost-accounting, 73
  effective vs. efficient, 71
  general ledger, 72, 73
  information systems auditors, 73
  integrated functions, 73–74
  IS functions, 21, 72–73
  ISs illustrated, 73
  managerial uses, 74
  online billing, 85
  payroll, 74
  price determination, 73
  purposes, 72
  recording transactions, 74–75
  reporting functions, 72, 73
  subsystems example, 10
  tracking all expenses, 74
accounts payable, 72, 73
accounts receivable, 72, 73
accurate information, 9,10, 33, 93. *See also* useful information
ACP, 403
Acrobat Reader (Adobe), 48
ActiveNet, 365
active server pages (ASPs), 230, 231, 260
activity diagrams, 395
actor, 395
Adaptive Software Development (ASD), 398

addresses. *See* IP numbers; memory, internal (main); Uniform Resource Locators
ad hoc queries, 226, 227
ad hoc reports, 227
ad hoc team, 390
ADSL. *See* asymmetric DSL
advertising
  Adware, 276
  B2C, 262–264
  banner ads, 263
  Eats2Go case study, 69
  methods, 84, 85, 90
  metrics, 263
  online, 83, 262–264
  pop-up ads, 84, 276
  reach percentage, 263
  spam, 16, 27, 84, 276
  traffic volume, 262
  unique visitor pages, 263
  unique visitors per month, 263
Adware, 276
affiliate programs, **46**, 268–269
Agency Data Systems, 50
agents of change, 23, 54
agile methods, 398–400
  defined, **398**
  development of, 388
  when not to use, 400–401
  when to use, 400, 401
agriculture
  DSS example, 328
  RFID applications, 205
AIM. *See* AOL Instant Messenger
airline industry
  alliances, 50, 266
  business intelligence and knowledge management, 375–376
  competitive advantages, 50–53
  engineering efficiency example, 76
  hotspot example, 194
  mechanical failure ESs, 337–338
  model management use, 323
  online reservations systems, 50
  reverse auctioning, 270
  success story, 51–53
algorithms
  defined, **319**
  encryption, 458–459
  neural networks using, 334
alliances, 45–47
  affiliate programs, 46-47

airline industry, 46, 266
  benefits, 45
  defined, **45**
  establishing, 39, 45–47
  examples, 46–47
  online, 266
  travel industry, 46–47, 266
ALU. *See* arithmetic logic units
analog signals, 189, 198
animal tracking, 205
antecedents, 333
antitheft measures, 205
antivirus software, **448**, 451
AOL Instant Messenger (AIM), 255
AP. *See* access points
Apache, 260
Apple iPod. *See* iPod
applets, **152**
appliances RFID applications, 205
application service providers (ASPs), 432
  alternative to in-house development, 414
  caveat emptor, 427–428
  defined, **425**
  example, 438–439
  vendors, 423–427
application software, 147, 154–158. *See also specific software types*; customed-designed software; packaged software
  activation, 154
  alternatives to in-house development, 414
  classifications, 414
  custom-designed, 154
  defined, **147**
  general features, 154–156
  general-purpose, 154
  groupware, 157
  hypermedia and multimedia, 156–157
  installation location, 425
  office productivity applications, 154–156
  3-D geographic software, 158, 159
  user development, 431
  virtual reality, 157–158
application-specific software, **154**
applications, **147**. *See also specific software*; application software; packaged software
  risks to, 444–450, 470

SUBJECT INDEX

ArcView, 339
arithmetic logic units (ALUs), **116**, 117–118
artificial intelligence (AI). *See also* expert systems
case study. *See* DeBoer Farms case study
defined, **332**
neural nets. *See* neural networks
ASD. *See* Adaptive Software Development
ASNA Visual RPG, 149
ASP. *See* active server pages; application service providers
assemblers, 149, 153
assembly languages, 147, **148**
asymmetric DSL (ADSL), 198–199
asymmetric encryption, **459**, 470
ATM. *See* automated teller machines
atomic transactions, **454**, 454–455, 470
attributes, 222
auctions online
B2B, 264–266
B2C, 270
C2C, 262
entrant barrier example, 41
exchanges vs., 264
Nazi items lawsuit, 299
new service advantage example, 42
reverse auctioning, 41, 270
audit trails, **455**, 455–456, 470
authentication, 457–459, **458**. *See also* encryption
authoring tools, Web page, 156
autocategorization, **368**, 370
automated teller machines (ATMs), 23, 34–35, 50, 101, 444, 449
automating
customer service, 40
sales forces, 86
automation advantage, 40, 51–53
automobile industry
agile methods, 400
design efficiency example, 79
promotional disks, 89
reengineering example, 50
supercomputer use, 113
Web failure example, 54–56

B

backbone (Internet), **192**
backup systems, 111, **452**, 470
backward compatibility, **133**
balance sheet, 72
bandwidth, 184–187. *See also* telecommunications; telecommunications media
baseband, 184
broadband, 184
defined, **184**
international commerce challenges, 293
measurements, 184
speeds, 184, 185, 196, 198
bank information systems, 23
CMSs, 74
data mining, 354
EFTs, 74
input devices, 121
MICR readers, 121
model management use, 323
online banking, 75
security and, 476–477
banner ads, **263**
bar codes, 15
EDI use, 274
monitor and control, 79
RFID microchips replacing, 203
scanning devices, 120
SCM using, 79
shipping industry use, 121–122
barriers, raising, 39, 41
baseband, **184**
BASIC. *See* Beginners All-purpose Symbolic Instruction Code
BearShare, 183
Beginners All-purpose Symbolic Instruction Code (BASIC), 149
benchmarking, **424**, 424–425
benefits management, 91
beta sites, **397**, 422
beta versions, **422**
BI. *See* business intelligence
Big Brother awards, 301
billing online, 85, 270–271
bill of materials (BOM), **78**
biometrics, **454**, 455, 470
bits (binary digits), **112**, 184
bits per second (bps), **184**
BizWorks software, 333–334
blackouts
defined, **443**

example, 469
UPS system protection, 443
bleeding edge, 53, **56**, 56–57, 65
blogs, **253**, 253–254, 298
Blue Gene, 113
Blue Performance software, 51
Bluetooth, 186, **195**, 204
BOM. *See* bill of materials
boundary router, 457
BPL. *See* Broadband over Power Line; electric power lines
bps. *See* bits per second
brainstorming, **75**
brick-and-mortar company, **257**
bridges, **189**
broadband. *See also specific broadband services*; telecommunications media
defined, **184**
growth, 198, 199
subscriber online purchases, 287
Broadband over Power Line (BPL), 187, 198, **202**
broadband telephoning, 202–203
brownouts, **443**
brute-force software, 446
B2B. *See* business-to-business trading
B2C. *See* business-to-consumer trading
budgets, 74
e-commerce control, 272–273
bugs, 149, 163, 176, 177, 233
buses
clock rates, 118
defined, **118**
throughput, 118
business, multimedia in, 157
business continuity plans, 464
business cycle, shortening, 278
business intelligence (BI), 312, 370
data mining and online analysis, 353–363
defined, **20, 353**
intangible benefits, 392
knowledge management, 363–369
business ISs. *See also specific functional areas/sectors*
effectiveness, efficiency in, 70–72
functional areas, 18–21, 71
home-based, 51
interdependence, 70–71
newly-spawned, 22

sectors, 19–21
telecommunications impact, 180–181
understanding ISs advantage, 73
business models, successful, 251, 262, 270
business plan
parts of, 3
writing, 3
business process outsourcing, 417
business recovery plans, **464**, 464–466, 470
business resumption plans, 464
business-to-business (B2B) trading, **262,** 262–266
advertising, 262–264
alliances. *See* alliances
ASPs. *See* application service providers
exchanges and auctions, 264–266
international. *See* global information systems
sales figures, 262–263
supplier network example, 54
business-to-consumer (B2C) trading, **262,** 266–273
advertising, 268–267
auctions online, 270
bill presentment and payment, 270–271
challenges, 268
consumer profiling, 268
content providers, 270
CRM application use, 268
dispersed workforce, 271
e-retailing. *See* e-retailing; e-tailing
international. *See* global information systems
m-commerce, 272–273
online advantages, 268
online traffic volume, 262
payment mechanisms, 270–271
reach percentage, 263
sales figures, 267
top ten sites, 269
unique visitor pages, 263
unique visitors per month, 263
buying. *See* purchasing
bytes, 232
defined, **112**
measurements, 112

C
C, 149, 153
CA. *See* certificate authority
cable
coaxial cable, 185, 186
modems, 190, 197
services, 197, 198
transmission speeds, 184
CAD. *See* computer-aided design
CADUCEUS diagnosis ES, 335
Caller ID, 85
CAM. *See* computer-aided manufacturing
cameras (digital)
converging technologies, 115
flash memory, 128–129
magnetic disks, 127
wireless communications, 194
canned software. *See* packaged software
capacity. *See also* speed
CPUs, 125
telecommunications, 184–202
careers, 22–27
CIOs, 25–26
CSOs, 25
CTOs, 25–26
database administrators, 24
network administrators, 24–25
programmer/analysts, 23–24
systems analysts, 23–24
Webmasters, 25
Carnivore monitoring program, 467
carpal tunnel syndrome, 123
car rental industry. *See* travel industry
Carrier Sense Multiple Access with Collision Detection (CSMA/CD), 193
CASE. *See* computer-aided software engineering
case studies
decision support and business intelligence. *See* DeBoer Farms case study
IS development. *See* QuickBiz Messengers case study
new business development. *See* Eats2Go case study

planning, acquisitions, and control. *See* Worldwide Host case study
Web-enabled commerce. *See* It Fits Outfits case study
cash flow management, 74
cash management, 74
cash management systems (CMSs), **74**
casinos and RFID technology, 82
CASM (cost per available seat-mile), 53
catalog databases, 261, 262
cathode-ray tube (CRT) monitors, 123–124
advantages, 124
color, 123–124
defined, **123**
LCDs vs., 124
mechanics, 123–124
picture sharpness, 124
resolutions, 124
CBIP, 403
CCP, 403
CDMA. *See* Code Division Multiple Access
CDMP, 403
CDs. *See* compact discs
cellular phones, 181–182. *See also* wireless communications
digital cameras, 115
features, 181–182
Internet access, 181–182
mobile commerce, 272
PDAs, 115
censorship, 298
central processing units (CPUs), 116–118. *See also* microprocessors
arithmetic logic units, 116, 117–118
clock rates, 116, 117, 118
control units, 116
data word (word), 117, 118
defined, **112**, 116
functions, 112
illustrated, 117
machine cycles, 116–117
microprocessor, 116
processing capacity, 112, 125
certificate authority (CA), **462**, 470
certification (professional), 402, 403, 404

Cessna Diagnostic and Repair ES, 337
CGI. *See* Common Gateway Interface scripts
characters, **219**
chatting online. *See* instant messaging
checkout systems, 121
chief information officers (CIOs), **25**, 25–26
   duties, 26–26
   performance satisfaction levels, 26
   planning ISs. *See* information systems planning
   sample help wanted ad, 26
   success traits, 26
chief security officers (CSOs), **25**
chief technology officers (CTOs), 25, 25–26
children (database), 318
Chrysler Comprehensive Compensation (C3), 400
churn, customer, 20, 355
CIOs. *See* chief information officers
ciphertext, **458**
circuit switching, **190**, 191
class diagrams, 395
classification (data mining), 354
clear GIF, 233
ClearResearch, 363
clickstream tracking, **255**, 361
clients (outsourcing), 421
clock rates, **117**
closed systems
   defined, **10**
   open vs., 10–11, 27
clustering, 113, 354, 355
CMSs. *See* cash management systems
coaxial cable, **185**, 186
COBOL. *See* COmmon Business Oriented Language
Code Division Multiple Access (CDMA), 196
code translations. *See* language translation
collaboration. *See also* groupware
   IS facilitating, 94
   projects, 93, 94
   software, 94
collaborative logistics, 94
college database example, 225
co-location service, **259**
color CRT monitors, 123–124

commands (OS processing), 159–160
COmmon Business Oriented Language (COBOL), 149, 153
Common Gateway Interface (CGI) scripts, 230, 260
compact discs (CDs)
   defined, **127**
   drive speeds, 128
   read-only memory (CD-ROM), 128
   recordable (CD-R), 128, 132
   rewritable (CD-RW), 128
   training with, 90
   types, 127–128
compatibility issues, 111, 133, 134, 403, 430
compensation management, 91
competition programs (e-tailing) 269
competitive advantage
   achieving, 39–48
   critical mass creating, 42
   defined, **38**
   Eats2Go case study, 37, 59
   first movers creating. *See* first movers
   multiple strategies achieving, 41, 42
   outsourcing risks, 420, 432
   standards creating, 58
   strategic advantage creating, 38, 50
   transient nature, 54, 64
competitive advantage initiatives, 39–48
   alliances, 39, 40, 45–47
   benefits of, 39
   differentiation, 39, 40, 43
   high switching costs, 39, 40, 41–42
   locking in suppliers/buyers, 47–48
   new product, service, 39, 40, 42–43
   product enhancement, 39, 40, 44–45
   raising barriers, 39, 40, 41
   reducing costs, 39, 40, 40
   service enhancement, 39, 40, 44–45
   summary list, 40
   unique product, service, 44–45
compilers, 153–154
   debugging process, 149
   defined, **153**

   illustrated, 153
   interpreters vs., 153–154
complete information, 9, 20. *See also* useful information
composite keys, **224**
computer-aided design (CAD)
   collaborative software, 94
   computers, 114
   defined, **75**, 96
   efficiency example, 75
   workstations, 114
computer-aided manufacturing (CAM), **75**, 114
computer-aided software engineering (CASE), 418, 419
computer classifications, 112–115
   mainframe computers, 113–114
   microcomputers, 114
   midrange computers, 114
   notebook computers, 114
   PDAs, 69, 86, 114
   portables, 114–115
   supercomputers, 113
   tablet computers, 114–115
   workstations, 114
computer communication
   bits (binary digits), 112
   byte measurements, 112
computer costs
   microcomputers (PCs), 114
   purchasing considerations, 131, 132–133
   storage, 131
   supercomputers, 113
computer crime. *See* security; security measures; security risks
computer networks. *See* telecommunications
computer telephony integration (CTI), 85
computer viruses, 447–449, 470
   antivirus software, 448
   defined, **447**
   logic bombs vs., 447–449
   Melissa virus, 447–448
   MSBlast worm, 451
   patches, 447, 451
   Sasser worm, 451
   Slammer worm, 448
   Sobig virus, 448
   Trojan horses, 448
   worms vs., 447–449

computer vision syndrome (CVS), 123
computers. *See also* computer communication; hardware; *specific components*
  advantages, 17
  buses, 118
  compatibility issues, 111, 133, 134
  costs. *See* computer costs
  employee use policies, 432
  evaluating, 132–133, 134
  expandability, 134
  health hazards, 123
  input. *See* input
  IS contributions, 14, 17
  MIPS, 118–119
  output. *See* output; reports
  PDAs, 69, 86
  ports, 132, 134
  power, 118–119, 132, 133, 134
  processing. *See* data processing
  purchasing considerations, 130–131
  speeds, 118–119
  storage. *See* external storage; external storage media; storage
  synergy, 13, 14
  system components, 9–12, 14, 17–18, 27
  throughput, 118
  time increments, 117
  trends, 13
  use statistics, 3
conclusions, 333
construction phase, 395
consumer clustering, 354, 355
consumer privacy, 16, 87–88, 233–234. *See also* privacy issues
  business perspective, 87
  consumer perspective, 87
  database tracking systems, 233–234
  data collection rules, 87–88
  defined, 87
  finances exposed, 233–234
  global information systems, 299
  Gram-Leach-Bliley law, 233
  health-care records, 234
  international laws, 301–303
  profiling issues, 84, 86
consumer profiling, 84, 86, **268**
consumer-to-consumer (C2C), 262
contention-based protocol, 193

content providers, 270
contracts
  crafting, 427
  packaged software, 425
control, loss of through outsourcing, 420, 432
controlling operations, 79–80
controls (systems), 451–456, 470
  access controls, 453–454
  atomic transactions, 454–455
  audit trails, 455–456
  backup systems, 111, 452
  data entry controls, 452
  defined, **451**
  program robustness, 452
control units, **116**
conversion, 396
  cut-over conversion, 396
  defined, **396**
  e-tailing, 269
  flash cut conversion, 396
  parallel conversion, 396
  phased conversion, 396
  pilot conversion, 397
  strategies, illustrated, 397
conversion rate, **269**
cookies, 233, **255**, 255–256, 268, 277, 361
Copy command, 159–160
cost-accounting systems, 72–74
cost/benefit analysis
  defined, **391**
  e-commerce, 272–273
  example, 391
  intangible benefits, 391
  systems development, 391
cost-effective information, 9. *See also* useful information
cost per available seat-mile (CASM), 53
costs
  computers. *See* computer costs
  ERP systems, 95
  external storage media, 131
  hardware evaluation form, 134
  outsourcing impact, 421, 432
  reducing, 39, 40, 419
  SIS development, 49
  software, 167, 168
cost savings with standardization planning, 387–388
country of destination principle, 300
country of origin principle, 299

Covisint, 54, 266
C++, 152, 153
CPUs. *See* central processing units
creating a standard, **48**
creating new and unique products or services, 40, **42**, 42–43
credit cards
  FAST system, 336
  fraud detection software, 334
  industry alliances, 46
  information security, 442
  input devices, 111, 119–122
  neural nets supporting, 334
  transaction process, 18
credit history
  ES use, 336
  firms, 19
  machines making decisions, 329–330
  minimizing risks, 348
credit worthiness decisions, 329–330, 336
crime. *See* security; security measures; security risks
critical mass, **42**
cross-promoted, 73
CRM. *See* customer relationship management
CRTs. *See* cathode-ray tube monitors
Crystal Analysis, 312
Crystal method, 398
CSMA/CD protocol. *See* Carrier Sense Multiple Access with Collision Detection
CSOs. *See* chief security officers
C3. *See* Chrysler Comprehensive Compensation
CTI. *See* computer telephony integration
CTOs. *See* chief technology officers
C2C sites. *See* consumer-to-consumer
cubes (information), 357
cultural differences (international trade), 296
culture, organizational. *See* organizational culture
current information, 9,10, 88. *See also* useful information
custom-designed software, 154, 167, 432
  defined, **415**
  outsourcing, 415–416
customer churn, 20, 355

customer relationship management (CRM), 19, 82–86
  behavior, predicting, 354–356
  customer service, 85–86
  databases, 225
  defined, **19**, **71**
  demographics, inferring, 356
  e-retailers using, 277
  global information uses, 311
  intelligence, 361
  loyalty programs, 356
  market research, 83
  personalizing service, 277
  profiling customers, 84, 86, 275, 277
  purchasing packaged software, 422, 426
  salesforce automation, 86
  target marketing, 84–85
customer service, 85–86
  automating, 40, 86
  case study, 107
  CRM, 86
  proactive approach, 278
cut-over conversion, **396**
CVS. *See* computer vision syndrome
cyberspace legal jurisdictions, 299–300
cycle time, 278

D

DAS. *See* direct access storage
dashboard, 258, **362**, 362–363, 370
data
  alteration, 446–447, 470
  as IS component, 14
  characters, 219, 220, 225
  defined, **7**, 14
  destruction, 446–447, 470
  encryption. *See* encryption
  hierarchy, 219, 220
  information vs., 7
  manipulation, 8
  program/data dependency, 218
  risks to, 444–450
  traditional file approach, 218–219
database administrators (DBAs)
  career duties, skills, 24
  defined, **24**, **221**
  responsibilities, 24
  sample help wanted ad, 24

database approach, **219**, 219–222
database management systems (DBMSs), 218–222
  database approach, 219–222
  defined, 219–220
  functions, 219–221
  hierarchy, 220
  languages, 227
  metadata, 228
  mismanagement, 232
  modeling, 229–230
  models, 222–226
  open source software, 163–165
  queries, 221
  security, 222
  targeting markets, 84–85
  tools, 155
  traditional file approach, 218–219
  vendors, 225
  Web, 230–231
database models, 222–226
  defined, 222
  hierarchical model, 220
  object-oriented model, 225–226
  overview, 222
  pros/cons, 222–226
  relational model. *See* relational databases
databases. *See also* database management systems (DBMSs)
  advantages, 218
  building, 219–222
  business impact, 218
  characters, 219
  data hierarchy, 219, 220
  defined, **11**
  dimensional, 357
  entities, 219
  fields, 219
  files, 219
  functions, 24
  illustrated, 20, 24
  models. *See* database models
  multidimensional, 357
  overview, 218
  process to data warehouse, 234–235
  QuickBiz Messengers case study, 105–108
  records, 219
  tracking every move, 233

traditional file approach vs., 218–219
  Web-based. *See* Web databases
data dictionary, **228**
data entry controls, 452
data flow diagrams (DFDs), 393–394, 404
  defined, **393**
  illustrated, 394
  symbols, 393, 394
  uses, 393–394
data integrity, **219**
data management module, **322**, 322–323
data marts, **232**
data mining, 85, 235, 312, 354, 370
  banking industry, 354
  classifications, 354
  clustering, 354, 355
  customer behavior, predicting, 354–356
  customer churn identification, 355
  customer intelligence, 361
  defined, **354**
  demographics, inferring, 356
  direct marketing, 355
  executive dashboards, 362–363
  forecasting, 354
  fraud detection, 354, 355, 455
  industries using, 354–356
  interactive marketing, 355
  loyalty programs, utilizing, 356
  marketing applications, 355
  marketing basket analysis, 355
  objectives, 354
  OLAP applications, 312, 357–361
  online analysis, 353–354
  sequence/path analysis, 354
  trend analysis, 355
data modeling, **229**, 229–230
data processing, 15. *See also specific stages*
  computer contribution, 17, 18
  defined, **15**
  speeds, 131
  stages, 15–17
data redundancy, **218**, 469, 470
data store, 393
data warehouses, 231–232
  accessibility, 233–234
  building, 235–236
  data marts vs., 232

data mining, 85, 235
defined, **20**, **232**
ETL process, 235–236
example, 233–234
functions, 231–232
hardware, 234–235
illustrated, 20
process to, 234–235
scalability, 235
data word (word), **117**, 118
datum, 7. *See also* data
DB Intelligent Miner, 355
DBAs. *See* database administrators
DBMS. *See* database management
systems
DB2, 225
DdoS. *See* distributed denial-of-
service
DeBoer Farms case study
background, 313
business challenges, 315
data mining and analysis,
352–353
DSS use/issues, 317–318
ES use, 313–315, 343
IT systems, 313–315
debugging. *See also* error detection
bugs, 233
defined, **149**
new IS systems, 397
decision, defined, 7
decision making. *See also* decision
support systems
case study, 6–7
choice phase, 319
design phase, 319
information needs, 7
intelligence phase, 319
models, 319
phases, 319
process, 318–319
semistructured problems, 320–321
structured problems, 319–321
support, 318
unstructured decisions, 320
unstructured problems, 319–321
decision support aids, 321
decision support systems (DSSs),
20, 316–350. *See also* decision
making
case study. *See* DeBoer Farms
case study
components, 322

data management module,
322–323
defined, 20, 27, **321**
dialog module, 325–326
electronic spreadsheets, 154
examples, 327–332
functions, 20, 322
graphical results, 325–326
illustrated, 322
linear regression model, 324–325
machines making decisions,
329–330
manager uses, 320
model management module,
323–325
overview, 20, 321–322
sensitivity analysis, 326–327
software, 322, 323–325, 327
systems intertwined with, 322
tax decision software, 328
Web-enabled, 330
dedicated servers, **258**
defacement, Web, 446–447
delivery. *See* implementation
phase (SDLC)
Delphi, 149
demilitarized zone (DMZ)
security, **456**
demographics, 356
denial of service (DoS), **450**, 470
desktop publishing, 155
devices
input, 17
output, 17
process, 17
storage, 17
DFDs. *See* data flow diagrams
(DFDs)
diagnosis ESs
mechanical systems, 337–338
medical systems, 335
dialog module, **325**, 325–326
dial-up connections, **190**, 198
differentiation
competitive advantage, 43
defined, **43**
digital cameras. *See* cameras (digital)
digital certificates, 462–463, 470
contents, 462
defined, **462**
encryption, 462–463
illustrated, 462, 463
issuers, 462

Digital Linear Tape (DLT), 126
digital signals, 85, 189, 190, 193, 202
digital signatures, **460**, 460–462
digital subscriber line (DSL), 190
ADSL, 198–199
defined, **198**
modems, 190
services, 197–198
transmission speeds, 184
digital versatile disks. *See* digital
video disks
digital video disks (DVDs), **128**
dimensional databases, **357**
direct access, **125**
direct access storage (DAS), 129
advantages, 129
defined, **125**, 129
media, 129
Directive on Data Privacy,
302–303, 329
disaster recovery plans, 464
Discern Expert, 336
distributed denial-of-service
(DDoS), **450**
DLT. *See* Digital Linear Tape
DMZ security. *See* demilitarized
zone security
DNS. *See* Domain Name System
documentation
system development, 398
user-developed applications,
398, 431, 432
domain, 332
domain names
defined, **251**
top-level, 251
Domain Name System (DNS), **192**
DoS. *See* denial of service
DOS (Disk Operating System), 55
dot-matrix printers, **125**
downstream, **197**
downtime, 260, 261, **442**, 468–469
Dreamweaver (Macromedia), 152
drilling down, **357**, 370
drivers, **161**
DSDM. *See* Dynamic Systems
Development Method
DSL. *See* digital subscriber line
DSSs. *See* decision support systems
duplication of resources, 431, 432
DVD/CD-RW drives, 128
DVDs. *See* digital video disks
Dvorak keyboards, 119

dynamic IP numbers, **192**
Dynamic Systems Development
    Method (DSDM), 398
dynamic Web page, **259**

E

EAN. *See* European Article Number
Eats2Go case study
    adding new line, 37
    advertising/promotion, 69–70
    business challenges, 6, 28,
        37–38, 59, 97
    competitive advantage, 37, 59
    data management, 7
    expansion considerations, 37, 69
    information systems, 7, 37
    making decisions, 6
    reports, 68
    solving problems, 6
    start-up planning, 1–4
    strategic planning, 37–38, 59
EBBP. *See* electronic bill present-
    ment and payment
e-commerce, **22**, 301, 302. *See also*
    business-to-business trading;
    business-to-consumer trading;
    e-commerce practices;
    e-commerce sites; e-retailing;
    e-tailing
    controls. *See* controls (systems)
    defined, 22
    establishing sites. *See* e-commerce
        sites
    evolution, 22
    fraud. *See* fraud detection
    information control, 273
    international commerce. *See*
        global information systems
    management challenges/solu-
        tions, 272–273
    scalability, 260, 261
    security. *See* security; security
        measures; security risks
e-commerce practices, 284–300. *See*
    also business-to-business trading;
    business-to-consumer trading
    alliances. *See* alliances
    ASPs. *See* application service
        providers
    auctions, 264–266
    customer service, 275–277
    example, 245–247
    FAQs, 278

fulfillment, 278
mobile technology, 272–273
owning customer experience, 277
proactive approach, 277
shortening business cycle, 278
targeting customers. *See* targeted
    marketing
transaction rules, 275–278
e-commerce sites, 257
    dedicated servers, 258
    electronic storefronts, 218, 267
    evaluating service providers,
        259–261
    hosting alternatives, 257–259
    ISP hosting, 257
    scalability, 260
    security. *See* security; security
        measures; security risks
    server options, 257
    technical support, 260
    virtual Web servers, 258
    Web hosting services, 259–261
    Web portals, 258
economical information, 9, 10
economic interests (international
    trade), 296–297
economic feasibility study, 389,
    391–392
    cost/benefit analysis, 391
    example, 391
    intangible benefits, 391–392
    ROI analysis, 391
    sample spreadsheet, 391
economic order quantity (EOQ), **78**
economics of information security,
    466–469
EDI. *See* electronic data interchange
education, multimedia in, 157
effectiveness
    defined, **70**
    efficiency vs., 70–72
efficiency
    defined, **70**
    effectiveness vs., 70–72
    mathematic equation, 70
    resource utilization, 431, 432
    telecommunications
        increasing, 181
EFT. *See* electronic funds transfer
802.11 standards. *See* IEEE 802.11
    standards
802.15 standards. *See* IEEE 802.15
    standards

802.16 standards. *See* IEEE 802.16
    standards
802.20 standards. *See* IEEE 802.20
    standards
EIM. *See* enterprise incentive
    management
electric power lines (BPL), 185, 187
electromagnetic interference
    (EMI), **185**
electronic bill presentment and
    payment (EBBP), 271
electronic commerce. *See*
    e-commerce; e-commerce prac-
    tices; e-commerce sites; e-retailing
electronic data interchange
    (EDI), 188
    value-added networks (VANs),
        273–275
electronic data processing
    auditor, 456
electronic funds transfer (EFT), **74**
electronic product code (EPC), **81**,
    203, 272
electronic spreadsheets. *See*
    spreadsheets
electronic storefronts, 218, 267
e-mail
    business communication, 180
    marketing, 16, 84, 321
    open source, 163
    spamming, 16, 84, 276
    viruses. *See* computer viruses
    Web-based e-mail, 252–253
embedding. *See* object linking and
    embedding
EMI. *See* electromagnetic interference
employee knowledge networks,
    364–367, **365**, 370
employee record management, 88
employees
    computer use policies, 432
    evaluations, 91
    IS careers. *See* careers
    outsourcing impact, 420, 432
    privacy, 16
    record management, 88
    skill acquisition, 430, 432
    telecommuting, 51, 181,
        200–201
encapsulation, **225**
encryption, 457–459, **458**, 470
    algorithms, 458
    asymmetric, 459

authentication, 457–459
ciphertext, 458
defined, **193**
example, 458
government export, 298
keys, 459–460
PGP software, 296
plaintext, 458
private key, 459
protocols, 193
public key, 459–460
secret key, 459, 460
symmetric, 459
engineering, 75–77
brainstorming, 75
business function interdependence, 75–77
CAD, 75
CAM, 75
design efficiency examples, 75–77
design technologies, 75–77
ISs illustrated, 76
IT contributions, 75–77
lead time, 75
rapid prototyping, 75, 77
time to market, 75, 77
enhancing existing products or
services, 39, 40, **44**, 44–45,
48–50
enterprise applications systems, **18**,
18–19, 27. *See also* enterprise
resource planning systems
enterprise incentive management
(EIM), 101
enterprise resource planning (ERP)
systems, 18–19, 95, 377
accessing, 464
alternative names, 18, 71
costs, 95
defined, **18**, **95**
failures, 469
features, 95
global business, 310
installing,
locking in buyers, 47–48
outsourcing. *See* outsourcing
purchasing packaged software,
422, 423
SCM systems, 71, 95
systems integration, 401
tailoring, 95
vendors, 95

enterprise software applications,
13, 49. *See also* enterprise
resource planning systems
Enterprise Virtual Operations
Center (EVOC), 214–215
entities, **219**
entity relationship (ER) diagram,
229, 229–230
EOQ. *See* economic order quantity
EPC. *See* electronic product code
ER diagram. *See* entity relationship
diagram
e-recruiting, 89–90
e-retailing, 267–269. *See also*
business-to-consumer trading;
e-commerce; e-commerce practices; e-commerce sites; e-tailing
pop-up ads, 84, 276
reach percentage, 263
traffic volume, 262
unique visitor pages, 263
unique visitors per month, 263
ergonomic keyboards, 119
ergonomics, **119**, 133, 134
ERP systems. *See* enterprise resource
planning systems
error detection
bugs, 149, 163, 176, 177
compilers vs. interpreters,
153–154
debugging, 149
telecommunications, 191
ES. *See* expert systems; expert systems examples
e-tailing, 267–268
affiliate programs, 268–269
competition, 269
conversion, 269
Ethernet, 192–193
defined, **192**
Gigabit Ethernet, 193
network cards, 190
ethical/social issues, 16–17
employee privacy, 16
freedom of speech, 16
IT professionalism, 17
legal jurisdictions, 299–300
machines making decisions,
329–330
Microsoft monopoly issue, 55–56
online annoyances, 16, 276–277
privacy issues. *See* consumer
privacy; privacy issues

software piracy, 166
spamming, 84, 276
telecommuting, 51, 181,
200–201
ETL (extracting, transformation,
loading) process
European Article Number (EAN), **300**
evaluating
external storage media, 130–132
hardware, 132–133, 134
software, 167–168
evaluations (employee), 91
EVOC. *See* Enterprise Virtual
Operations Center
exabyte, 232
Excel (Microsoft) 57, 149, 154,
155, 348
exchanges, 264–266
executive dashboards, 362–363, 370
EXNUT Irrigator Pro software, 337
expertise, 332
expert systems (ESs), 20, 332–350.
See also expert systems examples
advantages, 20
components, 332–334
defined, **20**, 27, **332**
development, 332
if-then rules, 332–333, 336
illustrated, 333
inference engines, 332
knowledge base, 332
purposes, 332–334
shared data resources, 20
expert systems (ESs) examples, 335
credit evaluation, 336
insider-trading detection, 336–337
irrigation, 337
mechanical failure diagnosis,
337–338
medical diagnosis, 335
medical management, 336
metal detection, 337
mineral exploration, 337
pest management, 337
telephone network mainte-
nance, 336
Extensible Hypertext Markup
Language (XHTML), **252**
Extensible Markup Language
(XML), **252**
EDI with, 275
functions, 252
nonproprietary language, 152

tags, 252
Web technologies, 274
external entities, 393
external memory, **112**
external storage, 125–132
external storage media, 125–132
    access modes, 125–127
    capacities, 130
    CDs. *See* compact discs
    comparison chart, 132
    costs, 131
    data volume requirements, 130
    direct access storage, 125, 129
    DVDs, 128
    evaluating, 130–132
    flash memory, 128–129
    floppy disks, 127
    life expectancy, 131
    magnetic disks, 127
    magnetic tapes, 126–127
    optical disks, 127–128
    optical tape, 128
    portability, 131
    reliability, 131, 133
    sequential storage, 125
    speed, 131
    storage purpose, 130
    trade-offs, 151
    virtual memory, 161
extracting, transformation, loading
    (ETL) process, 235–236
extranets
    business contributions, 264–266
    cost savings, 265
    defined, **264**
    functions, 264–265
    illustrated, 264–265
Extreme Programming (XP), 398,
    399–400
EyeD Mouse, 454
eye strain, 123

F
facsimiles. *See* faxes
Falcon software, 334
FAQs. *See* Frequently Asked
    Questions
farm industry
    case study. *See* DeBoer Farms
    case study
    irrigation ESs, 337
    pest management ESs, 337

FAST. *See* Financial Analysis
    Support Techniques
faxes, **182**
FDD. *See* Feature Driven
    Development
feasibility studies, 404
    defined, **390**
    economic, 389, 391–392
    operational, 389, 392
    technical, 389, 390
Feature Driven Development
    (FDD), 398
FedScope, 358
fields, **219**
file, **219**
file management, 155
file sharing (P2P), 183
file transfer, 252–253
File Transfer Protocol (FTP), **252**,
    252–253
finance ISs, 74–75
    analysis functions, 74
    business function interdepend-
    ence, 74–75
    cash management, 74
    CMSs, 74
    credit worthiness decisions,
    329–330, 336
    EFTs, 74
    goal, 74
    illustrated, 74
    investment analysis and
    service, 75
    IS contributions, 22, 74–75
    management objectives, 74
    multi-dimensional management
    tools, 84
    optimizing earning power, 74–75
    transaction speeds, 75
Financial Analysis Support
    Techniques (FAST), 336
financial planning, improve
    through outsourcing, 418
financial services DSS example,
    331–332
fingerprint access controls, 454
Firefox, 163, 164, 463
firewalls, 163, **456**, 456–457, 470
first-generation languages, 148
first movers
    bleeding edge, 56–57
    competitive advantage, 42

defined, **42**
late movers vs., 53
limited benefit, 42, 56–57
risks, 56–57
Web success and, 42–43
fixed costs reduced through out-
    sourcing, 418, 432
fixed wireless, 198, **199**, 201
flash cut conversion, **396**
flash drives, **126**
flash memory, **128**, 128–129, 132
flash ROM, 112
Flash software, 48
flat-panel monitors, **124**
floppy disks. *See* magnetic disks
FoodPro, 327
food production DSS example,
    327–328
forecasting (data mining), 354
foreign key, **225**
forms online. *See* Common
    Gateway Interface scripts
FORTRAN (FORmula TRANslation),
    149, 153
4GLs. *See* fourth-generation
    languages
fourth-generation languages
    (4GLs), 148, 149
    advantages, 148–149
    comparison chart, 148
    disadvantages, 148–149
    popular languages, 148–149
    3GL vs., 148–149
frame relay, **191**
fraud detection
    data mining for, 354, 355
    data warehousing, 231
    DSSs, 331
    electronic bill presentment and
    payment, 271
    neural networks for, 334
    PayPal, 287
    phishing, 277
freedom of speech, 16, 299
free software, 163, 165
    graphics, 155
    open source software, 163–165
    remote collaboration, 94
    suite, 155
Frequently Asked Questions (FAQs),
    86, 278
FrontPage (Microsoft), 152, 260

FTP. *See* File Transfer Protocol
fulfillment, **267**, 278
Future Bank, 101

G

Gaim, 255
GAIN. *See* Global Aviation
 Information Network
gas stations, purchase
 technology, 182
GB. *See* gigabyte
Gbps, 184
GDP (gross domestic product), 91, 94
general ledger, 72, 73
General Public License (GPL), 166
general-purpose application software, **154**
geographical information systems
 (GISs), 338–341
 components, 339
 defined, **20**, 27, **338**
 examples, 20–21, 338–340
 functions, 20–21, 339–340
 illustrated, 339, 341
 vendors, 340
GEO satellites. *See* geostationary
 satellites
geostationary (GEO) satellites, 186
Gigabit Ethernet, **193**
giga bps, 184
gigabyte (GB), 112
GISs. *See* geographical information
 systems
GLBA. *See* Gramm-Leach-Bliley law
Global Aviation Information
 Network (GAIN), 375–376
global information systems,
 288–304
 bandwidth challenges, 293
 case study, 289–290, 305
 challenges, 293–304
 conflicting interests, 296–297
 cultural differences, 296
 defined, **290**
 field size challenges, 294
 intellectual property issues,
 41, 297
 international commerce, 291–293
 language challenges, 294,
 295–296
 legal barriers, 295, 301
 legal jurisdictions, 299–300

multinational organizations,
 290–291
 payment mechanisms, 295
 political challenges, 297–298
 privacy laws, 301–303
 regulations, 294–295
 software, 297
 standards, 298–301
 tariffs, 294–295
 technological challenges,
 293–294
 time zones, 304
 web commerce, 291–293
globalization, 366, 416
global positioning systems (GPS),
 21, 176
 converging technologies, 115
 satellite, 199
 3-D geographic software, 158, 159
Global System for Mobile (GSM), 196
Global Trade Item Numbers
 (GTINs), 301
glocalization, **292**
GoLive, 152
GoreTex, 376
GoToMyPC software, 444
government
 Big Brother awards, 301
 censorship, 298
 crime and terrorism, protection
 against, 467, 470
 global politics, 297–298
 international commerce regulations, 301–303
 international laws. *See* legal
 issues (international)
 jurisdiction, 299–300
GPL. *See* General Public License
Gramm-Leach-Bliley law (GLBA),
 233, 442
graphical information
 databases, 325–326
 DSSs, 325–326
 trend analysis, 355
graphical user interfaces (GUIs),
 152, 225, 227
graphics software, 155
gross domestic product (GDP), 91, 94
groupware, 157
 collaborative projects, 94
 defined, **157**
 software, 157

GSM. *See* Global System for Mobile
GTINs. *See* Global Trade Item
 Numbers
GUIs. *See* graphical user interfaces

H

hackers, 442, 477
handheld computers, 114. *See also*
 personal digital assistants
handheld devices. *See* cameras (digital); personal digital assistants
hard copies, output devices, 112
hard disks, **127**. *See also* magnetic
 disks
hard drives. *See* magnetic disks
hardware, 109–144. *See also specific
 components*
 as IS component, 13, 14
 compatibility issues, 111, 133, 134
 components, 111–112
 data warehousing, 234–235
 defined, **111**
 evaluating, 132–133, 134
 footprint, 133, 134
 input devices. *See* input devices
 language understood, 203
 networking, 189–190
 purchasing considerations,
 132–133, 134
 scalability, 129, 133
 security risks, 443–444, 470
 support, 134
 updating, 133–135
 vendors, 417
 warranty, 134
 wireless cards, 132
HCM. *See* human capital
 management
HDTV. *See* high definition television
health-care industry
 database management
 systems, 234
 ES applications, 335, 336
 HIPAA, 234
 medical diagnosis ESs, 335
 medical management ESs, 336
 modeling, 349
 RFID applications, 205
health hazards, 123
Health Insurance Portability and
 Accountability Act of 1996
 (HIPPA), 234, 442
hierarchical database model, 220

high definition television (HDTV), 251
higher-level programming
　advantages, 148–149
　disadvantages, 148–149
hijacking, **450**, 450–451, 470
HIPPA. *See* Health Insurance Portability and Accountability Act of 1996
hits, 261
holes (security), 444
home pages, 43, 233, 330. *See also* Web pages
Home Publishing (Microsoft), 155
honeypots, **447**
honeytokens, **447**
host, **192**
hosting services, 257–259
　selecting, considerations, 259–261
host language, 227
hot sites, **466**, 470
hotspots
　airline example, 194
　cities with, 195
　defined, **193**
　m-commerce, 272
　VoIP technology, 202–203
HTML. *See* Hypertext Markup Language
HTTP. *See* Hypertext Transfer Protocol
HTTPS. *See* Hypertext Transfer Protocol Secure
HTTP Secure. *See* Hypertext Transfer Protocol Secure
hubs, **189**
human capital management (HCM), 102
human resource (HR) management, 88. *See also* employees
　benefits management, 91
　business function interdependence, 71–72
　compensation management, 91
　employee record management, 88
　evaluation, 91
　IS contributions, 22
　ISs illustrated, 89
　IT resources. *See* information systems management
　performance evaluations, 91
　promotion, 88, 90
　recruiting activities, 88

semistructured problems, 321
　training, 90
Hurricane Katrina, 464
hypermedia, **156**, 156–157
hypertext, 156
Hypertext Markup Language (HTML), 252
　defined, **252**
　functions, 252
　nonproprietary language, 152
　tags, 252
Hypertext Transfer Protocol (HTTP)
　defined, **251**
　functions, 251–252
Hypertext Transfer Protocol Secure (HTTPS), **251**, **460**, 470

I
ICQ, 255
ID device, 467
identity theft, 271, 444–446, **445**, 470
IE. *See* Internet Explorer
IEEE 802.11 standards, **193**, 193–194, 196
IEEE 802.15 standards, 195, 196
IEEE 802.16 standards, 195, 196
IEEE 802.20 standards, 195, 196
if-then rules, 332–333, 336
Illustrator, 155, 157
IM. *See* instant messaging
imaging devices, 111, **122**
I-mode standard, 272
impact analysis (business recovery plan), 465
impact printers, **125**
implementation phase (SDLC), 396, 404
　conversion phase, 396
　cut-over conversion, 396
　defined, **396**
　delivery, 396
　flash cut conversion, 396
　illustrated, 397
　parallel conversion, 396
　phased conversion, 396
　pilot conversion, 397
　project management. *See* project management
　shortened through outsourcing, 419, 432
　steps, 396

support, 425
　training, 396
impression, **263**
inference engines, **332**
information. *See also* information systems (ISs); useful information
　business intelligence, **20**, 312
　content providers, 270
　data vs., 7
　defined, **7**
　e-commerce control, 272–273
　generating, 8–9
　graphical, 325
　islands of, 431, 432
　multiple dimensions, 75
　OLAP applications, 312
　processes creating, 9
　theft, 444–446, 470
information cubes, 357
information maps, **12**, 12–13
information systems (ISs). *See also* business Iss
　applications risks, 444–450
　careers, 32–27
　categories, 18–21
　college degrees, 12
　components, 17, 27
　contributions, 7–17
　data risks, 444–450
　defined, **11**
　development. *See specific development phases*; systems development; systems development life cycle
　hardware risks, 443–444
　in business functions, 21–22
　in organizations, 13
　managers and, 11, 22–26
　planning, 385–386, 388
　purposes, 7
　risks to, 442–450
　security. *See* controls (systems); security; security measures; security risks
　standardization planning, benefits of, 387–388, 404
　steps in planning, 386–387
　trends supporting use, 13
　types of, 18–21
information systems auditors, **456**
information systems management careers. *See* careers

multinational organizations, 290–291

staff time, freeing up, 431, 432

information technology (IT)

competitive advantage, 39–40

defined, **13**

outsourcing, 417–421

professionalism, 17, 402, 404

professionals' reaction, managing, 428

resource management. *See* information systems management

infrared input devices, 15

inheritance, **225**

initial public offering (IPO), 66

ink-jet printer, 124, 125

input

defined, **15**

process, 15

process, output and, 8–9

transaction recording, 15

input and output (I/O) devices, 119–125

input devices, 111, 119–122

banking industry devices, 121

bar code scanners, 121–122

credit cards, 121

defined, **111**

imaging devices, 122

keyboards, 111, 119

mice, 111

MICR devices, 121

optical recognition devices, 120–121

shipping industry use, 121–122

source data devices, 120–122

speech recognition devices, 111, 115, 122

touch screens, 120

trackballs, 119–120

trackpads, 119–120

wireless, 120

insider-trading ES detection, 336–337

instant messaging (IM), **254**, 254–255

instant transactions, 181

insurance, mapping risk, 350

insurance fraud prevention, 334

intangible benefits, 391–392

integrated software, 102, 155, 157, 294

integration. *See* systems integration

intellectual property, 41, 297

intelligent interface, 361

interaction diagrams, 395

interactive marketing, 355

interface, smooth, 415, 432

internal memory, **112**. *See also* memory, internal (main)

international commerce, 291–292. *See also* global information systems

Internet. *See also specific applications*; Internet applications; World Wide Web

advertising, 84–85

backbone, 192

defined, 22

employee recruiting, 88–90

extranet routing, 190

facilitating JIT, 79

government use, 74

intranet routing, 190

marketing. *See* marketing

market research, 83

mechanics. *See* Internet mechanics

Microsoft monopoly issue, 55–56

mobile browsing, 54, 85

networking services, 197–202

pop-up ads, 84, 276

P2P file sharing, 183

TCP/IP, 192

wireless connections, 69, 79–80, 86, 193–197

Internet access

cable. *See* cable

cellular phones, 181–181

dial-up connections, 184, 188, 190

DSL. *See* digital subscriber line

IP numbers, 192

ISPs, 189, 192, 199, 202

modems, 189–190

wireless, 69, 79–80, 86

Internet appliances, 125, 126–127

Internet applications. *See also* Web technologies

blogs, 253–254

e-mail. *See* e-mail

FTP, 243–254

newsgroups, 253

telephoning, 202–203

Web browsers. *See specific browsers*; Web browsers

Internet Explorer (IE; Microsoft)

antitrust lawsuit, 55

digital certificate, 463

dominating market, 57, 164

mapping risk, 350

market share, 55

risks, 445

setting standard, 55

Internet mechanics, 191–197

DNS servers, 192

domain names, 251–252

IP numbers, 192

URLs, 251–252

Internet networking services. *See* telecommunications services

Internet Protocol (IP), 189

Internet Protocol numbers. *See* IP numbers (addresses)

Internet service providers (ISPs)

defined, **189**

hosting services, 257–259

resolving domain names, 251–252

wireless, 199, 201

interpreters

compilers vs., 153–154

defined, **153**

error detection, 153

pros/cons, 153

intranets

defined, **88**, **264**

functions, 88, 91, 190, 264, 272, 339

inventory control. *See also* manufacturing sector; supply chain management

BOMs, 78

business function interdependence, 77–78

components list, 78

EOQ, 78

ISs illustrated, 78

MRP, 78–79

optimal raw materials, 78

red zone, 363

retail sector, 15

source data input devices, 121–122

trends, 94

investigation (systems analysis), 389, 390

investment

analysis and service, 75

downtime losses, 260, 261

insider-trading detection ES, 336–337
semistructured problems, 321
I/O devices. *See* input and output devices
IP. *See* Internet Protocol
IP numbers (addresses)
    address components, 251
    defined, **192**
    domain name resolution, 251–252
    registering, 251
IPO. *See* initial public offering
iPod, 254
IrfanView, 155
irrigation ES, 337
ISA, 403
islands of information, 431, 432
I.S.P., 403
ISPs. *See* Internet service providers
IS professionals. *See specific job titles*; careers; managers
ISs. *See* information systems
IT. *See* information technology
It Fits Outfits case study
    blogs and chats, 250
    business concept, 245–246
    business planning, 246
    connecting to customers, 249
    e-commerce, 247
    establishing Web operations, 249, 280
    e-zine, 250
    global expansion, 289–290, 305
    virtual world, 249–250
    warehousing, supply and IT, 246

J

Java, 152, 153
JavaScript, 152
Java servlets, 230, 260
Java2EE, 152
JetBlue case study, 51–53
    automating services, 51–52
    CASM, 53
    cost reductions, 51, 53
    electronic ticketing, 51
    enhanced service, 51–53
    flight planning, 51–52
    ground communication, 52
    innovative routing, 52
    late mover advantage, 53
    maintenance systems, 52
    paperless systems, 51–52

performance data, 51–52
strategic advantages, 51–53
JIT. *See* just-in-time
join operation, 227
join table, **225**
jurisdiction (government), 299–300
just-in-time (JIT)
    defined, **79**
    example, 79
    Internet facilitating, 79
    mechanics, 79
    RFID tags facilitating, 203–204

K

KaZaA, 183
KB. *See* kilobyte
Kbps, 184
keyboards, 111, 119
    Dvorak keyboard, 119
    ergonomic, 119
    illustrated, 115
    QWERTY keyboard, 119
keyfob, 464
keys (database), 222, 224
    composite key, 224
    foreign key, 225
    primary key, 224
keys (encryption), 193, 459, 460, 470
keystroke logging, **444**
keywords, 13, 230, 312
kilobyte (KB), 112
KM. *See* knowledge management
knowledge base, **332**
knowledge management (KM), 363–364, 370
    autocategorization, 368–369
    defined, **363**
    employee knowledge networks, 364–367
    intangible benefits, 392
    organizational knowledge, capturing and sorting, 364
    software, 278
    web, knowledge from, 367–368
knowledge workers
    defined, 12
    IS requirements, 12
konbini, 295

L

LAMP, 260
language differences (international trade), 294, 295–296

language translation, 153–154
    compilers, 153–154
    interpreters, 153–154
    source code into object code, 153
    3GLs, 148–149
    types, 147–152
LANs. *See* local area networks
laptop computers, 114
laser printers, 124, 125
late mover, **53**
LCDs. *See* liquid crystal displays
LD. *See* Lean Development
leading edge
    bleeding edge vs., 56–57
    failure risk, 56–57
lead time, 75, 143, 430, 432
Lean Development (LD), 398
leased lines, 188, 190
legacy systems, 401
    starting without, 53
    systems integration, 401
legal issues (international), 301
    consumer protection, 299
    country of destination principle, 300
    country of origin principle, 299
    cultural differences, 296
    EU vs. U.S. privacy laws, 301–303
    free speech, 299
    intellectual property, 41, 297
    jurisdictions, 299–301
    language differences, 295
    privacy. *See* consumer privacy; privacy issues
    regulations, 294–295
    security, 296–297
    tariffs, 294–295
LEO satellites. *See* low earth orbit satellites
licensing, 165–167, 432
    alternative to in-house development, 414
    applications, 422
    fees, 418, 432
    software benefits, 422–423
    software risks, 423
    steps in ready-made software, 423–425
life cycle, 389. *See also* systems development life cycle
LimeWire, 183

linear regression models, 324–325
Linux, 161, 162, 163, 164, 260
liquid crystal displays (LCDs)
    active matrix displays, 124
    CRTs vs., 124
    defined, **124**
    mechanics, 124
livestock management, 205
load balancing, **257**
local area networks (LANs)
    defined, **187**
    hardware, 189–190
    media transmission speeds, 184
    peer-to-peer, 183, 188
    protocols, 191–192
    scalability, 188
    security issue, 188
    twisted pairs for, 185
    wireless, 188
locking in, 39, 47–48
    buyers, 47–48
    creating standards for, 39, 47–48
    defined, **47**
    suppliers, 47–48
logic bombs, 447–449, **449**, 470
logistics, collaborative, 94
Lotus Development SmartSuite, 155
Lotus Notes, 34
low earth orbit (LEO) satellites, 186
lower-level programming, 148–149
loyalty programs, 356

M
Mac OS X, 152, 161–162, 163
machine cycles, 116–117
    clock rates, 117
    defined, **117**
    illustrated, 117
    system clocks, 117
    time increments, 117
machine language, **148**
Macromedia Dreamweaver. *See* Dreamweaver
magnetic disks
    cameras using, 128
    comparison chart, 132
    cost history, 127
    current media, 127
    defined, **127**
    direct access storage, 127
    disadvantages, 127
    hard disks, 127
    RAID systems, 130

storage volumes, 127
types, 127
USB ports connecting, 126, 127
magnetic-ink character recognition (MICR) devices, **121**
magnetic tapes, 126–127
    advantages, 126–127
    comparison chart, 132
    defined, **126**
    features, 126–127
    sequential storage, 126–127
mainframe computers, 113–114
    costs, 113
    defined, **113**
    features, 113–114
main memory. *See* memory, internal (main)
maintenance
    fees, 418, 432
    outsourcing, 415, 432
    support, 397, 398
MAN. *See* metropolitan area network
management information systems (MISs), 18–21
    defined, **18**
    evolution, 18–21
    shared data resources, 22, 32
managers
    accounting ISs use, 72–74
    e-commerce challenges, 272–273
    information uses, 11–13
    IS planning participation, 386–387
    semistructured problems, 320–321
    SISs comprehension importance, 48, 49
    spreadsheets empowering, 154
    strategic ideas from, 45
    systems thinking, 11–13
    telecommunications affecting, 180–181
Manifesto for Agile Software Development, 398
manufacturing ISs, 77–82. *See also* inventory control; supply chain management
    automation advantage, 38–39
    business function interdependence, 77–79
    business intelligence and knowledge management, 376–377
    contributions, 18–19

controlling operations, 79–80
enterprise applications systems, 18, 19
ISs illustrated, 78
IT contributions, 77–79
JIT manufacturing, 79
monitoring operations, 79–80
MPS, 79
MRP, 79
MRP II, 79
OLAP application example, 312
optimizing performance, 80
RFID applications, 205
sample goals, 10
scheduling activities, 78, 79
manufacturing resource planning (MRP II), 79
    defined, **79**
    JIT, 79
    MPS, 79
manufacturing sector, 18
many-to-many relationship, **225**
mapping software, 350
maps. *See* geographical information systems
market basket analysis, 355
marketing, 82–86. *See also* sales
    business function interdependence, 82–83
    computer telephony integration, 85
    consumer profiling, 84, 86, 290, 294, 336
    data collection, 82–83
    data mining techniques, 85, 354–356
    direct, 355
    e-mail messages, 84, 85
    graphical decision assistance, 325–326
    interactive, 355
    IS contributions, 22, 83–86
    ISs illustrated, 83
    online, 86
    privacy issues. *See* consumer privacy; privacy issues
    research, 83
    semistructured problems, 321
    sensitivity analysis, 326–327
    targeted, 84–85
    telemarketing, 84
    trend analysis, 355
marketing to one, 354

market research, 83
master production schedule (MPS), **79**
material requirements planning and purchasing, 78–79
materials requirement planning (MRP), 78–79
  BOMs, 78
  calculating future needs, 78–79
  components list, 78
  defined, **78**
  EOQ, 78
  example, 244
  optimal raw materials, 78
  software, 78
MB. *See* megabyte
Mbps, 184
MBWA. *See* Mobile Broadband Wireless Access
m-commerce (mobile commerce), **272**, 272–273
mechanical failure ES, 337–338
media. *See* external storage media
Media Player (Microsoft), 55
medical diagnosis ES, 335
medical industry. *See* health-care industry
medical management ES, 336
medium, 184–185. *See also* telecommunications media
mega bps, 184
megabyte (MB), 112
Melissa virus, 447–448
memory, external. *See* external storage; external storage media
memory, internal (main), 112
  addresses, 125
  allocation, 161
  primary memory, 112, 116–118
  RAM. *See* random access memory
  ROM, 112
  volatile vs. nonvolatile, 136
message digest, **460**
messenger case study. *See* QuickBiz Messengers case study
metadata, **228**
metal detection ES, 337
metropolitan area network (MAN), **188**, 204
mice. *See* mouse
MICR. *See* magnetic-ink character recognition devices
microchips, speeds, 131

microcomputers (PCs), 114
  costs, 114
  defined, **114**
  evolution, 114
  microprocessor chips, 116
  speeds, 114, 131
  workstations, 114
Microdrive storage disk, 128
Micro Focus COBOL, 149
microprocessors. *See also* central processing units
  defined, **116**
  functions, 116
  mechanics, 116
  semiconductors, 116
microseconds, 117
Microsoft Access. *See* Access
Microsoft Excel. *See* Excel
Microsoft FrontPage. *See* FrontPage
Microsoft Home Publishing. *See* Home Publishing
Microsoft Internet Explorer. *See* Internet Explorer
Microsoft Media Player, 55
Microsoft Office. *See* Office
Microsoft Outlook. *See* Outlook
Microsoft PowerPoint. *See* PowerPoint
Microsoft Publisher. *See* Publisher
Microsoft Windows. *See* Windows
Microsoft Windows 2000. *See* Windows 2000
Microsoft Windows 2003. *See* Windows 2003
Microsoft Windows 95. *See* Windows 95
Microsoft Windows 98. *See* Windows 98
Microsoft Windows Me. *See* Windows Me
Microsoft Windows NT. *See* Windows NT
Microsoft Windows XP. *See See* Windows XP
Microsoft Word. *See* Word
microwaves
  characteristics, 185, 186
  defined, **186**
  satellite microwave, 186
  terrestrial microwave, 186
  transceiver dishes, 186
  transmission speeds, 184
midrange computers, **114**

millions of instructions per second (MIPS), **118**, 118–119
Millipede, 125
milliseconds, 117
mineral exploration ESs, 337
MIPS. *See* millions of instructions per second
mirrors, **257**
mission-critical applications, **465**
mission statements
  defined, **386**
  examples, 387
  IS, 386
  planning context, 386–387
Mobile Broadband Wireless Access (MBWA), **195**
mobile commerce. *See* m-commerce
mobile devices, 272
mobile Web browsing, 84
model management module, **323,** 323–325
models
  database. *See* database models
  defined, **319**
  linear regression model, 324–325
modems
  defined, **189**
  functions, 189–190
  types, 190
modulation
  analog, 189, 198
  modems, 189
modules. *See* scalability
monitoring, operations, 79–80
monitors, 123–124
  color, 123–124
  CRTs, 123–124
  flat-panel, 124
  illustrated, 124
  LCDs, 124
  pixels, 123
  purchasing considerations, 130–131, 132
  resolutions, 124
  types, 123–124
monopoly issue, 55–56
Morpheus, 183
motherboard, **112**
mouse, 111, **119**, 119–120
MPLS. *See* Multi-Protocol Label Switching
MPS. *See* master production schedule

MP3, 254
MRP. *See* materials requirement
    planning
MRP II. *See* manufacturing resource
    planning
Mr. Rounder, 175
MSBlast worm, 451
MS-DOS, 162
MSN Messenger, 255
multidimensional databases, **357**
multimedia software, 156–157
    business use, 157
    defined, **156**
    education use, 157
    research use, 157
    training use, 90, 157
multinational organizations,
    290–291
multiprocessing, **113**. *See also* par-
    allel processing
Multi-Protocol Label Switching
    (MPLS), 191
multitasking, 116
multithreading, **116**
music, 9
MVS. *See* OS390
MYCIN diagnosis ES, 335
MySQL, 163, 260

N
NAFTA. *See* North American Free
    Trade Agreement
name-your-price auction, **270**
nanoseconds, 117
nanotechnology, 125
NAS. *See* network-attached storage
natural disasters, 443, 464, 470
natural language, 148
Nazi items auction, 299
Netscape browsers
    challenging Microsoft, 55, 57
    losing domination, 42, 57
    market share, 42
NetWare, 161, 162
network administrator career, **24**
    duties, skills, 24
    sample help wanted ad, 25
network-attached storage (NAS), **129**
network commerce, 22
network interface card (NIC), **189**
networks, 187–191
    access points, 193
    bridges, 189

contention, 193
defined, **187**
extranets, 264–266
hardware, 189–190
hubs, 189
interface cards, 230
intranets, 264, 272
leased lines, 188, 190
local. *See* local area networks
metropolitan area network, 188
neural nets. *See* neural networks
nodes, 187
peer-to-peer LANs, 188
personal area network, 189
private. *See* private networks
protocols, 191–197
public lines. *See* public networking
risks to, 470
routers, 189
scalability, 188
services. *See* telecommunications
    services
setting up, 189–190
switches, 189
switching techniques, 190–191
telephone. *See* telephone net-
    works
trusted, 456–457
types, 187
VPNs. *See* virtual private networks
wide area. *See* wide area net-
    works
wireless. *See* wireless
    communications
WLANs, 188
network technology, future of
    broadband telephoning,
    202–203
    converging technologies, 204
    radio frequency identification,
    203–204, 205–206
neural networks (nets), 333
    business application, 333
    defined, **333**
    detecting fraud, 334
    examples, 333–334
    insurance industry application,
    334
    medical application, 335
newsgroups, 253
NIC. *See* network interface card

Nielsen NetRatings, 269
nodes
    contention, 193
    defined, **187**
    LAN protocols, 191–192
    WAN protocols, 193
nonimpact printers, **125**
nonmalicious mishaps, 449–450
nonvolatile memory, 136
North American Free Trade
    Agreement (NAFTA), 290
Norton SystemWorks, 163
notebook computers, **114**

O
object code
    defined, **153**
    source code vs., 153
Objectivity/DB OODB, 226
object linking and embedding
    (OLE), 155, 156
object-oriented databases (OODBs),
    225–226
    encapsulation, 225
    features, 225–226
    inheritance, 225
    objects, 225
    pros/cons, 225–226
    vendors, 226
object-oriented DBMs (OODBMSs),
    225, 225–226
object-oriented programming
    (OOP) languages, 150–152
    advantages, 151
    defined, **150**
    development ease, 151–152
    example, 151
    features, 151
    GUI development, 152
    maintenance ease, 151–152
    objects in, 151
    popular languages, 152
    reusing code, 150
    tools for the Web, 152
Object Pascal, 152
object relational databases, 225
objects
    OOPs, 150–152
    relational databases, 225
ObjectStore OODB, 226
OC. *See* Optical Carrier
OC-3, 198
OC-12, 198

OC-48, 198
OC-768, 239, 201
OCR. *See* optical character recognition
Office (Microsoft), 41, 155, 422
OfficeOne, 155
office productivity applications, 154–156
offshore work, 366
off-shoring, 86, **416**, 420
off-the-shelf software. *See* packaged software
oil industry, gas station purchase technology, 182
OLAP. *See* online analytical processing applications
OLE. *See* object linking and embedding
On Demand, 438
one-to-many relationship, **225**
online analytical processing (OLAP)
  applications, 370
  business intelligence, 353
  customer intelligence, 361
  data mining, 353–357
  data warehousing, 236
  defined, **357**
  examples, 312, 360–361
  executive dashboards, 362–363
  features, 357–361
  power of, 357–360
  processing speed, 359, 360
  tables, 357, 359
  Web-based, 357
Online Audience Analysis, 368
online banking, 34–35,50
online billing, 85
online operations risks, 450–451
OODBMSs. *See* object-oriented DBMs
OODBs. *See* object-oriented databases
OOP. *See* object-oriented programming languages
OpenOffice.org, 163, 164
Open Skies software, 51, 52
open source software, **163**, 163–165
open systems
  closed vs., 10–11, 27
  defined, **10**
operating systems (OSs), 159. *See also specific OSs*
  controlling CPU, 159–161
  current, 161–163
  defined, **159**

drivers, 161
functions, 161–163
illustrated, 160
increasing services, 161
memory allocation, 161
multiprocessing, 113
multitasking, 116
open source, 163–165
plug-and-play, 161
popular systems, 161–163
stability, 162
system management, 161
types, 162
trends, 162
user interfaces, 161
utilities, 159
virtual memory use, 161
operational feasibility study, 389, 392
operations, plans for, 386
opportunities, recognizing, 38
optical bar recognition, 120, 121–122
optical carrier (OC)
  bandwidth, 184–187
  defined, **201**
  fibers, 185, 186
  services, 198, 201
optical character recognition (OCR), 120–121
optical disks, 127–128
  categories, 127–128
  CDs. *See* compact discs
  defined, **127**
  direct access storage, 125–126, 129
  DVDs, 128
  recording technology, 115, 128
optical fiber, 185–186
  advantages, 185
  features, 185–186
  mechanics, 185–186
  OC fibers, 186
  telephone network use, 185–186
  transmission speeds, 184
optical mark recognition, 120–121
optical tape, 128, 132
Oracle, 48, 217, 225, 226, 322, 437
order entering systems and agile methods, 401
organizational culture, **392**, 415, 430, 432
organizational knowledge, 364
organizational structure. *See* information systems management
OS390 (formerly MVS), 162

OS/400, 162
Outlook (Microsoft), 155, 364, 447, 448
output. *See also* reports
  defined, 15
  hard copies, 112
  input, process and, 8–9
  MIS evolution, 18–21
  process, 15
output devices, 123–125
  defined, **15**, 112
  dot-matrix printers, 125
  hardcopy devices, 127
  impact printers, 125
  monitors. *See* monitors
  nonimpact printers, 124
  printers, 124–125
  soft-copy devices, 141–145
  speech output, 122
outsourcers. *See* vendors, outsourcing
outsourcing, 415, 432
  advantages, 418–420, 432
  alternative to in-house development, 414
  benefits from, 419
  case study, 613–614
  competitive advantage risks, 420
  consulting, 419
  control loss with, 420
  core business attention, 419, 432
  costs, 419, 421
  custom-designed applications, 415–416
  defined, **415**
  examples, 437–439
  financial planning improvement, 418
  fixed costs reduced, 419
  good fit to culture, 415, 432
  good fit to need, 415, 432
  implementation cycle, 419
  IT services, 417–418
  know-how, highly qualified, 419, 432
  licensed fees reduced, 418
  long-term, 417–418
  maintenance from, 415, 418
  personnel impact, 419, 420
  risks, 420–422, 432
  smooth interface, 415
  strategic advantage potential, 415
  support, 419

typical services for, 417–418
vendors, 417–418

P

packaged software, 167–168, 432.
 See also specific software types
 advantages, 167, 432
 ASPs providing. *See* application
  service providers
 availability, 167–168
 code type, 147–154
 costs, 167
 defined, **154**
 desktop publishing, 155
 disadvantages, 168
 evaluating, 167
 hypermedia features, 156–157
 integrated software, 167–168
 licensing, 423–425, 432
 modification difficulties, 423, 432
 networking, 167
 purchasing, 165–168, 432
 quality, 167
 risks, 432
 spreadsheets, 154
 suites, 155–156
 support, 167
 testing, 168
 vendors, 152, 167
 word processors, 154
packet, **191**
packet sniffing devices, 467
packet switching, 191
 defined, **191**
 frame relay, 191
 illustrated, 191
 mechanics, 191
 pros/cons, 191
 TCP/IP, 192
padlock (digital certificates), 463
Paintship, 155
palm computers, 114
Palm OS, 162
PAN. *See* personal area network
paper use, 8
parallel conversion, **396**
parallel processing, **113**
parameters, **319**
parents (database), 225
partial information, 10
Pascal, 149
passwords. *See* access controls
Paste command, 160

patches, 447, 451
patents, 41, 46
path analysis (data mining), 354
PATRIOT Act. *See* Uniting and
 Strengthening America by
 Providing Appropriate Tools
 Required to Intercept and
 Obstruct Terrorism PATRIOT Act
patriotism, 467
payment mechanisms, 295
payments, wireless, 182–183
payroll, 74
 agile methods, 401
 cost-accounting integration, 74
PB. *See* petabyte
PCs. *See* microcomputers
PDAs. *See* personal digital assistants
peer-to-peer (P2P) file sharing, **183**
peer-to-peer LANs, **188**
people tracking, 205
performance evaluations, 91
periodicals online. *See* content
 providers
peripheral devices, 126, 132, 133,
 134, 160, 189. *See also specific
 devices*
PERL. *See* Practical Extraction
 Report Language
permissive model, 166
persona, 285–286
personal area network (PAN),
 189, 195
personal computers. *See*
 microcomputers
personal digital assistants (PDAs)
 cell phones as, 114, 181–182
 defined, **114**
 features, 114–115
 salesforce automation, 86
 stylus, 114
 touch screens, 120
 wireless connections, 69,
  79–80, 114
Personal Information Protection
 Law, 455
personnel costs reduced through
 outsourcing, 418, 432
pest management ES, 337
petabyte (PB), 112
PGP. *See* Pretty Good Privacy
pharmaceuticals RFID
 applications, 205
phased conversion, **396**

phishing, **271**, 276–277, 446
Photoshop, 155
PhotoSuite, 155
PHP, 152, 260
physical components diagrams, 395
picoseconds, 117
pilot conversion, 397
piloting, **397**
piracy (software), 166
pixels, **123**
plaintext, **458**
PLC. *See* Power Line Communication
plug-and-play devices, 161
plug-and-play (PnP) OSs, **161**
plug-ins, 163, 185
PnP Oss. *See* plug-and-play OSs
podcast, **254**
politics (global), 297–298
PolyAnalyst, 364, 375–376
pop-up ads, 84, 276
portable computers, 189, 272. *See
 also* personal digital assistants
portable languages, 227
portals, 258
ports
 defined, **132**
 purchasing considerations,
  132, 134
 types, 132
 USB, 126, 127
power (computer), 118–119, 132,
 133, 134. *See also* computer classifications; speed
Power Line Communication
 (PLC), 187
PowerPC chips, 116, 162
PowerPoint (Microsoft), 154, 155,
 364
Practical Extraction Report
 Language (PERL), 163, 260
Prairie Crop Protection Planner, 328
presentation tools, 154
Pretty Good Privacy (PGP), 296
primary key, **224**
primary memory, 112, 116–117,
 118, 119, 128
printers, 15, 124–125
 dot-matrix, 125
 I/O devices, 124–125
 impact, 125
 ink-jet, 124, 125
 laser, 124, 125
 nonimpact, 124

output quality, 124–125
purchasing, 124
speed, 124
switching costs, 42
types, 124–125
privacy issues. *See also* consumer privacy
  business perspective, 87
  cookies, 233, 255–256, 268, 277
  data collection rules, 87–88
  defined, 87
  employee, 16
  international laws, 301–303
  m-commerce, 273
  review procedures, 87–88
  spyware, 276–277
  U.S. vs. EU laws, 301–303
  violation awards, 302
private-key encryption, 459, 470
private networks
  cell phones, 189
  satellite systems, 186–187
  VPNs, 190
  WANs, 188–189
problems
  defined, 7
  semistructured, 320
  structured, 319–321
  unstructured, 319–321
problem solving. *See also* decision making; decision support systems
  case study, 6–7
  decisions for, 6
  information requirements, 7
  opportunity recognition vs., 38
procedures
  as IS component, 14
  defined, 14
process devices, 17
Process Health Assessment Tool, 376–377
processes
  defined, **8**, 393
  input, output and, 8–9
processing. *See* data processing
product information RFID applications, 205
production rules. *See* if-then rules
productivity
  defined, **70**
  extranet contributions, 264
  Internet contributions, 264
  intranet contributions, 264

products
  competitive advantage from, 39, 42–43
  creating new, 39, 42–43
  differentiating, 39, 43
  effective vs. efficient, 70–71
  enhancing, 39, 44–45
professionalism, 16
profiling customers, 84, 86, 275, 277
program/data dependency, 218
programmable. *See* structured problems
programmer/analysts, 22–24
programming, **147**
programming languages, 147–152
  assembly, 147
  assembly languages, 148
  bugs, 163
  compilers, 153–154
  debugging, 149
  defined, **148**
  English-like, 148
  evolution, 148–149
  first-generation, 148
  fourth-generation, 148–149
  generations overview, 148–149
  higher-level pros/cons, 148–149
  interpreters, 153–154
  lower-level pros/cons, 148–149
  machine language, 147
  object-oriented, 150–152
  portability, 167
  reusing code, 151
  second-generation, 148–149
  third-generation, 148–149
  translating languages, 148–149
  visual programming, 149–150
programmers, 22–24, **23**
programs. *See* application software; operating systems; packaged software; *specific software*
project management
  illustrated, 155
  software, 155
  tools, 155
project operation, 227
promotion, 88–90
proposal, requesting, 424
proprietary software, **163**, 166
proprietary technologies, 256
protocols, 191–197. *See also specific protocol names*; standards
  contention, 193

defined, **191**
encryption. *See* encryption
Ethernet, 192–193
Internet URLs, 251–252
LAN, 191–192
mobile communications, 196–197
networks, 191–197
TCP/IP, 192
WAN, 192–193
wireless, 193–196
prototyping, **388**
proxy servers, **456**, 456–457
P2P. *See* peer-to-peer file sharing
public-key encryption, 459–460, 470
public networking
  encryption. *See* encryption
  security risks, 181
  VPNs, 190, 264–266
  WANs, 188–189
Publisher (Microsoft), 155
PUFF diagnosis ES, 335
purchased applications. *See* packaged software
purchasing
  external storage media, 132–133
  hardware, 132–133, 134
  licensing, 165
  printers, 125
  software, 167
pure-play company, **257**
Python, 260

Q

Quark, 155
queries, 221
  ad-hoc, 226, 227
QuickBiz Messengers case study, 105–108
  background, 105–108
  business challenges, 108
  communications technology, 105–106, 179–180
  competition, 179–180
  customer service, 107
  data management, 217
  expansion considerations, 106, 137
  external storage backups, 125–132
  hardware considerations, 110–111, 137

intranet and extranet consideration, 180
IS development, 107
network provider decision, 180
performance evaluations, 147
software considerations, 146–147, 170
staffing challenges, 146–147
tracking delivery data, 110
QWERTY keyboards, 119

R
radio frequency (RF), 186
radio frequency identification (RFID), 47, **81**, 81–82, 122, 183, 203–204, 205–206, 272, 301
radio frequency interference (RFI), **185**
radio waves, 185
RAID. *See* Redundant Array of Independent Disks
raising barriers to entrants, 39, **41**
RAM. *See* random access memory
random access memory (RAM)
defined, **112**
functions, 112
speeds, 112
rapid prototyping
benefits, 77
defined, **75**
mechanics, 75, 77
Rapt Buy application, 322
Rational Unified Process (RUP), 398
reach percentage, **263**
read-only memory (ROM)
defined, **112**
flash ROM, 112
functions, 112
ready-to-use software. *See* packaged software
Really Simple Syndication (RSS), **253**, 254
records, **219**
recovery measures, 464–466
business recovery plans, 464–466
hot site providers, 466
planning, 466
planning providers, 466
Recovery Point Objective (RPO), 476
Recovery Time Objective (RTO), 476

recruiting employees, 89–90
e-recruiting, 89–90
qualifying prospects, 90
recruitment, 88–90
reducing costs, 39, **40**
case study, 51
redundancies, 469, 470
Redundant Array of Independent Disks (RAID), **130**, **452**, 453
red zone inventory, 363
reengineering
auto industry example, 50
defined, **49**, 58
goal of, 50
implementing SISs, 49–50
registering IP addresses, 251
regulations. *See* legal issues (international); privacy issues
relational databases
attributes, 222
composite keys, 224
designing, 222
example, 222–223
foreign key, 225
join table, 225
keys, 222, 224
linking, 224
link types (diagrams), 223
many-to-many relationship, 225
one-to-many relationship, 225
operations, 222–225
primary key, 224
relations, 222
tables, 222
tuples, 222
relational model, **222**, 222–225
relational operations, 226–227
defined, **226**
metadata, 228
schema, 228
Structured Query Language, 227
relevant information, 10, 87. *See also* useful information
repeaters, **189**
repetitive-stress injuries (RSI), 123
Report Program Generator (RPG) languages, 149
reports
accounting systems, 72, 73
OLAP applications, 312
request for information (RFI), **424**
requests for proposals (RFPs), **424**

requirements
defining, 389, 392
system requirements, 392, 404
research, multimedia in, 157
resolutions, **124**
resumes online, 90
retailing online. *See* e-commerce; e-commerce practices; e-commerce sites; e-retailing
retail sector
DSS example, 327–328
RFID applications, 205, 272
self-checkout systems, 121
training program example, 90
retinal access controls, 454
Return Exchange, 355
return on investment (ROI), **391**, 437, 466
revenue management, 331, 356
Revenue Management System, 331
reverse auctioning, 41, **270**
RF. *See* radio frequency
RFI. *See* radio frequency interference; request for information
RFID. *See* radio frequency identification
RFPs. *See* requests for proposals
Rich Site Summary (RSS), **253**, 254
risk assessment, 465
risks
assessing financial, 75
bleeding (leading) edge, 53, 56–57, 65
first movers, 56–57
information systems, 442–450
mapping, 350
online operations, 450–451
robustness, 452, 470
ROI. *See* return on investment (ROI)
ROM. *See* read-only memory
root access, 259
routers, **189**, 457
RPG. *See* Report Program Generator languages
RPO. *See* Recovery Point Objective
RSI. *See* repetitive-stress injuries
RSS. *See* Really Simple Syndication; Rich Site Summary
RTO. *See* Recovery Time Objective
RUP. *See* Rational Unified Process

SUBJECT INDEX

S

SaaS. *See* software as a service
SABRE online reservations, 50
Safe Harbor, **303**
sales, 86. *See also* marketing
    business function interdepend-
    ence, 72
    m-commerce, 272
    privacy issues. *See* consumer pri-
    vacy; privacy issues
    sales force automation, 86
salesforce automation, 86
SAN. *See* storage area network
SAP applications, 437, 464
Sarbanes-Oxley Corporate
    Governance Act (SOX), 421,
    442, 456
satellite, 186–187, 198, 199
    microwave, 185
    transmission, 186–187
Sasser worm, 451
scalability
    case study. *See* Worldwide Host
    case study
    data warehouses, 235
    defined, **133**, **188**
    e-commerce, 260, 261
    hardware, 129, 133
    updating hardware and, 133–135
    Web sites, 260, 261
    wireless LANS, 188
scanning devices, 122, 182
schemas, 228
    building databases, 228
    data types, 228
    DDL example, 228,
    defined, **228**
    example, 228
scientific interests (international
    trade), 296–297
SCM. *See* supply chain management
screens. *See* monitors
scripting
    CGI scripts, 230, 260
    Java, 152
    JavaScript, 152
Scrum method, 398
SDLC. *See* systems development life
    cycle
SDRF. *See* Symmetrix Data Remote
    Facility
SDSL. *See* Symmetric DSL
search advertising, **263**

search engines, company use, 368
second-generation languages,
    148–149
secret key, 459, 460, 470
Secure ID, 454, 464
Secure Sockets Layer (SSL), 460
security. *See also* security measures;
    security risks
    controls. *See* controls (systems)
    DBMSs, 221
    economics of, 466–469
    fraud detection, 354, 355
    goals, 442
    intellectual property, 41
    international trade, 296–297
    national, 467
    personal data, 88–87
    risks to information systems,
    442–450
    specialized, 415, 432
    spending, 468, 470
    user-developed applications,
    431, 432
security measures, 456–464
    authentication, 457–462
    digital certificates, 462–463
    digital signatures, 460–462
    downside, 463–464
    downtime, 468–469
    economics of, 466–469
    encryption. *See* encryption
    firewalls, 456–457
    measures, 456–464
    proxy servers, 456–457
    public-key encryption, 459–460
    Transport Layer Security, 460
    vendors, 454
security risks, 442–456
    blackouts, 443
    brownouts, 443
    computer viruses. *See* computer
    viruses
    data alteration/destruction,
    446–447
    data risks, 444–450
    denial of service, 450
    distributed DoS, 450
    fraud. *See* fraud detection
    hardware risks, 443–444
    hijacking, 450
    identity theft, 444–446
    information theft, 444–446
    keystroke logging, 444

    logic bombs, 447–449
    natural disasters, 443
    nonmalicious mishaps, 449–450
    public networking, 181, 190
    social engineering, 445
    terrorism, 466, 467
    vandalism, 444
    Web defacement, 446–447
    worms, 447–449
select operation, 227
self-checkout systems, 121
semantic layer, 361
semiconductors, 116
semistructured problems, 320–321
    defined, **320**
    examples, 320–321
    managers and, 320
sensitivity analysis, **327**, 326–327
sequence (data mining), 354
sequential storage
    advantages, 125
    defined, **125**
    disadvantages, 125
    illustrated, 126
    program/data dependency, 218
servers
    dedicated servers, 258
    defined, **188**
    e-commerce options, 258–259
    load balancing, 257
    owing and maintaining, 257
    virtual Web servers, 258
service-level agreements, **421**, 432
services
    alliances strengthening, 39, 45–47
    automating, 40, 51
    competitive advantage from, 39,
    42–43, 51, 52–53
    creating new, 39, 42–43
    differentiating, 39, 43
    enhancing, 39, 44–45, 52–53
    software, 425–428
service sector, 13
servlets. *See* Java servlets
shared data resources, 19, 22. *See*
    also data warehouses; databases
    file sharing (P2P), 183
shared hosting, **257**
shipping, 80–81
shipping industry
    model management use, 323
    source data input devices,
    121–122

shopping RFID applications, 205
single sign-on (SSO), **463**
SISs. *See* strategic information systems
sit.wav file. *See* Special Information Tone file
Slammer worm, 448
Smalltalk, 152
Sobig virus, 448
social engineering, **445**
social engineers, 445
social issues. *See* ethical/social issues
software, 145–177. *See also specific software*; application software; packaged software
applications, 147, 154–158
compatibility issues, 111, 133, 134
costs, 167, 168
defined, **147**
evaluating, 167–168
free, 163, 165
IS planning. *See* information systems, planning
licensing, 165–167, 422–425
locking in buyers, 47–48
marketing data collection, 82–83
memory location, 159
new product advantage example, 42–43
open source, 163–165
outsourcing, 415–421
overview, 147
patches, 447, 451
piracy, 166
programming languages and — development tools, 147–152
proprietary, 163
purchasing, 167
standards, 48, 58
switching costs, 41
system. *See* operating systems; system software
vendors, 152, 417, 423
software as a service (SaaS), **425**, 425–428, 432, 438
software by subscription, 425
Solaris (Sun Microsystems), 162, 165
solid state disk (SSD), **129**
source code
defined, **153**
object code vs., 153–154

source data input devices, 111, 118, 120–122
banking industry, 121
bar codes, 121–122
credit cards, 121
defined, **120**
MICR devices, 121
shipping industry, 121–122
source data technology, 120–121
source data technology, 120–121
SOX. *See* Sarbanes-Oxley Corporate Governance Act
spamming, 16, 27, 84, 276, 445
Special Information Tone (sit.wav) file, 84
speech, freedom of, 16
speech output, 15
speech recognition, 15, 122
converging technologies, 115
defined, **122**
features, 122
input devices, 111
limitations, 122
speed
bandwidth, 184–187
computers, 123
microchips, 116
OLAP applications, 312
SpeedPass, 182
SpoofStick, 271
spreadsheets, 154
functions, 154
integrated software, 154–156
popular program, 154–156
suites, 155–156
switching cost, 41
spyware, **256**, 276, 361, 444
SQL. *See* Structured query language
SQL Server, 225, 226, 311, 312, 448–449
SSD. *See* solid state disk
SSL. *See* Secure Sockets Layer
SSO. *See* single sign-on
SSPs. *See* storage service providers
staffing. *See* employees; human resource management
standardization, benefits in planning, 387–388, 404
standards. *See also specific standards*; protocols
creating, 48, 58
global ISs, 298–301

planning ISs, 387–388
software, 48, 58
StarOffice (Sun Microsystems), 41, 155
state diagrams, 395
static IP numbers, **192**
stock trading online. *See* investment
storage, 17. *See also* external storage; external storage media
defined, **15**
devices, 17
storage area network (SAN), **130**, 143
storage service providers (SSPs), **428**
story, 399
strategic advantage. *See also* competitive advantage; competitive advantage initiatives
airline success story, 51–53
custom software for, 415, 432
defined, **38**
strategic information systems (SISs), 48–54
competitive advantage, 50–51
consideration steps, 49
creating, 49
defined, **38**
economic justification, 49
ideas comprising, 48
planning, 49
reengineering changes, 49–50
requirements, 49
understanding, reasons, 45
strategic planning
CEO perspective, 39
defined, 386
Eats2Go case study, 37–38, 59
IS planning, 386
strategy, 38–39
defined, 38
IS contributions, 38–39
opportunities vs. problem solving, 38
streaming video/audio, 254
stress, from computers, 123
structured problems, 319–321
algorithms, 319
defined, 319
examples, 319
illustrated, 319
parameters, 319
Structured Query Language (SQL), **227**, 360
stylus, **114**

subsystems
defined, **9**, 31
examples, 9–10
suites, **155**, 155–156
supercomputers
defined, **113**
functions, 113
parallel processing, 113
suppliers, locking in, 39, 47–48
supply chain
activities, 77
defined, **77**
on the Web, 273–275
supply chain management (SCM),
77–77, 273–275
benefits, 274
collaboration, 274
combined with CRM and ERP, 71
cycle time, 278
databases, 225
defined, **18**, **77**
EDI, 273–274
ERP systems supporting, 71, 95
extranet use, 274
failures, 469
GDP statistics, 91, 94
interorganizational—systems,
91–94
manufacturing resource planning, 79
material requirements planning
and purchasing, 78–79
monitoring and control, 79–80
outsourcing. *See* outsourcing
planning. *See* information systems, planning
purchasing packaged software,
167–168, 422, 423
reducing inventory levels, 274
RFID, 81–82
shipping, 80–81
shipping collaboration, 274
software, 76, 77, 273–274
systems integration, 401
trust factor, 93
warehousing collaboration, 94
support (new systems), 397–398,
404
availability, 134
defined, **397**
outsourcing and, 419, 432
packaged software, 167–168

providing, 430
standardization in planning, 388
switches, **189**
switching costs, 39, **41**, 41–42
switching techniques, 190–191
applications, 190–191
circuit switching, 191
packet switching, 191
Symmetric DSL (SDSL), 198
symmetric encryption, **459**, 470
Symmetrix Data Remote Facility
(SDRF), 476
synergy
defined, **13**
human/computer qualities, 13
system board. *See* motherboard
system clocks, **117**
system management, 161
system requirements, **392**, 404, 424
system software, 158–163
defined, **147**
functions, 159–163
operating systems, 159
systems
closed vs. open, 10–11, 27
defined, **9**
effective vs. efficient, 70–72
examples, 9
subsystems relationships, 9–10
systems acquisitions
case study. *See* Worldwide Host
case study
licensing applications, 422–425
options and priorities, 414–415
outsourcing, 415–421
software as a service, 425–428
user application development,
428–431
systems analysis, 389
defined, **389**
economic feasibility study, 389,
391–392
illustrated, 390
investigation, 389, 390
operational feasibility study,
389, 392
requirements definition, 390,
392, 404
steps, 389–390
technical feasibility study,
389, 390
systems analysts, **23**, 23–24
agents of change, 23

career duties, skills, 23–24
roles illustrated, 23
sample help wanted ad, 23
systems design, 392–393, 404
construction phase, 395
data flow diagrams, 393–394
defined, **392**
flowcharts, 393, 394
testing phase, 396
Unified Modeling Language,
394–395
systems development. *See also*
specific development phases; systems development life cycle
agile methods, 398–401
planning information systems,
385–398
principles of, 388
systems integration, 401–403
systems development life cycle
(SDLC), 388–389, 404, 423
agile methods vs., 398–401
analysis. *See* systems analysis
construction phase, 395
cut-over conversion, 396
data flow diagrams, 393–394
defined, **388**
design phase. *See* systems design
economic feasibility study, 389,
391–392
implementation, 396, 404
investigation, 389, 390
operational feasibility study,
389, 392
parallel conversion, 396
phased conversion, 396
pilot conversion, 397
requirements definition, 389,
392, 404
support phase, 397–398, 404
technical feasibility study,
389, 390
testing phase, 396
unified modeling language
(UML), 394–395
systems implementation, 396, 404
cut-over conversion, 396
parallel conversion, 396
phased conversion, 396
pilot conversion, 397
systems integration, **401**, 401–403
systems planning, 385–386
steps in, 386–387

benefits of standardization planning, 387–388, 404
to development, 388
systems support, 397, 404
systems thinking
advantages, 11–12
defined, 12

T
tables (relational databases), **222**
tablet computers
defined, **114**
features, 114–115
tactical planning
defined, 386
IS planning, 386
tags, 219
tailored software. *See also* custom-designed software; systems design; systems development; systems development life cycle
defined, **415**
ERP systems, 92
tapes. *See* magnetic tapes; optical tape
targeted marketing, 84–85
consumer profiling, 84, 86
cookies, 255–256, 361
computer telephony integration, 85
data mining techniques, 85, 354–356
defined, **84**
telemarketing, 84–85
tariffs, 294–295
TaxCut software, 328
tax decision software, 328
tax planning DSS example, 328–329
TB. *See* terabyte
Tbps, 184
TCP/IP. *See* Transmission Control Protocol/Internet Protocol
team projects. *See* collaboration; groupware
technical feasibility study, 389
technology convergence, **115**
telecommunications, 17. *See also* cellular phones; networks; *specific network types*; telephone networks; wireless communications
automating sales forces, 86

bandwidth, 184–187
business impact, 180–181
cellular phones, 182
computer telephony integration, 85
daily use, 181–184
defined, **17**, **180**
distributing data, 181
error detection, 191
ES use, 336
faxes, 182
gas station purchase technology, 182
improving communication, 180–181
incoming call system, 32–33
increasing efficiency, 181
instant messaging, 254–255
Internet telephoning, 202–203
P2P file sharing, 183
peer-to-peer file sharing, 183
protocols. *See* protocols; standards
repeaters, 189
speeds, 184–187
switching costs, 41
switching techniques, 190–191
toll plaza technology, 182–183
transaction speeds, 181
transmission rates, 184
videoconferencing, 182
voice mail, 180
Web-empowered commerce, 184
wireless payments and warehousing, 182–183
telecommunications media, 184–187
capacities (speeds), 184–187
characteristics, 187–191
coaxial cable, 185, 186
described, 184, 185
DSL. *See* digital subscriber line
electric power lines, 185, 187
microwaves, 185
networking, 185, 187–191
optical fiber, 185, 186
radio transmission, 186
satellite transmission, 186–187
terrestrial microwave, 186
twisted pair, 185
telecommunications services, 197–202
BPL, 198, 202
cable, 197, 198

capacities (speeds), 184–187
dial-up, 198
DSL. *See* digital subscriber line
fixed wireless, 198, 199, 201
gigabit Ethernet, 193
optical carrier, 198, 201
satellite, 186–187, 198, 199
summary list, 198
T1 lines, 198, 199
T3 lines, 198, 199
telecommuting, 51, 181, 200–201
telemarketing
ending annoying, 84
IT use, 84–85, 86
targeted marketing, 84–85
telephone networks
ES use, 336
maintenance ES, 336
modem use, 189
structure, 185, 188
telephoning online, 202–203
televisions
converging technologies, 115
marketing on, 85
telework, 200
tera bps, 284
terabyte (TB), 112
terrestrial microwave, 186
terrorism, 214, 296, 466, 467
TestAnalyst, 375
testing
packaged software, 167–168
systems designs, 395, 396
theft (information), 444–446
thin clients, 144
third-generation languages (3GLs), 148–149
compiler, 153
4GLs vs., 148–149
comparison chart, 148
3-D geographic software, 158, 159
3GLs. *See* third-generation languages
three nines, 427
throughput, **118**
thumb drives, 128
Thunderbird, 163, 164
time to market, **75**, 77
time zones, 304
TLD. *See* top-level domain
tolerance, 130
toll plaza technology, 182–183

T1 lines, 198, **199**
top-level domain (TLD)
    defined, **251**
    examples, 251–252
touch screens, **120**
toy industry example, 157
TPM. *See* transactions per minute
TPS. *See* transaction-processing
    system
trackback software, 253
trackballs, **119**, 119–120
trackpads, **119**, 119–120
traditional file approach, 218–219
    data integrity, 219
    data redundancy, 218
    defined, **218**
    program/data dependency, 218
traffic volume, 262
training(employee), 90
    cost reduction example, 90
    multimedia software, 90, 157
    new system use, 396
    standardization in planning, 388
transaction, **15**
transactional databases, 232, 234,
    236, 322
transaction-processing system (TPS)
    defined, **15**
    example, 18
    functions, 18, 72
    mechanics, 72
    sharing data, 18
transactions
    alliances tracking, 46
    defined, 15
    fulfillment, 278
    instant, 181
    online business rules, 275–278
    owning customer experience, 277
    personalizing service, 277
    shortening business cycle, 278
    speeds, 80
    targeting customers. *See* targeted
        marketing
transactions per minute (TPM), 119
transceiver dishes, 186
transistors, 116
Transmission Control
    Protocol/Internet Protocol
    (TCP/IP), 192
    defined, **192**
    IP numbers, 192

transmission rates, **184**, 196,
    197, 201
transportation industry applica-
    tions, 205, 213
Transportation Recall
    Enhancement Accountability
    and Documentation Act, 311
Transport Layer Security (TLS),
    460, 470
travel industry
    alliances, 46–47, 266, 278
    case study. *See* Worldwide Host
        case study
    model management use, 323
tree model. *See* hierarchical data-
    base model
trend analysis, 355
Trillian, 255
Trojan horses, **448**
trucking business. *See* shipping
    industry
trust, 93
trusted network, 456–457
T3 lines, 198, **199**
turnkey solution, 258
tuples, 222
TurboTax software, 328
Tux the penguin, 164
twisted pair, **185**

U

UML. *See* Unified Modeling
    Language
Unicode, 294
Unified Modeling Language (UML),
    394, 394–395, 404
Uniform Resource Locators (URLs)
    defined, **251**
    domain names, 251–252
    example, 251–252
    file location, 251
    protocols, 251
    segment names, 251
uninterruptible power supply (UPS)
    systems, **443**
unique visitor pages, 263
unique visitors per month, 263
Uniting and Strengthening
    America by Providing
    Appropriate Tools Required to
    Intercept and Obstruct Terrorism
    (PATRIOT) Act, 467
Universal Product Code (UPC), **300**

universal serial bus (USB) ports,
    126, 127
UNIX OSs, 162, 163
unstructured decisions, 320
unstructured problems
    defined, **319**
    illustrated, 319
    overview, 319–321
UPC. *See* Universal Product Code
updating, hardware, 133–135
UPS. *See* uninterruptible power sup-
    ply systems
upstream, **197**
uptime, **427**
URLs. *See* Uniform Resource
    Locators
USB. *See* universal serial bus ports
USB drive, **128**
USB flash drive, 128
use case diagrams, 395
useful information
    case study, 6–7
    characteristics, 9
    example, 9
user application development,
    428, 432
    advantages, 430–431, 432
    alternative to in-house develop-
        ment, 414
    defined, **428**
    managing, 428–430
    risks, 430–431
user IDs. *See* access controls
user interface, 161
utilities, **160**, 160–161

V

value-added networks (VANs), **188**,
    188–189, 274
vandalism, 444
VANs. *See* value-added networks
vendors
    antivirus software, 448, 451
    bankruptcies, 423, 432
    business intelligence tools, 362
    business recovery plans, 465
    contracts, 624
    database management
        systems, 225
    digital certificates, 462
    ERP systems, 95, 362
    executive dashboards, 362
    GISs, 340

hardware, 417
modification difficulties, 423, 432
object-oriented databases, 226
outsourcing, 417–418
packaged software, 152, 423–425
personnel turnover, 423
proposals from, 424, 432
reliability, 131, 133
screening, 424
security devices, 454
selecting, 424
software, 417
supercomputers, 113
Ventura, 155
VeriChip, 204
Versant OODB, 226
videoconferencing, **182**
video displays/monitors, 15
virtual memory, **161**
virtual private networks (VPNs)
access, 464
defined, **190**
extranets, 264–266
intranets, 264, 272
virtual private server, **258**
virtual reality (VR), **157**, 157–158
virtual Web servers, 258
viruses. *See* computer viruses
vision. *See* mission statements
Visual Basic, 149, 152, 153
Visual C++, 149
visual programming language,
149–150
defined, **149**
features, 149
languages, 150
voice mail, 180
Voice over Internet Protocol (VoIP),
51, 53
defined, **202**
hotspot technology, 204
Internet telephoning, 191,
202–203
voiceprints, 454
voice recognition systems, 15, 111.
See also speech recognition
VoIP. *See* Voice over Internet
Protocol
volatile memory, 125, 136
VPN. *See* virtual private networks
VR. *See* virtual reality

W
walk-through, 395
WAN. *See* wide area networks
warehousing, 182–183
warranty, 134
waste management RFID applications, 205
waterfall development, 389, 398, 401
Watson (data application), 364
web, knowledge from, 367–368
Web Affinity Analysis software, 361
Web-based e-mail, 252–253
Web browsers. *See also specific
browsers*
dialog module, 325
interpreting HTML, 252
market, 42–43, 55
open source software, 163–165
Web databases, 230–231
common uses, 230
interfaces, 230
keywords, 230
security, 231
Web defacement, 446–447, 470
Web-empowered enterprises,
22, 184
Web-enabled enterprise, 262–273
advertising, 262–264
auctions, 264–266, 270
bill presentment and payment,
270–271
B2B trading, 262–266
B2C trading, 266–273
business growth and changes, 251
content providers, 270
dispersed workforce, 271
e-tailing, 267–269
exchanges, 264–266
example, 249–248
global information systems,
291–292
m-commerce, 272–273
online business alliances, 266
reverse auctions, 270
rules for success, 275–278
supply chains, 273–275
technology review, 251–256
Web site options, 257–262
Web hosting services, **257**
Webmaster, **25**
Web page authoring tools
defined, **156**
functions, 152, 156

hypermedia features, 156–157
popular programs, 152
Web page editors, 41. *See also* Web
page authoring tools
Web pages
authoring tools. *See* Web page
authoring tools
creating, 252–253, 257
design rules, 261
home pages, 43, 233, 330
translation, 293, 296
Web portals, 258
Web sites, 257. *See also* e-commerce
sites
business, design rules, 261, 262
dedicated servers, 258
DSS example, 330
electronic storefronts, 218, 267
evaluating service providers,
259–261
home pages, 43, 233, 330
host considerations, 259–261
hosting alternatives, 257–259
hosting service, 257–259
hosting specialists, 257–261
HTML, 152, 252
ISP hosting, 257–259
markup languages, 252
servers, owning and maintaining, 257
virtual Web servers, 258
Web portals, 258
XML, 252
Web software. *See also* Web
technologies
CGI scripts, 230, 260
cookies, 255–256
HTML, 152
invading privacy, 233–234
Java, 152
JavaScript, 152
spyware, 276
Tools, 152
Web page editors. *See* Web page
authoring tools; Web page
editors
XHTML standard, 252
XML, 152
Web technologies, 251
blogs, 253–254
cookies, 255–256, 361
file transfer, 252–253
HTML and XML, 252

HTTP, 251–252
instant messaging, 254–255
podcasting, 254
proprietary technologies, 256
RSS, 253
WEP. *See* Wired Equivalent Privacy
what if (sensitivity) analysis, **327**
wide area networks (WANs),
  188–189
  common carrier leases, 188
  defined, **188**
  hardware, 189
  personal, 189
  private, 188
  protocols, 192–193
  public, 188
  types, 188–189
  VANs, 188–189
Wi-Fi Protected Access (WPA), 193
Wi-Fi (wireless fidelity)
  technology, 186
  defined, **193**
  hotspots, 194, 195, 244
  IEEE 802.11 standards,
    193–194, 196
  IEEE 802.15 standards, 195, 196
  IEEE 802.16 standards, 195, 196
  IEEE 802.20 standards, 195, 196
  m-commerce, 272–273
  protocols, 193–196
  standards, 193–194, 195, 196
WiMax. *See* Worldwide
  Interoperability for Microwave
  Access
Windows, 55, 165, 260, 448, 451
Windows 2000, 162, 451
Windows 2003, 162
Windows 95, 162
Windows 98, 55, 162
Windows Me, 162
Windows NT, 162
Windows OSs (Microsoft),
  55–56, 122

Windows XP, 122, 161, 162, 451
Wingcast telematics, 54
Wired Equivalent Privacy
  (WEP), 193
wireless communications
  cell phones. *See* cellular phones
  fixed wireless, 198, 199, 201
  hotspots, 194, 195, 244
  IEEE 802.11 standards,
    193–194, 196
  IEEE 802.15 standards, 195, 196
  IEEE 802.16 standards, 195, 196
  IEEE 802.20 standards, 195, 196
  Internet connections, 69,
    79–80, 86
  m-commerce, 272–273
  payments, 182–183
  PDAs featuring, 69, 79–80
  popular technologies, 195
  protocols, 193–196
wireless fidelity. *See* Wi-Fi technology
wireless input devices, 120
wireless ISP (WISP), 199, 201
wireless LANs (WLANs), 64, **188**
WISP. *See* wireless ISP
WLANs. *See* wireless LANs
word (data word), 117
Word (Microsoft), 154, 296, 364, 447
Wordfast, 296
WordPerfect, 154
WordPro, 154
word processors, 154
workforce, dispered, 271
workstations
  defined, **114**
  functions, 114
Worldwide Host case study
  alternative ISs sources, 384
  background, 379–382
  database development, 385
  investigating existing systems, 398

outsourcing issues, 413–414
security issues, 441
systems acquisitions, 413–414
systems planning and development, 383–385
Web site defaced, 441
Worldwide Interoperability for
  Microwave Access (WiMAX),
  195, 204
World Wide Web (WWW). *See also*
  Internet
  affiliate programs, 46–47
  alliances, 45–47
  automating customer service,
    40, 86
  failures, 54, 56
  success stories/principles, 51–53
worms, **447**, 447–449, 470. *See also*
  computer viruses
  MSBlast worm, 451
  Sasser worm, 451
  Slammer worm, 448
WPA. *See* Wi-Fi Protected Access
WWW. *See* Internet; World
  Wide Web

X
XHTML, **252**
XML. *See* Extensible Markup
  Language
XP. *See* Extreme Programming

Y
Yahoo! Messenger, 255
yield management DSS example,
  330, 330–331, 356

Z
zombies, 450

A

AANDS, 270
ABF Freight System, 213
Accenture, 368, 417
Acer, 124
ACLU. *See* American Civil Liberties Union
Acxiom, 268
Adams, Robert, 64–65
Adobe, 48, 155, 157
A.G. Edwards, 354
Agency.com, Ltd., 285
AIG. *See* American International Group
Air Canada, 266
Air New Zealand, 266
Albertson's Inc., 65
Alcatel, 455
Amazon.com, 19, 39, 41, 42, 46–47, 50–51, 85, 267, 269, 356, 387, 409, 450
AMD, 161
Amerada Hess, 164
American Airlines, 50, 266
American Civil Liberties Union (ACLU), 467
American Express, 122, 303, 336, 442
American Express CA, 462
American International Group (AIG), 348
American Optometric Association, 123
American Stock Exchange (AMEX), 336
AmeriVault, 452, 453
AMEX. *See* American Stock Exchange
AMR Corp., 50
Anti-Phishing Working Group, 277
AOK, 126
AOL, 42, 55, 189, 255, 263
Apple Computer, 162, 254, 270, 287
Archimedes, 349
ARPA. *See* U.S. Department of Defense Advanced Research Projects Agency
AskMe Corporation, 365, 366–367
AT&T, 162, 199, 200–201, 417
Aurora Information Systems, 327
Austrian Airlines, 266
Avant Force, 43
Avenue A, 255, 361

B

BAE Automated Systems, Inc., 410
Baltz, Chris, 213
Bank of America (BofA), 232, 354, 449, 476–477
Barnes & Noble, 41, 274
Baseline Business Graphics, 350
Beckman Coulter Inc., 93
BellSouth, 188
Ben & Jerry's, 360–361
Berkeley Software Distribution (BSD), 166
BidPay, 287
Bigstep, 258
BillPoint, 287
Blockbuster Inc., 251, 452
BN.com, 41
Boeing, 194
BofA. *See* Bank of America
Borland, 149
Bornemann Associates, 51
British Airways, 194
British Telecom, 200–201
BSA. *See* Business Software Alliance
BSD. *See* Berkeley Software Distribution
Business Objects SA, 312, 362
Business Software Alliance (BSA), 166
Butterfield, Peter, 311
Buy.com, 19, 46, 230, 267

C

Cablevision, 202
Callidus Software, 101
Canada Post, 102–103
Canadian Pacific Railway, 338
Capgemini, 417
Capital Group Cos., 215
Capital One Financial Corp., 70
Captiva, 122
CardSystems Solutions, 442
Catalyst Design Group, 409
CAUCE. *See* Coalition Against Unsolicited Commercial E-mail
CDS Business Mapping, 350
CERT/CC. *See* Computer Emergency Response Team/Coordination Center
Cessna, 337
Charles Schwab, 44
ChemConnect, 264–265
Chicago Medical Center, 336
Choice Hotels, 265, 409–410

ChoiceBuy.com, 265
ChoicePoint, 268
Cinergy, 202
CIO Magazine, 12
Circuit City, 47
Cisco Systems, 79, 203, 298, 438
CitiBank, 263
CKE Restaurants, 356
Clarion, 409
Claritas, 285
Clear Forest Corp., 363
Click Tactics, 286
CMS Energy, 422
CNN, 450
Coalition Against Unsolicited Commercial E-mail (CAUCE), 276
Cognos, 357, 362
Cohen, Jeff, 53
Coldwater Creek, 269
Comcast, 186, 202
Comergent, 409
Comfort Inn, 409
Commerce Bank, 33–35
Commission Junctions, 269
Compaq, 55
Computer Associates International, 333–334
Computer Emergency Response Team/Coordination Center (CERT/CC), 448, 450
Computer Sciences Corp. (CSC), 39, 387, 417, 418, 420, 425
Compuware Corp., 266
comScore, 263
Consumer Reports, 101, 448
ConsumerConnect.com, 54
Continental Airlines, 266, 449
Corel, 154, 155
Corio, 425
Costco, 235, 243
Cray Inc., 113
Crittenden, Mickey, 143
CSC. *See* Computer Sciences Corp.
CVS, 90, 360

D

DaimlerChrysler, 54, 164, 400
Dana Corp., 182
Dash Group, 51
Datanautics, Inc., 330
Deep Blue, 334
Deep Junior, 334
DeepGreen Financial, 331–332

Dell Computers, 40, 45, 164
Delta Airlines, 53, 266
Delta Song, 53
Denver International Airport, 410–411
Detroit Coffee Co., 287
Deutsche Bank, 417
Deutsche Telecom, 201
Digital Signature Trust Co., 462
Direct Marketing Association (DMA), 276
DirecTV, 53
Disney, 201, 213–214
DMA. *See* Direct Marketing Association
DoCoMo, 272
Domino's Pizza, 400
Doran-Collins, Marianne, 285
Dorenfest Group, 175
DoubleClick, 255, 361
Douglas, Brad, 409
Dow Chemical Co., 271, 363
Dow Jones, 368
DPAs. *See* European Data Protection Authorities
Drugstore.com, 361

E
eBay, 42, 43, 264, 269, 270, 287, 303, 450
EconoLodge, 409
eCount, 287
Eddie Bauer, 361
Eddy, David, 349
EDS. *See* Electronic Data Systems
Electronic Data Systems (EDS), 214, 364, 417
Electronic Privacy Information Center (ERIC), 467
Eli Lilly & Co., 271
eMarketer, 263
EMC, 130
Empire Blue Cross Blue Shield, 334
Engage, 361
Engelbart, Douglas, 120
Entopia Inc., 365
EPA. *See* U.S. Department Environmental Protection Agency
Equinix, 468
ERIC. *See* Electronic Privacy Information Center
Ernst & Young, 203

ERSI, 340
Esler, Jamie, 102
Etterman, Al, 438, 439
EU. *See* European Union
European Data Protection Authorities (DPAs), 303
European Union (EU), 55–56, 289, 290, 299–300, 302–303, 329–330
EverGreen Data Continuity, 466
Expedia, 44, 266, 361, 384
Experian, 445
ExxonMobile, 182

F
FAA. *See* Federal Aviation Authority
Factiva, 368
Fair, Isaac, and Corporation, 334
Fairchild Semiconductor, 310
Farahi, Babak, 66
FastClick, 255
FBI, 214, 271, 467, 477
Federal Aviation Authority (FAA), 52, 375–376
FedEx, 32–33, 46, 102, 121, 278, 477
Financial Executives International, 39, 387
First Capital Bank, 3
First Data, 417
First Union Corp., 101–102
FleetBoston Financial, 476–477
Fluor Daniel, 158
Ford Motor Company, 54, 79–80, 182
FordDirect.com, 54, 56
Forrester Research Inc., 115, 266
Fortune, 376
Free Software Association, 163, 166
FTD.com, 269
Fujitsu, 113, 114

G
G&T Conveyor Co., 410
Gallup, 102 , 445
Garmin, 115
Gartner Group, 85, 200–201, 445, 476, 477
Gates, Bill, 55, 56
GBDe. *See* Global Business Dialogue on Electronic Commerce
General Electric Corp., 337
General Mills, 94
General Motors Corp., 50, 54, 93, 94, 194

GeoSim, 158
Gillette, 190, 203
Global Business Dialogue on Electronic Commerce (GBDe), 293
GlobalSign NV, 462
GNY. *See* Greater New York Insurance Companies
Gold, David, 64–65
Goodyear, 94
Google, 43, 252, 258, 263, 298, 368
Gore, W. L., 376
Grand Rental Station, 362
Greater New York Insurance Companies (GNY), 350
Greater New York Mutual Insurance Company, 350
Greater New York Taxpayers Association, 350
Guess, 355

H
Hackensack University Medical Center, 175
Hallmark, 190
Hamon Corp., 202
Hardee's, 356
Harrah's Entertainment, 331, 356
Hart, Christopher, 375
Hewlett-Packard (HP), 46, 55, 114, 130, 164, 165, 417
HighJump Software, 64, 65
Hitachi, 113
HNC Software, 334
Holden Humphrey Co., 426
Home and Garden Showplace, 362
Home Depot Inc., 57, 121
Honda, 312
Hotwire, 384
HP. *See* Hewlett-Packard
Humana, Inc., 90
Hyperion, 357

I
IBM, 43, 55, 92, 113, 114, , 116, 122, 125, 130, 162, 164, 165, 225, 290, 350, 334, 355, 409, 417, 420, 466
IBM Global Services, 43, 55, 425, 426
ICANN. *See* Internet Corporation for Assigned Names and Numbers
ICCP. *See* Institute for Certification of Computer Professionals

IDC. *See* International Data Corp.
Incentive Systems, 101
Induserve Supply, 362
Infogain, 311
InnoCentive Inc., 271
Institute for Certification of
    Computer Professionals (ICCP),
    402, 403
Institution of Medicine, 175
Institution of Safe Medicine
    Practices, 175
Insurance Company of Greater
    New York, 350
Intel Corp., 116, 161, 164, 290
Intelltext, 364
InterBiz Solutions, 333
International Data Corp. (IDC),
    165, 166, 363, 427
International League against
    Racism and Anti-Semitism
    (LICRA), 299
International Telework Association
    & Council, 200
Internet Corporation for
    Assigned Names and Numbers
    (ICANN), 251
iPhrase Technologies, Inc., 368
iTunes Music Store, 287
ITW Foilmark, 190
i2 Technologies, 423
iValueHost, 258

J
Japan Airlines, 194
Japan Post, 455
Jaschan, Sven, 451
J.D. Powers, 311, 312
JDS Fitel, 438
JDS Uniphase (JDSU), 438–439
JDSU. *See* JDS Uniphase
Jennings, Michael, 376
JetBlue, 51–53
Jiang, Juju, 444
Johnson, Samuel, 363
J.P. Morgan Chase, 417, 420

K
Kaiser Permanente, 349
Kasparov, Garry, 334
Keen, 264
Keynote Systems, Inc., 44

Kia Motors, 310–312
Kidrobot, 157
Kinko's, 444
Kroger Co., 64

L
Lakewest Group, 437
Land's End, 269, 277, 361
Lawrence Livermore National
    Laboratory, 113
Leiner Health Products Inc., 243–245
Levchin, Max, 286
LICRA. *See* International League
    against Racism and Anti-Semitism
LightYear Capital, 331
LinkShare, 269
llbean.com, 269
Lloyd, Timothy, 449
Loebner, Hugh, 332
Lotus Development Corporation,
    42, 154, 155
Lowe's, 57
Lufthansa, 194, 266

M
Macromedia Inc., 48, 409
Macy's West, 215
MainStay Suites, 409
MandrakeSoft, 164
MapInfo, 340
Marshall Field's, 47
MasterCard International, 286,
    303, 442
McAfee, 448, 451
McCarthy, Neil, 437
McCormick & Co., 94
McDonald's, 292
Megaputer Intelligence, Inc.,
    364, 375
Merrill Lynch, 44
Mervyn's, 47
MessageLabs Inc., 448
Metaldyn, 418
Metropolitan South Africa, 142
MGI, 155
Michael Wesetly Clothing, 376
Microsoft, 41, 42, 48, 55–56, 55–56,
    57, 122, 149, 152, 154, 155, 161,
    162, 164, 165, 166, 217, 225,
    226, 227, 228, 260, 296, 298,
    348, 350, 447–449, 451, 463
Millbrook, 350

Mitsubishi Tokyo Financial
    Group, 455
Mobilcom, 355
Monster.com, 23
Morgan Stanley, 165
Morris Air, 51
Motorola, 162, 364, 417, 420
Movement against Racism
    (MRAP), 299
Mozilla, 43, 163
MRAP. *See* Movement against Racism
Mrs. Fields Cookies, 327
MSN, 255, 263
Multivision, 66
Myers Industries, 334

N
Narayanan, Paul, 348
NASA, 201
Nasser, Jacques, 54, 56
National Academy of Sciences, 175
National Highway Traffic Safety
    Administration (NHTSA),
    311, 312
National Institute of Occupational
    Safety and Health. *See* U.S.
    National Institute of
    Occupational Safety and Health
NavaSol, 182
Navic Networks, 85
NBC, 201
NEC, 113
Neeleman, David, 51
Netflix, 251
Netscape Corporation, 42, 55, 57
Network Alliance, 130
New York Times, 254
Newcity, Michael, 213
NextLinx, 294, 310
Nextel, 213
NHTSA. *See* National Highway
    Traffic Safety Administration
Nielsen Corporation, 269
Nike Inc., 423
99 Cents Only Stores, 64–65
NIOS U.S. National Institute of
    Occupational Safety and Health
Nippon TV, 201
Nissan, 54
Nistevo Corporation, 94
Norelco, 290
Northwest Airlines, 266
Novell, 162, 165

NTT DoCoMo, 272
Nuance Communications, 455
Nunz-Aponte, Rafael, 447

O
Objectivity Inc., 226
Occupational Safety and Health
Administration (OSHA), 123
Office Depot, 274, 360
Omega Engineering, 449
OneWorld, 266
OpenTV, 85
Oracle Corp., 48, 95, 101, 166, 225,
322, 357, 362, 375, 425, 426,
437, 438
Orbitz, 44, 266, 278
OSHA. *See* Occupational Safety and
Health Administration
Overstock.com, 242–243, 259, 287

P
Pacific Bell, 336
Palm, 162
Participate Systems Inc., 365
Party Central, 362
PayPal, 267, 286–287
PC Magazine, 168
PC World, 168
PEFA.com, 265
PeopleAdmin, Inc., 90
PeopleSoft, 428
Perot Systems Corp., 417, 418
PGW. *See* Philadelphia Gas Works
Philadelphia Gas Works (PGW), 464
Philips, 290
PI. *See* Privacy International
Pitney Bowes, 200
Pixar Animation Studios, 164
Pollo Tropical, 340
Polonski, Joe, 437
Priceline.com, 41, 46, 266
PrimarySource.com, 410
Privacy International (PI), 301
Procter & Gamble, 48, 93, 203,
271, 274
proflowers.com, 269
Progress Software Inc., 226
ProPay, 287

Q
Qualcomm Inc., 54
Quality, 409

Quantum, 126
QuantumBio Inc., 113
Quark, 155
QVC, 269

R
Ramirez, Jose, 377
Rapt, Inc., 322
Rational Software Group, 409
Raytheon, 158
Red Hat, 164, 165
Renault, 54
Retek, 437
Return Exchange, 355
Rock County, Wisconsin, 143–144
Rodeway Inn, 409
RSA, 454
Ruby Tuesday, 359, 360

S
Sabre Inc., 50
SAFLINK Corp., 455
Salesforce.com, 425
Sam's Club, 243
Samsung, 115, 121
San Jose Police Officers Association,
176–177
SAP AG, 48, 95, 101, 166, 322, 362,
428, 437
SAS Institute, 362, 377
Saturn, 50
Saylor's Pizza, 287
Scandanavian Airlines, 194, 266
Sears, 47, 418
SecuGen Corporation, 454
Seiden, Mark, 477–478
Shopping.com, 231
Siebel, 362
SIIA. *See* Software & Information
Industry Association
Silva, Luiz Inacio da, 165
Simon, Herbert, 319
Simpson Industries, 426
Sirius, 42
SkyTeam, 266
Slater, Dave, 1–4, 37–38, 59
Sleep Inn, 409
Sloan-Kettering Cancer Research
Institute, 446
Slocum, Kathy, 3
Smith, Nikole, 409
Software & Information Industry
Association (SIIA), 166

Sony, 116
Southwest Airlines, 44, 51, 375
Sovereign Bank, 285–286
Sports Authority, 355
sportsmanguide.com, 269
Sprint, 188, 199
Stallman, Richard, 163
Standish Group, 95, 442
Stanford Research Institute, 120
Staples, 355
Star Alliance, 266
State Street Corporation, 41
Strohl Systems, 466
Sun Microsystems, 41, 155, 162,
165, 322
Sunbelt, 445
SunGard, 466, 476
SunGard Availability Services, 466
SuSE, 164
Symantec, 163, 448, 451
Synygy, 101

T
Tacit Systems Inc., 365
Taiwan, 55
Tallán, Inc., 285
Target Corp., 19, 47, 267
Taylor, Lari Sue, 476
Taylor Rental, 362
Ted, 53
Teledesic LLC, 186
Tenet Healthcare Corporation, 418
Thiel, Peter, 286
3M, 65
TiVo, 165
Tommy Hilfiger, 164
Torvalds, Linus, 162, 164
Toshiba, 116
Towers Perrin, 427
Toyota, 215, 312
TRADOS Inc., 296
Travelocity, Inc., 44, 50, 278, 384
True Value, 362
TruServ, 362
Turing, Alan, 332
Tymnet, 188

U
uBid, 264, 270
UCC. *See* Uniform Code Council
UEFJ. *See* Union of French Jewish
Students
Uniform Code Council (UCC), 300

Union of French Jewish Students (UEFJ), 299
Uniphase, 438
Unisys, 113, 417
United Airlines, 53, 266, 273, 410–411
University of California, 448
University of California, San Diego, 450
University of Illinois, Chicago, 336
University of Pennsylvania, 158
University of Wisconsin, Madison, 448
UPS, 102, 121, 263, 278
U.S. Bureau of Labor Statistics, 22, 47, 123
U.S. Census Bureau, 267, 429
U.S. Chamber of Commerce, 348
U.S. Department of Agriculture, 328, 337
U.S. Department of Commerce, 91, 303
U.S. Department of Defense, 195
U.S. Department of Defense Advanced Research Projects Agency (ARPA) , 201
U.S. Department Environmental Protection Agency (EPA), 8
U.S. Department of Homeland Security, 214

U.S. Department of Justice, 55
U.S. Department of Labor, 123
U.S. Federal Trade Commission, 299
U.S. National Institute of Occupational Safety and Health (NIOS)
U.S. Office of Personnel Management, 358
U.S. Postal Service, 467
U.S. Robotics (USR), 368–369
U.S. Supreme Court, 183
U.S. White House, 450
USi. *See* USinternetworking
USinternetworking (USi), 425, 426

V
VA Software, 165
Varig, 266
Ventoro LLC, 420
Venus Swimwear, 255
Verio, 258
VeriSign Inc., 462
Verizon, 185, 188
Versant Corporation, 226
VGM Club, 410
Visa International, 286, 442
Visible World, 85
Vonage, 202

W
Wachovia, 101–102
Walton, Avis, 64–65
Wal-Mart, 47–48, 59, 93, 127, 203, 235, 243, 251, 267, 270, 274
Wawa, 432–433, 464
Wells Fargo & Co., 23
World Trade Organization, 298
Worldwide, 466

X
Xcel, 142
XeoMatrix, 362
Xerox, 152
XM, 42
X3D Fritz, 334

Y
Yahoo!, 42, 54, 255, 258, 263, 269, 298, 299, 368
Yahoo! Auctions, 42, 303
Yamaha Corp., 215

Z
Zimmerman, Phillip, 296
Zohn-h, 447